[CONTACTS 2008]

97th edition published by The Spotlight, 7 Leicester Place, London WC2H
t: 020 7437 7631 f: 020 7437 5881 e-mail: info@spotlight.com www.sp

What is Contacts?

Contacts is the essential handbook for everyone working or wanting to work in the entertainment industry. It has been published by The Spotlight since 1947. It contains over 5000 listings for companies, services and individuals across all branches of Television, Stage, Film and Radio. These are updated annually to bring you the most accurate information available.

Also watch out for the 'information pages', designed to tell you more about those listed and why you might want to contact them. They include valuable advice from key industry figures - especially helpful if you are just starting out in the industry.

As ever, please send any feedback or suggestions for the next edition to marketing@spotlight.com

How can I / my company appear in the next edition of Contacts?

Contacts is published annually. If you would like to appear in the next edition please contact:

e: advertising@spotlight.com   t: 020 7437 7631 for advertising
e: info@spotlight.com   t: 020 7437 7631 for free, text-only entries

How do I buy copies of Contacts?

To purchase additional copies of Contacts, please e-mail sales@spotlight.com, visit www.spotlight.com/shop or call 020 7440 5026. It is also available from most good bookshops.

Contents

Index To Advertisers See page 380

[CONTACTS 2008]

A

Agents
Advertising
Agents & Personal Managers

Key to areas of specialization:
C Cabaret F Films G General M Musicals
Md Models PM Personal Managers
S Singing TV Television V Variety

For information regarding membership of the
Personal Managers' Association please contact:
Personal Managers' Association Limited
1 Summer Road, East Molesley, Surrey KT8 9LX
t: 020 8398 9796 Website: www.thepma.com
∗ Denotes PMA Membership

For information regarding membership of the
Co-operative Personal Management Association
please contact: Secretary
CPMA, c/o 1 Mellor Road, Leicester LE3 6HN
t: 07981 902525 Website: www.cpma.com
● Denotes CPMA Membership

Children's & Teenagers'
Dance
Literary & Play

For information regarding membership of the
Personal Managers' Association please contact:
Personal Managers' Association Limited
1 Summer Road, East Molesley, Surrey KT8 9LX
t: 020 8398 9796 Website: www.thepma.com
∗ Denotes PMA Membership

Presenters
Voice-Over
Walk-on & Supporting Artists

For information regarding membership of National
Association of Supporting Artistes Agents (NASAA)
Website: www.nasaa.org.uk
■ Denotes NASAA Membership

Animals
Arts Centres
Arts Councils

[CONTACTS 2008]

ABBOT MEAD VICKERS BBDO Ltd
151 Marylebone Road
London NW1 5QE
Website: www.amvbbdo.com
Fax: 020-7616 3600   Tel: 020-7616 3500

AKA
1st Floor
115 Shaftesbury Avenue
London WC2H 8AF
Website: www.akauk.com
e-mail: aka@akauk.com
Fax: 020-7836 8787   Tel: 020-7836 4747

BARTLE BOGLE HEGARTY
60 Kingly Street
London W1B 5DS
Fax: 020-7437 3666   Tel: 020-7734 1677

BDH/TBWA
St Paul's, 781 Wilmslow Road
Didsbury Village
Manchester M20 2RW
Website: www.bdhtbwa.co.uk
e-mail: info@bdhtbwa.co.uk
Fax: 0161-908 8601   Tel: 0161-908 8600

BURNETT Leo Ltd
Warwick Building
Kensington Village
Avonmore Road
London W14 8HQ
Fax: 020-7348 3855   Tel: 020-7751 1800

CDP
9 Lower John Street
London W1F 9DZ
Fax: 020-7437 5445   Tel: 020-7437 4224

CELEBRITY ENDORSEMENTS
PO Box 981
Wallington
Surrey SM6 8JU
Website: www.celebrityendorsements.co.uk
e-mail: info@nmp.co.uk
Fax: 020-8404 2621   Tel: 020-8669 3128

COGENT ELLIOT
Heath Farm, Hampton Lane
Meriden, West Midlands CV7 7LL
Website: www.cogent.co.uk
Fax: 0121-627 5038   Tel: 0121-627 5040

DDB LONDON
12 Bishops Bridge Road
London W2 6AA
Fax: 020-7402 4871   Tel: 020-7258 3979

DEWYNTERS
48 Leicester Square
London WC2H 7QD
Website: www.dewynters.com
Fax: 020-7321 0104   Tel: 020-7321 0488

DONER CARDWELL HAWKINS
26-34 Emerald Street
London WC1N 3QA
Website: www.dch.co.uk
Fax: 020-7437 3961   Tel: 020-7400 1230

DRAFT LONDON
55 Newman Street, London W1T 3EB
Website: www.draft.fcb.com
Fax: 020-7947 8001   Tel: 020-7947 8000

EURO RSCG LONDON
Cupola House
15 Alfred Place, London WC1E 7EB
Fax: 020-7467 9210
Tel: 020-7240 4111

GOLLEY SLATER & PARTNERS (LONDON) Ltd
12 Margaret Street
London W1W 8JQ
Fax: 020-7255 6490
Tel: 020-7255 6400

GREY LONDON
The Johnson Building
77 Hatton Garden
London EC1N 8JS
Fax: 020-3037 3001
Tel: 020-3037 3000

JWT Ltd
1 Knightsbridge Green
London SW1X 7NW
Website: www.jwt.co.uk
e-mail: firstname.lastname@jwt.com
Fax: 020-7656 7010
Tel: 020-7656 7000

LEAGAS DELANEY LONDON Ltd
1 Alfred Place
London WC1E 7EB
Website: www.leagasdelaney.com
Fax: 020-7758 1760
Tel: 020-7758 1758

LEITH AGENCY The
37 The Shore
Edinburgh EH6 6QU
Fax: 0131-561 8601
Tel: 0131-561 8600

LOWE & PARTNERS
60 Sloane Avenue
London SW3 3XB
Website: www.loweworldwide.com
Fax: 020-7584 9557
Tel: 020-7584 5033

McCANN-ERICKSON ADVERTISING Ltd
7-11 Herbrand Street
London WC1N 1EX
Fax: 020-7837 3773
Tel: 020-7837 3737

MEDIACOM
124 Theobalds Road
London WC1X 8RX
Fax: 020-7158 5999
Tel: 020-7158 5500

MEDIAJUNCTION
40A Old Compton Street
Soho
London W1D 4TU
Website: www.mediajunction.co.uk
e-mail: mailbox@mediajunction.co.uk
Fax: 020-7439 0794
Tel: 020-7434 9919

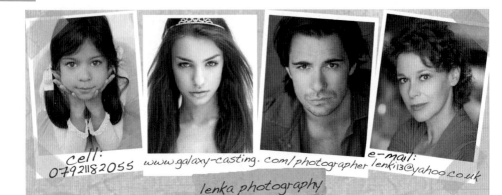

cell: 07921182055 www.galaxy-casting.com/photographer e-mail: lenki13@yahoo.co.uk

lenka photography

MUSTOES
2-4 Bucknall Street
London WC2H 8LA
Website: www.mustoes.co.uk
Fax: 020-7379 8487 Tel: 020-7379 9999

OGILVY GROUP UK
10 Cabot Square
Canary Wharf, London E14 4QB
Fax: 020-7345 9000 Tel: 020-7345 3000

PUBLICIS Ltd
82 Baker Street, London W1U 6AE
Website: www.publicis.co.uk
Fax: 020-7487 5351 Tel: 020-7935 4426

RKCR / Y & R
Greater London House
Hampstead Road
London NW1 7QP
Fax: 020-7611 6011 Tel: 020-7404 2700

RPM 3
William Blake House
8 Marshall Street
London W1F 7EJ
Fax: 020-7439 8884 Tel: 020-7434 4343

SAATCHI & SAATCHI
80 Charlotte Street
London W1A 1AQ
Fax: 020-7637 8489 Tel: 020-7636 5060

SMEE'S ADVERTISING Ltd
3-5 Duke Street
London W1U 3BA
Fax: 020-7935 8588 Tel: 020-7486 6644

TBWA/LONDON
76-80 Whitfield Street
London W1T 4EZ
Fax: 020-7573 6667 Tel: 020-7573 6666

TMP WORLDWIDE
Chancery House
53-64 Chancery Lane
London WC2A 1QS
Website: www.tmpw.com
Fax: 020-7406 5001 Tel: 020-7406 5000

TV MANAGEMENTS
Brink House, Avon Castle
Ringwood, Hants BH24 2BL
e-mail: etv@tvmanagements.com Tel: 01425 475544

WCRS
5 Golden Square
London W1F 9BS
Website: www.wcrs.com
Fax: 020-7806 5099 Tel: 020-7806 5000

YOUNG & RUBICAM Ltd
Greater London House
Hampstead Road, London NW1 7QP
Fax: 020-7611 6570 Tel: 020-7387 9366

Who are Agents and Personal Managers?

There are hundreds of Agents and Personal Managers in the UK, representing thousands of actors and artists. It is their job to promote their clients to casting opportunities and negotiate contracts on their behalf. In return they take commission ranging from 10-15%. Larger agencies can have hundreds of clients on their books, smaller ones may only have a handful. A personal manager is someone who manages an artist's career on a more one-on-one basis. Co-operative agencies are staffed by actors themselves, who take turns to handle the administrative side of the agency and promote themselves to casting opportunities as a team. Agents usually try to represent a good range of artists (age, sex, type) to fill the diverse role types required by casting directors.

How should I use these listings?

If you are an actor getting started in the industry, or looking to change your agent, the following pages will supply you with up-to-date contact details for many of the UK's leading agencies. Every company listed is done so by written request to us. Members of the Personal Managers' Association (PMA) are shown with the symbol * in this book. Members of the Co-operative Personal Management Association (CMPA) are labelled with the symbol • in this book. When writing to agencies, try to research the different companies instead of just sending a 'blanket' letter to every single one. This way you can target your approaches to the most suitable agencies and avoid wasting their time (and yours). Remember that agents receive hundreds of letters each week, so try to keep your communication concise, and be professional at all times. If you include a stamped-addressed envelope (SAE) you will increase your chances of getting a reply (make sure it is big enough so that they can return your 10 x 8 photo and that it has sufficient postage). We also recommend that your letter has some kind of focus: perhaps you are telling them about your next showcase, or where they can see you currently appearing on stage. Include a photograph which has your name written on the back. Only send showreels if you have checked with the agency first.

Should I pay an agent to join their books? Or sign a contract?

Equity (the actors' trade union) does not recommend that artists pay an agent to join their client list. Before signing a contract, you should be very clear about the terms and commitments involved. For advice on both of these issues, or if you experience any problems with a current agent, we recommend that you contact Equity www.equity.org.uk. They also publish the booklet 'You and your Agent' which is free to all Equity members.

How do I become an agent?

Budding agents will need to get experience of working in an agent's office, usually this is done by working as an assistant. It can be extremely hard work, and you will be expected to give up a lot of your evenings to attend productions. There are two organisations you may find it useful to contact: the Agents' Association www.agents-uk.com and the Personal Managers' Association www.thepma.com

FIONA KEDDIE opened the books of Keddie Scott Associates Ltd, in 2003. The agency has since expanded to include an office of two agents in Cardiff (KSA-Wales), and an office in Glasgow (KSA-Scotland). Fiona works from the head office in London alongside associate agent, Anna Loose. With a background in acting, Fiona continues to perform whilst overseeing the Management of KSA Ltd.

The entertainment industry is one of constant change and it is of utmost importance for agents and actors to stay on top of these movements. Technology, for one, is developing at such a fast pace that we must always remain familiar with new software and systems which better assist with the managing of clients (for agents) or managing yourself (as an actor).

I could give masses of advice to actors seeking representation, but here are the most important points which I feel should be taken on board:

- Do your research and know who you are writing to. There is nothing worse than receiving 'Dear Sir/Madam' or 'FAO All Agents' or worst of all 'Dear Sirs' in an office managed entirely by women! If you can not be bothered to take the time to find the names and information on an agency, why should they be interested in finding out more about you?

- Keep letters concise and reference any possible contact you may have had with the agency before. Note why you are writing to that agent in particular. What is it that most attracts you to that specific agency?

- Submissions by email will be accepted by many agents but be wary, try to find out how an individual prefers to receive your details. Do not, under any circumstances, send large photo files. They clog up an agent's inbox and can result in preventing them carrying out their work until your information has been properly downloaded. This will not bode well; an agent's office is **very** busy. If your IT skills are not of a level to reduce file sizes, get help or send details by post. Photographs must be of professional quality and of exact likeness. CVs should be truthful, informative and always up-to-date. Do not list walk-on or supporting artist work, only bona fide professional acting credits.

- It is not always necessary to send a glossy 10X8 with a postal submission, and certainly not necessary to send two! It can be helpful to send a copy of a demo or showreel; it is expensive to have these duplicated. If you would like your details returned, you must include a SAE which is sufficient in size and postage for its contents.

- Prepare for your interview. Do further research on the agency and if possible, know what their clients are doing. Most importantly, know what areas the agency deals in. There is no point in writing to an agent who specialises in Musical Theatre if you are not a singer! Additionally, have a list of questions prepared. Remember, you are both assessing and being assessed in an interview, the aim is to establish whether this will be a good two-way working relationship.

- If you have been approached by a number of agents, make sure you contact them all, thank them for their interest and, wherever possible, meet with each one. Similarly, if an agent offers you representation, always contact them even if you have chosen to join another company. This is common courtesy and it is important that you do not burn any bridges.

It has to be said that getting an agent is not the be-all-and-end-all. There are plenty of ways in which an actor can market him/herself. Hard work, dedication and impeccable organisational skills are paramount. Establish and enjoy your life outside of performing. It will do you no good to find yourself depressed in between jobs. Your life will become a rollercoaster of highs and lows, so you must be prepared to have the mental capacity to balance your feelings and allow you to cope.

For more information please visit www.ks-ass.co.uk

1984 PERSONAL MANAGEMENT Ltd•
PM Co-operative
Suite 508, Davina House
137 Goswell Road
London EC1V 7ET
Website: www.1984pm.com
e-mail: info@1984pm.com
Fax: 020-7250 3031   Tel: 020-7251 8046

21ST CENTURY ACTORS MANAGEMENT Ltd•
Co-operative
E10 Panther House
38 Mount Pleasant
London WC1X 0AN
Website: www.21stcenturyactors.co.uk
e-mail: mail@21stcenturyactors.co.uk   Tel: 020-7278 3438

2MA Ltd
(Sports & Stunts)
Spring Vale, Tutland Road
North Baddesley
Hants SO52 9FL
Website: www.2ma.co.uk
e-mail: info@2ma.co.uk
Fax: 023-8074 1355   Tel: 023-8074 1354

A & B PERSONAL MANAGEMENT Ltd*
PM (Write)
Suite 330, Linen Hall
162-168 Regent Street
London W1B 5TD
e-mail: billellis@aandb.co.uk
Fax: 020-7038 3699   Tel: 020-7434 4262

EXTREME SPORTS

DANCERS

ACROBATS

DIVERS

www.2ma.co.uk

A Beautiful Image
PHOTOGRAPHY

020 8568 2122

debal@abeautifulimage.com

LIVERPOOL BASED PHOTOGRAPHER
Stephanie de Leng

Leanne Best, best newcomer 2006

Tel: **0151 476 1563**   Mobile: **07740 927765**

lookandsee@mac.com

www.stephaniedeleng.co.uk

A@B (AGENCY AT BODYWORK)
25-29 Glisson Road, Cambridge CB1 2HA
e-mail: agency@bodyworkds.co.uk
Fax: 01223 358923   Tel: 01223 309990

A & J MANAGEMENT
242A The Ridgeway, Botany Bay, Enfield EN2 8AP
Website: www.ajmanagement.co.uk
e-mail: info@ajmanagement.co.uk
Fax: 020-8342 0842   Tel: 020-8342 0542

A-LIST LOOKALIKES & ENTERTAINMENTS Ltd
4th Floor Calls Landing
36-38 The Calls,
Leeds LS2 7EW
Website: www.alistlookalikes.co.uk
e-mail: info@alistlookalikes.co.uk   Tel: 0113-243 6245

A PLUS
(16-26 year olds)
2 Foresters Cottages
Barnet Wood Road, Bromley BR2 8HJ
Website: www.kidsplusagency.co.uk
e-mail: office@kidsplusagency.co.uk Tel/Fax: 020-8462 4666

ABA (ABACUS ADULTS)
The Studio
4 Bailey Road, Westcott
Dorking, Surrey RH4 3QS
Fax: 01306 877813   Tel: 01306 877144

ABBOTT June ASSOCIATES
55 East Road, London N1 6AH
e-mail: jaa@thecourtyard.org.uk
Fax: 020-7251 6018   Tel: 020-7250 0520

ACADEMY CASTINGS
Blue Square
272 Bath Street, Glasgow G2 4JR
Website: www.academycastings.co.uk
e-mail: robert@academycastings.co.uk
Fax: 0141-354 8876   Tel: 0141-354 8873

ACCESS ARTISTE MANAGEMENT
PO Box 39925, London EC1V 0WN
Website: www.access-associates.co.uk
e-mail: mail@access-associates.co.uk   Tel: 020-8505 1094

ACROBAT PRODUCTIONS
(Artists & Advisors)
12 Oaklands Court
Hempstead Road, Watford WD17 4LF
Website: www.acrobatproductions.com
e-mail: roger@acrobatproductions.com   Tel: 01923 224938

ACT OUT AGENCY
22 Greek Street, Stockport, Cheshire SK3 8AB
e-mail: ab22actout@aol.com   Tel/Fax: 0161-429 7413

ACTING ASSOCIATES
PM
71 Hartham Road, London N7 9JJ
Website: www.actingassociates.co.uk
e-mail: fiona@actingassociates.co.uk Tel/Fax: 020-7607 3562

ACTIVATE DRAMA SCHOOL
Priestman Cottage
Sea View Road, Sunderland SR2 7UP
e-mail: activate_agcy@hotmail.com
Fax: 0191-551 2051   Tel: 0191-565 2345

ACTOR MUSICIANS @ ACCESS
PO Box 39925, London EC1V 0WN
Website: www.access-associates.co.uk
e-mail: musicians@access-associates.co.uk Tel: 020-8505 1094

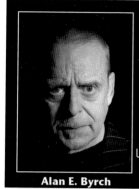

ACTORS AGENCY
1 Glen Street, Tollcross, Edinburgh EH3 9JD
Website: www.stivenchristie.co.uk
e-mail: info@stivenchristie.co.uk
Fax: 0131-228 4645   Tel: 0131-228 4040

ACTORS ALLIANCE•
Co-operative
Disney Place House, 14 Marshalsea Road, London SE1 1HL
e-mail: actors@actorsalliance.co.uk   Tel/Fax: 020-7407 6028

ACTORS' CREATIVE TEAM•
Co-operative
Albany House, 82-84 South End, Croydon CR0 1DQ
Website: www.actorscreativeteam.co.uk
e-mail: office@actorscreativeteam.co.uk
Fax: 020-8239 8818   Tel: 020-8239 8892

ACTORS DIRECT Ltd
Gainsborough House
109 Portland Street
Manchester M1 6DN
Website: www.actorsdirect.org.uk
e-mail: actorsdirect@aol.com
Mobile: 07985 760226   Tel/Fax: 0161-237 1904

ACTORS FILE The•
PM Co-operative
Spitfire Studios
63-71 Collier Street
London N1 9BE
Website: www.theactorsfile.co.uk
e-mail: mail@theactorsfile.co.uk
Fax: 020-7278 0364   Tel: 020-7278 0087

ACTORS' GROUP The (TAG)•
PM Co-operative
21-31 Oldham Street
Manchester M1 1JG
Website: www.theactorsgroup.co.uk
e-mail: enquiries@theactorsgroup.co.uk Tel/Fax: 0161-834 4466

ACTORS IN SCANDINAVIA
Tarkk'ampujankatu 14
00150 Helsinki, Finland
Website: www.actors.fi
e-mail: laura@actors.fi
Fax: 00 358 9 68 40 4422   Tel: 00 358 9 68 40 440

ACTORS INTERNATIONAL Ltd
Conway Hall
25 Red Lion Square
London WC1R 4RL
e-mail: mail@actorsinternational.co.uk
Fax: 020-7831 8319   Tel: 020-7242 9300

ACTORS IRELAND
Crescent Arts Centre
2-4 University Road
Belfast BT7 1NH
Website: www.actorsireland.com
e-mail: geraldine@actorsireland.com   Tel: 028-9024 8861

ACTOR'S TEMPLE The
13 Warren Street, London W1T 5LG
Website: www.actorstemple.com
e-mail: info@actorstemple.com
Mobile: 07771 734670   Tel: 020-7383 3535

ACTORS WORLD CASTING
13 Briarbank Road
London W13 0HH
Website: www.actors-world-production.com
e-mail: katherine@actors-world-production.com
                              Tel: 020-8998 2579

ACTORUM Ltd
PM Co-operative
3rd Floor
21 Foley Street
London W1W 6DR
Website: www.actorum.com
e-mail: actorum2@ukonline.co.uk
Fax: 020-7636 6975   Tel: 020-7636 6978

ADAMS Juliet MODELS & TALENT CASTINGS AGENCY
19 Gwynne House
Challice Way
London SW2 3RB
Website: www.julietadams.co.uk
e-mail: bookingdesk@julietadams.co.uk
Fax: 020-8671 9314   Tel: 020-8671 7673

AFFINITY MANAGEMENT
The Coach House
Down Park
Turners Hill Road
Crawley Down
West Sussex RH10 4HQ
e-mail: jstephens@affinitymanagement.co.uk
Fax: 01342 715800   Tel: 01342 715275

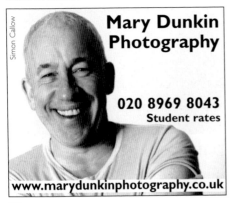

AGENCY Ltd The
(Teri Hayden)
47 Adelaide Road
Dublin 2
Ireland
Website: www.the-agency.ie
e-mail: info@tagency.ie
Fax: 00 353 1 6760052   Tel: 00 353 1 6618535

AGENCY PLANITOLOGY
Studio G7
Shakespeare Business Centre
245A Coldharbour Lane
London SW9 8RR
Website: www.agencyplanitology.co.uk
e-mail: info@agencyplanitology.co.uk
Fax: 020-7326 5768   Tel: 020-7733 2995

AHA
(See HOWARD Amanda ASSOCIATES Ltd)

AIM (ASSOCIATED INTERNATIONAL MANAGEMENT)*
45-53 Sinclair Road
London W14 0NS
Website: www.aimagents.com
e-mail: info@aimagents.com
Fax: 020-7300 6656   Tel: 020-7300 6506

ALANDER AGENCY
TV F S V
10 Ingram Close
Stanmore
Middlesex HA7 4EW   Tel: 020-8954 7685

MARCO WINDHAM
PHOTOGRAPHER
020 7737 5954   07768 330 027

ALEXANDER PERSONAL MANAGEMENT Ltd
Pinewood Studios, Pinewood Rd, Iver Heath, Bucks SL0 0NH
Website: www.apmassociates.net
e-mail: apm@apmassociates.net
Fax: 01753 639205   Tel: 01753 639204

ALL TALENT UK
Central Chambers, 93 Hope Street, Glasgow G2 6LD
Website: www.alltalentuk.co.uk
e-mail: enquiries@alltalentuk.co.uk
Fax: 0141-221 8883   Tel: 0141-221 8887

ALLSORTS DRAMA FOR CHILDREN
(In Association with Sasha Leslie Management)
34 Pember Road, London NW10 5LS
e-mail: sasha@allsortsdrama.com   Tel/Fax: 020-8969 3249

Esme Eliot

Paul Keating

ROBERT WORKMAN Superb casting photographs
Tel: 020 7385 5442   www.robertworkman.demon.co.uk

ALLSORTS THEATRICAL AGENCY
Suite 1 & 2 Marlborough Business Centre
96 George Lane, London E18 1AD
Website: www.allsortsagency.com
e-mail: bookings@allsortsagency.com
Fax: 020-8989 5600   Tel: 020-8989 0500

ALPHA PERSONAL MANAGEMENT Ltd•
PM Co-operative
Studio B4
3 Bradbury Street
London N16 8JN
Website: www.alphaactors.com
e-mail: alpha@alphaactors.com
Fax: 020-7241 2410   Tel: 020-7241 0077

ALRAUN Anita REPRESENTATION*
(Write with SAE, no e-mails)
5th Floor, 28 Charing Cross Road
London WC2H 0DB
e-mail: anita@cjagency.demon.co.uk
Fax: 020-7379 6865   Tel: 020-7379 6840

ALTARAS Jonathan ASSOCIATES Ltd*
11 Garrick Street
Covent Garden
London WC2E 9AR
e-mail: kathryn@jaa.ndirect.co.uk
Fax: 020-7836 6066   Tel: 020-7836 8722

ALVAREZ MANAGEMENT
33 Ludlow Way, London N2 0JZ
e-mail: sga@alvarezmanagement.fsnet.co.uk
        Tel: 020-8883 2206

ALW ASSOCIATES
1 Grafton Chambers
Grafton Place, London NW1 1LN
e-mail: alweurope@onetel.com
Fax: 020-7813 1398   Tel: 020-7388 7018

A M ENTERTAINMENTS
Suite 1, Townsend House
22-25 Dean Street, London W1D 3RY
e-mail: hilsjago@amentertainments.com
Mobile: 07970 524234   Tel: 020-7734 4588

AMBER PERSONAL MANAGEMENT Ltd
189 Wardour Street
London W1F 8ZD   Tel: 020-7734 7887

28 St Margaret's Chambers
5 Newton Street, Manchester M1 1HL
Website: www.amberltd.co.uk
e-mail: info@amberltd.co.uk
Fax: 0161-228 0235   Tel: 0161-228 0236

AMC MANAGEMENT
(Anna McCorquodale)
43 St Maur Road, London SW6 4DR
e-mail: anna@amcmanagement.co.uk
Fax: 020-7371 9048   Tel: 020-7731 1721

AMCK MANAGEMENT Ltd
103 Westbourne Studios
242 Acklam Road
Notting Hill, London W10 5JJ
Website: www.amck.tv
e-mail: info@amck.tv
Fax: 020-7524 7789   Tel: 020-7524 7788

AMERICAN AGENCY The
14 Bonny Street
London NW1 9PG
Website: www.americanagency.tv
e-mail: americanagency@btconnect.com
Fax: 020-7482 4666   Tel: 020-7485 8883

ANA (Actors Network Agency)•
PM Co-operative
55 Lambeth Walk
London SE11 6DX
Website: www.ana-actors.co.uk
e-mail: info@ana-actors.co.uk
Fax: 020-7735 8177   Tel: 020-7735 0999

ANDREWS Amanda AGENCY
30 Caverswall Road
Blythe Bridge
Stoke-on-Trent
Staffordshire ST11 9BG
e-mail: amanda.andrews.agency@tesco.net
Mobile: 07711 379770   Tel/Fax: 01782 393889

ANDREWS HAMILTON Ltd*
BCM Box 3054
London WC1N 3XX
Website: www.andrewshamilton.com
e-mail: info@andrewshamilton.com
Fax: 020-8551 3685   Tel: 020-8491 7904

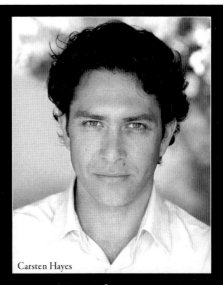

Artist Management
adults   children

Byron's Management
Tel: 020 8444 4445
Fax: 020 8444 4040
byronsmanagement@aol.com
www.byronsmanagement.co.uk

ANGEL Susan & FRANCIS Kevin Ltd*
(Write, no e-mails)
1st Floor
12 D'Arblay Street
London W1F 8DU
e-mail: agents@angelandfrancis.co.uk
Fax: 020-7437 1712   Tel: 020-7439 3086

ANTONY Christopher ASSOCIATES
The Old Dairy
164 Thames Road
London W4 3QS
Website: www.christopherantony.co.uk
e-mail: info@christopherantony.co.uk
Fax: 020-8742 8066   Tel: 020-8994 9952

ANUBIS AGENCY Ltd
Mobile: 07748 608821   Tel/Fax: 0870 0852288

A.P.M. ASSOCIATES (Linda French)
(See ALEXANDER PERSONAL MANAGEMENT Ltd)

ARAENA/COLLECTIVE
10 Bramshaw Gardens
South Oxhey
Herts WD19 6XP   Tel/Fax: 020-8428 0037

ARC ENTERTAINMENTS
10 Church Lane
Redmarshall
Stockton on Tees
Cleveland TS21 1EP
Website: www.arcents.co.uk
e-mail: arcents@aol.com   Tel: 01740 631292

ARCADIA ASSOCIATES
18B Vicarage Gate
London W8 4AA
e-mail: info.arcadia@btopenworld.com
                                      Tel/Fax: 020-7937 0264

ARENA ENTERTAINMENT CONSULTANTS
(Corporate Entertainment)
Regent's Court
39 Harrogate Road, Leeds LS7 3PD
Website: www.arenaentertainments.co.uk
e-mail: stars@arenaentertainments.co.uk
Fax: 0113-239 2016   Tel: 0113-239 2222

ARENA PERSONAL MANAGEMENT Ltd
Co-operative
Room 11
East Block, Panther House
38 Mount Pleasant
London WC1X 0AP
Website: www.arenapmltd.co.uk
e-mail: arenapmltd@aol.com   Tel/Fax: 020-7278 1661

A R G (ARTISTS RIGHTS GROUP Ltd)*
4 Great Portland Street, London W1W 8PA
e-mail: argall@argtalent.com
Fax: 020-7436 6700   Tel: 020-7436 6400

ARGYLE ASSOCIATES
PM (Richard Argyle) (SAE for Unsolicited Mail)
St John's Buildings
43 Clerkenwell Road, London EC1M 5RS
e-mail: argyle.associates@virgin.net
Fax: 0871 4336130   Tel: 020-7608 2095

Robert Kilroy-Silk   Ruth Shephard   Anthony Marsh   Michelle C

Howard Sayer Photographer
www.howardsayer.com   m: 07860 559891   howard@howardsayer.com

ARTIST MANAGEMENT UK Ltd
PO Box 96
Liverpool L9 8WY
Website: www.artistmanagementuk.com
e-mail: chris@artistmanagementuk.com   Tel: 0151-523 6222

ARTS MANAGEMENT
First Floor
10 Goddard Place
Maidenbower
West Sussex RH10 7HR
Website: www.artsmanagement.co.uk
e-mail: artsmanagementltd@hotmail.com
Mobile: 07764 801167   Tel: 01293 885746

ARTSWORLD INTERNATIONAL MANAGEMENT Ltd
1 Farrow Road
Whaplode Drove
Nr Spalding PE12 0TS
e-mail: bob@artsworld.freeserve.co.uk   Tel: 01406 330099

ARUN Jonathan Ltd
Studio 9
33 Stannary Street
London SE11 4AA
e-mail: jonathan@jonathanarun.com   Tel: 020-7840 0123

ASHCROFT ACADEMY OF DRAMATIC ART & AGENCY
Malcolm Primary School
Malcolm Road
Penge
London SE20 8RH
Website: www.ashcroftacademy.com
e-mail: geraldi.gillma@btconnect.com
Mobile: 07799 791586   Tel/Fax: 01634 856900

ASHCROFT Sharron MANAGEMENT Ltd
Dean Clough
Halifax
West Yorkshire HX3 5AX
Website: www.sharronashcroft.com
e-mail: info@sharronashcroft.com
Fax: 01422 343417   Tel: 01422 343949

ASQUITH & HORNER
PM (Write with SAE)
The Studio
14 College Road
Bromley
Kent BR1 3NS
Fax: 020-8313 0443   Tel: 020-8466 5580

ASSOCIATED ARTS
(Directors, Designers, Lighting Designers)
8 Shrewsbury Lane
London SE18 3JF
Website: www.associated-arts.co.uk
e-mail: karen@associated-arts.co.uk
Fax: 020-8856 8189   Tel: 020-8856 4958

ASSOCIATED SPEAKERS
(Lecturers & Celebrity Speakers)
24A Park Road
Hayes
Middlesex UB4 8JN   Tel: 020-8848 9048

ASTRAL ACTORS MANAGEMENT
7 Greenway Close
London NW9 5AZ
Website: www.astralactors.com
e-mail: info@astralactors.com
Fax: 020-8200 3694   Tel: 020-8728 2782

Eva Pope

Lee Williams

Paris Jefferson

P H O T O G R A P H E R

07876 586601

AUSTIN WEBSTER PERSONAL MANAGEMENT
9 Moss Lane
Romford, Essex RM1 2PT
Website: www.andmanagement.co.uk
e-mail: info@andmanagement.co.uk   Tel: 01708 787517

AVALON MANAGEMENT GROUP Ltd
4A Exmoor Street, London W10 6BD
Website: www.avalonuk.com
e-mail: enquiries@avalonuk.com
Fax: 020-7598 7300   Tel: 020-7598 8000

AVENUE ARTISTES Ltd
C G TV
8 Winn Road, Southampton SO17 1EN
Website: www.avenueartistes.com
e-mail: info@avenueartistes.com   Tel: 023-8055 1000

AWA - ANDREA WILDER AGENCY
23 Cambrian Drive
Colwyn Bay, Conwy LL28 4SL
Website: www.awagency.co.uk
e-mail: casting@awagency.co.uk
Fax: 07092 249314   Mobile: 07919 202401

AXM*
Actors' Exchange Management
PM Co-operative
206 Great Guildford Business Square
30 Great Guildford Street, London SE1 0HS
Website: www.axmgt.com
e-mail: info@axmgt.com
Fax: 020-7261 0408   Tel: 020-7261 0400

AZA ARTISTES
(Existing Clients only)
652 Finchley Road
London NW11 7NT   Tel: 020-8458 7288

BALLROOM, LONDON THEATRE OF
(Ballroom/Social Dancers for Film/TV/Theatre)
24 Montana Gardens
Sutton, Surrey SM1 4FP
Website: www.londontheatreofballroom.com
e-mail: office@londontheatreofballroom.com
Mobile: 07958 784462   Tel: 020-8722 8798

B A M ASSOCIATES
Benets Cottage, Dolberrow, Churchill, Bristol BS25 5NT
Website: www.ebam.tv
e-mail: casting@ebam.tv   Tel: 01934 852942

BARKER Gavin ASSOCIATES Ltd*
(Gavin Barker, Michelle Burke)
2d Wimpole Street, London W1G 0EB
Website: www.gavinbarkerassociates.co.uk
e-mail: steven@gavinbarkerassociates.co.uk
Fax: 020-7499 3777   Tel: 020-7499 4777

BASHFORD Simon
(See GLOBAL ARTISTS)

B.A.S.I.C./JD AGENCY
C V S
3 Rushden House
Tatlow Road, Glenfield
Leicester LE3 8ND
e-mail: jonny.dallas@ntlworld.com   Tel/Fax: 0116-287 9594

BECKER Paul
e-mail: paul@paulbeckerltd.com
Fax: + 972 3 761 7144   Tel + 972 52 528 1645

BELCANTO LONDON ACADEMY MANAGEMENT
(Children & Young Adults)
Performance House, 20 Passey Place
Eltham, London SE9 5DQ
e-mail: bla@dircon.co.uk
Fax: 020-8850 9944   Tel: 020-8850 9888

BELFRAGE Julian ASSOCIATES*
Adam House
14 New Burlington Street
London W1S 3BQ
Fax: 020-7287 8832   Tel: 020-7287 8544

BELL Olivia Ltd*
189 Wardour Street
London W1F 8ZD
e-mail: info@olivia-bell.co.uk
Fax: 020-7439 3485   Tel: 020-7439 3270

BENJAMIN Audrey AGENCY
278A Elgin Avenue, Maida Vale, London W9 1JR
e-mail: a.benjamin@btconnect.com
Fax: 020-7266 5480   Tel: 020-7289 7180

BETTS Jorg ASSOCIATES*
Gainsborough House
81 Oxford Street, London W1D 2EU
e-mail: agents@jorgbetts.com
Fax: 020-7903 5301   Tel: 020-7903 5300

DIRECT PERSONAL MANAGEMENT

formerly Direct Line Personal Management

Personal Manager: Daphne Franks

e-mail: daphne.franks@directpm.co.uk

website: www.directpm.co.uk

LONDON
St. John's House
16 St. John's Vale
London SE8 4EN
Tel/fax 020 8694 1788

LEEDS
Park House
62 Lidgett Lane
Leeds LS8 1PL
Tel/fax 0113 266 4036

BILLBOARD PERSONAL MANAGEMENT
Unit 5
11 Mowll Street
London SW9 6BG
Website: www.billboardpm.com
e-mail: billboardpm@btconnect.com
Fax: 020-7793 0426   Tel: 020-7735 9956

BILLY MARSH DRAMA Ltd
(Actors & Actresses)
(See MARSH Billy DRAMA Ltd)

BIRD AGENCY
(Personal Performance Management)
Birkbeck Centre, Birkbeck Road
Sidcup, Kent DA14 4DE
Fax: 020-8308 1370   Tel: 020-8308 6994

BLOND Rebecca ASSOCIATES
69A Kings Road
London SW3 4NX
e-mail: info@rebeccablondassociates.com
Fax: 020-7351 4600   Tel: 020-7351 4100

BLOOMFIELDS MANAGEMENT*
34 South Molton Street
London W1K 5BP
Website: www.bloomfieldsmanagement.com
e-mail: emma@bloomfieldsmanagement.com
Fax: 020-7493 4449   Tel: 020-7493 4448

BLUE WAND MANAGEMENT
2nd Floor
12 Weltje Road
Hammersmith, London W6 9TG
e-mail: bluewand@btinternet.com   Tel: 020-8741 2038

BMA MODELS
346 High Street
Marlow House
Berkhamsted, Herts HP4 1HT
Website: www.bmamodels.com
e-mail: info@bmamodels.com
Fax: 01442 879879   Tel: 01442 878878

BODENS AGENCY
PM
Bodens Studios & Agency
99 East Barnet Road
New Barnet, Herts EN4 8RF
Website: www.bodensagency.com
e-mail: info@bodensagency.com
Fax: 020-8449 5212   Tel: 020-8447 0909

BOYCE Sandra MANAGEMENT*
1 Kingsway House
Albion Road
London N16 0TA
Website: www.sandraboyce.com
e-mail: info@sandraboyce.com
Fax: 020-7241 2313   Tel: 020-7923 0606

BRAIDMAN Michelle ASSOCIATES*
2 Futura House
169 Grange Road
London SE1 3BN
e-mail: info@braidman.com
Fax: 020-7231 4634   Tel: 020-7237 3523

BRAITHWAITE'S THEATRICAL AGENCY
8 Brookshill Avenue
Harrow Weald
Middlesex HA3 6RZ   Tel: 020-8954 5638

BREAK A LEG MANAGEMENT Ltd
Units 2/3 The Precinct
Packington Square
London N1 7UP
Website: www.breakalegman.com
e-mail: agency@breakalegman.com
Fax: 020-7359 3660   Tel: 020-7359 3594

BROADCASTING AGENCY
Unit 36, Pall Mall Deposit
124-128 Barlby Road
London W10 6BL
Website: www.broadcastingagency.co.uk
e-mail: info@broadcastingagency.co.uk
Fax: 020-8960 9689   Tel: 020-8960 5020

Steve Lawton

PHOTOGRAPHY LONDON

07973 307487

www.stevelawton.com

Student rates

Steven Webb, Gerard McCarthy, Helen Koya
Nathalie Cox, Robert Kazinsky, Natalie Anderson
Trey Farley, Anna Walton, Adam-Jon Fiorentino

Joanna Page

Nigel Harman

chris baker

photographer

www.chrisbakerphotographer.com

020 8441 3851

e: chrisbaker@photos2000.demon.co.uk

"Still the best!"

BROOD MANAGEMENT
Regent House
291 Kirkdale SE26 4QD
Website: www.broodmanagement.com
e-mail: broodmanagement@aol.com
Fax: 020-8776 6968   Tel: 020-8778 6673

BROOK Dolly AGENCY
PO Box 5436
Dunmow CM6 1WW
e-mail: dollybrookcasting@btinternet.com
Fax: 01371 875996   Tel: 01371 875767

BROOK Valerie AGENCY
10 Sandringham Road
Cheadle Hulme
Cheshire SK8 5NH
e-mail: colinbrook@freenetname.co.uk
Fax: 0161-488 4206   Tel: 0161-486 1631

BROOKS Claude ENTERTAINMENTS
19 Sussex Place
Slough
Berks SL1 1NH
Fax: 01753 520424   Tel: 01753 520717

BROWN & SIMCOCKS*
PM (Write)
1 Bridgehouse Court
109 Blackfriars Road
London SE1 8HW
e-mail: mail@brownandsimcocks.co.uk
Fax: 020-7928 1909   Tel: 020-7928 1229

BROWNING Malcolm*
Lafone House, Unit 2.4
The Leathermarket
Weston Street
London SE1 3ER
e-mail: info@malcolmbrowning.com
Fax: 0870 4581766   Tel: 020-7378 1053

BRUNSKILL MANAGEMENT Ltd*
PM M S TV (Write)
Suite 8A
169 Queen's Gate, London SW7 5HE
e-mail: contact@brunskill.com
Fax: 020-7589 9460   Tel: 020-7581 3388

The Courtyard
Edenhall
Penrith, Cumbria CA11 8ST
e-mail: admin@brunskill.com
Fax: 01768 881850   Tel: 01768 881430

BSA Ltd
(See HARRISON Penny BSA Ltd)

BUCHANAN Bronia ASSOCIATES Ltd*
Nederlander House
7 Great Russell Street
London WC1B 3NH
Website: www.buchanan-associates.co.uk
e-mail: info@buchanan-associates.co.uk
Fax: 020-7631 2034   Tel: 020-7631 2004

BURNETT GRANGER CROWTHER Ltd*
(Barry Burnett, Lindsay Granger, Lizanne Crowther)
3 Clifford Street
London W1S 2LF
Website: www.bgcltd.org
e-mail: associates@bgcltd.org
Fax: 020-7287 3239   Tel: 020-7437 8008

Nick Miles 2006   Lucy-Jo Hudson 2007

PHOTOGRAPHY BY PETER SIMPKIN

T: 020 8883 2727   M: 07973 224 084   E: petersimpkin@aol.com

www.petersimpkin.co.uk

BWH AGENCY Ltd The*
Barley Mow Business Centre
10 Barley Mow Passage
Chiswick, London W4 4PH
Website: www.thebwhagency.co.uk
e-mail: info@thebwhagency.co.uk
Fax: 020-8996 1662   Tel: 020-8996 1661

BYRON'S MANAGEMENT
(Children & Adults)
76 St James Lane, Muswell Hill, London N10 3DF
Website: www.byronsmanagement.co.uk
e-mail: byronscasting@aol.com
Fax: 020-8444 4040   Tel: 020-8444 4445

C.A. ARTISTES MANAGEMENT
26-28 Hammersmith Grove
London W6 7BA
Website: www.caartistes.com
e-mail: casting@caartistes.com   Tel: 020-7967 8067

CALON•
(Formerly Cardiff Casting)
Co-operative Actors Management
Chapter Arts Centre
Market Road
Cardiff CF5 1QE
Website: www.cardiffcasting.co.uk
e-mail: admin@cardiffcasting.co.uk   Tel: 029-2023 3321

photography

CHALKY WHYTE

HEADSHOTS-£150

FEE INCLUDES ALL SHOTS PRESENTED ON CD
+ 2 PRINTS SIZE 10 X 8 ins

t. 020 8960 9654
m.07880735912

email:chalkywhyte@supanet.com
website: www.chalkywhyte.co.uk

Representing Bilingual Actors and Actresses English, French, American etc.

CBA International.

M 07789 991032
E cba_office@yahoo.co.uk

C.B.A. Contact Cindy Brace
31 rue Milton, 75009 Paris, France
T (33) 1 4526 33 42. **F:** (33) 1 4874 51 42
E c_b_a@club-internet.fr
W www.cindy-brace.com

CAM*
PM (Write)
First Floor
55-59 Shaftesbury Avenue
London W1D 6LD
Website: www.cam.co.uk
e-mail: info@cam.co.uk
Fax: 020-7734 3205   Tel: 020-7292 0600

CAMBELL JEFFREY MANAGEMENT
(Set, Costume, Lighting Directors)
11A Greystone Court
South Street
Eastbourne BN21 4LP
e-mail: cambell@theatricaldesigners.co.uk
Fax: 01323 411373   Tel: 01323 411444

CAMPBELL Alison MODEL & PROMOTION AGENCY
381 Beersbridge Road
Belfast BT5 5DT
Website: www.alisoncampbellmodels.com
e-mail: info@alisoncampbellmodels.com
Fax: 028-9080 9808   Tel: 028-9080 9809

CANONGATE
9 Waters Close
Leith
Edinburgh EH6 6RB
Website: www.canongate.com
e-mail: al@canongate.com
Fax: 0131-555 2021   Tel: 0131-555 4455

CAPITAL VOICES
(Anne Skates) (Session Singers, Studio, Stage, TV & Film)
PO Box 364
Esher
Surrey KT10 9XZ
Website: www.capitalvoices.com
e-mail: capvox@aol.com
Fax: 01372 466229   Tel: 01372 466228

CAREY Roger ASSOCIATES*
PM
Suite 909
The Old House
Shepperton Film Studios
Studios Road
Shepperton, Middlesex TW17 0QD
e-mail: info@rogercarey.f25.com
Fax: 01932 569602   Tel: 01932 582890

CARNEY Jessica ASSOCIATES*
PM Write
4th Floor
23 Golden Square, London W1F 9JP
e-mail: info@jcarneyassociates.co.uk
Fax: 020-7434 4173   Tel: 020-7434 4143

CAROUSEL EVENTS
(Entertainment for Corporate & Private Events)
Ivy House
35 High Street
Bushey
Herts WD23 1BD
Website: www.carouselevents.co.uk
e-mail: enquiries@carouselevents.co.uk
Fax: 0845 3374981   Tel: 0845 3374980

CARR Norrie AGENCY
Holborn Studios
49-50 Eagle Wharf Road
London N1 7ED
Website: www.norriecarr.com
e-mail: info@norriecarr.com
Fax: 020-7253 1772   Tel: 020-7253 1771

CARTEURS
170A Church Road
Hove, East Sussex BN3 2DJ
Website: www.stonelandsschool.co.uk
Fax: 01273 770444   Tel: 01273 770445

KAREN SCOTT PHOTOGRAPHY

07958 975 950
www.karenscottphotography.com

SHEILA BURNETT
PHOTOGRAPHY

Simon Pegg   Imelda Staunton

Patsy Palmer   Ewan McGregor

020 7289 3058
www.sheilaburnett-photography.com
Student Rates

ETHNICS ARTISTE AGENCY

Talent of Colour. Talent of Foreign Language.

| Film | TV | Radio | Commercials | Theatre
| Photographic Work | Voice Overs

T: 020-8523 4242
F: 020-8523 4523

CASAROTTO MARSH Ltd
(Film Technicians)
Waverley House, 7-12 Noel Street, London W1F 8GQ
Website: www.casarotto.co.uk
e-mail: casarottomarsh@casarotto.co.uk
Fax: 020-7287 9128   Tel: 020-7287 4450

CASTAWAY ACTORS AGENCY
30-31 Wicklow Street, Dublin 2, Ireland
Website: www.irish-actors.com
e-mail: castaway@clubi.ie
Fax: 00 353 1 6719133   Tel: 00 353 1 6719264

CASTCALL & CASTFAX
(Casting & Consultancy Service)
106 Wilsden Avenue, Luton LU1 5HR
Website: www.castcall.co.uk
e-mail: casting@castcall.co.uk
Fax: 01582 480736   Tel: 01582 456213

CASTING COUCH The
(Moira Townsend) (E-mail submissions only)
213 Trowbridge Road
Bradford-on-Avon, Wiltshire BA15 1EU
e-mail: moiratownsend@yahoo.co.uk   Mobile: 07932 785807

CASTING DEPARTMENT The
Elysium Gate, Unit 15
126-128 New Kings Road, London SW6 4LZ
e-mail: jillscastingdpt@aol.com
Fax: 020-7736 2221   Tel: 020-7384 0388

CASTING SUITE AGENCY The
8-10 Lower James Street, London W1F 9EL
Website: www.thecastingsuite.co.uk
e-mail: agency@thecastingsuite.co.uk
Fax: 020-7494 0803   Tel: 020-7534 5757

CASTING UK
10 Coptic Street, London WC1A 1NH
Website: www.castinguk.com
e-mail: info@castinguk.com   Tel: 020-7580 3456

C B A INTERNATIONAL
166 Waverley Avenue
Twickenham TW2 6DL
e-mail: cba_office@yahoo.co.uk   Mobile: 07789 991032

(Cindy Brace)
31 rue Milton
75009 Paris, France
Website: www.cindy-brace.com
e-mail: c_b_a@club-internet.fr
Fax: 00 33 148 74 51 42   Tel: 00 33 145 26 33 42

C C A MANAGEMENT*
PM (Write) (Actors and Technicians)
Garden Level
32 Charlwood Street, London SW1V 2DY
e-mail: cca@ccamanagement.co.uk
Fax: 020-7630 7376   Tel: 020-7630 6303

CCM•
Co-operative
Panther House, 38 Mount Pleasant, London WC1X 0AP
Website: www.ccmactors.com
e-mail: casting@ccmactors.com   Tel: 020-7278 0507

CDA
(See DAWSON Caroline ASSOCIATES)

CELEBRITY GROUP The
13 Montagu Mews South, London W1H 7ER
Website: www.celebrity.co.uk
e-mail: info@celebrity.co.uk   Tel: 0871 2501234

CENTRAL LINE•
PM Co-operative
11 East Circus Street, Nottingham NG1 5AF
Website: www.the-central-line.co.uk
e-mail: centralline@btconnect.com   Tel: 0115-941 2937

CENTRE STAGE AGENCY*
7 Rutledge Terrace
South Circular Road, Dublin 8, Ireland
e-mail: geraldinecenterstage@eircom.net
                        Tel/Fax: 00 353 1 4533599

CHAMBERS MANAGEMENT
23 Long Lane, Barbican, London EC1A 9HL
Website: www.chambersmgt.co.uk
e-mail: hannah@chambersmgt.com
Fax: 020-7796 3676   Tel: 020-7796 3588

CHAPMAN AGENCY
BSA
Millennium Point, G2
Curzon Street, Birmingham B4 7XG
e-mail: chapmanagency@bsa.uce.ac.uk
Fax: 0121-331 7221   Tel: 0121-331 7220

CHARLESWORTH Peter & ASSOCIATES
68 Old Brompton Road, London SW7 3LQ
e-mail: info@petercharlesworth.co.uk
Fax: 020-7589 2922   Tel: 020-7581 2478

CHATTO & LINNIT Ltd
123A Kings Road, London SW3 4PL
e-mail: info@chattolinnit.com
Fax: 020-7352 3450   Tel: 020-7352 7722

Mike S. Photography

Most types of photography undertaken Studio or location

Contact Mike on: t: 0121 323 4459   m: 07850 160311
e: mike@mbmphoto.fsnet.co.uk w: www.mikephotos.co.uk

stage

film

movies **Drama**

www.hobsons-international.com

theatre

television   commercials

Corporate & promos

videos **Commercial**

idents

travel & sport

news **Presenters** music

documentaries

entertainment

HOBSON'S | 62 Chiswick High Road | T] +44 (0)20 8995 3628
London W4 1SY | F] +44 (0)20 8996 5350

Alistair McGowan   Rachel Weisz

CAROLE LATIMER Photography

T: 020 7727 9371   www.carolelatimer.com   e-mail: carole.latimer@freenet.co.uk

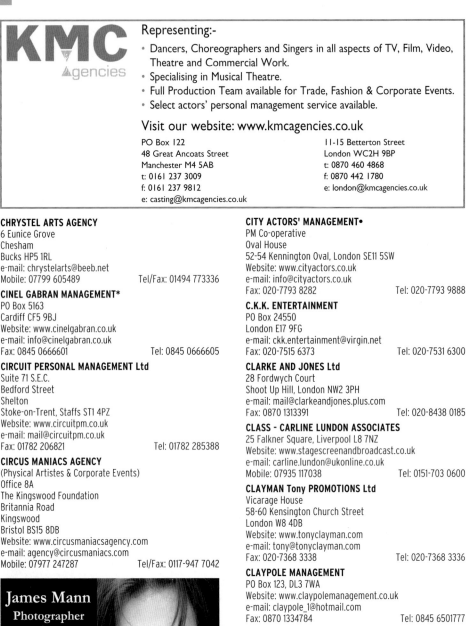

KMC Agencies

Representing:-
- Dancers, Choreographers and Singers in all aspects of TV, Film, Video, Theatre and Commercial Work.
- Specialising in Musical Theatre.
- Full Production Team available for Trade, Fashion & Corporate Events.
- Select actors' personal management service available.

Visit our website: www.kmcagencies.co.uk

PO Box 122
48 Great Ancoats Street
Manchester M4 5AB
t: 0161 237 3009
f: 0161 237 9812
e: casting@kmcagencies.co.uk

11-15 Betterton Street
London WC2H 9BP
t: 0870 460 4868
f: 0870 442 1780
e: london@kmcagencies.co.uk

CHRYSTEL ARTS AGENCY
6 Eunice Grove
Chesham
Bucks HP5 1RL
e-mail: chrystelarts@beeb.net
Mobile: 07799 605489   Tel/Fax: 01494 773336

CINEL GABRAN MANAGEMENT*
PO Box 5163
Cardiff CF5 9BJ
Website: www.cinelgabran.co.uk
e-mail: info@cinelgabran.co.uk
Fax: 0845 0666601   Tel: 0845 0666605

CIRCUIT PERSONAL MANAGEMENT Ltd
Suite 71 S.E.C.
Bedford Street
Shelton
Stoke-on-Trent, Staffs ST1 4PZ
Website: www.circuitpm.co.uk
e-mail: mail@circuitpm.co.uk
Fax: 01782 206821   Tel: 01782 285388

CIRCUS MANIACS AGENCY
(Physical Artistes & Corporate Events)
Office 8A
The Kingswood Foundation
Britannia Road
Kingswood
Bristol BS15 8DB
Website: www.circusmaniacsagency.com
e-mail: agency@circusmaniacs.com
Mobile: 07977 247287   Tel/Fax: 0117-947 7042

CITY ACTORS' MANAGEMENT•
PM Co-operative
Oval House
52-54 Kennington Oval, London SE11 5SW
Website: www.cityactors.co.uk
e-mail: info@cityactors.co.uk
Fax: 020-7793 8282   Tel: 020-7793 9888

C.K.K. ENTERTAINMENT
PO Box 24550
London E17 9FG
e-mail: ckk.entertainment@virgin.net
Fax: 020-7515 6373   Tel: 020-7531 6300

CLARKE AND JONES Ltd
28 Fordwych Court
Shoot Up Hill, London NW2 3PH
e-mail: mail@clarkeandjones.plus.com
Fax: 0870 1313391   Tel: 020-8438 0185

CLASS - CARLINE LUNDON ASSOCIATES
25 Falkner Square, Liverpool L8 7NZ
Website: www.stagescreenandbroadcast.co.uk
e-mail: carline.lundon@ukonline.co.uk
Mobile: 07935 117038   Tel: 0151-703 0600

CLAYMAN Tony PROMOTIONS Ltd
Vicarage House
58-60 Kensington Church Street
London W8 4DB
Website: www.tonyclayman.com
e-mail: tony@tonyclayman.com
Fax: 020-7368 3338   Tel: 020-7368 3336

CLAYPOLE MANAGEMENT
PO Box 123, DL3 7WA
Website: www.claypolemanagement.co.uk
e-mail: claypole_1@hotmail.com
Fax: 0870 1334784   Tel: 0845 6501777

CLIC AGENCY
Rhoslwyn
Rhoslsaf, Nr. Caernarfon
Gwynedd LL54 7NF
Website: www.clicagency.co.uk
e-mail: clic@btinternet.com   Tel: 01286 831001

CLOUD NINE AGENCY
96 Tiber Gardens
Treaty Street, London N1 0XE
Website: www.cloudnineagency.co.uk
e-mail: cloudnineagency@blueyonder.co.uk
Tel/Fax: 020-7278 0029

James Mann
Photographer

London

07742814160

james@actors-photography.com
Chris Harrison

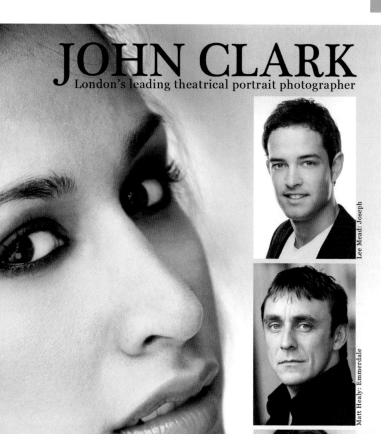

CMP MANAGEMENT
8-30 Galena Road
Hammersmith
London W6 0LT
e-mail: info@ravenscourt.net
Fax: 020-8741 1786   Tel: 020-8741 3400

COCHRANE Elspeth PERSONAL MANAGEMENT*
(Helen Smith)
16 Trinity Close
The Pavement
London SW4 0JD
e-mail: info@elspethcochrane.co.uk   Tel: 020-7622 3566

COLE KITCHENN PERSONAL MANAGEMENT Ltd
212 Strand
London WC2R 1AP
Website: www.colekitchenn.com
e-mail: stuart@colekitchenn.com
Fax: 020-7353 9639   Tel: 020-7427 5680

COLLINS Shane ASSOCIATES*
11-15 Betterton Street
Covent Garden
London WC2H 9BP
Website: www.shanecollins.co.uk
e-mail: info@shanecollins.co.uk
Fax: 0870 460 1983   Tel: 020-7470 8864

COLLIS MANAGEMENT
182 Trevelyan Road
London SW17 9LW
e-mail: marilyn@collismanagement.co.uk
Fax: 020-8682 0973   Tel: 020-8767 0196

COMEDY CLUB Ltd The
2nd Floor
28-31 Moulsham Street
Chelmsford
Essex CM2 0HX
Website: www.hahaheehee.com
e-mail: info@hahaheehee.com
Fax: 01245 255507   Tel: 0870 0425656

COMIC VOICE MANAGEMENT
2nd Floor
28-31 Moulsham Street
Chelmsford
Essex CM2 0HX
Website: www.comicvoice.com
e-mail: info@comicvoice.com
Fax: 01245 255507   Tel: 0870 0425656

COMMERCIAL AGENCY Ltd The
(See TCA)

COMPLETE ARTISTES
N&S Tower
4 Selsdon Way
City Harbour
London E14 9GL
Website: www.completeartistes.com
e-mail: lisa.dawson@nasnet.co.uk
Fax: 020-7308 6001   Tel: 020-7308 5351

CONTI Italia AGENCY Ltd
S M TV F (Write or Phone)
23 Goswell Road
London EC1M 7AJ
e-mail: agency@italiaconti.co.uk
Fax: 020-7253 1430   Tel: 020-7608 7500

CONWAY Clive CELEBRITY PRODUCTIONS Ltd
32 Grove Street
Oxford OX2 7JT
Website: www.celebrityproductions.info
e-mail: info@celebrityproductions.org
Fax: 01865 514409   Tel: 01865 514830

CONWAY VAN GELDER GRANT Ltd*
PM
3rd Floor
18-21 Jermyn Street
London SW1Y 6HP
Fax: 020-7287 1940   Tel: 020-7287 0077

COOKE Howard ASSOCIATES*
19 Coulson Street
Chelsea
London SW3 3NA
Fax: 020-7591 0155   Tel: 020-7591 0144

COOPER Tommy AGENCY The
(Comedy, Magicians)
6 Marlott Road
Poole
Dorset BH15 3DX
Website: www.tommycooperremembered.co.uk
Mobile: 07860 290437   Tel: 01202 666001

CORNER Clive ASSOCIATES
3 Bainbridge Close
Ham
Middlesex TW10 5JJ
e-mail: cornerassociates@aol.com   Tel/Fax: 020-8332 1910

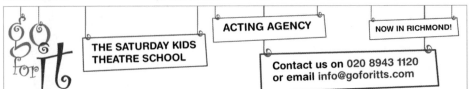

CORNISH Caroline MANAGEMENT Ltd
(Technicians Only)
12 Shinfield Street
London W12 0HN
Website: www.carolinecornish.co.uk
e-mail: carolinecornish@btconnect.com
Fax: 020-8743 7887   Tel: 020-8743 7337

COULSON Lou ASSOCIATES Ltd*
1st Floor
37 Berwick Street
London W1F 8RS
e-mail: info@loucoulson.co.uk
Fax: 020-7439 7569   Tel: 020-7734 9633

COULTER MANAGEMENT AGENCY Ltd*
(Anne Coulter)
333 Woodlands Road
Glasgow G3 6NG
e-mail: cmaglasgow@btconnect.com
Fax: 0141-357 6676   Tel: 0141-357 6666

COVENT GARDEN MANAGEMENT
5 Denmark Street
London WC2H 8LP
Website: www.coventgardenmanagement.com
e-mail: agents@coventgardenmanagement.com
Fax: 020-7240 8409   Tel: 020-7240 8400

CPA MANAGEMENT
The Studios
219B North Street
Romford
Essex RM1 4QA
Website: www.cpamanagement.co.uk
e-mail: david@cpamanagement.co.uk
Fax: 01708 766077   Tel: 01708 766444

CRAWFORDS
PO Box 44394
London SW20 0YP
Website: www.crawfords.tv
e-mail: cr@wfords.com
Fax: 020-3258 5037   Tel: 020-8947 9999

CREATIVE MEDIA
PM (Write)
11 Asquith Road
Bentley
Doncaster DN5 0NS
Mobile: 07787 784412   Tel: 01302 812233

CREATIVE MEDIA MANAGEMENT*
(No Actors - Film, TV & Theatre Technical Personnel only)
3B Walpole Court
Ealing Studios
Ealing Green
London W5 5ED
Website: www.creativemediamanagement.com
e-mail: enquiries@creativemediamanagement.com
Fax: 020-8566 5554   Tel: 020-8584 5363

CREDITS ACTORS AGENCY Ltd
29 Lorn Road
London SW9 0AB
e-mail: credits@actors29.freeserve.co.uk
                                      Tel: 020-7737 0735

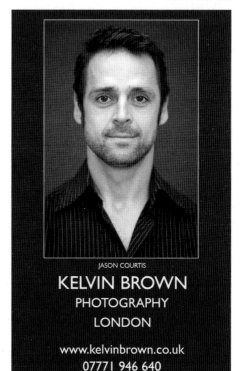

CRESCENT MANAGEMENT•
PM Co-operative
10 Barley Mow Passage
Chiswick
London W4 4PH
e-mail: mail@crescentmanagement.co.uk
Fax: 020-8987 0207   Tel: 020-8987 0191

CROWD PULLERS
(Street Performers)
14 Somerset Gardens
London SE13 7SY
e-mail: jhole@crowdpullers.co.uk
Fax: 020-8469 2147   Tel: 020-8469 3900

CRUICKSHANK CAZENOVE Ltd*
(Directors, Designers, Choreographers)
97 Old South Lambeth Road
London SW8 1XU
e-mail: office@cruickshankcazenove.com
Fax: 020-7582 6405   Tel: 020-7735 2933

CS MANAGEMENT
The Croft, 7 Cannon Road
Southgate, London N14 7HE
Website: www.csmanagementuk.com
e-mail: carole@csmanagementuk.com
Fax: 020-8886 7555   Tel: 020-8886 4264

C.S.A.
(Christina Shepherd Advertising)
4th Floor, 45 Maddox Street
London W1S 2PE
e-mail: csa@shepherdmanagement.co.uk
Fax: 020-7499 7535   Tel: 020-7499 7534

CSM (ARTISTS)
PM
Room 212
77 Oxford Street
London W1D 2ES
e-mail: csmartists@aol.com
Fax: 020-8842 4132   Tel: 020-7659 2399

CURTIS BROWN GROUP Ltd*
Haymarket House
28-29 Haymarket, London SW1Y 4SP
e-mail: actorsagents@curtisbrown.co.uk
Fax: 020-7393 4401   Tel: 020-7393 4400

D Lisa MANAGEMENT Ltd
PO Box 4050, Bracknell RG42 9BZ
e-mail: agents@lisad.co.uk   Tel/Fax: 01344 643568

DALY PEARSON ASSOCIATES
(David Daly & Paul Pearson)
586A King's Road
London SW6 2DX
Website: www.dalypearson.co.uk
e-mail: agent@dalypearson.co.uk
Fax: 020-7610 9512   Tel: 020-7384 1036

DALY PEARSON ASSOCIATES (MANCHESTER)
16 King Street
Knutsford WA16 6DL
Website: www.dalypearson.co.uk
e-mail: north@dalypearson.co.uk
Fax: 01565 755334   Tel: 01565 631999

DALZELL & BERESFORD Ltd
26 Astwood Mews
London SW7 4DE
Fax: 020-7341 9412   Tel: 020-7341 9411

DANCERS
1 Charlotte Street, London W1T 1RD
Website: www.features.co.uk
e-mail: info@features.co.uk
Fax: 020-7636 1657   Tel: 020-7636 1473

DARRELL Emma MANAGEMENT
(Producers, Directors & Writers)
Hazelbank
3 Chalfont Lane
Chorleywood, Herts WD3 5PR
e-mail: emma.mc@virgin.net
Fax: 01923 284064   Tel: 01923 284061

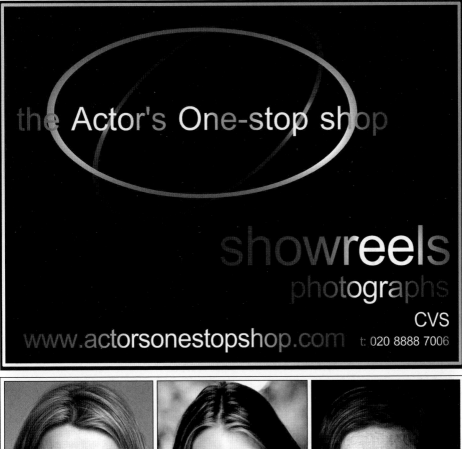

Terry Sweeney   Lauren Cohan   Elizabeth Marmur

ric bacon
07970 970799
www.ricbacon.co.uk

DAVID ARTISTES MANAGEMENT AGENCY Ltd The
F TV Md (Write)
26-28 Hammersmith Grove
London W6 7BA
Website: www.davidagency.net
e-mail: casting@davidagency.net   Tel: 020-7967 7001

DAVIS Chris MANAGEMENT Ltd*
Tenbury House, 36 Teme Street
Tenbury Wells, Worcestershire WR15 8AA
Website: www.cdm-ltd.com   e-mail: info@cdm-ltd.com
Fax: 01584 819076   Tel: 01584 819005

DAVIS Lena, JOHN BISHOP ASSOCIATES
Cotton's Farmhouse
Whiston Road, Cogenhoe
Northants NN7 1NL   Tel: 01604 891487

DAWSON Caroline ASSOCIATES*
125 Gloucester Road
London SW7 4TE
e-mail: cda@cdalondon.com
Fax: 020-7373 1110   Tel: 020-7373 3323

DEALERS AGENCY BELFAST
22-31 Waring Street
Belfast BT1 2DX
Website: www.dealersagency.co.uk
e-mail: patrickduncan609@msn.com
Fax: 028-9043 6699   Tel: 028-9024 2726

DENMAN CASTING AGENCY
Burgess House
Main Street, Farnsfield
Notts NG22 8EF   Tel/Fax: 01623 882272

DENMARK STREET MANAGEMENT●
PM Co-operative (Write SAE)
Suite 4
Clarendon Buildings
25 Horsell Road, Highbury N5 1XL
Website: www.denmarkstreet.net
e-mail: mail@denmarkstreet.net
Fax: 020-7607 8085   Tel: 020-7700 5200

DEREK'S HANDS AGENCY
(Hand & Foot Modelling)
26-28 Hammersmith Grove
London W6 7BA
Website: www.derekshands.com
e-mail: casting@derekshands.com   Tel: 020-8834 1609

de WOLFE Felix*
PM (Write)
Kingsway House
103 Kingsway
London WC2B 6QX
e-mail: info@felixdewolfe.com
Fax: 020-7242 8119   Tel: 020-7242 5066

DIAMOND MANAGEMENT*
31 Percy Street, London W1T 2DD
e-mail: agents@diman.co.uk
Fax: 020-7631 0500   Tel: 020-7631 0400

DIESTENFELD Lily
(Personal Manager for 50+ ages)
(No unsolicited Mail/Calls from Actors)
28B Alexandra Grove
London N12 8HG   Tel: 020-8446 5379

Picture Credits Sinitta *actresss and singer*, Natalie Palys *Madness of King George*, Sir Richard Branson *Duo Magazine*, Andy Hamilton *Whitbread*, Anabel Kutay *ballerina and dancer Phantom of the Opera*, Miss Pinto and Rat, Benjamin and Rebecca Green *dancers*

Will C specialises in actors, actresses and personalities in advertising, editorial, film and television. He has been principal photographer on over 30 major films and 40 commercials. Actors and actresses portraits can be taken in our fully equipped film and digital studio in NW2 - just 15 minutes from Marble Arch or Baker Street.

Tokyo • New York • Amsterdam • Paris • London

DIMPLES THEATRICAL ACADEMY
84 Kirkhall Lane
Leigh
Lancs WN7 5QQ
e-mail: info@dimplesacademy.com
Fax: 01942 262232   Tel: 01942 262012

DIRECT PERSONAL MANAGEMENT•
(Personal Manager: Daphne Franks)
St John's House
16 St John's Vale
London SE8 4EN
Website: www.directpm.co.uk
e-mail: daphne.franks@directpm.co.uk   Tel/Fax: 020-8694 1788

Park House
62 Lidgett Lane
Leeds LS8 1PL   Tel/Fax: 0113-266 4036

DOE John ASSOCIATES
26 Noko
3/6 Banister Road
London W10 4AR
Website: www.johndoeassociates.com
e-mail: info@johndoeassociates.com
Mobile: 07979 558594   Tel: 020-8960 2848

DON CAPO ENTERTAINMENT PRODUCTIONS
Suite B
5 South Bank Terrace
Surbiton
Surrey KT6 6DG
Website: www.doncapo.com
e-mail: info@doncapo.com
Mobile: 07884 056405   Tel/Fax: 020-8390 8535

DOUBLE ACT CELEBRITY LOOK ALIKES
PO Box 25574
London NW7 3GB
Website: www.double-act.co.uk
e-mail: info@double-act.co.uk
Fax: 020-8201 1795   Tel: 020-8381 0151

DOUBLEFVOICES
(Singers Agency)
1 Hunters Lodge
Bodiam
East Sussex TN32 5UE
e-mail: rob@doublefvoices.com
Mobile: 07976 927764   Tel: 01580 830071

DOWNES PRESENTERS AGENCY
96 Broadway
Bexleyheath
Kent DA6 7DE
Website: www.presentersagency.com
e-mail: downes@presentersagency.com   Tel: 020-8304 0541

DP MANAGEMENT
1 Euston Road
London NW1 2SA
e-mail: danny@dpmanagement.org
Fax: 020-7278 3466   Tel: 020-7843 4331

DQ MANAGEMENT
Suite 21
Kingsway House
134-140 Church Road
Hove
East Sussex BN3 2DL
Website: www.dqmanagement.com
e-mail: info@dqmanagement.com
Fax: 01273 779065   Tel: 01273 721221

DRB ENTERTAINMENT AGENCY
28 Blakes Quay
Gas Works Road
Reading
Berks RG1 3EN
Website: www.drbentertainment.co.uk
e-mail: info@drbentertainment.co.uk
Mobile: 07772 446627   Tel: 0118-958 3936

Personal Management

(Formerly known as Michael Garrett Associates)

Agents:
Simon Bashford
Michael Garrett
Niki Winterson

GLOBAL ARTISTS

23 Haymarket London SW1Y 4DG
Tel: 020 7839 4888 Fax: 020 7839 4555
email: info@globalartists.co.uk
www.globalartists.co.uk
www.theatricalagent.co.uk

Members of the Personal Managers' Association

Michael Garrett Associates Ltd. Registered No. 4404385
Registered Office: 23 Haymarket, London SW1Y 4DG

Anna-Maria Nabirye

Steve McFadden

Heather Peace

DREW Bryan Ltd
PM Write
Mezzanine
Quadrant House
80-82 Regent Street
London W1B 5AU
e-mail: bryan@bryandrewltd.com
Fax: 020-7437 0561   Tel: 020-7437 2293

DUDDRIDGE Paul MANAGEMENT
32 Rathbone Place
London W1T 1JJ
Website: www.paulduddridge.com
e-mail: mail@paulduddridge.com
Fax: 020-7580 3480   Tel: 020-7580 3580

EARLE Kenneth PERSONAL MANAGEMENT
214 Brixton Road
London SW9 6AP
Website: www.entertainment-kennethearle.co.uk
e-mail: kennethearle@agents-uk.com
Fax: 020-7274 9529   Tel: 020-7274 1219

EARNSHAW Susi MANAGEMENT
PM
68 High Street
Barnet, Herts EN5 5SJ
Website: www.susiearnshaw.co.uk
e-mail: casting@susiearnshaw.co.uk
Fax: 020-8364 9618   Tel: 020-8441 5010

EAST 15 MANAGEMENT
(Only represent E15 Graduates)
East 15 Acting School
Rectory Lane
Loughton
Essex IG10 3RY
e-mail: e15management@yahoo.com
Mobile: 07748 704718   Tel/Fax: 020-8508 3746

EDEN Shelly ASSOCIATES Ltd
The Old Factory
Minus One House
Lyttelton Road
London E10 5NQ
e-mail: shellyeden@aol.com   Tel/Fax: 020-8558 3536

EDLER Debbie MANAGEMENT (DEM)
37 Russet Way
Peasedown St John
Bath BA2 8ST
Website: www.dem.1colony.com
e-mail: dem2005@eircom.net   Tel/Fax: 01761 436631

EJA ASSOCIATES
Lower Ground Floor
86 Vassall Road
London SW9 6JA
e-mail: ejaassociates@aol.com
Mobile: 07891 632946   Tel: 020-7564 2688

EKA MODEL & ACTOR MANAGEMENT
The Warehouse Studios
Glaziers Lane
Culcheth
Warrington WA3 4AQ
Website: www.eka-agency.com
e-mail: kate@eka-agency.com
Fax: 01925 767563   Tel: 01925 761087

ELLIOTT AGENCY Ltd The
10 High Street
Shoreham-by-Sea BN43 5DA
Website: www.elliottagency.co.uk
e-mail: elliottagency@btconnect.com   Tel: 01273 454111

ELLIS Bill Ltd
(See A & B PERSONAL MANAGEMENT Ltd)

ELLITE MANAGEMENT
The Dancer
8 Peterson Road
Wakefield WF1 4EB
Website: www.elliteproductions.co.uk
e-mail: enquiries@ellitemanagement.co.uk
Mobile: 07957 631510   Tel: 0845 6525361

EMPTAGE HALLETT*
14 Rathbone Place
London W1T 1HT
e-mail: mail@emptagehallett.co.uk
Fax: 020-7580 2748   Tel: 020-7436 0425

2nd Floor
3-5 The Balcony
Castle Arcade
Cardiff CF10 1BU
e-mail: claire.lincoln@emptagehallett.co.uk
Fax: 029-2034 4206   Tel: 029-2034 4205

ENGLISH Doreen '95
(Write or Phone)
4 Selsey Avenue
Aldwick, Bognor Regis
West Sussex PO21 2QZ   Tel/Fax: 01243 825968

EPSTEIN June ASSOCIATES
(Write)
Flat 1
62 Compayne Gardens
London NW6 3RY
e-mail: june@june-epstein-associates.co.uk
Fax: 020-7328 0684   Tel: 020-7328 0864

ESOTERIC ENTERTAINMENTS Ltd
(For Psychics & Mystics)
Maidstone TV Studios
New Cut Road
Vintners Park
Maidstone, Kent ME14 5NZ
Website: www.esoteric-e.co.uk
e-mail: info@esoteric-e.co.uk   Tel: 01622 684504

ESSANAY*
PM (Write)
PO Box 44394
London SW20 0YP
e-mail: info@essanay.co.uk
Fax: 020-3258 5037   Tel: 020-8549 4472

ET-NIK-A PRIME MANAGEMENT & CASTINGS Ltd
30 Great Portland Street
London W1W 8QU
Website: www.etnikapmc.com
e-mail: info@etnikapmc.com
Fax: 020-7299 3558   Tel: 020-7299 3555

ETHNICS ARTISTE AGENCY
86 Elphinstone Road
Walthamstow, London E17 5EX
Fax: 020-8523 4523   Tel: 020-8523 4242

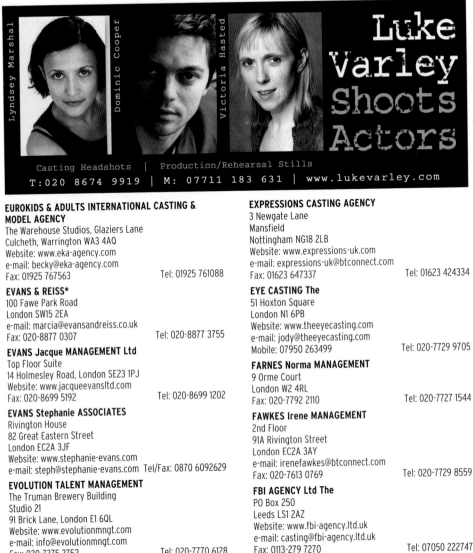

EUROKIDS & ADULTS INTERNATIONAL CASTING & MODEL AGENCY
The Warehouse Studios, Glaziers Lane
Culcheth, Warrington WA3 4AQ
Website: www.eka-agency.com
e-mail: becky@eka-agency.com
Fax: 01925 767563
Tel: 01925 761088

EVANS & REISS*
100 Fawe Park Road
London SW15 2EA
e-mail: marcia@evansandreiss.co.uk
Fax: 020-8877 0307
Tel: 020-8877 3755

EVANS Jacque MANAGEMENT Ltd
Top Floor Suite
14 Holmesley Road, London SE23 1PJ
Website: www.jacqueevansltd.com
Fax: 020-8699 5192
Tel: 020-8699 1202

EVANS Stephanie ASSOCIATES
Rivington House
82 Great Eastern Street
London EC2A 3JF
Website: www.stephanie-evans.com
e-mail: steph@stephanie-evans.com Tel/Fax: 0870 6092629

EVOLUTION TALENT MANAGEMENT
The Truman Brewery Building
Studio 21
91 Brick Lane, London E1 6QL
Website: www.evolutionmngt.com
e-mail: info@evolutionmngt.com
Fax: 020-7375 2752
Tel: 020-7770 6128

EXPRESSIONS CASTING AGENCY
3 Newgate Lane
Mansfield
Nottingham NG18 2LB
Website: www.expressions-uk.com
e-mail: expressions-uk@btconnect.com
Fax: 01623 647337
Tel: 01623 424334

EYE CASTING The
51 Hoxton Square
London N1 6PB
Website: www.theeyecasting.com
e-mail: jody@theeyecasting.com
Mobile: 07950 263499
Tel: 020-7729 9705

FARNES Norma MANAGEMENT
9 Orme Court
London W2 4RL
Fax: 020-7792 2110
Tel: 020-7727 1544

FAWKES Irene MANAGEMENT
2nd Floor
91A Rivington Street
London EC2A 3AY
e-mail: irenefawkes@btconnect.com
Fax: 020-7613 0769
Tel: 020-7729 8559

FBI AGENCY Ltd The
PO Box 250
Leeds LS1 2AZ
Website: www.fbi-agency.ltd.uk
e-mail: casting@fbi-agency.ltd.uk
Fax: 0113-279 7270
Tel: 07050 222747

PETER HALL
P H O T O G R A P H Y

t: 020 8981 2822   m: 07803 345495

peter@peterhall.fsnet.co.uk   www.peterhall-photo.co.uk

S T U D E N T   R A T E S

Lime Actors Agency & Management Ltd

Nemesis House / 1 Oxford Court / Bishopsgate / Manchester / M2 3WQ
0161 236 0827 / www.limemanagement.tv / georgina@limemanagement.co.uk

FEAST MANAGEMENT Ltd*
10 Primrose Hill Studios
Fitzroy Road
London NW1 8TR
e-mail: office@feastmanagement.co.uk
Fax: 020-7586 9817   Tel: 020-7586 5502

FEATURES
1 Charlotte Street
London W1T 1RD
Website: www.features.co.uk
e-mail: info@features.co.uk
Fax: 020-7636 1657   Tel: 020-7637 1487

FIELD Alan ASSOCIATES
3 The Spinney
Bakers Hill
Hadley Common
Herts EN5 5QJ
e-mail: alanfielduk@aol.com
Fax: 020-8447 0657   Tel: 020-8441 1137

FILM RIGHTS Ltd
PM (Write)
Mezzanine
Quadrant House
80-82 Regent Street, London W1B 5AU
Fax: 020-7734 0044   Tel: 020-7734 9911

FINCH & PARTNERS
6 Heddon Street
London W1B 4BS
Website: www.finchandpartners.com
e-mail: kat@finchandpartners.com
Fax: 020-7287 6420   Tel: 020-7851 7140

FIRST ACT PERSONAL MANAGEMENT
2 Saint Michaels
New Arley, Coventry CV7 8PY
Website: www.spotlightagent.info/firstact
e-mail: firstactpm@aol.com
Fax: 01676 542777   Tel: 01676 540285

FIRST ARTIST ENTERTAINMENT Ltd
3 Tenterden Street, London W1S 1TD
Website: www.firstnci.com
Fax: 020-3205 2140   Tel: 020-7096 9999

FIRST CALL MANAGEMENT
29-30 Dame Street
Dublin 2, Ireland
e-mail: fcm@indigo.ie
Fax: 00 353 1 679 8353   Tel: 00 353 1 679 8401

FITZGERALD Sheridan MANAGEMENT
(For representation write only with SAE. No Phone Calls)
87 Western Road
Upton Park
London E13 9JE   Tel: 020-8471 9814

FLAIR TALENT
46 Barry Road
East Dulwich, London SE22 0HU
Website: www.flairtalent.com
e-mail: aaron@flairtalent.com   Tel: 020-8693 8649

FLETCHER ASSOCIATES
(Broadcast & Media)
25 Parkway
London N20 0XN
Fax: 020-8361 8866   Tel: 020-8361 8061

FLETCHER JACOB
(Artist Management)
First Floor
77 Leonard Street, London EC2A 4QS
e-mail: info@fletcherjacob.co.uk
Fax: 020-7168 8738   Tel: 020-7613 7234

FOSTER Sharon MANAGEMENT
15A Hollybank Road
Birmingham B13 0RF
Website: www.sharonfoster.co.uk
e-mail: mail@sharonfoster.co.uk   Tel: 0121-443 4865

FOX Clare ASSOCIATES
(Designers & Lighting Designers)
9 Plympton Road
London NW6 7EH
Website: www.clarefox.co.uk
e-mail: cimfox@yahoo.co.uk   Tel/Fax: 020-7328 7494

FRENCH Linda
(See ALEXANDER PERSONAL MANAGEMENT Ltd)

FRESH AGENTS Ltd
Suite 5, Saks House
19 Ship Street
Brighton BN1 1AD
Website: www.freshagents.co.uk
e-mail: info@freshagents.co.uk   Tel: 0845 4080998

FRESH MANAGEMENT
7 Marshall Road
Levenshulme
Manchester M19 2EG
e-mail: freshmanagement@btconnect.com
                                     Tel/Fax: 0161-434 8333

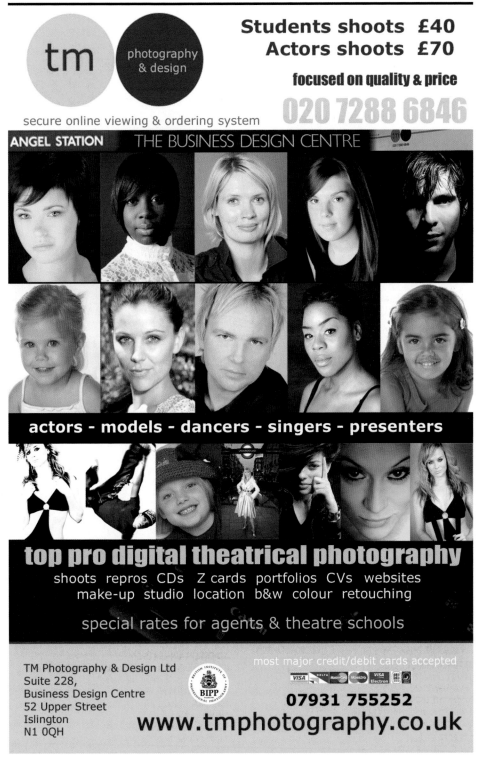

pure.

exclusive representation of professional actors

contact. debbie pine
pure. actors agency and management ltd
a. 44 salisbury road, manchester m41 0rb t. 0161 747 2377 m. 07808 295 230
f. 0161 746 9886 e. enquiries@pure-management.co.uk **www.pure-management.co.uk**

FRESH PARTNERS Ltd
19-21 Nile Street
London N1 7LL
Website: www.fresh-partners.com
e-mail: hello@fresh-partners.com
Fax: 020-7241 2749   Tel: 020-7566 1774

FRONTLINE ACTORS AGENCY DUBLIN
30-31 Wicklow Street
Dublin 2, Ireland
Website: www.frontlineactors.com
e-mail: frontlineactors@eircom.net   Tel: 00 353 1 6359882

FUNKY BEETROOT CELEBRITY MANAGEMENT Ltd
(Actors, TV Celebrities, Casting & Personal Management)
PO Box 143
Faversham
Kent ME13 9LP
Website: www.funky-beetroot.com
e-mail: info@funky-beetroot.com
Fax: 01227 752300   Tel: 01227 751549

FUSHION PUKKA BOSH
(London & New York)
27 Old Gloucester Street
London WC1N 3XX
e-mail: enquirieslondon@fushion-uk.com
Fax: 08700 111020   Tel: 08700 111100

GAGAN Hilary ASSOCIATES*
PM
187 Drury Lane
London WC2B 5QD
e-mail: hilary@hgassoc.freeserve.co.uk
Fax: 020-7430 1869   Tel: 020-7404 8794

GALLOWAYS ONE
15 Lexham Mews
London W8 6JW
e-mail: hugh@gallowaysone.com
Fax: 020-7376 2416   Tel: 020-7376 2288

GARDNER HERRITY Ltd*
(Kerry Gardner & Andy Herrity)
24 Conway Street
London W1T 6BG
e-mail: info@gardnerherrity.co.uk
Fax: 020-7388 0688   Tel: 020-7388 0088

GARRETT Michael
(See GLOBAL ARTISTS)

GARRICKS*
Angel House
76 Mallinson Road
London SW11 1BN
e-mail: info@garricks.net
Fax: 020-7801 0088   Tel: 020-7738 1600

GAY Noel
19 Denmark Street
London WC2H 8NA
Website: www.noelgay.com
Fax: 020-7287 1816   Tel: 020-7836 3941

GILBERT & PAYNE
Room 236, 2nd Floor
Linen Hall
162-168 Regent Street
London W1B 5TB
e-mail: ee@gilbertandpayne.com
Fax: 020-7494 3787   Tel: 020-7734 7505

GLASS Eric Ltd
25 Ladbroke Crescent
Notting Hill, London W11 1PS
e-mail: eglassltd@aol.com
Fax: 020-7229 6220   Tel: 020-7229 9500

GLOBAL ARTISTS*
23 Haymarket
London SW1Y 4DG
Website: www.globalartists.co.uk
e-mail: info@globalartists.co.uk
Fax: 020-7839 4555   Tel: 020-7839 4888

GLYN MANAGEMENT
The Old School House
Brettenham
Ipswich IP7 7QP
e-mail: glyn.management@tesco.net
Fax: 01449 736117   Tel: 01449 737695

GO ENTERTAINMENTS Ltd
(Circus Artistes, Chinese State Circus, Cirque Surreal,
Bolshoi Circus "Spirit of The Horse")
The Arts Exchange
Congleton
Cheshire CW12 1JG
Website: www.arts-exchange.com
e-mail: info@arts-exchange.com
Fax: 01260 270777   Tel: 01260 276627

STAND UP DRAMA® PRESENTS
London's leading acting showcase...

DIGESTIBLE DRAMA WITH A DRINK!
Where actors, writers, casting directors and agents meet.
The first Wednesday, Thursday & Friday of every month.
For actors looking for industry exposure, performance experience or to secure representation.

WHY CHOOSE LONDON BITES?

- **AWARD WINNING** Winner of "Best Producer" at The Fringe Report Awards.
- **3 NIGHTS** Actors perform on 3 nights for increased exposure.
- **HIGH STANDARDS** All actors are pre-auditioned and rehearsed.
- **REPUTATION** Founded 2005 Stand Up Drama has earned an unrivalled reputation.
- **PROFESSIONAL SHOW** London Bites is an entertaining and interactive performance.
- **UNIQUE ATMOSPHERE** Our shows take place in a beautiful bar, where audience can enjoy a drink whilst being entertained.
- **LIVE AUDIENCE** Industry can see first hand how each of our actors communicate with our theatre-going audience.
- **INFORMATION** Every actor is listed on our website, with a link to their Spotlight page, so they can always be found by industry.
- **INDUSTRY** We invite industry through our sponsors The Spotlight.

AND I QUOTE

"..a resounding success. Well done." - THE STAGE

"Stand Up Drama is a most welcome venture by actors, for actors". - FRONTLINE MANAGEMENT

"I am doing great since my appearance in London Bites. I got a show from it, which led to an agent, which led to a job on TV this year. So Stand Up Drama does work." Past Performer 06

"Professionally everything is going really well thanks to London Bites. I had a meeting with 2 different agents and they both offered me a place. Performer Feb 07

"Highly entertaining, professional performances, great ambience" Audience member, April 07

AND NOW: STAND UP DRAMA® PRESENTS

CARDIFF BITES Are you an actor based in Wales and looking for somewhere to perform? Apply now for Stand Up Drama's Cardiff Bites.

TO APPLY TO PERFORM EMAIL TALENT@STANDUPDRAMA.COM

WWW.STANDUPDRAMA.COM   SPONSORED BY

© COPYRIGHT 2007 STAND UP DRAMA

GOLDMAN KING
(Comedians, Comic Performers, Actors, Studio Warm-ups,
Voice-overs)
21 Red Lion Street
London WC1R 4PS
Website: www.goldmanking.com
e-mail: contacts@goldmanking.com   Mobile: 07980 241505

GORDON & FRENCH*
(Write)
12-13 Poland Street, London W1F 8QB
Website: www.gordonandfrench.co.uk
e-mail: mail@gordonandfrench.net
Fax: 020-7734 4832   Tel: 020-7734 4818

GOSS Gerald Ltd
19 Gloucester Street, London SW1V 2DB
e-mail: info@geraldgoss.co.uk
Fax: 020-7592 9301   Tel: 020-7592 9202

G.O.T MANAGEMENT
38 Garrison Court, Mount Garrison
Hitchin, Herts SG4 9AA
e-mail: info@gotproductions.co.uk   Tel: 01462 420400

GRAHAM David PERSONAL MANAGEMENT (DGPM)
The Studio
107A Middleton Road
London E8 4LN
e-mail: infodgpm@aol.com   Tel/Fax: 020-7241 6752

GRANTHAM-HAZELDINE Ltd
Suite 605, The Linen Hall
162-168 Regent Street, London W1B 5TG
e-mail: agents@granthamhazeldine.com
Fax: 020-7038 3739   Tel: 020-7038 3737

GRAY Darren MANAGEMENT
(Specialising in representing/promoting Australian Artists)
2 Marston Lane
Portsmouth, Hampshire PO3 5TW
Website: www.darrengraymanagement.co.uk
e-mail: darren.gray1@virgin.net
Fax: 023-9267 7227   Tel: 023-9269 9973

GRAYS MANAGEMENT & ASSOCIATES
PM
Panther House
38 Mount Pleasant, London WC1X 0AP
Website: www.graysman.com
e-mail: grays.man@btconnect.com
Fax: 020-7278 1091   Tel: 020-7278 1054

GREEN & UNDERWOOD
PM (Write)
PO Box 44394, London SW20 0YP
e-mail: info@greenandunderwood.com
Fax: 020-3258 5037   Tel: 020-8546 2614

GREGOR Katherine ASSOCIATES
PM (For representation send e-mail only)
The Colombo Centre
34-68 Colombo Street
London SE1 8DP
Website: www.katherinegregorassociates.co.uk
e-mail: agent@katherinegregorassociates.co.uk
                              Tel/Fax: 020-7261 9466

GREIG Miranda ASSOCIATES Ltd*
92 Englewood Road, London SW12 9NY
e-mail: mail@mirandagreigassoc.co.uk
Fax: 020-7228 1400   Tel: 020-7228 1200

Sophia Di Martino

Zaid Munir

michael pollard
photographer
manchester

tel : 0161 456 7470
email : info@michaelpollard.co.uk
website : www.michaelpollard.co.uk

studio/location/student rates

Jacob Dramatics Management *"Your Ladder To Success"*

No.4 Raby Drive   East Herrington   Sunderland   Tyne and Wear SR3 3QE

T: 0191 5512 954   **F:** 0191 5512 954   **E:** jacobjky@aol.com

GRESHAM Carl GROUP
PO Box 3, Bradford
West Yorkshire BD1 4QN
Website: www.carlgresham.com
e-mail: gresh@carlgresham.co.uk
Fax: 01274 827161   Tel: 01274 735880

GRIDMODELS Ltd
(Model Agency)
8 Kerry Path
Arklow Road, London SE14 6DY
Website: www.gridmodels.com
e-mail: info@gridmodels.com
Fax: 020-7993 5758   Tel: 020-7993 6512

GRIFFIN Sandra MANAGEMENT
6 Ryde Place, Richmond Road
East Twickenham, Middlesex TW1 2EH
e-mail: office@sandragriffin.com
Fax: 020-8744 1812   Tel: 020-8891 5676

GUBBAY Louise ASSOCIATES
26 Westmore Road
Tatsfield, Kent TN16 2AX
Website: www.louisegubbay.com
e-mail: louise@louisegubbay.com   Tel: 01959 573080

GURNETT J. PERSONAL MANAGEMENT Ltd
12 Newburgh Street, London W1F 7RP
Website: www.jgpm.co.uk
e-mail: mail@jgpm.co.uk
Fax: 020-7287 9642   Tel: 020-7440 1850

HALL JAMES PERSONAL MANAGEMENT
20 Abbey Close
Pinner, Middlesex HA5 2AW
Website: www.halljames.co.uk
e-mail: info@halljames.co.uk
Fax: 020-8868 5825   Tel: 020-8429 8111

HALLY Yvette MANAGEMENT
121 Grange Road
Rathfarnham
Dublin 14, Ireland
e-mail: yhmgt@eircom.net
Fax: 00 353 1 4933076   Tel: 00 353 1 4933685

HAMBLETON Patrick ASSOCIATES
Top Floor
136 Englefield Road
London N1 3LQ
e-mail: patrick@patrickhambleton.co.uk
Fax: 0870 2848554   Tel: 020-7424 5832

HAMILTON HODELL Ltd*
5th Floor
66-68 Margaret Street
London W1W 8SR
Website: www.hamiltonhodell.co.uk
e-mail: info@hamiltonhodell.co.uk
Fax: 020-7636 1226   Tel: 020-7636 1221

HandE CASTING ADVERTISING AGENCY
Epping Film Studios
Brickfield Business Centre
Thornwood High Road
Epping
Essex CM16 6TH
Website: www.hande.org
e-mail: caa@hande.org
Fax: 01992 570601   Tel: 01992 570662

HARGREAVES Alison MANAGEMENT
(Designers/Lighting Designers/Directors)
27 Hamilton Road
London NW10 1NS
Website: www.alisonhargreaves.co.uk
e-mail: agent@alisonhargreaves.co.uk Tel: 020-8438 0112

HARRIS AGENCY Ltd The
52 Forty Avenue
Wembley Park
Middlesex HA9 8LQ
e-mail: theharrisagency@btconnect.com
Fax: 020-8908 4455   Tel: 020-8908 4451

HARRISON Penny BSA Ltd
Trinity Lodge
25 Trinity Crescent
London SW17 7AG
e-mail: harrisonbsa@aol.com
Fax: 020-8672 8971   Tel: 020-8672 0136

HARVEY VOICES
54-55 Margaret Street
London W1W 8SH
Website: www.harveyvoices.co.uk   Tel: 020-7952 4361

HAT MANAGEMENT
(Neil Howarth)
24 Thornley Rise
Audenshaw
Manchester M34 5JX
e-mail: hat.mgmt@hotmail.co.uk
Mobile: 07775 744438   Tel: 0161-370 8648

Nick Gregan
PHOTOGRAPHY

**The easiest and the best headshot you'll ever have -
By one of London's premier theatrical photographers.**

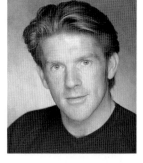

For contemporary, natural headshots for the acting profession, contact Nick on
Tel: 020 85333003 I Mobile: 07774 421878 I www.nickgregan.com
email:info@nickgregan.com

ROSIE STILL - 020 8857 6920 - *www.rosiestillphotography.com*

| Chris Jarvis | Debra Stephenson | Charlie Clements | Bella Emberg | Christopher Parker |

Discounts for SPOTLIGHT & Drama Students - View the results instantly on my laptop
Take whole shoot home on cd - Relaxed & friendly atmosphere - Own South London studio

HATSTAND CIRCUS
(Special Skills Perfomers)
98 Milligan Street
West Ferry
London E14 8AS
Website: www.hatstandcircus.co.uk
e-mail: helenahatstand@btconnect.com
Tel/Fax: 020-7538 3368

HATTON McEWAN*
PM (Write) (Stephen Hatton, Aileen McEwan
James Penfold)
PO Box 37385
London N1 7XF
Website: www.thetalent.biz
e-mail: info@thetalent.biz
Fax: 020-7251 9081   Tel: 020-7253 4770

H C A
(See COOKE Howard ASSOCIATES)

HENRIETTA RABBIT CHILDREN'S ENTERTAINMENTS AGENCY Ltd
(Magiciennes, Punch & Judy, Balloonologists, Stiltwalkers, Face Painters, Jugglers etc)
The Warren, 12 Eden Close, York YO24 2RD
Website: www.henriettarabbit.co.uk
e-mail: info@henriettarabbit.co.uk   Tel: 0800 0965653

HENRY'S AGENCY
53 Westbury
Rochford, Essex SS4 1UL
Website: www.henrysagency.co.uk
e-mail: info@henrysagency.co.uk   Tel/Fax: 01702 541413

HICKS Jeremy ASSOCIATES
114-115 Tottenham Court Road
London W1T 5AH
Website: www.jeremyhicks.com
e-mail: info@jeremyhicks.com
Fax: 020-7383 2777   Tel: 020-7383 2000

HILL Edward MANAGEMENT
Dolphin House
2-5 Manchester Street BN2 1TF
e-mail: info@edagent.com   Tel: 0870 0673505

HILTON Elinor ASSOCIATES
2nd Floor
28 Charing Cross Road
London WC2H 0DB
Website: www.elinorhilton.com
e-mail: info@elinorhilton.com
Fax: 020-7836 3982   Tel: 020-7240 2555

HINDIN Dee ASSOCIATES
(Existing Clients only)
9B Brunswick Mews
Great Cumberland Place
London W1H 7FB
Fax: 020-7258 0651   Tel: 020-7723 3706

HIRED HANDS
12 Cressy Road, London NW3 2LY
Website: www.hiredhandsmodels.com
e-mail: hiredhandsagency@aol.com   Tel: 020-7267 9212

HOBBS Liz GROUP Ltd
(Artiste Management)
65 London Road
Newark, Notts NG24 1RZ
Website: www.lizhobbsgroup.com
e-mail: casting@lizhobbsgroup.com
Fax: 0870 3337009   Tel: 0870 0702702

HOBSON'S ACTORS
62 Chiswick High Road
Chiswick
London W4 1SY
Website: www.hobsons-international.com
e-mail: actors@hobsons-international.com
Fax: 020-8996 5350   Tel: 020-8995 3628

HOLLOWOOD Jane ASSOCIATES Ltd
Apartment 17
113 Newton Street
Manchester M1 1AE
e-mail: janehollowood@ukonline.co.uk
Fax: 0161-237 9142   Tel: 0161-237 9141

HOLLY Dave ARTS MEDIA SERVICES
The Annexe
23 Eastwood Gardens
Felling, Tyne & Wear NE10 0AH
Fax: 0191-438 2722   Tel: 0191-438 2711

HOLMES Kim SHOWBUSINESS ENTERTAINMENT AGENCY Ltd
8 Charles Close
Ilkeston, Derbyshire DE7 5AF
Fax: 0115-930 9636   Tel: 0115-930 5088

HOPE Sally ASSOCIATES*
108 Leonard Street
London EC2A 4XS
Website: www.sallyhope.biz
e-mail: casting@sallyhope.biz
Fax: 020-7613 4848   Tel: 020-7613 5353

PLA

PAT LOVETT ASSOCIATES

Pat Lovett, Dolina Logan

43 Chandos Place London WC2N 4HS Tel: 020 7379 8111 Fax: 020 7379 9111

5 Union Street Edinburgh EH1 3LT Tel: 0131 478 7878 Fax: 0131 478 7070 www.pla-uk.com

HORSEY Dick MANAGEMENT Ltd
Suite 1
Cottingham House, Chorleywood Road
Rickmansworth, Herts WD3 4EP
Website: www.dhmlimited.co.uk
e-mail: roger@dhmlimited.co.uk
Mobile: 07850 112211 Tel: 01923 710614

HOWARD Amanda ASSOCIATES Ltd*
21 Berwick Street, London W1F 0PZ
Website: www.amandahowardassociates.co.uk
e-mail: mail@amandahowardassociates.co.uk
Fax: 020-7287 7785 Tel: 020-7287 9277

HOWARD Richard ASSOCIATES
6 Upper Hollingdean Road, Brighton BN1 7GA
Website: www.richardhowardassociates.co.uk
e-mail: info@richardhowardassociates.co.uk
Tel/Fax: 01273 539530

HOWE Janet CHILDREN'S CASTING & MODELLING AGENCY
The Pie Factory, 101 Broadway
Salford Quays, Manchester M50 2EQ
Mobile: 07801 942178 Tel/Fax: 0161-263 0633
e-mail: info@janethowe.com

The Works Media Centre, 36 White House Street
Hunslet, Leeds LS10 1AD Tel/Fax: 0113-242 5225

56 The Ironmarket, Newcastle-Under-Lyme
Staffordshire ST5 1PE Tel/Fax: 01782 661777

HOWELL Philippa
(See PHPM)

HUDSON Nancy ASSOCIATES Ltd
3rd Floor, 50 South Molton Street
Mayfair, London W1K 5SB
Website: www.nancyhudsonassociates.com
e-mail: agents@nancyhudsonassociates.com
Tel: 020-7499 5548

HUNTER Bernard ASSOCIATES
13 Spencer Gardens
London SW14 7AH
Fax: 020-8392 9334 Tel: 020-8878 6308

HUNWICK HUGHES Ltd*
(Formerly 41 Management)
Suite 2FF
45A George Street, Edinburgh EH2 2HT
Website: www.hunwickhughes.com
e-mail: maryam@hunwickhughes.com
Fax: 0131-225 4535 Tel: 0131-225 3585

I-MAGE CASTINGS
Regent House Business Centre
Suite 22, 24-25 Nutford Place
Marble Arch
London W1H 5YN
Website: www.i-mage.uk.com
e-mail: jane@i-mage.uk.com
Fax: 020-7725 7004 Tel: 020-7725 7003

ICON ACTORS MANAGEMENT
Tanzaro House
Ardwick Green North, Manchester M12 6FZ
Website: www.iconactors.net
e-mail: info@iconactors.net
Fax: 0161-273 4567 Tel: 0161-273 3344

IMAGE MANAGEMENT
The Media Centre
94 Roundhill Crescent
Brighton
East Sussex BN2 3FR
Website: www.imagemanagement.co.uk
e-mail: mail@imagemanagement.co.uk
Fax: 01273 680689 Tel: 01273 695290

I.M.L.•
PM Co-operative
The White House
52-54 Kennington Oval
London SE11 5SW
Website: www.iml.org.uk
e-mail: iml.london@btconnect.com Tel/Fax: 020-7587 1080

IMPACT INTERNATIONAL MANAGEMENT
2nd Floor
16-18 Balderton Street, London W1K 6TN
e-mail: colin@impactinternationalgroup.com
Fax: 020-7495 6515 Tel: 020-7495 6655

INDEPENDENT TALENT GROUP Ltd*
(Formerly ICM, London)
Oxford House
76 Oxford Street
London W1D 1BS
Fax: 020-7323 0101 Tel: 020-7636 6565

INDEPENDENT THEATRE WORKSHOP The
2 Mornington Road
Ranelagh
Dublin 6, Ireland
Website: www.independent-theatre-workshop.com
e-mail: info@independent-theatre-workshop.com
Tel/Fax: 00 353 1 4968808

profile
p h o t o g r a p h y
www.profile-london.com

high quality digital
student rates
digital retouching
images on CD

t: 020 7289 1088
m: 07971 431 798
e: info@profile-london.com

Deborah Algeo   Christian Contreras   Helen Watkins

INSPIRATION MANAGEMENT
PM Co-operative
Room 227
The Aberdeen Centre
22-24 Highbury Grove
London N5 2EA
Website: www.inspirationmanagement.org.uk
e-mail: mail@inspirationmanagement.eclipse.co.uk
Tel: 020-7704 0440

INTER-CITY CASTING
PM
Portland Tower
Portland Street
Manchester M1 3LF
Website: www.iccast.co.uk
e-mail: mail@iccast.co.uk   Tel/Fax: 0161-238 4950

INTERNATIONAL ARTISTES Ltd*
4th Floor
Holborn Hall
193-197 High Holborn
London WC1V 7BD
e-mail: reception@internationalartistes.com
Fax: 020-7404 9865   Tel: 020-7025 0600

INTERNATIONAL COLLECTIVE ARTIST MANAGEMENT
Golden Cross House
8 Duncannon Street
The Strand
London WC2N 4JF
Website: www.internationalcollective.co.uk
e-mail: enquiries@internationalcollective.co.uk
Fax: 020-7484 5100   Tel: 020-7484 5080

INTERNATIONAL MODEL MANAGEMENT Ltd
(Incorporating Yvonne Paul Management)
Elysium Gate
Unit 15
126-128 New Kings Road
London SW6 4LZ
e-mail: info@immmodels.com
Fax: 020-7736 2221   Tel: 020-7384 0300

INTERNATIONAL THEATRE & MUSIC Ltd
(Piers Chater Robinson)
Garden Studios
11-15 Betterton Street
Covent Garden, London WC2H 9BP
Website: www.internationaltheatreandmusic.com
e-mail: info@internationaltheatreandmusic.com
Fax: 020-7379 0801   Tel: 020-7470 8786

JAA
(See ALTARAS Jonathan ASSOCIATES Ltd)

JABBERWOCKY AGENCY
(Children, Teenagers & Adults)
Glassenbury Hill Farm
Glassenbury Road
Cranbrook, Kent TN17 2QF
Website: www.jabberwockyagency.com
e-mail: keith@jabberwockyagency.com
Mobile: 07899 983090   Tel: 01622 871851

JACOB DRAMATICS MANAGEMENT
No 4 Raby Drive
East Herrington
Sunderland
Tyne & Wear SR3 3QE
e-mail: jacobjky@aol.com   Tel/Fax: 0191-551 2954

JAFFREY MANAGEMENT Ltd*
(Jennifer Jaffrey)
The Double Lodge
Pinewood Studios
Iver Heath, Bucks SLO 0NH
Website: www.jaffreyactors.co.uk
e-mail: castings@jaffreyactors.co.uk
Fax: 01753 785163   Tel: 01753 785162

JAMESON Joy Ltd
PM
21 Uxbridge Street
Kensington, London W8 7TQ
e-mail: joy@jote.freeuk.com
Fax: 020-7985 0842   Tel: 020-7221 0990

JAMES Susan
(See SJ MANAGEMENT)

JAY Alex PERSONAL MANAGEMENT
8 Higher Newmarket Road
Newmarket
Gloucestershire GL6 0RP
e-mail: alexjay@alex-jay-pm.freeserve.co.uk
Tel/Fax: 01453 834783

JB ASSOCIATES*
4th Floor
Manchester House
84-86 Princess Street
Manchester M1 6NG
Website: www.j-b-a.net
e-mail: info@j-b-a.net
Fax: 0161-237 1809   Tel: 0161-237 1808

AM LONDON

ACTORS HEADSHOTS

HOLLY DAVIDSON

CONNIE FISHER

JEREMY EDWARDS

JOHN BARROWMAN

PETER SERAFINOWICZ

FIONA ALDRIDGE

LILY ROBINSON

JAKE CANUSO

MODEL, DANCE & PERFORMER PORTFOLIOS

WWW.AM-LONDON.COM

PHOTOGRAPHERS CLAIRE ALEXANDER & CASEY MOORE

STUDIO: 020 7193 1868   MOBILE: 07972 826 065

John Colclough A d v i s o r y

Practical independent guidance for actors and actresses

t: 020 8873 1763   e: john@johncolclough.org.uk   www.johncolclough.co.uk

---

JEFFREY WHITE & SILVEY ASSOCIATES*
PM
9-15 Neal Street
London WC2H 9PW
e-mail: info@jwsassociates.co.uk
Fax: 020-7240 0007   Tel: 020-7240 7000

J.G.M.
15 Lexham Mews
London W8 6JW
Website: www.jgmtalent.com
e-mail: mail@jgmtalent.com
Fax: 020-7376 2416   Tel: 020-7376 2414

JIGSAW ARTS MANAGEMENT
64-66 High Street
Barnet
Herts EN5 5SJ
Website: www.jigsaw-arts.co.uk/agency
e-mail: admin@jigsaw-arts.co.uk
Fax: 020-8447 4531   Tel: 020-8447 4534

JLM PERSONAL MANAGEMENT*
(Sharon Henry, Sarah Lee)
4th Floor, Holborn Hall
193-197 High Holborn
London WC1V 7BD
e-mail: info@jlmpm.co.uk
Fax: 020-7404 9865   Tel: 020 7025 0630

J.M. MANAGEMENT
(Personal representation to a small number of
Actors/Actresses in film work)
20 Pembroke Road
North Wembley
Middlesex HA9 7PD   Tel/Fax: 020-8908 0502

JOHNSON WHITELEY Ltd
12 Argyll Mansions
Hammersmith Road, London W14 8QG
e-mail: jwltd@freeuk.com
Fax: 020-7348 0164   Tel: 020-7348 0163

JOHNSTON & MATHERS ASSOCIATES Ltd
PO Box 3167
Barnet EN5 2WA
Website: www.johnstonandmathers.com
e-mail: johnstonmathers@aol.com
Fax: 020-8449 2386   Tel: 020-8449 4968

JPA MANAGEMENT
30 Daws Hill Lane
High Wycombe
Bucks HP11 1PW
Website: www.jackiepalmer.co.uk
e-mail: jackie.palmer@btinternet.com
Fax: 01494 510479   Tel: 01494 520978

K ENTERTAINMENTS Ltd
The Bridge
12-16 Clerkenwell Road
London EC1M 5PQ
Website: www.ktalent.co.uk   Tel: 020-7324 6350

KAL MANAGEMENT
(Write)
95 Gloucester Road
Hampton, Middlesex TW12 2UW
Website: www.kaplan-kaye.co.uk
e-mail: kaplan222@aol.com
Fax: 020-8979 6487   Tel: 020-8783 0039

KANAL Roberta AGENCY
82 Constance Road
Twickenham
Middlesex TW2 7JA
e-mail: roberta.kanal@dsl.pipex.com
Tel/Fax: 020-8894 7952   Tel: 020-8894 2277

KARUSHI MANAGEMENT
Unit 10
5-7 Wenlock Road, London N1 7SB
Website: www.karushi.com
e-mail: lisa@karushi.com
Fax: 0845 9005522   Tel: 0845 9005511

KASTKIDZ
40 Sunnybank Road
Unsworth, Bury BL9 8HF
Website: www.kastkidz.com
e-mail: kastkidz@ntlworld.com
Fax: 0161-796 7073   Mobile: 07905 646832

KD ASSOCIATES
12 The Drive
Northampton NN1 4SH
Website: www.kdassociates.biz
e-mail: kd.associates@virgin.net   Tel: 01604 715598

KEDDIE SCOTT ASSOCIATES Ltd
107-111 Fleet Street, London EC4A 2AB
e-mail: fiona@ks-ass.co.uk   Website: www.ks-ass.co.uk
Fax: 020-7936 9100   Tel: 020-7936 9058

(KSA-WALES)
3 Orchard Place, Canton, Cardiff CF11 9DY
e-mail: wales@ks-ass.co.uk
Mobile: 07917 272298   Tel/Fax: 029-2021 9396

(KSA-SCOTLAND)
430 Tantallon Road, Glasgow G41 3HR
e-mail: scotland@ks-ass.co.uk   Mobile: 07980 121728

KELLY'S KIND
(Dance, Models, Choreographers, Actors & Make-up Artists)
Third Floor
17-18 Margaret Street
London W1W 8RP
e-mail: office@kellyskind.co.uk   Tel: 0870 8701299

KELLY MANAGEMENT Ltd
2nd Floor, Hammer House
117 Wardour Street
London W1F 0UN
Website: www.kelly-management.com
e-mail: robert@kelly-management.com
Fax: 020-7434 1007   Tel: 020-7434 9955

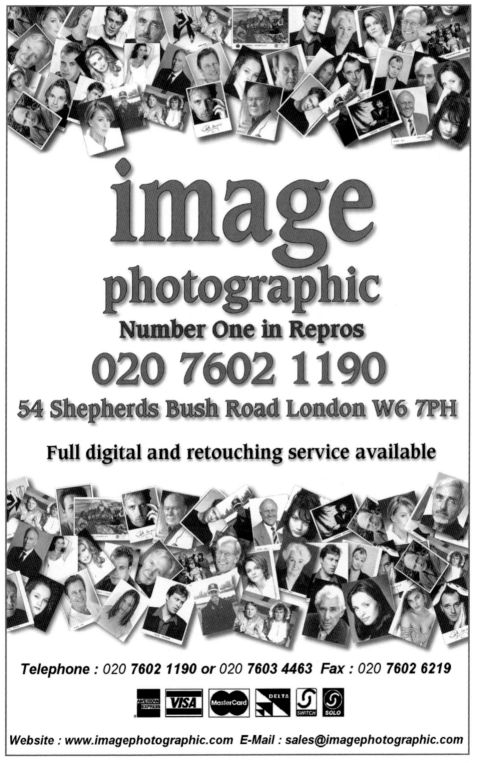

KENIS Steve & Co*
Royalty House
72-74 Dean Street, London W1D 3SG
e-mail: sk@sknco.com
Fax: 020-7287 6328   Tel: 020-7434 9055

KENT Tim ASSOCIATES Ltd
(Tim Kent & Julie Fox)
The Coach House
Pinewood Studios
Pinewood Road
Iver Heath, Bucks SL0 0NH
e-mail: castings@tkassociates.co.uk
Fax: 01753 655622   Tel: 01753 655517

KEW PERSONAL MANAGEMENT
PO Box 53974
London SW15 5SQ
Website: www.kewpersonalmanagement.com
e-mail: info@kewpersonalmanagement.com
                                    Tel: 020-8788 1166

KING Adrian ASSOCIATES*
33 Marlborough Mansions
Cannon Hill, London NW6 1JS
e-mail: akassocs@aol.com
Fax: 020-7435 4100   Tel: 020-7435 4600

K M C AGENCIES Ltd
11-15 Betterton Street
London WC2H 9BP
e-mail: london@kmcagencies.co.uk
Fax: 0870 4421780   Tel: 0870 4604868

PO Box 122
48 Great Ancoats Street
Manchester M4 5AB
e-mail: casting@kmcagencies.co.uk
Fax: 0161-237 9812   Tel: 0161-237 3009

KNIGHT AYTON MANAGEMENT
114 St Martin's Lane
London WC2N 4BE
Website: www.knightayton.co.uk
e-mail: info@knightayton.co.uk
Fax: 020-7836 8333   Tel: 020-7836 5333

KNIGHT Ray CASTING
21A Lambolle Place
London NW3 4PG
Website: www.rayknight.co.uk
e-mail: casting@rayknight.co.uk
Fax: 020-7722 2322   Tel: 020-7722 1551

KORT Richard ASSOCIATES
Theatre House
2-4 Clasketgate
Lincoln LN2 1JS
Website: www.richardkortassociates.com
e-mail: richardkort@dial.pipex.com
Fax: 01522 511116   Tel: 01522 526888

KREATE PROMOTIONS
Unit 232
30 Great Guildford Street
London SE1 0HS
e-mail: kreate@kreatepromotions.co.uk
Fax: 020-7401 3003   Tel: 020-7401 9007

KREMER ASSOCIATES
(See MARSH Billy DRAMA Ltd)

KSA - SCOTLAND
(See KEDDIE SCOTT ASSOCIATES Ltd)

KSA - WALES
(See KEDDIE SCOTT ASSOCIATES Ltd)

L.A. MANAGEMENT
10 Fairoak Close
Kenley
Surrey CR8 5LJ
Website: www.lamanagement.biz
e-mail: info@lamanagement.biz
Mobile: 07963 573538   Tel: 020-8660 0142

LADIDA
Cambridge Theatre
Earlham Street
Seven Dials
London WC2H 9HU
Website: www.ladidagroup.com
e-mail: m@ladidagroup.com
Fax: 020-7287 0300   Tel: 020-7287 0600

LAINE Betty MANAGEMENT
The Studios
East Street
Epsom, Surrey KT17 1HH
e-mail: enquiries@betty-laine-management.co.uk
                              Tel/Fax: 01372 721815

LAINE MANAGEMENT Ltd
Laine House, 131 Victoria Road
Hope, Salford M6 8LF
Website: www.lainemanagement.co.uk
e-mail: info@lainemanagement.co.uk   Tel: 0161-789 7775

michael douglas

alicia silverstone

dennis quaid

thora birch

stella rimington

spike lee

sean bean

martin scorsese

lemar

jonell elliott

bruce morrison

james fain

vin diesel

kerry newell

ray thacker

kelly clarkson

isabella cave

kevin power

polly parsons

ankit love

jamiehughesphotography

m: 07850-122977   f: 020-8355 8773   jamie@jamiehughesphotography.com
www.jamiehughesphotography.com

Success

THEATRICAL AGENTS • ACTORS
DANCERS • SINGERS
MODELS • PRESENTERS
CHOREOGRAPHERS

ROOM 236, LINEN HALL
162-168 REGENT STREET
LONDON W1B 5TB
TEL: 020 7734 3356 FAX: 020 7494 3787
www.successagency.co.uk
e-mail: ee@successagency.co.uk

LANGFORD ASSOCIATES Ltd
17 Westfields Avenue
Barnes
London SW13 0AT
e-mail: barry.langford@btconnect.com
Fax: 020-8878 7078   Tel: 020-8878 7148

LE BARS Tessa MANAGEMENT*
(Existing Clients Only)
54 Birchwood Road
Petts Wood, Kent BR5 1NZ
Website: www.galtonandsimpson.com
e-mail: tessa.lebars@ntlworld.com
Mobile: 07860 287255   Tel: 01689 837084

LEE GARRETT Anna MANAGEMENT
24-26 Arcadia Avenue
Finchley Central
London N3 2JU
Website: www.annaleegarrett.net
e-mail: contact@annaleegarrett.net   Tel: 020-8144 1142

LEE Wendy MANAGEMENT
2nd Floor
36 Langham Street
London W1W 7AP
e-mail: wendy-lee@btconnect.com   Tel: 020-7580 4800

LEE'S PEOPLE: RAPID TALENT
90 Long Acre
London WC2E 9RZ
Website: www.rapidtalent.co.uk
e-mail: enquiries@rapidtalent.co.uk Tel: 020-7734 5775

LEHRER Jane ASSOCIATES*
100A Chalk Farm Road
London NW1 8EH
Website: www.janelehrer.com
e-mail: janelehrer@aol.com
Fax: 020-7482 4899   Tel: 020-7482 4898

LEIGH MANAGEMENT
14 St David's Drive
Edgware
Middlesex HA8 6JH
e-mail: leighmanagement@aol.com Tel/Fax: 020-8951 4449

LEIGH Mike ASSOCIATES
37 Marylebone Lane
London W1U 2NW
Website: www.mikeleighassoc.com
Fax: 020-7486 5886   Tel: 020-7935 5500

LESLIE Sasha MANAGEMENT
(In Association with Allsorts Drama for Children)
34 Pember Road
London NW10 5LS
e-mail: sasha@allsortsdrama.com   Tel/Fax: 020-8969 3249

LIME ACTORS AGENCY & MANAGEMENT Ltd
Nemesis House
1 Oxford Court
Bishopsgate, Manchester M2 3WQ
Website: www.limemanagement.tv
e-mail: georgina@limemanagement.co.uk
Fax: 0161-228 6727   Tel: 0161-236 0827

LINKS MANAGEMENT
34-68 Colombo Street
London SE1 8DP
Website: www.links-management.co.uk
e-mail: agent@links-management.co.uk
                                  Tel/Fax: 020-7928 0806

LINKSIDE AGENCY
21 Poplar Road
Leatherhead
Surrey KT22 8SF
e-mail: linkside_agency@yahoo.co.uk   Tel: 01372 802374

LINTON MANAGEMENT
3 The Rock
Bury BL9 0JP
e-mail: carol@linton.tv
Fax: 0161-761 1999   Tel: 0161-761 2020

LITTLE ACORN MODELLING INTERNATIONAL Ltd
London House
271-273 King Street
Hammersmith
London W6 9LZ
Fax: 020-8390 4935   Tel: 020-8390 8023

LONDON MUSICIANS Ltd
(Orchestral Contracting)
Cedar House, Vine Lane
Hillingdon, Middlesex UB10 0BX
e-mail: mail@londonmusicians.co.uk
Fax: 01872 863557   Tel: 01895 252555

LONG Eva AGENTS
107 Station Road
Earls Barton
Northants NN6 0NX
e-mail: evalongagents@yahoo.co.uk
Fax: 01604 811921   Mobile: 07736 700849

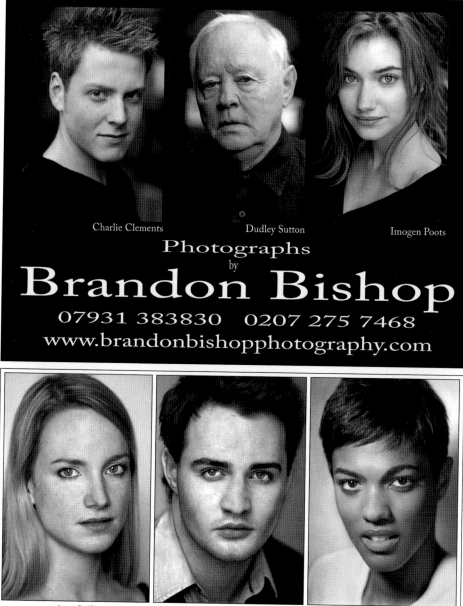

LONGRUN ARTISTES AGENCY
(Gina Long)
3 Chelsworth Drive
Plumstead Common
London SE18 2RB
Website: www.longrunartistes.co.uk
e-mail: gina@longrunartistes.co.uk   Mobile: 07748 723228

LOOKALIKES (Susan Scott)
106 Tollington Park
London N4 3RB
Website: www.lookalikes.info
e-mail: susan@lookalikes.info
Fax: 020-7281 1263   Tel: 020-7281 8029

LOOKS
PO Box 42783, London N2 0UF
Website: www.lookslondon.com
e-mail: lookslondonltd@btconnect.com
Fax: 020-8442 9190   Tel: 020-8341 4477

LOVETT Pat ASSOCIATES
(See PLA)

LSW PROMOTIONS
PO Box 31855
London SE17 3XP
Website: www.londonshakespeare.org.uk/promos
e-mail: londonswo@hotmail.com   Tel/Fax: 020-7793 9755

LUXFACTOR GROUP (UK) The
Fleet Place, 12 Nelson Drive
Petersfield, Hampshire GU31 4SJ
Website: www.luxfactor.co.uk
e-mail: info@luxfactor.co.uk
Fax: 0845 3700588   Tel: 0845 3700589

LYNE Dennis AGENCY*
108 Leonard Street
London EC2A 4RH
e-mail: info@dennislyne.com
Fax: 020-7739 4101   Tel: 020-7739 6200

MACFARLANE CHARD ASSOCIATES Ltd*
33 Percy Street
London W1T 2DF
Website: www.macfarlane-chard.co.uk
e-mail: enquiries@macfarlane-chard.co.uk
Fax: 020-7636 7751   Tel: 020-7636 7750

MACFARLANE CHARD ASSOCIATES IRELAND
14 Hagan's Court
Lad Lane
Dublin 2, Ireland
e-mail: derick@macfarlane-chard.co.uk
Fax: 00 353 1 661 9967   Tel: 00 353 1 661 9969

MACNAUGHTON LORD 2000 Ltd*
(Writers, Designers, Directors,
Choreographers/Composers/Lyricists/Musical Directors/
Lighting Designers)
19 Margravine Gardens
London W6 8RL
Website: www.ml2000.org.uk
e-mail: info@ml2000.org.uk
Fax: 020-8741 7443   Tel: 020-8741 0606

MADELEY Paul ASSOCIATES
17 Valley Road, Arden Park
Bredbury, Stockport
Cheshire SK6 2EA
e-mail: celebritypr@amserve.com   Tel/Fax: 0161-430 5380

harry rafique
photography

07986 679 498
www.hr-photographer.co.uk
020 7266 5398

MAIDA VALE SINGERS
(Singers for Recordings, Theatre, Film, Radio & TV)
7B Lanhill Road
Maida Vale
London W9 2BP
Website: www.maidavalesingers.co.uk
e-mail: maidavalesingers@cdtenor.freeserve.co.uk
Mobile: 07889 153145   Tel/Fax: 020-7266 1358

MAIN ARTISTS
34 South Molton Street
London W1K 5BP
Website: www.mainartists.com
e-mail: andrew@mainartists.com
Fax: 0870 1280003   Tel: 020-7495 4955

MAITLAND MANAGEMENT
PM (Anne Skates)
PO Box 364
Esher
Surrey KT10 9XZ
Website: www.maitlandmusic.com
e-mail: maitmus@aol.com
Fax: 01372 466229   Tel: 01372 466228

MANAGEMENT 2000
23 Alexandra Road, Mold, Flintshire CH7 1HJ
Website: www.management-2000.co.uk
e-mail: jackey@management-2000.co.uk
          Tel/Fax: 01352 771231

MANS Johnny PRODUCTIONS Ltd
PO Box 196
Hoddesdon, Herts EN10 7WG
Website: www.johnnymansproductions.co.uk
e-mail: real@legend.co.uk
Fax: 01992 470516   Tel: 01992 470907

MANSON Andrew PERSONAL MANAGEMENT Ltd*
288 Munster Road, London SW6 6BQ
Website: www.andrewmanson.com
e-mail: post@andrewmanson.com
Fax: 020-7381 8874   Tel: 020-7386 9158

MARCH MODELS
The Aberdeen Centre
22-24 Highbury Grove, London N5 2EA
Website: www.marchmodels.com
e-mail: hello@marchmodels.com
Fax: 020-7704 6085   Tel: 020-7704 6950

Markham & Marsden
Personal Management for Actors & Directors
in the fields of Film, Television, Theatre, Radio & Voice Work

405 Strand London WC2R 0NE
t: 020 7836 4111   f: 020 7836 4222
e: info@markham-marsden.com   w: markham-marsden.com

Take control of your career: Join a Co-op

Agents marked with a • are members of the
Co-operative Personal Management Association
phone: 07981 902525
email: cpmauk@yahoo.co.uk **web:** www.cpma.co.uk

MARCUS & McCRIMMON MANAGEMENT
1 Heathgate Place
75 Agincourt Road
Hampstead
London NW3 2NU
Website: www.marcusandmccrimmon.com
e-mail: info@marcusandmccrimmon.com
Fax: 020-8347 0006　　　　　Tel: 020-8347 0007

MARKHAM & FROGGATT Ltd*
PM (Write)
4 Windmill Street
London W1T 2HZ
Website: www.markhamfroggatt.com
e-mail: admin@markhamfroggatt.co.uk
Fax: 020-7637 5233　　　　　Tel: 020-7636 4412

MARKHAM & MARSDEN Ltd*
405 Strand
London WC2R 0NE
Website: www.markham-marsden.com
e-mail: info@markham-marsden.com
Fax: 020-7836 4222　　　　　Tel: 020-7836 4111

MARSH Billy ASSOCIATES Ltd*
76A Grove End Road
St Johns Wood
London NW8 9ND
Website: www.billymarsh.co.uk
e-mail: talent@billymarsh.co.uk
Fax: 020-7449 6933　　　　　Tel: 020-7449 6930

MARSH Billy DRAMA Ltd
(Actors & Actresses)
11 Henrietta Street
Covent Garden
London WC2E 8PY
e-mail: info@billymarshdrama.co.uk
Fax: 020-7379 7272　　　　　Tel: 020-7379 4800

MARSH Sandra MANAGEMENT
(Film Technicians)
Waverley House
7-12 Noel Street
London W1F 8GQ
Website: www.casarotto.co.uk
e-mail: casarottomarsh@casarotto.co.uk
Fax: 020-7287 9128　　　　　Tel: 020-7287 4450

MARSHALL Ronnie AGENCY
S F M PM TV (Write or Phone)
66 Ollerton Road
London N11 2LA　　　　Tel/Fax: 020-8368 4958

MARSHALL Scott PARTNERS Ltd*
2nd Floor
15 Little Portland Street
London W1W 8BW
e-mail: smpm@scottmarshall.co.uk
Fax: 020-7636 9728　　　　　Tel: 020-7637 4623

MARTIN Carol PERSONAL MANAGEMENT
19 Highgate West Hill
London N6 6NP
Fax: 020-8340 4868　　　　　Tel: 020-8348 0847

MAY John
Top Floor
46 Golborne Road, London W10 5PR
e-mail: may505@btinternet.com　　Tel: 020-8962 1606

MAYER Cassie Ltd*
5 Old Garden House
The Lanterns
Bridge Lane
London SW11 3AD
e-mail: info@cassiemayerltd.co.uk
Fax: 020-7350 0890　　　　　Tel: 020-7350 0880

MBA (Formerly John Mahoney Management)
Concorde House
18 Margaret Street
Brighton BN2 1TS
Website: www.mbagency.co.uk
e-mail: mba.concorde@virgin.net
Fax: 01273 818306　　　　　Tel: 01273 685970

McKINNEY MACARTNEY MANAGEMENT Ltd
(Technicians)
The Barley Mow Centre
10 Barley Mow Passage
London W4 4PH
Website: www.mckinneymacartney.com
e-mail: mail@mckinneymacartney.com
Fax: 020-8995 2414　　　　　Tel: 020-8995 4747

McLEAN Bill PERSONAL MANAGEMENT
PM (Write)
23B Deodar Road
London SW15 2NP　　　　　Tel: 020-8789 8191

McLEAN-WILLIAMS MANAGEMENT
Thames Wharf Studios
Rainville Road, London W6 9HA
Website: www.mclean-williams.com
e-mail: info@mclean-williams.com
Fax: 020-3080 0111　　　　　Tel: 020-7610 2929

McLEOD HOLDEN ENTERPRISES Ltd
Priory House
1133 Hessle Road, Hull HU4 6SB
Website: www.mcleod-holden.com
e-mail: peter.mcleod@mcleod-holden.com
Fax: 01482 353635　　　　　Tel: 01482 565444

McREDDIE Ken ASSOCIATES Ltd*
PM
36-40 Glasshouse Street
London W1B 5DL
Website: www.kenmcreddie.com
e-mail: email@kenmcreddie.com
Fax: 020-7734 6530　　　　　Tel: 020-7439 1456

CASTING PHOTOS

Black & White - Colour
Ready While You Wait

Passport Photo Service
449 Oxford Street
London W1
Tel: 020 7629 8540

Opposite Selfridges Est 1953
www.passportphoto.co.uk

MCS AGENCY
47 Dean Street
London W1D 5BE
Website: www.mcsagency.co.uk
e-mail: info@mcsagency.co.uk
Fax: 020-7734 9996   Tel: 020-7734 9995

MEDIA LEGAL
PM F TV Voice-overs (Existing Clients only)
West End House, 83 Clarendon Road
Sevenoaks, Kent TN13 1ET   Tel: 01732 460592

MHM
Heather Barn
Cryers Hill Lane
High Wycombe, Bucks HP15 6AA
Website: www.mhmagents.com
e-mail: mhmagents@gmail.com
Fax: 01494 716448   Tel: 01494 711400

MILNER David MANAGEMENT
40 Whitehall Road
London E4 6DH
e-mail: milner.agent@btinternet.com
                   Tel/Fax: 020-8523 8086

MIME THE GAP
(Mime & Physical Theatre Specialists)
23 Manor Place
Staines
Middlesex TW18 1AE
Website: www.mimethegap.com   Mobile: 07970 685982

MINT MANAGEMENT
1 Sheencroft Cottages
Bessels Way, Blewbury
Didcot, Oxon OX11 9ED
e-mail: lisi@mintman.co.uk
Mobile: 07792 107644   Tel/Fax: 01235 851165

MIRTH CONTROL MANAGEMENT Ltd
50A Crayford Road
Islington, London N7 0ND
Website: www.mirthcontrol.org.uk
e-mail: leanna@mirthcontrol.org.uk
Mobile: 07976 283456   Mobile: 07976 560580

MITCHELL MAAS McLENNAN
Offices of Millennium Dance 2000
Hampstead Town Hall Centre
213 Haverstock Hill
London NW3 4QP
Website: www.mmm2000.co.uk
e-mail: agency@mmm2000.co.uk   Tel/Fax: 01767 650020

ML 2000 Ltd
(See MACNAUGHTON LORD 2000 Ltd)

MONDI ASSOCIATES Ltd
Unit 3 O, Cooper House
2 Michael Road
London SW6 2AD
Website: www.mondiassociates.com
e-mail: michelle@mondiassociates.com
                   Mobile: 07817 133349

MONTAGU ASSOCIATES
Ground Floor
13 Hanley Road
London N4 3DU
e-mail: montagus@btconnect.com   Tel: 020-7263 3883

MOORE Jakki MANAGEMENT
18 Main Street
Haverigg
Cumbria LA18 4EX
e-mail: jakki@jakkimoore.com
Mobile: 07967 612784   Tel: 01229 776389

MORGAN & GOODMAN
Mezzanine
Quadrant House
80-82 Regent Street
London W1B 5RP
e-mail: mg1@btinternet.com
Fax: 020-7494 3446   Tel: 020-7437 1383

MORGAN Lee MANAGEMENT
The Strand
Golden Cross House
8 Duncannon Street
London WC2N 4JF
Website: www.leemorganmanagement.co.uk
e-mail: leemorganmgnt@aol.com
Fax: 020-7484 5100   Tel: 020-7484 5331

MORRIS Andrew MANAGEMENT
Penthouse Offices
60 Reachview Close
Camden Town
London NW1 0TY
e-mail: morrisagent@yahoo.co.uk
Mobile: 07918 636775   Tel/Fax: 020-7482 0451

MOUTHPIECE MANAGEMENT
PO Box 145
Inkberrow
Worcestershire WR7 4ZG
Website: www.mouthpiecemanagement.co.uk
e-mail: karin@mouthpiecemanagement.co.uk
Mobile: 07900 240904   Tel: 01527 850149

MPC ENTERTAINMENT
(Write or Phone)
MPC House 15-16 Maple Mews
Maida Vale, London NW6 5UZ
Website: www.mpce.com
e-mail: mpc@mpce.com
Fax: 020-7624 4220   Tel: 020-7624 1184

MR.MANAGEMENT
29 Belton Road
Brighton
East Sussex BN2 3RE
e-mail: mr.management@ntlworld.com
Fax: 020-8579 6360   Tel: 01273 232381

Treating people with respect will gain one acceptance and improve business.

Tao Zhu Gong, 500BC

Brebners offers much more than accountancy services and business advice. We offer trust, reliability and a truly personal service.

Whether you are just starting out or are more established, our committed and specialist team offers a full range of services to help your business succeed.

Please call Michael Burton, Raef Gregory or Hazel Milne on 020 7734 2244 for a free and confidential discussion.

BREBNERS

CHARTERED ACCOUNTANTS
& BUSINESS ADVISERS

THE QUADRANGLE 180 WARDOUR STREET LONDON W1F 8LB TEL: 020 7734 2244
EMAIL: PARTNERS@BREBNERS.COM WEB: WWW.BREBNERS.COM

BILLY MARSH DRAMA LIMITED
LINDA KREMER ASSOCIATES
Personal Management / Representation
Film   Television   Theatre   Commercials

11 Henrietta Street, Covent Garden, London WC2E 8PY
Tel: 020 7379 4800   Fax: 020 7379 7272   E-mail: info@billymarshdrama.co.uk

MUGSHOTS AGENCY
153 Buckhurst Avenue
Carshalton, Surrey SM5 1PD
e-mail: becky@mugshots.co.uk
Fax: 020-8296 8056   Tel: 020-8296 0393

MURPHY Elaine ASSOCIATES
Suite 1
50 High Street, London E11 2RJ
e-mail: elaine@elainemurphy.co.uk
Fax: 020-8989 1400   Tel: 020-8989 4122

MUSIC INTERNATIONAL
M
13 Ardilaun Road
London N5 2QR
Website: www.musicint.co.uk
e-mail: music@musicint.co.uk
Fax: 020-7226 9792   Tel: 020-7359 5183

MV MANAGEMENT
Ralph Richardson Memorial Studios
Kingfisher Place
Clarendon Road, London N22 6XF
e-mail: theagency@mountview.ac.uk
Fax: 020-8829 1050   Tel: 020-8889 8231

MYERS MANAGEMENT
63 Fairfields Crescent
London NW9 0PR   Tel/Fax: 020-8204 8941

NARROW ROAD COMPANY The*
22 Poland Street
London W1F 8QH
e-mail: agents@narrowroad.co.uk
Fax: 020-7439 1237   Tel: 020-7434 0406

182 Brighton Road
Coulsdon, Surrey CR5 2NF
e-mail: coulsdon@narrowroad.co.uk
Fax: 020-8763 2558   Tel: 020-8763 9895

2nd Floor, Grampian House
144 Deansgate
Manchester M3 3EE
e-mail: manchester@narrowroad.co.uk
                               Tel/Fax: 0161-833 1605

NE REPRESENTATION
38 Coniscliffe Road
Darlington DL3 7RG
Website: www.nerepresentation.co.uk
e-mail: info@nerepresentation.co.uk
Fax: 01325 488390   Tel: 01325 488385

NEVS AGENCY
Regal House
198 King's Road, London SW3 5XP
Website: www.nevs.co.uk
e-mail: getamodel@nevs.co.uk
Fax: 020-7352 6068   Tel: 020-7352 4886

NEW CASEY AGENCY
The Annexe
129 Northwood Way
Northwood HA6 1RF   Tel: 01923 823182

NEW FACES Ltd
2nd Floor, The Linen Hall
162-168 Regent Street
London W1B 5TB
Website: www.newfacestalent.co.uk
e-mail: val@newfacestalent.co.uk
Fax: 020-7287 5481   Tel: 020-7439 6900

NFD - THE FILM & TV AGENCY
PO Box 76
Leeds LS25 9AG
Website: www.film-tv-agency.com
e-mail: info@film-tv-agency.com   Tel/Fax: 01977 681949

NICHOLSON Jackie ASSOCIATES
PM
Suite 44, 2nd Floor
Morley House, 320 Regent Street
London W1B 3BD
Fax: 020-7580 4489   Tel: 020-7580 4422

N M MANAGEMENT
16 St Alfege Passage
Greenwich, London SE10 9JS
e-mail: nmmanagement@hotmail.com
Tel: 020-7581 0947   Tel: 020-8853 4337

NMP MANAGEMENT
PO Box 981
Wallington, Surrey SM6 8JU
Website: www.nmpmanagement.co.uk
e-mail: management@nmp.co.uk
Fax: 020-8404 2621   Tel: 020-8669 3128

NORTH OF WATFORD ACTORS AGENCY
Co-operative
Bridge Mill, Hebden Bridge
West Yorks HX7 8EX
Website: www.northofwatford.com
e-mail: info@northofwatford.com
Fax: 01422 846503   Tel: 01422 845361

NORTH WEST ACTORS
36 Lord Street
Radcliffe
Manchester M26 3BA
Website: www.northwestactors.co.uk
e-mail: northwestactors@btinternet.com
Tel/Fax: 0161-724 6625

NORTHERN LIGHTS MANAGEMENT Ltd
Dean Clough Mills
Halifax
West Yorks HX3 5AX
e-mail: northern.lights@virgin.net
Fax: 01422 330101
Tel: 01422 382203

NORTHERN PROFESSIONALS
(Casting, Technicians, Action Safety, Boat & Diving
Equipment Hire)
21 Cresswell Avenue
North Shields
Tyne & Wear NE29 9BQ
Website: www.northernprocasting.co.uk
e-mail: bill@northernprocasting.co.uk
Fax: 0191-296 3243
Tel: 0191-257 8635

NORTHONE MANAGEMENT•
HG08 Aberdeen Studios
Highbury Grove
London N5 2EA
Website: www.northone.co.uk
e-mail: actors@northone.co.uk
Fax: 020-7359 9449
Tel: 020-7359 9666

NS ARTISTES MANAGEMENT
10 Claverdon House
Holly Bank Road
Billesley, Birmingham B13 0QY
Website: www.nsmanagement.co.uk
e-mail: nsmanagement@fsmail.net
Tel: 0121-684 5607

NSM*
(Natasha Stevenson Management Ltd)
Studio 7C
Clapham North Arts Centre
Voltaire Road
London SW4 6DH
Website: www.natashastevenson.co.uk
e-mail: inbox@natashastevenson.co.uk
Fax: 020-7720 5565
Tel: 020-7720 3355

NUMBER ONE CASTING & MODEL MANAGEMENT Ltd
408F The Big Peg
120 Vyse Street
The Jewellery Quarter
Birmingham B18 6NF
Website: www.numberonemodelagency.co.uk
e-mail: info@numberonemodelagency.co.uk
Tel: 0121-233 2433

NUTOPIA PERSONAL MANAGEMENT
(Ferris Entertainment)
Number 8
132 Charing Cross Road
London WC2H 0LA
Website: www.ferrisentertainment.com
Mobile: 07801 493133

NYLAND MANAGEMENT Ltd
20 School Lane
Heaton Chapel
Stockport SK4 5DG
Website: www.nylandmanagement.com
e-mail: nylandmgmt@freenet.co.uk   Tel/Fax: 0161-442 2224

Lydia Watson

Ava de Souza
P h o t o g r a p h e r

t: 020 8392 9093   www.avadesouza.co.uk

Lazarus No No

gustavo camilo
info@gcamilophotography.com
www.gcamilophotography.com
+44 7947 888 247

OFF THE KERB PRODUCTIONS
22 Thornhill Crescent
London N1 1BJ
Fax: 020-7700 4646   Tel: 020-7700 4477

3rd Floor
Hammer House
113-117 Wardour Street
London W1F 0UN
Website: www.offthekerb.co.uk
e-mail: info@offthekerb.co.uk
Fax: 020-7437 0647   Tel: 020-7437 0607

OI OI AGENCY
Pinewood Film Studios
Pinewood Road
Iver Heath
Bucks SLO ONH
Website: www.oioi.org.uk
e-mail: info@oioi.org.uk
Fax: 01753 655622   Tel: 01753 655514

OLIVER & OLIVER
67 Bannister Close
Greenford
Middlesex UB6 0SW
e-mail: olivernoliver@gmail.com   Tel: 08712 775090

ONE MAKE UP/ONE PHOTOGRAPHIC Ltd
4th Floor
48 Poland Street
London W1F 7ND
Website: www.onemakeup.com
e-mail: info@onemakeup.com
Fax: 020-7287 2313   Tel: 020-7287 2311

ONSCREEN AGENCY.COM
No 199,
2 Lansdowne Row
Mayfair
London W1J 6HL
Website: www.onscreenagency.com
e-mail: info@onscreenagency.com
Fax: 020-7493 4935   Tel: 020-7193 7547

OPERA & CONCERT ARTISTS
M Opera
75 Aberdare Gardens
London NW6 3AN
e-mail: enquiries@opera-and-concert-artists.co.uk
Fax: 020-7372 3537   Tel: 020-7328 3097

ORDINARY PEOPLE
(Actors and Models)
16 Camden Road
London NW1 9DP
Website: www.ordinarypeople.co.uk
e-mail: info@ordinarypeople.co.uk
Fax: 020-7267 5677   Tel: 020-7267 7007

ORIENTAL CASTING AGENCY Ltd (Peggy Sirr)
(Afro/Asian Artists) (Write or Phone)
1 Wyatt Park Road
Streatham Hill
London SW2 3TN
Website: www.orientalcasting.com
e-mail: peggy.sirr@btconnect.com
Fax: 020-8674 9303   Tel: 020-8671 8538

OTTO PERSONAL MANAGEMENT Ltd•
PM Co-operative
S.I.F.
5 Brown Street
Sheffield S1 2BS
Website: www.ottopm.co.uk
e-mail: admin@ottopm.co.uk
Fax: 0114-279 5225   Tel: 0114-275 2592

PADBURY David ASSOCIATES
44 Summerlee Avenue
Finchley
London N2 9QP
Website: www.davidpadburyassociates.com
e-mail: info@davidpadburyassociates.com
    Tel/Fax: 020-8883 1277

PAN ARTISTS AGENCY Ltd
Cornerways
34 Woodhouse Lane
Sale
Cheshire M33 4JX
Website: www.panartists.co.uk
e-mail: panartists@btconnect.com
Mobile: 07952 018175   Tel: 0800 6349147

PANTO PEOPLE
3 Rushden House
Tatlow Road
Glenfield
Leicester LE3 8ND
e-mail: jonny.dallas@ntlworld.com   Tel/Fax: 0116-287 9594

PARAMOUNT INTERNATIONAL MANAGEMENT
Talbot House
204-226 Imperial Drive
Harrow, Middlesex HA2 7HH
Website: www.ukcomedy.com
e-mail: mail@ukcomedy.com
Fax: 020-8868 6475 Tel: 020-8429 3179

PARSONS & BROOK
37 Berwick Street
London W1F 8RS
e-mail: info@parsonsandbrook.co.uk
Fax: 020-7287 8016 Tel: 020-7434 0398

P B J MANAGEMENT Ltd*
(Comedy)
7 Soho Street
London W1D 3DQ
Website: www.pbjmgt.co.uk
e-mail: general@pbjmgt.co.uk
Fax: 020-7287 1191 Tel: 020-7287 1112

PC THEATRICAL & MODEL AGENCY
(Large Database of Twins)
12 Carlisle Road
Colindale
London NW9 0HL
Website: www.twinagency.com
e-mail: twinagy@aol.com
Fax: 020-8933 3418 Tel: 020-8381 2229

PELHAM ASSOCIATES*
PM (Peter Cleall)
The Media Centre
9-12 Middle Street
Brighton BN1 1AL
Website: www.pelhamassociates.co.uk
e-mail: petercleall@pelhamassociates.co.uk
Fax: 01273 202492 Tel: 01273 323010

PEMBERTON ASSOCIATES Ltd*
193 Wardour Street
London W1F 8ZF
Fax: 020-7734 2522 Tel: 020-7734 4144

Express Networks
1 George Leigh Street
Manchester M4 5DL
Website: www.pembertonassociates.com
e-mail: general@pembertonassociates.com
Fax: 0161-235 8442 Tel: 0161-235 8440

PEPPERPOT PROMOTIONS
(Bands)
Suite 20B
20-22 Orde Hall Street
London WC1N 3JW
e-mail: chris@pepperpot.co.uk
Fax: 01255 473107 Tel: 020-7405 9108

PERFORMANCE ACTORS AGENCY•
PM Co-operative
137 Goswell Road, London EC1V 7ET
Website: www.performanceactors.co.uk
e-mail: info@performanceactors.co.uk
Fax: 020-7251 3974 Tel: 020-7251 5716

PERFORMERS DIRECTORY & AGENCY
(Actors, Dancers, Models and Extras)
PO Box 29942, London SW6 1FL
Website: www.performersdirectory.co.uk
e-mail: performersdirectory@yahoo.com Tel: 020-7610 6677

Kay Headley

Ewa Cichon

PERFORMING ARTS*
(Directors, Designers, Choreographers, Lighting Designers)
6 Windmill Street
London W1T 2JB
Website: www.performing-arts.co.uk
e-mail: info@performing-arts.co.uk
Fax: 020-7631 4631   Tel: 020-7255 1362

PERSONAL APPEARANCES
20 North Mount
1147-1161 High Road
Whetstone N20 0PH
Website: www.personalappearances.biz
e-mail: patsy@personalappearances.biz
                    Tel/Fax: 020-8343 7748

PFD*
PM
Drury House
34-43 Russell Street
London WC2B 5HA
Website: www.pfd.co.uk
e-mail: postmaster@pfd.co.uk
Fax: 020-7836 9544   Tel: 020-7344 1010

PHD ARTISTS
24 Montana Gardens
Sutton
Surrey SM1 4FP
Website: www.phdartists.com
e-mail: office@phdartists.com   Tel: 020-7241 6601

PHILLIPS Frances*
89 Robeson Way
Borehamwood
Hertfordshire WD6 5RY
Website: www.francesphillips.co.uk
e-mail: derekphillips@talk21.com
Mobile: 07957 334328   Tel: 020-8953 0303

PHPM
(Philippa Howell Personal Management)
184 Bradway Road
Sheffield S17 4QX
e-mail: philippa@phpm.co.uk   Tel/Fax: 0114-235 3663

PHYSICK Hilda
PM (Write)
78 Temple Sheen Road
London SW14 7RR
Fax: 020-8876 5561   Tel: 020-8876 0073

PICCADILLY MANAGEMENT
PM
23 New Mount Street
Manchester M4 4DE
e-mail: piccadilly.management@virgin.net
Fax: 0161-953 4001   Tel: 0161-953 4057

PINEAPPLE AGENCY
Montgomery House
159-161 Balls Pond Road
London N1 4BG
Website: www.pineappleagency.com
e-mail: pineapple.agency@btconnect.com
Fax: 020-7241 3006   Tel: 020-7241 6601

PLA*
(LOVETT Pat ASSOCIATES)
5 Union Street
Edinburgh EH1 3LT
Website: www.pla-uk.com
e-mail: edinburgh@pla-uk.com
Fax: 0131-478 7070   Tel: 0131-478 7878

43 Chandos Place
London WC2N 4HS
e-mail: london@pla-uk.com
Fax: 020-7379 9111   Tel: 020-7379 8111

PLAIN JANE
PO Box 2730
Romford, Essex RM7 1AB
Website: www.plain-jane.co.uk
e-mail: info@plain-jane.co.uk   Mobile: 07813 667319

PLATER Janet MANAGEMENT Ltd
D Floor
Milburn House
Dean Street
Newcastle upon Tyne NE1 1LF
Website: www.janetplatermanagement.co.uk
e-mail: magpie@tynebridge.demon.co.uk
Fax: 0191-233 1709   Tel: 0191-221 2490

PLUNKET GREENE ASSOCIATES
(In conjunction with James Sharkey Assocs Ltd)
(Existing Clients only)
PO Box 8365
London W14 0GL
Fax: 020-7603 2221   Tel: 020-7603 2227

POLLYANNA MANAGEMENT Ltd
1 Knighten Street
Wapping, London E1W 1PH
Website: www.pollyannatheatre.com
e-mail: aliceharwood@talktalk.net
Fax: 020-7480 6761   Tel: 020-7481 1911

POOLE Gordon AGENCY Ltd
The Limes
Brockley
Bristol BS48 3BB
Website: www.gordonpoole.com
e-mail: agents@gordonpoole.com
Fax: 01275 462252   Tel: 01275 463222

POPLAR MANAGEMENT
22 Knightswood
Woking, Surrey GU21 3PY
e-mail: poplarmanagement@hotmail.co.uk
                    Tel/Fax: 01483 828056

www.jk-photography.net 07816 825578

£145
inc. hair & make-up
All images on CD

JK PHOTOGRAPHY

POWER MODEL MANAGEMENT CASTING AGENCY
PO Box 1198, Salhouse
Norwich NR13 6WD
Website: www.powermodel.co.uk
e-mail: info@powermodel.co.uk   Tel: 01603 721287

POWER PROMOTIONS
PO Box 61, Liverpool L13 0EF
Website: www.powerpromotions.biz
e-mail: tom@powerpromotions.co.uk
Fax: 0870 7060202   Tel: 0151-230 0070

PREGNANT PAUSE AGENCY
(Pregnant Models, Dancers, Actresses)
11 Matham Road, East Molesey KT8 0SX
Website: www.pregnantpause.co.uk
e-mail: sandy@pregnantpause.co.uk   Tel: 020-8979 8874

PRICE GARDNER MANAGEMENT
PO Box 59908, London SW16 5QH
Website: www.pricegardner.co.uk
e-mail: info@pricegardner.co.uk
Fax: 020-7381 3288   Tel: 020-7610 2111

PRINCIPAL ARTISTES
PM (Write only)
4 Paddington Street, Marylebone, London W1U 5QE
Fax: 020-7486 4668   Tel: 020-7224 3414

PRODUCTIONS & PROMOTIONS Ltd
Apsley Mills Cottage, London Road
Hemel Hempstead, Herts HP3 9QU
Website: www.prodmotions.com
e-mail: reception@prodmotions.com
Fax: 0845 0095540   Tel: 01442 233372

PROSPECTS ASSOCIATIONS
(Singers, Sessions, Voice Overs for TV, Film & Commercials)
28 Magpie Close
Forest Gate
London E7 9DE   Tel: 020-8555 3628

PURE ACTORS AGENCY & MANAGEMENT Ltd
44 Salisbury Road
Manchester M41 0RB
Website: www.pure-management.co.uk
e-mail: enquiries@pure-management.co.uk
Fax: 0161-746 9886   Tel: 0161-747 2377

PURELY TALENT CASTING
(See GUBBAY Louise ASSOCIATES)

PVA MANAGEMENT Ltd
Hallow Park
Worcestershire WR2 6PG
e-mail: clients@pva.co.uk
Fax: 01905 641842   Tel: 01905 640663

QUICK Nina ASSOCIATES
(See TAYLOR Brian ASSOCIATES)

RAGE MODELS
Tigris House
256 Edgware Road
London W2 1DS
Website: www.ragemodels.org
e-mail: ragemodels@ugly.org
Fax: 020-7402 0507   Tel: 020-7262 0515

RAINBOW REPRESENTATION
45 Nightingale Lane
Crouch End
London N8 7RA
e-mail: rainbowrp@onetel.com   Tel/Fax: 020-8341 6241

RAMA GLOBAL Ltd
Huntingdon House
278-290 Huntingdon Street
Nottingham NG1 3LY
Website: www.rama-global.co.uk
e-mail: admin@rama-global.co.uk
Fax: 0115-948 3696   Tel: 0115-952 4333

RANDALL RICHARDSON ACTORS MANAGEMENT
2nd Floor
145-157 St John Street
London EC1V 4PY
Website: www.randallrichardson.co.uk
e-mail: mail@randallrichardson.co.uk
Fax: 0870 7623212   Tel: 020-7060 1645

RAVENSCOURT MANAGEMENT
8-30 Galena Road
Hammersmith
London W6 0LT
e-mail: info@ravenscourt.net
Fax: 020-8741 1786   Tel: 020-8741 0707

RAW AGENCY
Studio 1
Bizzy House
73A Mayplace Road West
Bexleyheath, Kent DA7 4JL
Website: www.raw-agency.com   Tel: 020-8303 2627 Ext 24

RAWHIDE COMEDY
PO Box 1127
Liverpool L69 3TL
Website: www.royalcourtliverpool.com
e-mail: info@rawhidecomedy.com
Fax: 0870 7871241   Tel: 0870 7871866

RAY KNIGHT CASTING
(See KNIGHT Ray CASTING)

RAZZAMATAZZ MANAGEMENT
Mulberry Cottage
Park Farm
Haxted Road, Lingfield RH7 6DE
e-mail: razzamatazzmanagement@btconnect.com
                                Tel/Fax: 01342 835359

RbA MANAGEMENT Ltd•
Co-operative PM
37-45 Windsor Street
Liverpool L8 1XE
Website: www.rbamanagement.co.uk
e-mail: info@rbamanagement.co.uk
Fax: 0151-709 0773   Tel: 0151-708 7273

RBM ACTORS
3rd Floor, 168 Victoria Street
London SW1E 5LB
Website: www.rbmactors.com
e-mail: info@rbmactors.com
Fax: 020-7630 6549   Tel: 020-7630 7733

RDF MANAGEMENT
3-6 Kenrick Place
London W1U 6HD
e-mail: debi.allen@rdfmanagement.com
Fax: 020-7317 2245   Tel: 020-7317 2251

REACTORS AGENCY
Co-operative
1 Eden Quay
Dublin 1
Ireland
Website: www.reactors.ie
e-mail: reactors@eircom.net
Fax: 00 353 1 8783182   Tel: 00 353 1 8786833

REAL PEOPLE, REAL TALENT
Half Moon Chambers
Chapel Walks
Manchester M2 1HN
Website: www.realpeople4u.com
e-mail: info@realpeople4u.com
Fax: 0161-832 5219   Tel: 0161-832 8259

Ella Kenion

Patrick Malahide

DAN HARWOOD-STAMPER
photographer

Tel: 07779 165777

www.danharwoodstamper.co.uk

Regan Rimmer Management   Theatre / Film / Television / Commercials

Debbie Rimmer
Suite 4
22 Little Russell Street
London
WC1A 2HS
t 020 7404 9957
f 020 7404 9958
e thegirls@regan-rimmer.co.uk

Leigh-Ann Regan
Ynyslas Uchaf Farm
Blackmill
Bridgend
CF35 6DW
t 01656 841841
f 01656 841 815
e regan-rimmer@btconnect.com

RE.ANIMATOR MANAGEMENT*
3rd Floor
The Priory
Syresham Gardens
West Sussex RH16 3LB
Website: www.reanimator.co.uk
e-mail: re.animator@gmail.com
Fax: 01444 447030   Tel: 01444 447020

RED CANYON MANAGEMENT
Website: www.redcanyon.co.uk
e-mail: info@redcanyon.co.uk
Mobile: 07939 365578   Mobile: 07931 381696

RED HOT ENTERTAINMENT
6 Farriers Mews
London SE15 3XP
Website: www.redhotentertainment.biz
e-mail: info@redhotentertainment.biz
Fax: 020-7635 8988   Tel: 020-7635 0403

RED ONION AGENCY
(Session Fixer for Singers, Musicians and Gospel Choirs)
26-28 Hatherley Mews
London E17 4QP
Website: www.redonion.uk.com
e-mail: events@redonion.uk.com
Fax: 020-8521 6646   Tel: 020-8520 4093

REDDIN Joan
PM (Write)
Hazel Cottage
Frogg's Island
Wheeler End Common
Bucks HP14 3NL   Tel: 01494 882729

REDROOFS ASSOCIATES
Harlequin House
26 Bath Road
Maidenhead
Berkshire SL6 4JT
Website: www.redroofs.co.uk
e-mail: agency@redroofs.co.uk
Fax: 01628 822461   Tel: 01628 822982

REGAN RIMMER MANAGEMENT
(Debbie Rimmer)
Suite 4
Little Russell House
22 Little Russell Street
London WC1A 2HS
e-mail: thegirls@regan-rimmer.co.uk
Fax: 020-7404 9958   Tel: 020-7404 9957

(Leigh-Ann Regan)
Ynyslas Uchaf Farm
Blackmill
Bridgend CF35 6DW
e-mail: regan-rimmer@btconnect.com
Fax: 01656 841815   Tel: 01656 841841

REGENCY AGENCY
F TV
25 Carr Road
Calverley
Leeds LS28 5NE   Tel: 0113-255 8980

REPRESENTATION UPSON EDWARDS
(Voice Coaches only)
51 Bounds Green Road
London N22 8HB
Website: www.voicecoach.tv
e-mail: sarahupson2006@btconnect.com
Fax: 056 007 56516   Tel: 020-8888 2525

REYNOLDS Sandra AGENCY
Md F TV
Shakespeare House
168 Lavender Hill
London SW11 5TF
Fax: 020-7387 5848   Tel: 020-7387 5858

Bacon House
35 St Georges Street
Norwich NR3 1DA
Website: www.sandrareynolds.co.uk
e-mail: info@sandrareynolds.co.uk
Fax: 01603 219825   Tel: 01603 623842

RHINO PERSONAL MANAGEMENT
Studio House
Delamare Road
Cheshunt
Hertfordshire EN8 9SH
Website: www.rhino-management.co.uk
e-mail: info@rhino-management.co.uk
Fax: 0845 3625457   Tel: 0845 3625456

RICHARD STONE PARTNERSHIP The
(See STONE Richard PARTNERSHIP The)

RICHARDS Lisa AGENCY
108 Upper Leeson Street
Dublin 4
Ireland
e-mail: info@lisarichards.ie
Fax: 00 353 1 6671256   Tel: 00 353 1 6375000

The Space
57-61 Mortimer Street
London W1W 8HS
Website: www.lisarichards.ie
e-mail: rose@lisarichards.ie   Tel: 020-3170 6205

RICHARDS Stella MANAGEMENT
(Existing Clients Only)
42 Hazlebury Road
London SW6 2ND
Fax: 020-7731 5082   Tel: 020-7736 7786

RIDGEWAY MANAGEMENT
Fairley House
Andrews Lane
Cheshunt
Herts EN7 6LB
e-mail: info@ridgewaystudios.co.uk
Fax: 01992 633844   Tel: 01992 633775

ROGUES & VAGABONDS MANAGEMENT Ltd•
PM Co-operative
The Print House
18 Ashwin Street
London E8 3DL
e-mail: rogues@vagabondsmanagement.com
Fax: 020-7249 8564   Tel: 020-7254 8130

ROLE MODELS
12 Cressy Road
London NW3 2LY
Website: www.rolemodelsagency.com
e-mail: info@rolemodelsagency.com   Tel: 020-7284 4337

ROSEBERY MANAGEMENT Ltd•
PM
Hoxton Hall
130 Hoxton Street
London N1 6SH
Website: www.roseberymanagement.com
e-mail: admin@roseberymanagement.com
Fax: 020-7503 0517   Tel: 020-7684 0187

ROSEMAN ORGANISATION The
51 Queen Anne Street
London W1G 9HS
Website: www.therosemanorganisation.co.uk
e-mail: info@therosemanorganisation.co.uk
Fax: 020-7486 4600   Tel: 020-7486 4500

ROSS BROWN ASSOCIATES
PM
Rosedale House
Rosedale Road
Richmond
Surrey TW9 2SZ
e-mail: sandy@rossbrown.eu
Fax: 020-8398 4111   Tel: 020-8398 3984

ROSS Frances MANAGEMENT
Higher Leyonne
Golant
Fowey
Cornwall PL23 1LA
Website: www.francesrossmanagement.com
e-mail: francesross@btconnect.com   Tel/Fax: 01726 833004

ROSSMORE PERSONAL MANAGEMENT*
70-76 Bell Street
London NW1 6SP
Website: www.rossmoremanagement.com
e-mail: agents@rossmoremanagement.com
Fax: 020-7258 0124   Tel: 020-7258 1953

ROUGH HANDS AGENCY The
The Pink House
7 Grosvenor Rise East
Walthamstow
London E17 9LB
e-mail: roughhandsagency@yahoo.co.uk
Mobile: 07932 573228   Mobile: 07976 838729

ROWE ASSOCIATES
33 Percy Street
London W1T 1DE
Website: www.growe.co.uk
e-mail: agents@growe.co.uk
Mobile: 07887 898220   Tel/Fax: 01992 308519

ROYCE MANAGEMENT
29 Trenholme Road
London SE20 8PP
e-mail: office@roycemanagement.co.uk
                             Tel/Fax: 020-8778 6861

RSM
(Cherry Parker)
15 The Fairway SS9 4QN
Website: www.rsm.uk.net
e-mail: info@rsm.uk.net
Mobile: 07976 547066   Tel: 01702 522647

RUBICON MANAGEMENT
27 Inderwick Road
Crouch End, London N8 9LB
e-mail: rubiconartists@blueyonder.co.uk
                             Tel/Fax: 020-8374 1836

RUDEYE DANCE AGENCY
PO Box 38743
London E10 5WN
Website: www.rudeye.com
e-mail: info@rudeye.com   Tel/Fax: 020-8556 7139

SANDERS Loesje Ltd*
(Designers, Directors, Choreographers, Lighting Designers)
Pound Square
1 North Hill
Woodbridge, Suffolk IP12 1HH
Website: www.loesjesanders.com
e-mail: loesje@loesjesanders.org.uk
Fax: 01394 388734   Tel: 01394 385260

SANGWIN ASSOCIATES*
8-30 Galena Road
Hammersmith
London W6 0LT
e-mail: info@sangwinassoc.com
Fax: 020-8741 1786   Tel: 020-8748 8698

SARABAND ASSOCIATES
(Sara Randall, Bryn Newton)
265 Liverpool Road
London N1 1LX
e-mail: brynnewton@btconnect.com
Fax: 020-7609 2370   Tel: 020-7609 5313

Simon & How Associates LTD

Talent Representatives

TV Film Commercial Theatre & Dance

Tel:0845 064 6666

Fax: 020 8553 4849

Email: info@simon-how.com

SASHAZE TALENT AGENCY
2 Gleannan Close
Omagh
Co. Tyrone BT79 7YA
Website: www.sashaze.com
e-mail: info@sashaze.com
Mobile: 07773 786098   Mobile: 07968 762942

SCA MANAGEMENT
TV F S M (Write)
77 Oxford Street
London W1D 2ES
Website: www.sca-management.co.uk
e-mail: agency@sca-management.co.uk
Fax: 020-7659 2116   Tel: 020-7659 2027

SCHNABL Peter
The Barn House
Cutwell, Tetbury
Gloucestershire GL8 8EB
Fax: 01666 502998   Tel: 01666 502133

SCOTT-PAUL YOUNG ENTERTAINMENTS Ltd
S.P.Y. Promotions & Productions
Northern Lights House
110 Blandford Road North
Langley, Nr Windsor, Berks SL3 7TA
Website: www.spy-ents.com
e-mail: castingdirect@spy-ents.com   Tel/Fax: 01753 693250

SCOTT Tim
284 Gray's Inn Road
London WC1X 8EB
e-mail: timscott@btinternet.com
Fax: 020-7278 9175   Tel: 020-7833 5733

SCREAM MANAGEMENT
The Pie Factory
101 Broadway
Media City
Manchester M50 2EQ
Website: www.screammanagement.com
e-mail: info@screammanagement.com
                             Tel/Fax: 0161-425 6495

SCRIMGEOUR Donald ARTISTS AGENT
(Dance)
49 Springcroft Avenue
London N2 9JH
Website: www.donaldsrimgeour.com
e-mail: vwest@dircon.co.uk
Fax: 020-8883 9751   Tel: 020-8444 6248

SEARS MANAGEMENT Ltd
2 Gumping Road
Orpington
Kent BR5 1RX
e-mail: lindasears@btconnect.com
Fax: 01689 862120   Tel: 01689 861859

SECOND SKIN AGENCY
Foxgrove House
School Lane
Seer Green
Beaconsfield, Bucks HP9 2QJ
e-mail: jenny@secondskinagency.com   Tel/Fax: 01494 730166

SEDGWICK Dawn MANAGEMENT
3 Goodwins Court
Covent Garden
London WC2N 4LL
Fax: 020-7240 0415   Tel: 020-7240 0404

Alan Rickman
Lindsay Duncan

FATIMAH NAMDAR
TEL 020 8341 1332 MOB 07973 287 535
e-mail: fn@fatimahnamdar.com
Student discount available

SHALIT GLOBAL MANAGEMENT
7 Moor Street
Soho
London W1D 5NB
e-mail: rich@shalitglobal.com
Fax: 020-7851 9156   Tel: 020-7851 9155

SHAPER Susan MANAGEMENT
5 Dovedale Gardens
465 Battersea Park Road
London SW11 4LR
e-mail: shapermg@btinternet.com
Fax: 020-7350 1802   Tel: 020-7585 1023

SHAW Vincent ASSOCIATES Ltd*
(Andy Charles)
186 Shaftesbury Avenue
London WC2H 8JB
Website: www.vincentshaw.com
e-mail: info@vincentshaw.com
Fax: 020-7240 2930   Tel: 020-7240 2927

SHEDDEN Malcolm MANAGEMENT
1 Charlotte Street
London W1T 1RD
Website: www.features.co.uk
e-mail: info@features.co.uk
Fax: 020-7636 1657   Tel: 020-7636 1876

SHEPHERD MANAGEMENT Ltd*
4th Floor
45 Maddox Street
London W1S 2PE
e-mail: info@shepherdmanagement.co.uk
Fax: 020-7499 7535   Tel: 020-7495 7813

SHEPPERD-FOX
5 Martyr Road
Guildford
Surrey GU1 4LF
Website: www.shepperd-fox.co.uk
e-mail: info@shepperd-fox.co.uk   Mobile: 07957 624601

SHOWSTOPPERS!
(Events Management & Entertainment)
42 Foxglove Close
Witham
Essex CM8 2XW
Website: www.showstoppers-group.com
e-mail: mail@showstoppers-group.com
Fax: 01376 510340   Tel: 01376 518486

S I A MANAGEMENT
Wessex
255 Brighton Road
Lancing, West Sussex BN15 8JP
Website: www.siamanagement.co.uk
e-mail: info@siamanagement.co.uk   Tel: 01903 529882

SIMON & HOW ASSOCIATES
90-92 Ley Street
Ilford
Essex IG1 4BX
Website: www.simon-how.com
e-mail: info@simon-how.com   Tel: 0845 0646666

SIMPSON FOX ASSOCIATES Ltd*
(Set, Costume and Lighting Designers, Directors,
Choreographers)
52 Shaftesbury Avenue
London W1D 6LP
e-mail: info@simpson-fox.com
Fax: 020-7494 2887   Tel: 020-7434 9167

SINGER Sandra ASSOCIATES
21 Cotswold Road
Westcliff-on-Sea, Essex SS0 8AA
Website: www.sandrasinger.com
e-mail: sandrasingeruk@aol.com
Fax: 01702 339393   Tel: 01702 331616

SINGERS INC/DANCERS INC Ltd
Golden Cross House
8 Duncannon Street
The Strand
London WC2N 4JF
Website: www.singersinc.co.uk
e-mail: enquiries@internationalcollective.co.uk
Fax: 020-7484 5100   Tel: 020-7484 5080

SIRR Peggy
(See ORIENTAL CASTING AGENCY Ltd)

SJ MANAGEMENT
8 Bettridge Road
London SW6 3QD
e-mail: sj@susanjames.demon.co.uk
Fax: 020-7371 0409   Tel: 020-7371 0441

SMART MANAGEMENT
The Aberdeen Centre
22-24 Highbury Grove
London N5 2EA
e-mail: smart.management@virgin.net   Tel: 020-7354 8822

Agency Management

Ice skaters, gymnasts,
circus artistes,
street theatre entertainers,
singers, dancers, magicians,
illusionists, choreographers,
directors, extras

AGENCY

Tel **01253 342426/7**   Fax: **01253 342702**
email: info@stageworkswwp.com   **www.stageworkswwp.com**

SMILE TALENT
The Office, Hope Cottage
London Road
Newport, Essex CB11 3PN
e-mail: info@smiletalent.com
Fax: 020-8457 2913   Tel: 020-8457 2702

SONGTIME/CHANDLER'S MANAGEMENT
10 Wallis Mews
Leatherhead, Surrey KT22 9DQ
Website: www.songtime.co.uk
e-mail: info@songtime.co.uk
Fax: 01372 362461   Tel: 020-8842 1242

SOPHIES PEOPLE
(Dancers & Choreographers)
40 Mexfield Road
London SW15 2RQ
Website: www.sophiespeople.com
e-mail: sophies.people@btinternet.com
Fax: 0870 7876447   Tel: 0870 7876446

SOUL MANAGEMENT
10 Coptic Street, London WC1A 1NH
Website: www.soulmanagement.co.uk
e-mail: info@soulmanagement.co.uk   Tel: 020-7580 1120

SPEAKERS CIRCUIT Ltd The
(After Dinner Speakers)
23 Tynemouth Street
Fulham, London SW6 2QS
e-mail: laura@allstarspeakers.co.uk
Fax: 01892 750089   Tel: 020-7371 7512

SPEAKERS CORNER
(Speakers, Presenters, Facilitation and Cabaret for the
Corporate Market)
Tigana House
Catlins Lane
Pinner
Middlesex HA5 2HG
Website: www.speakerscorner.co.uk
e-mail: info@speakerscorner.co.uk
Fax: 020-8868 4409   Tel: 020-8866 8967

SPIRE CASTING
PO Box 372
Chesterfield S41 0XW
Website: www.spirecasting.com
e-mail: mail@spirecasting.com   Tel: 07900 517707

SPLITTING IMAGES LOOKALIKES AGENCY
25 Clissold Court
Greenway Close
London N4 2EZ
Website: www.splitting-images.com
e-mail: info@splitting-images.com
Fax: 020-8809 6103   Tel: 020-8809 2327

SPORTABILITY Ltd
(Sporting Personalities)
Unit 2
23 Green Lane
Dronfield
Derbyshire S18 2LL
Fax: 01246 290520   Tel: 01246 292010

Pete Bartlett
Photography

e info@petebartlett.com
i www.petebartlett.com
t 07971653994

SPORTS MODELS
1A Calton Avenue
Dulwich Village
London SE21 7DE
Website: www.sportsmodels.com
e-mail: info@sportsmodels.com
Mobile: 07973 863263
Tel: 020-8299 8800

SPORTS OF SEB Ltd
31 Ivor Place, London NW1 6DA
Website: www.sportsofseb.com
e-mail: info@sportsofseb.com
Mobile: 07740 359770
Tel: 020-7723 1889

SPORTS WORKSHOP PROMOTIONS Ltd
(Sports Models)
PO Box 878
Crystal Palace
National Sports Centre
London SE19 2BH
e-mail: info@sportspromotions.co.uk
Fax: 020-8776 7772
Tel: 020-8659 4561

SPYKER Paul MANAGEMENT
PO Box 48848
London WC1B 3WZ
e-mail: belinda@psmlondon.com
Fax: 020-7462 0047
Tel: 020-7462 0046

SRA PERSONAL MANAGEMENT
Suite 84
The London Fruit and Wool Exchange
Brushfield Street
London E1 6EP
e-mail: agency@susanrobertsacademy.co.uk
Tel: 01932 863194
Tel: 020-7655 4477

STACEY Barrie PROMOTIONS
Apartment 8
132 Charing Cross Road
London WC2H 0LA
Website: www.barriestacey.com
e-mail: hopkinstacey@aol.com
Fax: 020-7836 2949
Tel: 020-7836 6220

STAFFORD Helen MANAGEMENT
14 Park Avenue
Bush Hill Park
Enfield EN1 2HP
e-mail: h-stafford@sky.com
Fax: 020-8372 0611
Tel: 020-8360 6329

STAGE AND SCREEN PERSONAL MANAGEMENT
20B Kidbrooke Grove
Blackheath SE3 0LF
Website: www.stageandscreenpm.com
e-mail: info@stageandscreenpm.com
Tel: 020-7193 4994

STAGE CENTRE MANAGEMENT Ltd•
PM Co-operative
41 North Road, London N7 9DP
Website: www.stagecentre.org.uk
e-mail: stagecentre@aol.com
Tel: 020-7607 0872

STAGEWORKS WORLDWIDE PRODUCTIONS
525 Ocean Boulevard
Blackpool FY4 1EZ
Website: www.stageworkswwp.com
e-mail: simon.george@stageworkswwp.com
Fax: 01253 343702
Tel: 01253 342427

STAR MANAGEMENT Ltd
16A Winton Drive
Glasgow G12 0QA
Website: www.starmanagement.co.uk
e-mail: star@starmanagement.co.uk
Tel: 0870 2422276

STARFISH ENTERPRISES Ltd
15 Leamington Road
Ainsdale
Southport
Merseyside PR8 3LB
Website: www.starfishents.co.uk
e-mail: info@starfishents.co.uk
Tel: 01704 573779

STARLINGS THEATRICAL AGENCY
45 Viola Close
South Ockendon
Essex RM15 6JF
Website: www.webspawner.com/users/starlings
e-mail: julieecarter@aol.com
Mobile: 07969 909284

STEVENSON Natasha MANAGEMENT Ltd
(See NSM)

STIRLING MANAGEMENT
37 Oldstead Grove
Ferncrest
Bolton
Lancs BL3 4XW
Website: www.stirlingmanagement.co.uk
e-mail: admin@stirlingmanagement.co.uk
Fax: 0844 4128689
Tel: 0845 0176500

STIVEN CHRISTIE MANAGEMENT
(Incorporating The Actors Agency of Edinburgh)
1 Glen Street
Tollcross, Edinburgh EH3 9JD
Fax: 0131-228 4645   Tel: 0131-228 4040

ST. JAMES'S MANAGEMENT
PM (Write SAE)
19 Lodge Close, Stoke D'Abernon
Cobham, Surrey KT11 2SG
Fax: 01932 863152   Tel: 01932 860666

STONE Ian ASSOCIATES
Suite 262
Maddison House, 226 High Street
Croydon CR9 1DF   Tel/Fax: 020-8667 1627

STONE Richard PARTNERSHIP The*
2 Henrietta Street, London WC2E 8PS
Website: www.thersp.com
e-mail: all@thersp.com
Fax: 020-7497 0869   Tel: 020-7497 0849

STRAIGHT LINE MANAGEMENT
(Division of Straight Line Productions)
58 Castle Avenue
Epsom, Surrey KT17 2PH
e-mail: hilary@straightlinemanagement.co.uk
Fax: 020-8393 8079   Tel: 020-8393 4220

STRANGE John MANAGEMENT
11 Ashley Street
Glasgow G3 6DR
Website: www.strangemanagement.co.uk
e-mail: lesley@strangemanagement.co.uk
Fax: 0141-333 9890   Tel: 0141-333 0233

SUCCESS
Room 236, 2nd Floor
Linen Hall
162-168 Regent Street
London W1B 5TB
Website: www.successagency.co.uk
e-mail: ee@successagency.co.uk
Fax: 020-7494 3787   Tel: 020-7734 3356

SUMMERS Mark MANAGEMENT
137 Freston Road
London W10 6TH
Website: www.marksummers.com
e-mail: info@marksummers.com
Fax: 020-7243 1987   Tel: 020-7229 8413

SUMMERTON Michael MANAGEMENT Ltd
(Choreographers & Dancers)
Mimosa House
Mimosa Street
London SW6 4DS
Website: www.michaelsummerton.com
e-mail: msminfo@btconnect.com
Fax: 020-7731 0103   Tel: 020-7731 6969

TAKE FLIGHT MANAGEMENT
Website: www.takeflightmanagement.com
e-mail: info@takeflightmanagement.com
                         Tel/Fax: 020-8835 8147

TALENT4MEDIA Ltd
Power Road Studios
114 Power Road, London W4 5PY
Website: www.unique-management.co.uk
e-mail: jc@uniquemgt.co.uk
Fax: 020-8987 6401   Tel: 020-8987 6400

Robert Glenister   Gemma Sutton   Paul Antony-Barber

J. BARBER
photography
07785 261513

TALENT ARTISTS Ltd*
(No Unsolicited Enquiries)
59 Sydner Road
London N16 7UF
e-mail: talent.artists@btconnect.com
Fax: 020-7923 2009   Tel: 020-7923 1119

TAVISTOCK WOOD
32 Tavistock Street
London WC2E 7PB
Website: www.tavistockwood.com
Fax: 020-7240 9029   Tel: 020-7257 8725

TAYLOR Brian ASSOCIATES*
50 Pembroke Road
Kensington
London W8 6NX
e-mail: briantaylor@nqassoc.freeserve.co.uk
Fax: 020-7602 6301   Tel: 020-7602 6141

TCA
(The Commercial Agency)
12 Evelyn Mansions
Carlisle Place
London SW1P 1NH
Website: www.thecommercialagency.co.uk
e-mail: mail@thecommercialagency.co.uk
Fax: 020-7233 8110   Tel: 020-7233 8100

TCG ARTIST MANAGEMENT
(Kristin Tarry, Rachel Cranmer-Gordon & Michael Ford)
Fourth Floor
6 Langley Street
London WC2H 9JA
Website: www.spotlightagent.info/tcgam
e-mail: info@tcgam.co.uk
Fax: 020-7240 3606   Tel: 020-7240 3600

T.G.R. DIRECT
88 Recreation Road
Poole, Dorset BH12 2AL
e-mail: tatianaroc.tgrdirect@virgin.net
Fax: 01202 721802   Tel: 01202 721222

THEATRE EXPRESS MANAGEMENT
(Write)
Spindle Cottage, Allens Farm
Digby Fen, Billinghay, Lincoln LN4 4DT
e-mail: info@theatre-express.com

THOMAS & BENDA ASSOCIATES Ltd
Top Floor, 15-16 Ivor Place
London NW1 6HS   Tel/Fax: 020-7723 5509

THOMPSON D.A. ASSOCIATES
22 Montefiore Street
Battersea, London SW8 3TL
e-mail: montifiore@aol.com
Fax: 020-7498 6548   Tel: 020-7622 6117

THOMPSON Jim
Herricks, School Lane
Arundel, West Sussex BN18 9DR
e-mail: jim@jthompson42.freeserve.co.uk
Fax: 01903 885887   Tel: 01903 885757

THOMPSON Peggy OFFICE The
PM
1st & 2nd Floor Offices
296 Sandycombe Road
Kew, Richmond
Surrey TW9 3NG
Fax: 020-8332 1127   Tel: 020-8332 1003

THOMSON Mia ASSOCIATES (MTA)
110 South Street
Eastbourne
East Sussex BN21 4LB
e-mail: info@miathomsonassociates.co.uk
Fax: 01323 417766   Tel: 01323 417817

THORNTON AGENCY
(Specialist Agency for Small People)
72 Purley Downs Road
South Croydon CR2 0RB
Website: www.dwarfs4hire.com
e-mail: thorntons.leslie@tinyworld.co.uk
                          Tel/Fax: 020-8660 5588

THRELFALL Katie ASSOCIATES
2A Gladstone Road, London SW19 1QT
e-mail: info@ktthrelfall.co.uk
Fax: 020-8543 7545   Tel: 020-8543 4344

THRESH Melody MANAGEMENT ASSOCIATES Ltd (MTM)
27 Ardwick Green North
Ardwick
Manchester M12 6FZ
e-mail: melodythreshmtm@aol.com
Fax: 0161-273 5455   Tel: 0161-273 5445

TILDSLEY Janice ASSOCIATES
47 Orford Road
London E17 9NJ
Website: www.janicetildsleyassociates.co.uk
e-mail: info@janicetildsleyassociates.co.uk
Fax: 020-8521 1174   Tel: 020-8521 1888

TINKER Victoria MANAGEMENT
(Technical, Non-Acting)
Birchenbridge House
Brighton Road
Mannings Heath, Horsham
West Sussex RH13 6HY   Tel/Fax: 01403 210653

TMG
(Lisa-Anne Campbell)
14 Hagan's Court, Lad Lane
Dublin 2, Ireland
e-mail: talentmanagementgroup@eircom.net
Fax: 00 353 1 661 9967   Tel: 00 353 1 661 9969

TOTAL VANITY Ltd
15 Walton Way, Aylesbury
Buckinghamshire HP21 7JJ
Website: www.totalvanity.com
e-mail: teresa.hellen@totalvanity.com
Mobile: 07739 381788   Mobile: 07710 780152

TOTS-TWENTIES
62 Buntingbridge Road
Newbury Park
Ilford, Essex IG1 7LR
Website: www.tots-twenties.co.uk
e-mail: sara@tots-twenties.co.uk
Fax: 020-8518 0212   Tel: 020-8518 0200

TRENDS AGENCY & MANAGEMENT Ltd
Sullom Lodge
Sullom Side Lane, Garstang PR3 1GH
Website: www.trendsgroup.co.uk
e-mail: info@trendsgroup.co.uk
Fax: 01253 407715   Tel: 0871 2003343

TROIKA*
3rd Floor
74 Clerkenwell Road
London EC1M 5QA
e-mail: info@troikatalent.com
Fax: 020-7490 7642   Tel: 020 7336 7868

TUCKER Tommy AGENCY
Suite 66
235 Earl's Court Road
London SW5 9FE
e-mail: TTTommytucker@aol.com   Tel: 020-7370 3911

TV MANAGEMENTS
Brink House, Avon Castle
Ringwood, Hants BH24 2BL
e-mail: etv@tvmanagements.co.uk
Fax: 01425 480123   Tel: 01425 475544

TWINS
(See PC THEATRICAL & MODEL AGENCY)

TWINS & TRIPLETS
(Identical Babies, Children, Teenagers & Adults for
Film/Television)
15 Holmhurst Road
Upper Belvedere DA17 6HW
e-mail: twinsontv@aol.com   Tel: 01322 440184

TWIST & FLIC SPORTS AGENCY
(Sports Model Agent)
1A Calton Avenue
Dulwich Village, London SE21 7ED
Website: www.sportsmodels.com
e-mail: info@sportsmodels.com
Mobile: 07973 863263   Tel: 020-8299 8800

TWITCH
5 Breakspears Mews
Brockley SE4 1PY
Website: www.twitch.uk.com
e-mail: info@twitch.uk.com
Mobile: 07932 656358   Mobile: 07747 770816

TWO'S COMPANY
244 Upland Road, London SE22 0DN
e-mail: graham@2scompanytheatre.co.uk
Fax: 020-8299 3714   Tel: 020-8299 4593

UGLY MODELS
Tigris House
256 Edgware Road, London W2 1DS
Website: www.ugly.org
e-mail: info@ugly.org
Fax: 020-7402 0507   Tel: 020-7402 5564

UNIQUE TALENT MANAGEMENT Ltd
(Dancers Only)
International House
Suite 501, 223 Regent Street
London W1H 2QD
Website: www.utm.org.uk
e-mail: info@utm.org.uk   Tel: 020-7569 8636

UNITED PRODUCTIONS
(Choreographers, Dancers, Stylists)
6 Shaftesbury Mews
Clapham
London SW4 9BP
Website: www.unitedproductions.biz
e-mail: lyndon@unitedproductions.biz
                          Tel/Fax: 020-7622 0840

UPBEAT MANAGEMENT
(Theatre Touring & Events - No Actors)
Larg House
Woodcote Grove
Coulsdon, Surrey CR5 2QQ
Website: www.upbeat.co.uk
e-mail: info@upbeat.co.uk
Fax: 020-8668 3922   Tel: 020-8668 3332

UPSON EDWARDS
(See REPRESENTATION UPSON EDWARDS)

URBAN HEROES
77 Wimpole Street
London W1G 9RU
Website: www.theurbanheroes.com
e-mail: justin@theurbanheroes.com
Fax: 0870 4792458   Tel: 020-7043 1072

URBAN TALENT
Nemesis House, 1 Oxford Court
Bishopsgate, Manchester M2 3WQ
Website: www.urbantalent.tv
e-mail: liz@nmsmanagement.co.uk
Fax: 0161-228 6727   Tel: 0161-228 6866

UVA MANAGEMENT Ltd
118-120 Kenton Road
Harrow, Middlesex HA3 8AL
e-mail: berko@uvamanagement.com
Mobile: 07716 777885   Tel: 0845 3700883

V A MANAGEMENT
145 Centrium
Stations Approach, Woking GU22 7PB
Website: www.viciousmanagement.com
e-mail: info@viciousmanagement.com
                          Mobile: 07940 658607

VACCA Roxane MANAGEMENT*
73 Beak Street
London W1F 9SR
Website: www.roxanevaccamanagement.com
Fax: 020-7734 8086   Tel: 020-7734 8085

VALLÉ ACADEMY THEATRICAL AGENCY The
The Vallé Academy Studios
Wilton House, Delamare Road
Cheshunt, Herts EN8 9SG
Website: www.valleacademy.co.uk
e-mail: agency@valleacademy.co.uk
Fax: 01992 622868   Tel: 01992 622861

VAMP JAZZ
(Artists & Musicians)
Ealing House
33 Hanger Lane, London W5 3HJ
e-mail: vampjazz@aol.com   Tel: 020-8997 3355

VIDAL-HALL Clare*
(Directors, Designers, Choreographers, Lighting Designers,
Composers)
57 Carthew Road, London W6 0DU
e-mail: info@clarevidalhall.com
Fax: 020-8741 9459   Tel: 020-8741 7647

VINE Michael ASSOCIATES
(Light Entertainment)
29 Mount View Road
London N4 4SS
e-mail: mpvine@aol.com
Fax: 020-8348 3277   Tel: 020-8348 5899

VisABLE PEOPLE
(Artists with Disabilities only)
Website: www.visablepeople.com
e-mail: louise@visablepeople.com   Tel: 01905 776631

WADE Suzann
9 Wimpole Mews
London W1G 8PG
Website: www.suzannwade.com
e-mail: info@suzannwade.com
Fax: 020-7486 5664   Tel: 020-7486 0746

WALMSLEY Peter ASSOCIATES
(No Representation, Do Not Write)
37A Crimsworth Road
London SW8 4RJ
e-mail: associates@peterwalmsley.net
Mobile: 07778 347312   Tel: 020-7787 6419

WARING & McKENNA*
11-12 Dover Street
Mayfair
London W1S 4LJ
Website: www.waringandmckenna.com
e-mail: dj@waringandmckenna.com
Fax: 020-7629 6466   Tel: 020-7629 6444

WEBSTER MANAGEMENT
75 Hewison Street
London E3 2HZ
e-mail: danniwebster@onetel.net   Mobile: 07708 154250

WELCH Janet PERSONAL MANAGEMENT
Old Orchard
The Street
Ubley
Bristol BS40 6PJ
e-mail: info@janetwelchpm.co.uk   Tel/Fax: 01761 463238

WESSON Penny*
(Directors)
26 King Henry's Road
London NW3 3RP
e-mail: penny@pennywesson.demon.co.uk
Fax: 020-7483 2890   Tel: 020-7722 6607

WEST CENTRAL MANAGEMENT
Co-operative
Room 4, East Block
Panther House
38 Mount Pleasant
London WC1X 0AN
Website: www.westcentralmanagement.co.uk
e-mail: mail@westcentralmanagement.co.uk
          Tel/Fax: 020-7833 8134

WEST END MANAGEMENT
(Maureen Cairns)
1st Floor, 84 Miller Street
Glasgow G1 1DT
Website: www.maureencairnsltd.com
e-mail: info@maureencairnsltd.com
Fax: 0141-226 8983   Tel: 0141-226 8941

WHATEVER ARTISTS MANAGEMENT Ltd
F24 Argo House
Kilburn Park Road
London NW6 5LF
Website: www.wamshow.biz
e-mail: info@wamshow.biz
Fax: 020-7372 5111   Tel: 020-7372 4777

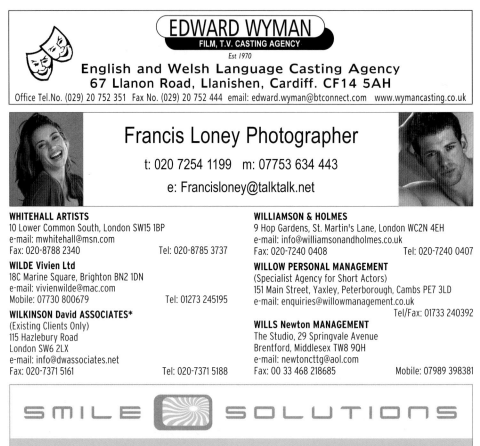

EDWARD WYMAN
FILM, T.V. CASTING AGENCY
Est 1970
English and Welsh Language Casting Agency
67 Llanon Road, Llanishen, Cardiff. CF14 5AH
Office Tel.No. (029) 20 752 351 Fax No. (029) 20 752 444 email: edward.wyman@btconnect.com www.wymancasting.co.uk

Francis Loney Photographer
t: 020 7254 1199   m: 07753 634 443
e: Francisloney@talktalk.net

WHITEHALL ARTISTS
10 Lower Common South, London SW15 1BP
e-mail: mwhitehall@msn.com
Fax: 020-8788 2340   Tel: 020-8785 3737

WILDE Vivien Ltd
18C Marine Square, Brighton BN2 1DN
e-mail: vivienwilde@mac.com
Mobile: 07730 800679   Tel: 01273 245195

WILKINSON David ASSOCIATES*
(Existing Clients Only)
115 Hazlebury Road
London SW6 2LX
e-mail: info@dwassociates.net
Fax: 020-7371 5161   Tel: 020-7371 5188

WILLIAMSON & HOLMES
9 Hop Gardens, St. Martin's Lane, London WC2N 4EH
e-mail: info@williamsonandholmes.co.uk
Fax: 020-7240 0408   Tel: 020-7240 0407

WILLOW PERSONAL MANAGEMENT
(Specialist Agency for Short Actors)
151 Main Street, Yaxley, Peterborough, Cambs PE7 3LD
e-mail: enquiries@willowmanagement.co.uk
                            Tel/Fax: 01733 240392

WILLS Newton MANAGEMENT
The Studio, 29 Springvale Avenue
Brentford, Middlesex TW8 9QH
e-mail: newtoncttg@aol.com
Fax: 00 33 468 218685   Mobile: 07989 398381

WILSON-GOUGH MANAGEMENT
2nd Floor, Hammer House
117 Wardour Street W1F 0UN
e-mail: info@wilson-gough.com
Fax: 020-7439 4173   Tel: 020-7439 4171

WINSLETT Dave ASSOCIATES
6 Kenwood Ridge, Kenley, Surrey CR8 5JW
Website: www.davewinslett.com
e-mail: info@davewinslett.com
Fax: 020-8668 9216   Tel: 020-8668 0531

WINTERSON Niki
(See GLOBAL ARTISTS)

WIS CELTIC MANAGEMENT
(Welsh, Irish, Scottish)
86 Elphinstone Road, Walthamstow, London E17 5EX
Fax: 020-8523 4523   Tel: 020-8523 4234

WISE BUDDAH TALENT
(Chris North)
74 Great Titchfield Street, London W1W 7QP
Website: www.wisebuddah.com
e-mail: chris.north@wisebuddah.com
Fax: 020-7307 7442   Tel: 020-7307 1600

WM MANAGEMENT
19 Havelock Street, London N1 0DA
e-mail: kate.whaley@virgin.net   Tel: 020-7278 8271

WMG MANAGEMENT EUROPE Ltd
(Sports Management Company)
5th Floor, 33 Soho Square, London W1D 3QU
Website: www.sfxsports.co.uk
Fax: 020-3230 1053   Tel: 020-7009 6000

WYMAN Edward AGENCY
F TV (English & Welsh Language)
67 Llanon Road
Llanishen, Cardiff CF14 5AH
Website: www.wymancasting.co.uk
e-mail: edward.wyman@btconnect.com
Fax: 029-2075 2444   Tel: 029-2075 2351

X-FACTOR MANAGEMENT Ltd
PO Box 44198, London SW6 4XU
Website: www.xfactorltd.com
e-mail: info@xfactorltd.com
Fax: 0870 2519560   Tel: 0870 2519540

XL MANAGEMENT
Edmund House, Rugby Road
Leamington Spa, Warwickshire CV32 6EL
Website: www.xlmanagement.co.uk
e-mail: office@xlmanagement.co.uk
Fax: 01926 811420   Tel: 01926 810449

YAT MANAGEMENT
Young Actors Management
70-72 Barnsbury Road, London N1 0ES
Website: www.yati.org.uk
e-mail: agent@yati.org.uk
Fax: 020-7833 9467   Tel: 020-7278 2101

YELLOW BALLOON PRODUCTIONS Ltd
(Mike Smith)
Freshwater House, Outdowns, Effingham, Surrey KT24 5QR
e-mail: yellowbal@aol.com
Fax: 01483 281502   Tel: 01483 281500

ZWICKLER Marlene & ASSOCIATES
1 Belgrave Crescent Lane, Edinburgh EH4 3AG
Website: www.mza-artists.com   Tel/Fax: 0131-343 3030

Daniel Coll

COLLETTE PARKER
Photographer

0794 4420625

www.colletteparker.co.uk

collette.parker@blueyonder.co.uk

studio/location

Sinead Marie Coll

International Casting & Model Agency
Tots : Children : Teens
Talented & professional actors for TV, Films, Commercials, Voice Overs
Our actors include:
Joshua Peacock, Amy Barlow, Finlay Moreton in Coronation Street
Luke Dingle in Emmerdale
Over 2000 Extras for Crowd/Classroom scenes!
Casting & Reception Facilities Manchester/Liverpool Area
All Children & Chaperones Licensed
We look forward to being of service to you
To access our online database
Ring: 01925 761088 email: castings@eka-agency.com
www.eka-agency.com

ALLSTARS
★ CASTING AGENCY ★
CHILDREN & TEENAGERS
TV, FILM & THEATRE WORK
★ TEL: 07739 359737 ★
EMAIL: allstarscasting@blueyonder.co.uk
★ www.allstarsweb.co.uk ★

A & J MANAGEMENT
242A The Ridgeway, Botany Bay, Enfield EN2 8AP
Website: www.ajmanagement.co.uk
e-mail: info@ajmanagement.co.uk
Fax: 020-8342 0842   Tel: 020-8342 0542

ABACUS AGENCY
The Studio, 4 Bailey Road, Westcott
Dorking, Surrey RH4 3QS
Website: www.abacusagency.co.uk
e-mail: admin@abacusagency.co.uk
Fax: 01306 877813   Tel: 01306 877144

ACADEMY MANAGEMENT
123 East Park Farm Drive, Charvil
Reading, Berks RG10 9UQ   Tel: 0118-934 9940

ACT OUT AGENCY
(Children, Teenagers & New Graduates)
22 Greek Street, Stockport, Cheshire SK3 8AB
e-mail: ab22actout@aol.com   Tel/Fax: 0161-429 7413

ACTIVATE DRAMA SCHOOL
(Drama School & Agency)
Priestman Cottage, Sea View Road, Sunderland SR2 7UP
e-mail: activate_agcy@hotmail.com   Tel: 0191-565 2345

ADAMS Juliet CHILD MODEL & TALENT AGENCY
19 Gwynne House, Challice Way, London SW2 3RB
Website: www.julietadams.co.uk
e-mail: bookingdesk@julietadams.co.uk
Fax: 020-8671 9314   Tel: 020-8671 7673

ALLSORTS DRAMA FOR CHILDREN
(In Association with Sasha Leslie Management)
34 Pember Road, London NW10 5LS
e-mail: sasha@allsortsdrama.com
Fax: 020-8969 3196   Tel: 020-8969 3249

ALLSORTS THEATRICAL AGENCY
Suite 1 & 2 Marlborough Business Centre
96 George Lane, London E18 1AD
Website: www.allsortsagency.com
e-mail: bookings@allsortsagency.com
Fax: 020-8989 5600   Tel: 020-8989 0500

ALLSTARS CASTING
PO Box 28, Walton, Liverpool L10 6NN
Website: www.allstarsweb.co.uk
e-mail: allstarscasting@blueyonder.co.uk
Fax: 0151-476 1135   Mobile: 07739 359737

ALPHABET KIDZ TALENT & MODELLING AGENCY
189 Southampton Way, London SE5 7EJ
Website: www.alphabetkidz.co.uk
e-mail: contact@alphabetkidz.co.uk
Fax: 020-7252 4341   Tel: 020-7252 4343

ANNA'S MANAGEMENT
(Formerly of ALADDIN'S CAVE)
25 Tintagel Drive, Stanmore, Middlesex HA7 4SR
e-mail: annasmanage@aol.com
Fax: 020-8238 2899   Tel: 020-8958 7636

AQUITAINE PERSONAL MANAGEMENT
PO Box 1896, Stanford-Le-Hope, Essex SS17 0WR
Website: www.apm.aquitaine.org.uk
e-mail: apm@aquitaine.org.uk   Tel: 01375 488022

ARAENA/COLLECTIVE
10 Bramshaw Gardens
South Oxhey, Herts WD19 6XP   Tel/Fax: 020-8428 0037

ARTS ACADEMY (T.A.A.) The
15 Lexham Mews, London W8 6JW
e-mail: jill@galloways.ltd.uk
Fax: 020-7376 2416   Tel: 020-7376 0267

Children, Teenagers & Babies available for TV/Film,
Commercials, Photographic, Theatre, Voiceovers and Extras

Naturally talented children with a multitude of different skills
and talents for all your casting needs

Our philosophy is
Fun, Energy, Enthusiasm,
Commitment, Equality and Diversity

alphabetkidz
www.alphabetkidz.co.uk
T: 020 7252 4343   F: 020 7252 4341   E: contact@alphabetkidz.co.uk

How do child actors get started?

If a child is interested in becoming an actor, they should try to get as much practical experience as possible. For example, joining the drama club at school, taking theatre studies as an option, reading as many plays as they can, and going to the theatre on a regular basis. They could also attend local youth theatres or drama groups. Some theatres offer evening or Saturday classes.

What are the chances of success?

As any agency or school will tell you, the entertainment industry is highly competitive and for every success story there are many children who will never be hired for paid acting work. Child artists and their parents should think very carefully before getting involved in the industry and be prepared for disappointments along the way.

What is the difference between stage schools and agencies?

Stage schools provide specialised training in acting, singing and dancing for the under 18's. They offer a variety of full and part-time courses. Please see the 'Drama Training, Schools and Coaches' section for listings (marked 'SS'). Children's and Teenagers' agencies specialise in the representation of child artists, promoting them to casting opportunities and negotiating contracts on their behalf. In return they will take commission, usually ranging from 10-15%. A number of agents are listed in the following pages. Always research an agency carefully to make sure it is suitable for your child. As a general rule, you should not pay an upfront joining fee. Some larger stage schools also have agencies attached to them.

Why do child actors need licenses? Who are chaperones?

Strict regulations apply to children working in the entertainment industry. These cover areas including the maximum number of performance hours per day / week, rest times, meal times and tutoring requirements. When any child under 16 performs in a professional capacity, the production company must obtain a Child Performance Licence from the child's Local Education Authority. Child artists must also be accompanied by a chaperone at all times when they are working. Registered chaperones are generally used instead of parents as they have a better understanding of the employment regulations involved, and they have professional experience of dealing with production companies. Registered chaperones have been police checked and approved by their local education authority to act *in loco parentis*. Always contact your local education authority if you have any questions or concerns.

What is the Spotlight Children and Young Performers directory?

Children who are currently represented by an agent or attend a stage school can appear in the Spotlight Children and Young Performers directory. This is a casting directory, used by production teams to source child artists for TV, film, stage or commercial work. Please speak to your child's school or agency about joining Spotlight.

SANDRA SINGER (M.I.E.A.P.) has been a Talent Agent since 1985. Since 1995 she has specialised in supplying clients for roles in Feature Films, Film, TV, Commercials and West End Musical Theatre. Sandra has a vocational Stage School, 'Singer Stage School', based in Leigh-on-Sea, Essex. Affiliated to her training school she has an agency called 'Sandra Singer Associates', where she represents child and adult clients.

In my opinion, if a parent is looking to allow their children to be involved in the entertainment business they need to remember the following:

I do not charge a fee for any child to join my agency. When finding an agent for your child, please check if they charge a joining fee. If they do: run a mile! If a child has potential, an agency should be pleased to represent them.

Young Children change their look so quickly (teeth falling out, braces, new hairstyles etc) that they need to be with an agent who can change the photograph of the child quickly, should they need to. So, for an agency, websites are my preference.

Once you or your child has joined an agency, the only thing you should pay for is for a great 'head and shoulders' promotional photograph, and an entry into Spotlight or a similar casting directory. Most agents use an experienced headshot photographer. My clients pay approx £40 for their photos, and then the annual fee to join Spotlight (website and book), currently this is £82.00.

As agents work on commission, this is where they should be making their money, not by charging you for expensive photographic portfolios (which you don't need), or from agency joining fees. If / when you get your first job, it is up to the agent to negotiate on your behalf, invoice the client and send you your payment minus commission. You need to ask in advance how much they take, and when you will be paid. My policy is seven days after we receive the payment from the client.

When children are very young, for auditions and castings it's all about their look. After 7+ it is still about the look initially (their photo), but then talent comes into play. When they get to audition, they must be able to cope with a script / choreography / singing etc. Competition is enormous and this is why good training is vital.

It can be a very-quick moving industry and artists must be prepared for this. We can suggest one of our clients for a job in the morning, hear back from the casting director that afternoon, with a script sent straight to the child to learn for an audition the next day, or maybe even that very same night!

The most important thing is the safety of child performers. Always make sure that your child is licenced to work. It is against the law for under-16s to work without one. This is for the interest and safety of the child.

Lastly, please don't live your dreams through your child. Encourage them 100% if this is what they want to do: but it really needs to come from the heart. To make it work, they really need to live to perform. They also need to enjoy themselves in this very hard - but wonderful - profession. I certainly do.

For more information please visit www.sandrasinger.com

ASHCROFT ACADEMY OF DRAMATIC ART & AGENCY
Malcolm Primary School
Malcolm Road, Penge, London SE20 8RH
Website: www.ashcroftacademy.com
e-mail: geraldi.gillma@btconnect.com
Mobile: 07799 791586   Tel/Fax: 01634 856900

AWA - ANDREA WILDER AGENCY
23 Cambrian Drive, Colwyn Bay, Conwy LL28 4SL
Website: www.awagency.co.uk
e-mail: casting@awagency.co.uk
Fax: 07919 202401   Mobile: 07092 249314

BABY BODENS
Bodens Studios & Agency
99 East Barnet Road, New Barnet, Herts EN4 8RF
Website: www.bodensagency.com
e-mail: info@bodensagency.com
Fax: 020-8449 5212   Tel: 020-8447 1035

BABYSHAK
Bizzy House, 73A Mayplace Road West
Bexleyheath, Kent DA7 4JL
Website: www.babyshak.com
e-mail: bookings@babyshak.com
Fax: 020-8303 2730   Tel: 020-8303 2627

BARDSLEY'S Pamela UNIQUE AGENCY
93 Bispham Road, Churchtown, Southport PR9 7DF
Website: www.pamelabardsleyschool.co.uk
e-mail: pamela_bardsley@hotmail.com
Mobile: 07969 774506   Tel: 01704 231101

BELCANTO LONDON ACADEMY Ltd
(Stage School & Agency)
Performance House
20 Passey Place, Eltham, London SE9 5DQ
e-mail: bla@dircon.co.uk
Fax: 020-8850 9944   Tel: 020-8850 9888

BIZZYKIDZ
Bizzy House, 73A Mayplace Road West
Bexleyheath, Kent DA7 4JL
Website: www.bizzykidz.com
e-mail: bookings@bizzykidz.com
Fax: 020-8303 2730   Tel: 020-8303 2627

BODENS AGENCY
99 East Barnet Road, New Barnet, Herts EN4 8RF
Website: www.bodensagency.com
e-mail: info@bodensagency.com
Fax: 020-8449 5212   Tel: 020-8447 1226

BOURNE Michelle ACADEMY & AGENCY The
Studio 1, 22 Dorman Walk, Garden Way, London NW10 0PF
Website: www.michellebourneacademy.co.uk
e-mail: info@michellebourneacademy.co.uk
Mobile: 07956 853564   Tel/Fax: 020-8451 8808

BRUCE & BROWN
203 Canalot Studios, 222 Kensal Road, London W10 5BN
Website: www.bruceandbrown.com
e-mail: info@bruceandbrown.com
Fax: 020-8964 0457   Tel: 020-8968 5585

BUBBLEGUM
Pinewood Studios, Pinewood Road
Iver Heath, Bucks SL0 0NH
Website: www.bubblegummodels.com
e-mail: kids@bubblegummodels.com
Fax: 01753 652521   Tel: 01753 632867

BYRON'S MANAGEMENT
(Babies, Children & Adults)
76 St James Lane, Muswell Hill, London N10 3DF
Website: www.byronsmanagement.co.uk
e-mail: byronscasting@aol.com
Fax: 020-8444 4040   Tel: 020-8444 4445

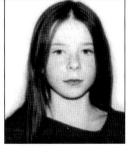

Altea Claveras, Charlotte Byker Grove

CAPITAL ARTS
Wyllyotts Centre, Darkes Lane, Potters Bar, Herts EN6 2HN
e-mail: capitalarts@btconnect.com
Mobile: 07885 232414   Tel/Fax: 020-8449 2342

CARR Norrie AGENCY
(Babies, Children & Adults)
Holborn Studios, 49-50 Eagle Wharf Road, London N1 7ED
Website: www.norriecarr.com
e-mail: info@norriecarr.com
Fax: 020-7253 1772   Tel: 020-7253 1771

CARTEURS THEATRICAL AGENCY
170A Church Road, Hove, East Sussex BN3 2DJ
Website: www.stonelandsschool.co.uk
e-mail: dianacarteur@stonelandsschool.co.uk
Fax: 01273 770444   Tel: 01273 770445

CHADWICK Jacqueline ACADEMY The
Oakdene Studios, Brewery Lane, Leigh WN7 2RJ
Website: www.jacquelinechadwickacademy.co.uk
e-mail: chadwickacademy@btconnect.com
Fax: 01942 609690   Tel: 01942 675747

CHILDSPLAY MODELS LLP
114 Avenue Road, Beckenham, Kent BR3 4SA
Website: www.childsplaymodels.co.uk
e-mail: info@childsplaymodels.co.uk
Fax: 020-8778 2672   Tel: 020-8659 9860

CHRYSTEL ARTS AGENCY
6 Eunice Grove, Chesham, Bucks HP5 1RL
e-mail: chrystelarts@beeb.net
Mobile: 07799 605489   Tel/Fax: 01494 773336

CIRCUS MANIACS AGENCY
(Circus, Theatre, Dance, Extreme Sports)
Office 8A, The Kingswood Foundation, Britannia Road
Kingswood, Bristol BS15 8DB
Website: www.circusmaniacsagency.com
e-mail: agency@circusmaniacs.com
Mobile: 07977 247287   Tel/Fax: 0117-947 7042

COLIN'S PERFORMING ARTS AGENCY
(Colin's Performing Arts Ltd)
The Studios, 219B North Street, Romford, Essex RM1 4QA
Website: www.colinsperformingarts.co.uk
e-mail: agency@colinsperformingarts.co.uk
Fax: 01708 766077   Tel: 01708 766444

CONTI Italia AGENCY Ltd
23 Goswell Road, London EC1M 7AJ
e-mail: agency@italiaconti.co.uk
Fax: 020-7253 1430   Tel: 020-7608 7500

CS MANAGEMENT
(Children & Young Adults)
The Croft, 7 Cannon Road, Southgate, London N14 7HE
Website: www.csmanagementuk.com
e-mail: carole@csmanagementuk.com
Fax: 020-8886 7555   Tel: 020-8886 4264

D & B MANAGEMENT & THEATRE SCHOOL
470 Bromley Road, Bromley, Kent BR1 4PN
Website: www.dandbperformingarts.co.uk
e-mail: bonnie@dandbmanagement.com
Fax: 020-8697 8100   Tel: 020-8698 8880

DD'S CHILDREN'S AGENCY
6 Acle Close, Hainault, Essex IG6 2GQ
Website: www.debdaystudio.com
e-mail: ddsagency@yahoo.co.uk
Mobile: 07725 556231   Tel: 020-8502 6866

DEBUT KIDS
25 Crossways
Shenfield, Essex CM15 8QX
Website: www.debutkids.co.uk
e-mail: team@debutkids.co.uk   Mobile: 07946 618328

DIMPLES MODEL & CASTING ACADEMY
(Children, Teenagers & Adults)
84 Kirk Hall Lane
Leigh, Lancs WN7 5QQ
e-mail: info@dimplesacademy.com
Fax: 01942 262232   Tel: 01942 262012

DMS AGENCY
30 Lakedale Road
Plumstead
London SE18 1PP   Tel/Fax: 020-8317 6622

DRAGON DRAMA
(Drama for Children)
347 Hanworth Road TW12 3EJ
Website: www.dragondrama.co.uk
e-mail: info@dragondrama.co.uk   Tel/Fax: 020-8255 8356

DRAMA STUDIO EDINBURGH The
19 Belmont Road, Edinburgh EH14 5DZ
Website: www.thedramastudio.co.uk
e-mail: thedra@thedramastudio.co.uk
Fax: 0131-453 3108   Tel: 0131-453 3284

EARNSHAW Susi MANAGEMENT
68 High Street, Barnet, Herts EN5 5SJ
Website: www.susiearnshaw.co.uk
e-mail: casting@susiearnshaw.co.uk
Fax: 020-8364 9618   Tel: 020-8441 5010

Artist Management
adults children

Byron's Management
Tel: 020 8444 4445
Fax: 020 8444 4040
byronsmanagement@aol.com
www.byronsmanagement.co.uk

ENGLISH Doreen '95
(Gerry Kinner)
4 Selsey Avenue, Aldwick, Bognor Regis
West Sussex PO21 2QZ　　　　Tel: 01243 825968

EUROKIDS & ADULTS INTERNATIONAL CASTING & MODEL AGENCY
The Warehouse Studios, Glaziers Lane
Culcheth, Warrington, Cheshire WA3 4AQ
Website: www.eka-agency.com
e-mail: becky@eka-agency.com
Fax: 01925 767563　　　　Tel: 01925 761088

EXPRESSIONS CASTING AGENCY
3 Newgate Lane, Mansfield, Nottingham NG18 2LB
e-mail: expressions-uk@btconnect.com
Fax: 01623 647337　　　　Tel: 01623 424334

FBI AGENCY Ltd The
PO Box 250, Leeds LS1 2AZ
e-mail: casting@fbi-agency.ltd.uk　　Tel/Fax: 07050 222747

FIORENTINI Anna THEATRE & FILM SCHOOL & AGENCY
25 Daubeney Road, Hackney, London E5 0EE
Website: www.annafiorentini.co.uk
e-mail: info@annafiorentini.co.uk
Mobile: 07779 125095　　　　Tel/Fax: 020-7682 1403

FOOTSTEPS THEATRE SCHOOL CASTING AGENCY
55 Pullan Avenue, Eccleshill, Bradford BD2 3RP
e-mail: helen@footsteps.fslife.co.uk
Tel/Fax: 01274 637429　　　　Tel: 01274 636036

FOX Betty AGENCY
Slade Road, Erdington, Birmingham B23 7PX
e-mail: bettyfox.school@virgin.net
Mobile: 07703 436045　　　　Tel/Fax: 0121-327 1020

GENESIS THEATRE SCHOOL & AGENCY
88 Hempland Close, Great Oakley
Corby, Northants NN18 8LT
e-mail: info@saracharles.com　　　Tel: 01536 460928

GLYNNE Frances THEATRE STUDENTS & MANAGEMENT
Flat 9, Elmwood, 6 The Avenue
Hatch End, Middlesex HA5 4EP
e-mail: franandmo@googlemail.com　　Mobile: 07950 918355

GOBSTOPPERS MANAGEMENT
37 St Nicholas Mount, Hemel Hempstead, Herts HP1 2BB
e-mail: chrisgobstoppers@btopenworld.com
Mobile: 07961 372319　　　　Tel: 01442 269543

GO FOR IT CHILDREN'S AGENCY
(Children & Teenagers)
47 North Lane, Teddington, Middlesex TW11 0HU
Website: www.goforitts.com
e-mail: agency@goforitts.com　　　Tel: 020-8943 1120

GOLDMAN'S Shana STAGE SCHOOL & AGENCY
74 Braemore Road, Hove, East Sussex BN3 4HB
Website: www.shana-goldmans.co.uk
e-mail: casting@shana-goldmans.co.uk
Mobile: 07967 203433　　　　Tel/Fax: 01273 329916

GP ASSOCIATES
4 Gallus Close, Winchmore Hill, London N21 1JR
Website: www.greasepaintanonymous.co.uk
e-mail: info@gpassociates.co.uk
Fax: 020-8882 9189　　　　Tel: 020-8886 2263

GRAYSTONS
843-845 Green Lanes, Winchmore Hill, London N21 2RX
e-mail: graystons@btinternet.com
Fax: 020-8364 2009　　　　Tel: 020-8360 5700

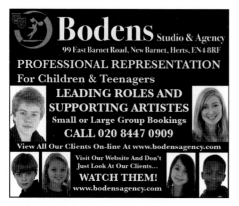

GREVILLE Jeannine THEATRICAL AGENCY
Melody House, Gillotts Corner
Henley-on-Thames, Oxon RG9 1QU
Fax: 01491 411533   Tel: 01491 572000

HARLEQUIN STUDIOS AGENCY FOR CHILDREN
122A Phyllis Avenue, Peacehaven
East Sussex BN10 7RQ   Tel: 01273 581742

HARRIS AGENCY Ltd The
52 Forty Avenue, Wembley Park
Middlesex HA9 8LQ
e-mail: theharrisagency@btconnect.com
Fax: 020-8908 4455   Tel: 020-8908 4451

HOBSON'S KIDS
62 Chiswick High Road, London W4 1SY
Website: www.hobsons-international.com
e-mail: kids@hobsons-international.com
Fax: 020-8996 5350   Tel: 020-8995 3628

HOWE Janet CHILDREN'S CASTING & MODELLING AGENCY
56 The Ironmarket
Newcastle-under-Lyme, Staffordshire ST5 1PE
e-mail: info@janethowe.com

The Pie Factory, 101 Broadway
Salford Quays, Manchester M50 2EQ   Tel/Fax: 0161-263 0633

Works Media Centre
36 White House Street
Hunslet, Leeds LS10 1AD   Tel/Fax: 0113-242 5225

INTER-CITY KIDS
Portland Tower, Portland Street, Manchester M1 3LF
Website: www.iccast.co.uk
e-mail: mail@iccast.co.uk   Tel/Fax: 0161-238 4950

JABBERWOCKY AGENCY
(Children, Teenagers & Adults)
Glassenbury Hill Farm, Glassenbury Road
Cranbrook, Kent TN17 2QF
Website: www.jabberwockyagency.com
e-mail: keith@jabberwockyagency.com
Fax: 01580 714346   Tel: 01622 871851

JB ASSOCIATES
(Children & Teenagers 10-18 Years)
4th Floor, Manchester House
84-86 Princess Street, Manchester M1 6NG
Website: www.j-b-a.net   e-mail: info@j-b-a.net
Fax: 0161-237 1809   Tel: 0161-237 1808

JIGSAW ARTS MANAGEMENT
(Representing Children & Young People from Jigsaw Performing Arts Schools)
64-66 High Street, Barnet, Herts EN5 5SJ
Website: www.jigsaw-arts.co.uk/agency   Tel: 020-8447 4534

JMB MANAGEMENT
PO Box 611, Banbury OX16 6EE
e-mail: managementjmb@yahoo.com   Mobile: 07814 768862

JOHNSTON & MATHERS ASSOCIATES Ltd
PO Box 3167, Barnet, Herts EN5 2WA
Website: www.johnstonandmathers.com
e-mail: johnstonmathers@aol.com
Fax: 020-8449 2386   Tel: 020-8449 4968

KASTKIDZ
40 Sunnybank Road
Unsworth, Bury BL9 8HF
Website: www.kastkidz.com
e-mail: kastkidz@ntlworld.com
Fax: 0161-796 7073   Mobile: 07905 646832

KELLY MANAGEMENT Ltd
2nd Floor, 117 Wardour Street, London W1F 0UN
Website: www.kelly-management.com
e-mail: robert@kelly-management.com
Fax: 020-7434 1007   Tel: 020-7434 9955

KENT Tim & FOX Julie CHILD TALENT
Pinewood Studios, Pinewood Road
Iver Heath, Bucks SL0 0NH
e-mail: childtalent@tkassociates.co.uk   Tel: 01753 655517

KENT YOUTH THEATRE AGENCY
Mulberry Croft, Mulberry Hill, Chilham CT4 8AJ
Website: www.kentyouththeatre.co.uk
e-mail: richard@kyt.org.uk   Tel/Fax: 01227 730177

STARDOM
CASTING AGENCY

**Bright Northern Kids
Theatre/Film/TV/
Photographic**

HANNAH WILKINSON
Sony Playstation TVC
(Worldwide)

TOM MILNER
Waterloo Rd
BBC

Tel/Fax: 01274 818051
Mob: 07740 091 019
Email: liz.stardom@btinternet.com
www.stardom.org.uk

Expressions
Academy of
Performing Arts   Casting Agency

CHILDREN & YOUNG ADULTS up to 21 years
TV · FILM · COMMERCIALS · THEATRE · MODELLING
Children Open License · Licensed Chaperones
www.expressions-uk.com
Children from London & All Over UK.

3, Newgate Lane, Mansfield, Nottingham NG18 2LB
Phone: 01623 424334 Fax: 01623 647337
e-mail: expressions-uk@btconnect.com

KIDS LONDON
67 Dulwich Road, London SE24 0NJ
Website: www.kidslondonltd.com
e-mail: kidslondon@btconnect.com
Fax: 020-7924 9766   Tel: 020-7924 9595

KIDS PLUS
2 Foresters Cottages, Barnet Wood Road, Bromley BR2 8HJ
Website: www.kidsplusagency.co.uk
e-mail: office@kidsplusagency.co.uk
Fax: 020-8462 9233   Tel: 020-8462 4666

KIDZ NATIONAL Ltd
10 Ellendale Grange, Manchester M28 7UX
Website: www.kidzltd.com   e-mail: info@kidzltd.com
Tel/Fax: 0870 2416260   Tel: 0870 2414418

KRACKERS KIDS THEATRICAL AGENCY
6-7 Electric Parade, Seven Kings Road, Ilford, Essex IG3 8BY
Website: www.krackerskids.co.uk
e-mail: krackerskids@hotmail.com   Tel/Fax: 01708 502046

LAMONT CASTING AGENCY
2 Harewood Avenue, Ainsdale, Merseyside PR8 2PH
Website: www.lamontcasting.co.uk
e-mail: diane@lamontcasting.co.uk   Mobile: 07736 387543

LESLIE Sasha MANAGEMENT
(In Association with Allsorts Drama for Children)
34 Pember Road, London NW10 5LS
e-mail: sasha@allsortsdrama.com   Tel/Fax: 020-8969 3249

LIFE AND SOUL THEATRE AGENCY
Oatfields, Dodds Lane, Piccotts End
Hemel Hempstead, Herts HP2 6JJ
Website: www.lifeandsoultheatreacademy.co.uk
e-mail: lifeandsoulta@hotmail.com   Tel/Fax: 01442 233050

Elisabeth Smith
The
MODEL AGENCY
for
• BABIES
• CHILDREN
• TEENAGERS
• FAMILIES

020-8863 2331 (5 LINES)   FAX 020-8861 1880
Website: http://www.elisabethsmith.co.uk
81 Headstone Road · Harrow · Middlesex · HA1 1PQ

LIL DEVILS AGENCY
1st Floor, 76 School Road, Tilehurst, Reading, Berks RG31 5AW
Website: www.lildevils.co.uk   e-mail: kids@lildevils.co.uk
Fax: 0118-941 7273   Tel: 0118-943 3057

LINTON MANAGEMENT
3 The Rock, Bury BL9 0JP
e-mail: carol@linton.tv
Fax: 0161-761 1999   Tel: 0161-761 2020

LITTLE ACORNS MODELLING INTERNATIONAL Ltd
London House, 271-273 King Street, London W6 9LZ
e-mail: acorns@dircon.co.uk
Fax: 020-8390 4935   Tel: 020-8390 8023

LITTLE ADULTS ACADEMY & MODELLING AGENCY Ltd
Studio 1, Essex House, 375-377 High Street
Stratford, London E15 4QZ
Website: www.littleadultsagency.co.uk
e-mail: info@littleadults.demon.co.uk
Fax: 020-8519 9797   Tel: 020-8519 9755

LIVE & LOUD
1st Floor, 84 Miller Street, Glasgow G1 1DT
e-mail: info@west-endmgt.com
Fax: 0141-226 8983   Tel: 0141-222 2942

MONDI ASSOCIATES Ltd
Unit 3 0, Cooper House
2 Michael Road, London SW6 2AD
Website: www.mondiassociates.com
e-mail: michelle@mondiassociates.com   Mobile: 07817 133349

MRS WORTHINGTON'S
(6-16 Years)
16 Ouseley Road, London SW12 8EF   Tel/Fax: 020-8767 6944

NFD - THE FILM AND TV AGENCY
PO Box 76, Leeds LS25 9AG
Website: www.film-tv-agency.com
e-mail: info@film-tv-agency.com   Tel/Fax: 01977 681949

NUTOPIA PERSONAL MANAGEMENT
(Ferris Entertainment)
Number 8, 132 Charing Cross Road, London WC2H 0LA
Website: www.ferrisentertainment.com   Mobile: 07801 493133

O'FARRELL STAGE & THEATRE SCHOOL
(Babies, Children, Teenagers & Young Adults)
36 Shirley Street, Canning Town, London E16 1HU
Mobile: 07956 941497   Tel: 020-7511 9444

ORR MANAGEMENT AGENCY
(Children, Teenagers & Adults)
1st Floor, 147-149 Market Street, Farnworth BL4 8EX
Website: www.orrmanagement.co.uk
e-mail: barbara@orrmanagement.co.uk
Mobile: 07773 227784   Tel: 01204 579842

PALMER Jackie AGENCY
30 Daws Hill Lane, High Wycombe, Bucks HP11 1PW
Website: www.jackiepalmer.co.uk
e-mail: jackie.palmer@btinternet.com
Fax: 01494 510479   Tel: 01494 520978

PAUL'S THEATRE AGENCY
Fairkytes Arts Centre, 51 Billet Lane
Hornchurch, Essex RM11 1AX
Website: www.paulstheatreschool.co.uk
e-mail: penny@paulstheatreschoolagency.co.uk
Fax: 01708 475286   Tel: 01708 446167

PC THEATRICAL & MODEL AGENCY
12 Carlisle Road, Colindale NW9 0HL
Website: www.twinagency.com
e-mail: twinagy@aol.com
Fax: 020-8933 3418   Tel: 020-8381 2229

PERFORMERS AGENCY Ltd
Southend Road, Corringham, Essex SS17 8JT
Website: www.performersagency.biz
e-mail: mandy@performersagency.biz
Fax: 01375 672353   Tel: 01375 672053

PHA YOUTH
Tanzaro House, Ardwick Green North, Manchester M12 6FZ
Website: www.pha-agency.co.uk
e-mail: youth@pha-agency.co.uk
Fax: 0161-273 4567   Tel: 0161-273 4444

POLLYANNA MANAGEMENT Ltd
1 Knighten Street, Wapping, London E1W 1PH
Website: www.pollyannatheatre.com
e-mail: aliceharwood@talktalk.net
Fax: 020-7480 6761   Tel: 020-7481 1911

POWER MODEL MANAGEMENT CASTING AGENCY
PO Box 1198, Salhouse, Norwich NR13 6WD
Website: www.powermodel.co.uk
e-mail: info@powermodel.co.uk
                                      Tel: 01603 721287

RASCALS MODEL AGENCY
13 Jubilee Parade, Snakes Lane East
Woodford Green, Essex IG8 7QG
Website: www.rascals.co.uk
e-mail: kids@rascals.co.uk
Fax: 020-8559 1035   Tel: 020-8504 1111

RAVENSCOURT MANAGEMENT
8-30 Galena Road, Hammersmith, London W6 0LT
e-mail: info@ravenscourt.net
Fax: 020-8741 1786   Tel: 020-8741 0707

REBEL SCHOOL OF THEATRE ARTS AND CASTING AGENCY
46 North Park Avenue, Roundhay, Leeds LS8 1EJ
e-mail: rebeltheatre@aol.com
Mobile: 07808 803637   Tel: 0113-305 3796

REDROOFS THEATRE SCHOOL AGENCY
Redroofs, Littlewick Green, Maidenhead SL6 3QY
Fax: 01628 822461   Tel: 01628 822982 Ext 1

REFLECTIONS AGENCY
9 Weavers Terrace, Fulham, London SW6 1QE
Website: www.reflectionsperfarts.tripod.com
e-mail: reflectionspa@yahoo.co.uk
Mobile: 07709 429354   Tel/Fax: 01322 410003

RHODES AGENCY
5 Dymoke Road, Hornchurch, Essex RM11 1AA
e-mail: rhodesarts@hotmail.com
Fax: 01708 730431   Tel: 01708 747013

Child Model Agency

Babies, Children, Teens, Families

66 Bidwell Gardens, London N11 2AU

TEL: 020 8888 4204 FAX: 020 8888 4584

Email: bookings@trulyscrumptious.co.uk

www.trulyscrumptious.co.uk

GP ASSOCIATES AGENCY

In association with Greasepaint Anonymous
Youth Theatre Company
Representing Children & Teenagers
Tel: 020 8886 2263 Fax: 020 8882 9189
E-mail: info@gpassociates.co.uk
www.greasepaintanonymous.co.uk
4 Gallus Close, Winchmore Hill, N21 1JR

RIDGEWAY MANAGEMENT
Fairley House, Andrews Lane, Cheshunt, Herts EN7 6LB
Website: www.ridgewaystudios.co.uk
e-mail: info@ridgewaystudios.co.uk
Fax: 01992 633844 Tel: 01992 633775

**ROSS David ACTING ACADEMY AND ACTORS
AGENCY The**
(David Ross Acting Ltd)
83 The Avenue, Sale, Cheshire M33 4YA
Website: www.davidrossacting.com
e-mail: info@davidrossacting.com
Mobile: 07957 862317 Tel: 0161-718 5835

SCALA KIDS CASTING
42 Rufford Avenue, Yeadon, Leeds LS19 7QR
Website: www.scalakids.com
e-mail: office@scalakids.com
Fax: 0113-250 8806 Tel: 0113-250 6823

SCALLYWAGS AGENCY Ltd
90-92 Ley Street, Ilford, Essex IG1 4BX
Website: www.scallywags.co.uk
e-mail: info@scallywags.co.uk
Fax: 020-8553 4849 Tel: 020-8553 9999

SCREAM MANAGEMENT
The Red Door, 32 Clifton Street
Blackpool, Lancs FY1 1JP
Website: www.screammanagement.com
e-mail: info@screammanagement.com
Fax: 01253 750829 Tel: 01253 750820

SEQUINS THEATRICAL AGENCY
8 Bideford Gardens, Bush Hill Park
Enfield, Middlesex EN1 2RP Tel: 020-8360 6601

SHARONA STAGE SCHOOL AGENCY & MANAGEMENT
82 Grennell Road, Sutton, Surrey SM1 3DN
Fax: 020-8642 2364 Tel: 020-8642 9396

SINGER Sandra ASSOCIATES
21 Cotswold Road, Westcliff-on-Sea, Essex SS0 8AA
Website: www.sandrasinger.com
e-mail: sandrasingeruk@aol.com
Fax: 01702 339393 Tel: 01702 331616

SMITH Elisabeth Ltd
81 Headstone Road, Harrow, Middlesex HA1 1PQ
Website: www.elisabethsmith.com
e-mail: models@elisabethsmith.com
Fax: 020-8861 1880 Tel: 020-8863 2331

SOLE KIDZ @ PINEAPPLE AGENCY
Montgomery House, 159-161 Balls Pond Road, London N1 4BG
Website: www.solecentral.org
e-mail: pineapple.agency@btconnect.com
Fax: 020-7241 3006 Tel: 020-7241 6601

SPEAKE Barbara AGENCY
East Acton Lane, London W3 7EG
e-mail: speakekids2@aol.com
Fax: 020-8740 6542 Tel: 020-8743 6096

SRA AGENCY
Suite 84, The London Fruit and Wool Exchange
Brushfield Street, London E1 6EP
e-mail: agency@susanrobertsacademy.co.uk
Tel: 01932 863194 Tel: 020-7655 4477

STAGE 84 YORKSHIRE SCHOOL OF PERFORMING ARTS
Old Bell Chapel, Town Ln, Idle, Bradford, W Yorks BD10 8PR
e-mail: valeriejackson@stage84.com
Mobile: 07785 244984 Tel: 01274 569197

Performing Arts School & Talent Agency
Training & representing talent 4yrs–adult
• Casting suite/Dance studio available
• Licensed chaperones

artemis STUDIOS 30 Charles Square, Bracknell, Berkshire
www.artemis-studios.co.uk • 01344 429403

The Stagecoach Agency (UK)

The UK's largest children's and young performers' agency.

We represent over 2,200 children and young performers aged between 4 and 20 all of whom attend one of our 620 schools throughout the whole of the U.K. We have members appearing in films, television, commercials, West End shows, regional theatre, voice-overs, radio drama, corporate video, photo-shoots, promotions, modelling and as background artists. The Stagecoach Agency can arrange and organize casting workshops and auditions throughout the UK. Our experienced staff will be pleased to offer you advice, or to help you with any enquiry.

Call us on: 0845 408 2468 (local rate) Or email: agent@stagecoachagency.co.uk
The Stagecoach Agency (UK), P.O. box 127, Ross-on Wye, HR9 6WZ
www.stagecoachagency.co.uk

STAGE CENTRAL CASTING
9 Alexandra Grove, Knaresborough
North Yorkshire HG5 0PH
Website: www.stagecentral.co.uk
e-mail: stagecentral@stagecentral.co.uk   Tel: 01423 540533

STAGECOACH AGENCY (UK) The
PO Box 127, Ross-on-Wye HR9 6WZ
Website: www.thestagecoachagency.co.uk
e-mail: agent@thestagecoachagency.co.uk
Fax: 0845 4082464   Tel: 0845 4082468

STAGE KIDS AGENCY
1 Greenfield, Welwyn Garden City, Herts AL8 7HW
Website: www.stagekids.co.uk   Tel: 01707 328359

STARDOM CASTING AGENCY & THEATRE SCHOOL
16 Pinebury Drive, Queensbury
Bradford BD13 2TA
e-mail: liz.stardom@btinternet.com
Mobile: 07740 091019   Tel/Fax: 01274 818051

STARLINGS THEATRICAL AGENCY
45 Viola Close, South Ockendon, Essex RM15 6JF
Website: www.webspawner.com/users/starlings
e-mail: julieecarter@aol.com   Mobile: 07969 909284

STARSTRUCK MANAGEMENT
85 Hewson Road, Lincoln, Lincolnshire LN1 1RZ
e-mail: starstruckacademy@hotmail.com   Tel: 01522 887894

STOMP! MANAGEMENT
Holcombe House, The Ridgeway
Mill Hill, London NW7 4HY
Website: www.stompmanagement.com
e-mail: stompmanagement@aol.com Tel/Fax: 020-8959 5353

STONELANDS SCHOOL OF BALLET & THEATRE ARTS
170A Church Road
Hove, East Sussex BN3 2DJ
Website: www.stonelandsschool.co.uk
e-mail: www@stonelandsschool.co.uk
Fax: 01273 770444   Tel: 01273 770445

TALENTED KIDS PERFORMING ARTS SCHOOL & AGENCY
23 Burrow Manor, Calverstown
Kilcullen, Co. Kildare, Ireland
Website: www.talentedkidsireland.com
e-mail: talentedkids@hotmail.com
Mobile: 00 353 87 2480348   Tel/Fax: 00 353 45 485464

TANWOOD
72 Nyland Road, Nythe, Swindon, Wilts SN3 3RJ
Website: www.tanwood.co.uk
e-mail: tanwood.agency2@ntlworld.com Mobile: 07774 517469

TELEVISION WORKSHOP The
(Birmingham Group)
ITV Central, Gas Street, Birmingham B1 2JT
e-mail: colin.edwards@itv.com
Fax: 0121-634 4835   Tel: 0121-634 4347

TELEVISION WORKSHOP The
(Nottingham Group)
Terry Lloyd House, Chetwynd Business Park
1 Regan Way, Chilwell, Nottingham NG9 6RZ
e-mail: ian.smith1@itv.com   Tel: 0844 8816643

THAMES VALLEY THEATRICAL AGENCY
Dorchester House, Wimblestraw Road
Berinsfield, Oxfordshire OX10 7LZ
Website: www.childactors.tv
e-mail: donna@childactors.tv   Tel/Fax: 01865 340333

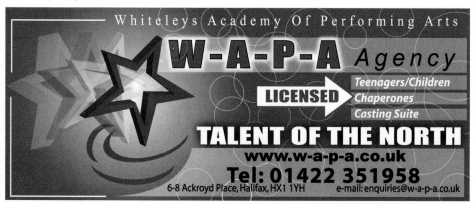

Whiteleys Academy Of Performing Arts

W-A-P-A Agency
Teenagers/Children
LICENSED Chaperones
Casting Suite

TALENT OF THE NORTH
www.w-a-p-a.co.uk
Tel: 01422 351958
6-8 Ackroyd Place, Halifax, HX1 1YH   e-mail: enquiries@w-a-p-a.co.uk

THOMPSON Jim CHILDREN'S SECTION
(Jenny Donnison)
Herricks, School Lane, Arundel, West Sussex BN18 9DR
Fax: 01903 885887   Tel: 01903 885757

TOTS-TWENTIES AGENCY
62 Buntingbridge Road, Newbury Park, Ilford, Essex IG2 7LR
Website: www.tots-twenties.co.uk
e-mail: sara@tots-twenties.co.uk
Fax: 020-8518 0212   Tel: 020-8518 0200

TRULY SCRUMPTIOUS Ltd
66 Bidwell Gardens, London N11 2AU
Website: www.trulyscrumptious.co.uk
e-mail: bookings@trulyscrumptious.co.uk
Fax: 020-8888 4584   Tel: 020-8888 4204

TUESDAYS CHILD
(Children, Teenagers & Adults)
Oakfield House, Springwood Way, Macclesfield SK10 2XA
Website: www.tuesdayschildagency.co.uk
e-mail: info@tuesdayschildagency.co.uk Tel/Fax: 01625 501765

TWINS
(See PC THEATRICAL & MODEL AGENCY)

UNIQUE TALENT MANAGEMENT Ltd
International House, Suite 501
223 Regent Street, London W1H 2QD
Website: www.utm.org.uk
e-mail: info@utm.org.uk   Tel: 020-7569 8636

URBAN ANGELS
7 Burnage Court, Lawrie Park Avenue, London SE26 6HS
e-mail: info@urbanangelsagency.com
Fax: 0870 8710046   Tel: 0870 8710045

VALLÉ ACADEMY THEATRICAL AGENCY
The Vallé Academy Studios, Wilton House
Delamare Road, Cheshunt, Herts EN8 9SG
Website: www.valleacademy.co.uk
e-mail: agency@valleacademy.co.uk
Fax: 01992 622868   Tel: 01992 622861

W-A-P-A CASTING AGENCY
6-8 Akroyd Place, Halifax, West Yorkshire HX1 1YH
Website: www.w-a-p-a.co.uk
e-mail: enquiries@w-a-p-a.co.uk   Tel/Fax: 01422 351958

WHITEHALL PERFORMING ARTS CENTRE
Rayleigh Road
Leigh-on-Sea, Essex SS9 5UU   Tel/Fax: 01702 529290

WILLIAMSON & HOLMES
9 Hop Gardens, St Martin's Lane, London WC2N 4EH
e-mail: info@williamsonandholmes.co.uk
Fax: 020-7240 0408   Tel: 020-7240 0407

WINGS AGENCY
(Affiliated to Angels Theatre School)
49 Midhurst Road
Fernhurst, Haslemere GU27 3EN
Website: www.angelstheatreschool.co.uk
e-mail: admin@wingsagency.co.uk
Fax: 01428 658990   Tel: 01428 658900

WYSE AGENCY
1 Hill Farm Road
Whittlesford, Cambs CB22 4NB
e-mail: frances.wyse@btinternet.com
Fax: 01223 839414   Tel: 01223 832288

YAT MANAGEMENT
70-72 Barnsbury Road, London N1 0ES
Website: www.yati.org.uk
e-mail: info@yati.org.uk
Fax: 020-7833 9467   Tel: 020-7278 2101

YOUNG ACTORS COMPANY Ltd The
3 Marshall Road, Cambridge CB1 7TY
Website: www.theyoungactorscompany.com
e-mail: info@theyoungactorscompany.com
Fax: 01223 416511   Tel: 01223 416474

YOUNG ACTORS FILE The
65 Stafford Street
Old Town, Swindon SN1 3PF
e-mail: young.actorsfile@tiscali.co.uk   Tel/Fax: 01793 423688

YOUNGBLOOD
BWH Agency, Barley Mow Centre
10 Barley Mow Passage, Chiswick, London W4 4PH
e-mail: info@thebwhagency.co.uk
Fax: 020-8996 1662   Tel: 020-8996 1661

YOUNGSTAR AGENCY
Youngstar Drama School
5 Union Castle House
Canute Road, Southampton SO14 3FJ
Website: www.youngstar.tv
e-mail: info@youngstar.tv
Fax: 023-8045 5816   Tel: 023-8033 9322

YOUNGSTARS
(Coralyn Canfor-Dumas)
4 Haydon Dell, Bushey, Herts WD23 1DD
e-mail: coralyncd@hotmail.com
Fax: 020-8950 5701   Mobile: 07966 176756

YOUNG 'UNS AGENCY
Sylvia Young Theatre School
Rossmore Road, Marylebone, London NW1 6NJ
e-mail: enquiries@youngunsagency.co.uk
Fax: 020-7723 1040   Tel: 020-7723 0037

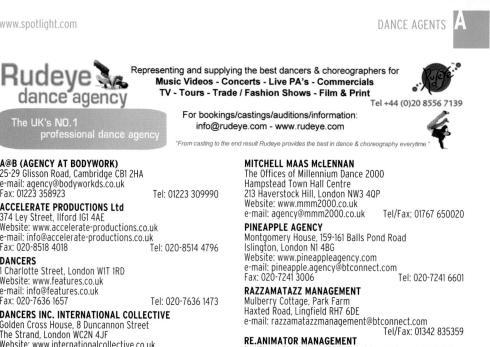

Rudeye dance agency

Representing and supplying the best dancers & choreographers for
**Music Videos - Concerts - Live PA's - Commercials
TV - Tours - Trade / Fashion Shows - Film & Print**
Tel +44 (0)20 8556 7139

For bookings/castings/auditions/information:
info@rudeye.com - www.rudeye.com

The UK's NO.1
professional dance agency

"From casting to the end result Rudeye provides the best in dance & choreography everytime."

A@B (AGENCY AT BODYWORK)
25-29 Glisson Road, Cambridge CB1 2HA
e-mail: agency@bodyworkds.co.uk
Fax: 01223 358923   Tel: 01223 309990

ACCELERATE PRODUCTIONS Ltd
374 Ley Street, Ilford IG1 4AE
Website: www.accelerate-productions.co.uk
e-mail: info@accelerate-productions.co.uk
Fax: 020-8518 4018   Tel: 020-8514 4796

DANCERS
1 Charlotte Street, London W1T 1RD
Website: www.features.co.uk
e-mail: info@features.co.uk
Fax: 020-7636 1657   Tel: 020-7636 1473

DANCERS INC. INTERNATIONAL COLLECTIVE
Golden Cross House, 8 Duncannon Street
The Strand, London WC2N 4JF
Website: www.internationalcollective.co.uk
e-mail: enquiries@internationalcollective.co.uk
Fax: 020-7484 5100   Tel: 020-7484 5080

FEATURES
1 Charlotte Street, London W1T 1RD
Website: www.features.co.uk
e-mail: info@features.co.uk
Fax: 020-7636 1657   Tel: 020-7637 1487

HEADNOD TALENT AGENCY
2nd Floor Office (Unit 4)
18 Kingsland Road, Shoreditch, London E2 8DA
Website: www.headnodagency.com
e-mail: nana@headnodagency.com   Tel/Fax: 020-7502 9478

JK DANCE PRODUCTIONS
South Manchester Film & Television Studios
Battersea Road, Stockport SK4 3EA
Website: www.jkdance.co.uk
e-mail: info@jkdance.co.uk   Tel: 01614 325222

K ENTERTAINMENTS Ltd
The Bridge, 12-16 Clerkenwell Road, London EC1M 5PQ
Website: www.kentsgroup.com
e-mail: mail@ktalent.com   Tel: 020-7324 6350

KEW PERSONAL MANAGEMENT
PO Box 53974, London SW15 2SQ
Website: www.kewpersonalmanagement.com
e-mail: info@kewpersonalmanagement.com
                                     Tel: 020-8788 1166

KMC AGENCIES
11-15 Betterton Street, London WC2H 9BP
e-mail: london@kmcagencies.co.uk
Fax: 0870 4421780   Tel: 0870 4604868

PO Box 122, 48 Great Ancoats Street, Manchester M4 5AB
e-mail: casting@kmcagencies.co.uk
Fax: 0161-237 9812   Tel: 0161-237 3009

LONGRUN ARTISTES
(Gina Long)
3 Chelsworth Drive, Plumstead Common, London SE18 2RB
Website: www.longrunartistes.co.uk
e-mail: gina@longrunartistes.co.uk   Mobile: 07748 723228

MBK DANCE & ENTERTAINEMENT
10 St Julians Close, London SW16 2RY
Website: www.mbkonline.co.uk
e-mail: info@mbkonline.co.uk
Fax: 020-8488 9121   Tel: 020-8664 6676

MITCHELL MAAS McLENNAN
The Offices of Millennium Dance 2000
Hampstead Town Hall Centre
213 Haverstock Hill, London NW3 4QP
Website: www.mmm2000.co.uk
e-mail: agency@mmm2000.co.uk   Tel/Fax: 01767 650020

PINEAPPLE AGENCY
Montgomery House, 159-161 Balls Pond Road
Islington, London N1 4BG
Website: www.pineappleagency.com
e-mail: pineapple.agency@btconnect.com
Fax: 020-7241 3006   Tel: 020-7241 6601

RAZZAMATAZZ MANAGEMENT
Mulberry Cottage, Park Farm
Haxted Road, Lingfield RH7 6DE
e-mail: razzamatazzmanagement@btconnect.com
                                     Tel/Fax: 01342 835359

RE.ANIMATOR MANAGEMENT
3rd Floor, The Priory, Syresham Gdns, W Sussex RH16 3LB
Website: www.reanimator.co.uk
e-mail: re.animator@gmail.com
Fax: 01444 447030   Tel: 01444 447020

RED & BLACK
Website: www.red-black.co.uk
e-mail: info@red-black.co.uk   Mobile: 07722 887277

RUDEYE
PO Box 38743, London E10 5WN
Website: www.rudeye.com
e-mail: info@rudeye.com   Tel/Fax: 020-8556 7139

SCRIMGEOUR Donald ARTISTS AGENT
49 Springcroft Avenue, London N2 9JH
e-mail: vwest@dircon.co.uk
Fax: 020-8883 9751   Tel: 020-8444 6248

SHOW TEAM PRODUCTIONS The
(Dancers & Choreographers)
18 Windmill Street, Brighton, Sussex BN2 0GN
Website: www.theshowteam.co.uk
e-mail: info@theshowteam.co.uk   Tel: 01273 671010

S.O.S.
31 Ivor Place, London NW1 6DA
Website: www.sportsofseb.com
e-mail: info@sportsofseb.com   Tel: 020-7723 1889

SUCCESS
Room 236, 2nd Floor, Linen Hall
162-168 Regent Street, London W1B 5TB
Website: www.successagency.co.uk
e-mail: ee@successagency.co.uk
Fax: 020-7494 3787   Tel: 020-7734 3356

TUCKER Tommy AGENCY
Suite 66, 235 Earls Court Road, London SW5 9FE
e-mail: TTTommytucker@aol.com   Tel: 020-7370 3911

TWITCH
5 Breakspears Mews, Brockley SE4 1PY
Website: www.twitch.uk.com
e-mail: info@twitch.uk.com
Mobile: 07932 656358   Mobile: 07747 770816

UNIQUE TALENT MANAGEMENT Ltd
International House, Suite 501
223 Regent Street, London W1H 2QD
Website: www.utm.org.uk
e-mail: info@utm.org.uk   Tel: 020-7569 8636

A & B PERSONAL MANAGEMENT Ltd*
Suite 330, Linen Hall
162-168 Regent Street, London W1B 5TD
e-mail: billellis@aandb.co.uk
Fax: 020-7038 3699   Tel: 020-7434 4262

ABNER STEIN
10 Roland Gardens
London SW7 3PH
e-mail: abner@abnerstein.co.uk
Fax: 020-7370 6316   Tel: 020-7373 0456

ACTAC
7 Isles Court, Ramsbury
Wiltshire SN8 2QW
Fax: 01672 520166   Tel: 01672 520274

AGENCY (LONDON) Ltd The*
24 Pottery Lane
Holland Park
London W11 4LZ
Website: www.theagency.co.uk
e-mail: info@theagency.co.uk
Fax: 020-7727 9037   Tel: 020-7727 1346

A J ASSOCIATES LITERARY AGENTS
Higher Healey House
Higher House Lane
White Coppice, Chorley PR6 9BT
e-mail: info@ajassociates.net   Tel/Fax: 01257 273148

A M HEATH & Co Ltd
(Fiction & Non-Fiction only)
6 Warwick Court, London WC1R 5DJ
Fax: 020-7242 2711   Tel: 020-7242 2811

A R G (Artists Rights Group Ltd)*
4 Great Portland Street
London W1W 8PA
e-mail: argall@argtalent.com
Fax: 020-7436 6700   Tel: 020-7436 6400

ASPER Pauline MANAGEMENT*
Jacobs Cottage, Reservoir Lane
Sedlescombe, East Sussex TN33 0PJ
e-mail: pauline.asper@virgin.net   Tel/Fax: 01424 870412

BERLIN ASSOCIATES*
14 Floral Street
London WC2E 9DH
Fax: 020-7632 5280   Tel: 020-7836 1112

BLAKE FRIEDMANN
(Novels, Non-Fiction & TV/Film Scripts)
122 Arlington Road
London NW1 7HP
Website: www.blakefriedmann.co.uk
e-mail: julian@blakefriedmann.co.uk
Fax: 020-7284 0442   Tel: 020-7284 0408

BRITTEN Nigel MANAGEMENT*
Riverbank House
1 Putney Bridge Approach
London SW6 3JD
e-mail: office@nbmanagement.com
Fax: 020-7384 3862   Tel: 020-7384 3842

BRODIE Alan REPRESENTATION Ltd*
6th Floor, Fairgate House
78 New Oxford Street
London WC1A 1HB
Website: www.alanbrodie.com
e-mail: info@alanbrodie.com
Fax: 020-7079 7999   Tel: 020-7079 7990

BURKEMAN Brie*
14 Neville Court
Abbey Road, London NW8 9DD
e-mail: brie.burkeman@mail.com
Fax: 0870 199 1029   Tel: 0870 199 5002

CANN Alexandra REPRESENTATION*
2 St Thomas Square
Newport, Isle of Wight PO30 1SN
e-mail: alex@alexandracann.co.uk
Fax: Tel: 01983 556866

CASAROTTO RAMSAY & ASSOCIATES Ltd*
Waverley House
7-12 Noel Street
London W1F 8GQ
Website: www.casarotto.uk.com
e-mail: agents@casarotto.uk.com
Fax: 020-7287 9128   Tel: 020-7287 4450

CLOWES Jonathan Ltd*
10 Iron Bridge House
Bridge Approach
London NW1 8BD
Fax: 020-7722 7677   Tel: 020-7722 7674

COCHRANE Elspeth PERSONAL MANAGEMENT*
16 Trinity Close
The Pavement
London SW4 0JD
e-mail: info@elspethcochrane.co.uk   Tel: 020-7622 3566

CREATIVE MEDIA
(No unsolicited scripts, first instance synopsis only)
11 Asquith Road
Bentley, Doncaster DN5 0NS
Mobile: 07787 784412   Tel: 01302 812233

CULVERHOUSE & JAMES Ltd
Suite 2, Galleon Buildings
16-18 Stanley Street
Southport PR9 0BY
Website: www.culverhousejames.co.uk
e-mail: enquiries@culverhousejames.co.uk
Fax: 01704 541144   Tel: 01704 542965

Shepperton Studios
Shepperton
Middlesex TW17 0QD
Fax: 01932 592233   Tel: 01932 592151

CURTIS BROWN GROUP Ltd*
5th Floor, Haymarket House
28-29 Haymarket
London SW1Y 4SP
e-mail: cb@curtisbrown.co.uk
Fax: 020-7393 4401   Tel: 020-7393 4400

DAISH Judy ASSOCIATES Ltd*
2 St Charles Place
London W10 6EG
Fax: 020-8964 8966   Tel: 020-8964 8811

DENCH ARNOLD AGENCY The*
10 Newburgh Street
London W1F 7RN
e-mail: contact@dencharnold.com
Fax: 020-7439 1355   Tel: 020-7437 4551

de WOLFE Felix*
Kingsway House
103 Kingsway, London WC2B 6QX
e-mail: info@felixdewolfe.com
Fax: 020-7242 8119   Tel: 020-7242 5066

Publishers of Plays • Agents for the Collection of Royalties
Specialist Booksellers
52 Fitzroy Street London W1T 5JR
Tel 020 7255 4300 (Bookshop) 020 7387 9373 (Enquiries)
Fax 020 7387 2161 www.samuelfrench-london.co.uk
e-mail: theatre@samuelfrench-london.co.uk

SAMUEL FRENCH LTD

DREW Bryan Ltd
Mezzanine, Quadrant House
80-82 Regent Street, London W1B 5AU
e-mail: bryan@bryandrewltd.com
Fax: 020-7437 0561   Tel: 020-7437 2293

FARNES Norma MANAGEMENT
9 Orme Court, London W2 4RL
Fax: 020-7792 2110   Tel: 020-7727 1544

FILLINGHAM Janet ASSOCIATES*
52 Lowther Road, London SW13 9NU
Website: www.janetfillingham.com
e-mail: info@jfillassoc.co.uk
Fax: 020-8748 7374   Tel: 020-8748 5594

FILM RIGHTS Ltd
Mezzanine, Quadrant House
80-82 Regent Street
London W1B 5AU
Website: www.filmrights.ltd.uk
e-mail: information@filmrights.ltd.uk
Fax: 020-7734 0044   Tel: 020-7734 9911

FITCH Laurence Ltd
Mezzanine, Quadrant House
80-82 Regent Street
London W1B 5AU
Fax: 020-7734 0044   Tel: 020-7734 9911

FOSTER Jill Ltd*
9 Barb Mews, London W6 7PA
Fax: 020-7602 9336   Tel: 020-7602 1263

FRENCH Samuel Ltd*
52 Fitzroy Street
Fitzrovia, London W1T 5JR
Website: www.samuelfrench-london.co.uk
e-mail: theatre@samuelfrench-london.co.uk
Fax: 020-7387 2161   Tel: 020-7387 9373

FUTERMAN, ROSE & ASSOCIATES
(TV/Film, Showbiz & Music Biographies)
17 Deanhill Road, London SW14 7DQ
Website: www.futermanrose.co.uk
e-mail: guy@futermanrose.co.uk
Fax: 020-8286 4860   Tel: 020-8255 7755

GILLIS Pamela MANAGEMENT
46 Sheldon Avenue, London N6 4JR
Fax: 020-8341 5564   Tel: 020-8340 7868

GLASS Eric Ltd
25 Ladbroke Crescent
Notting Hill, London W11 1PS
e-mail: eglassltd@aol.com
Fax: 020-7229 6220   Tel: 020-7229 9500

HALL Rod AGENCY Ltd The*
6th Floor, Fairgate House
78 New Oxford Street, London WC1A 1HB
Website: www.rodhallagency.com
e-mail: office@rodhallagency.com
Fax: 0845 6384094   Tel: 020-7079 7987

HANCOCK Roger Ltd*
4 Water Lane, London NW1 8NZ
e-mail: info@rogerhancock.com
Fax: 020-7267 0705   Tel: 020-7267 4418

HIGHAM David ASSOCIATES Ltd*
5-8 Lower John Street
Golden Square
London W1F 9HA
e-mail: dha@davidhigham.co.uk
Fax: 020-7437 1072   Tel: 020-7434 5900

HOSKINS Valerie ASSOCIATES Ltd*
20 Charlotte Street, London W1T 2NA
e-mail: vha@vhassociates.co.uk
Fax: 020-7637 4493   Tel: 020-7637 4490

HOWARD Amanda ASSOCIATES Ltd*
21 Berwick Street
London W1F 0PZ
Website: www.amandahowardassociates.co.uk
e-mail: mail@amandahowardassociates.co.uk
Fax: 020-7287 7785   Tel: 020-7287 9277

HURLEY LOWE MANAGEMENT*
27 Rosenau Crescent, London SW11 4RY
e-mail: kate@hurleylowemanagement.com
                                 Tel: 020-7978 7325

INDEPENDENT TALENT GROUP Ltd*
(Formerly ICM, London)
Oxford House
76 Oxford Street, London W1D 1BS
Fax: 020-7323 0101   Tel: 020-7636 6565

KASS Michelle ASSOCIATES*
85 Charing Cross Road, London WC2H 0AA
e-mail: office@michellekass.co.uk
Fax: 020-7734 3394   Tel: 020-7439 1624

KENIS Steve & Co*
Royalty House
72-74 Dean Street, London W1D 3SG
e-mail: sk@sknco.com
Fax: 020-7287 6328   Tel: 020-7434 9055

MACFARLANE CHARD ASSOCIATES Ltd*
33 Percy Street, London W1T 2DF
Website: www.macfarlane-chard.co.uk
e-mail: louise@macfarlane-chard.co.uk
Fax: 020-7636 7751   Tel: 020-7636 7750

MACNAUGHTON LORD 2000 Ltd*
19 Margravine Gardens
London W6 8RL
Website: www.ml2000.org.uk
e-mail: info@ml2000.org.uk
Fax: 020-8741 7443   Tel: 020-8741 0606

MANN Andrew Ltd*
1 Old Compton Street
London W1D 5JA
e-mail: info@manscript.co.uk
Fax: 020-7287 9264   Tel: 020-7734 4751

MANS Johnny PRODUCTIONS Ltd
PO Box 196, Hoddesdon
Herts EN10 7WQ
Website: www.johnnymansproductions.co.uk
e-mail: real@legend.co.uk
Fax: 01992 470516   Tel: 01992 470907

MARJACQ SCRIPTS Ltd
34 Devonshire Place
London W1G 6JW
Website: www.marjacq.com
e-mail: enquiries@marjacq.com
Fax: 020-7935 9115   Tel: 020-7935 9499

MARVIN Blanche*
21A St Johns Wood High Street
London NW8 7NG
e-mail: blanchemarvin17@hotmail.com
Tel/Fax: 020-7722 2313

M.B.A. LITERARY AGENTS Ltd*
62 Grafton Way, London W1T 5DW
Website: www.mbalit.co.uk
e-mail: agent@mbalit.co.uk
Fax: 020-7387 2042   Tel: 020-7387 2076

McLEAN Bill PERSONAL MANAGEMENT
23B Deodar Road
London SW15 2NP   Tel: 020-8789 8191

ML 2000 Ltd
(See MACNAUGHTON LORD 2000 Ltd)

MORRIS William AGENCY (UK) Ltd
52-53 Poland Street
London W1F 7LX
Fax: 020-7534 6900   Tel: 020-7534 6800

NARROW ROAD COMPANY The*
182 Brighton Road
Coulsdon, Surrey CR5 2NF
e-mail: richardireson@narrowroad.co.uk
Fax: 020-8763 2558   Tel: 020-8763 9895

PFD*
Drury House
34-43 Russell Street, London WC2B 5HA
Website: www.pfd.co.uk
e-mail: postmaster@pfd.co.uk
Fax: 020-7836 9539   Tel: 020-7344 1000

PLAYS AND MUSICALS
Lantern House
84 Littlehaven Lane
Horsham, West Sussex RH12 4JB
Website: www.playsandmusicals.co.uk
e-mail: sales@playsandmusicals.co.uk
Fax: 0700 5938843   Tel: 0700 5938842

POLLINGER Ltd
9 Staple Inn, Holborn
London WC1V 7QH
Website: www.pollingerltd.com
e-mail: info@pollingerltd.com
Fax: 020-7242 5737   Tel: 020-7404 0342

ROSICA COLIN Ltd
1 Clareville Grove Mews
London SW7 5AH
Fax: 020-7244 6441   Tel: 020-7370 1080

SAYLE SCREEN Ltd*
(Screenwriters & Directors for Film & TV)
11 Jubilee Place, London SW3 3TD
Fax: 020-7823 3363   Tel: 020-7823 3883

SEIFERT Linda MANAGEMENT*
22 Poland Street, London W1F 8QQ
e-mail: contact@lindaseifert.com
Fax: 020-7292 7391   Tel: 020-7292 7390

SHARLAND ORGANISATION Ltd*
The Manor House
Manor Street, Raunds, Northants NN9 6JW
e-mail: tsoshar@aol.com
Fax: 01933 624860   Tel: 01933 626600

SHEIL LAND ASSOCIATES Ltd*
(Literary, Theatre & Film)
52 Doughty Street
London WC1N 2LS
e-mail: info@sheilland.co.uk
Fax: 020-7831 2127   Tel: 020-7405 9351

STEEL Elaine*
(Writers' Agent)
110 Gloucester Avenue, London NW1 8HX
e-mail: ecmsteel@aol.com
Fax: 020-8341 9807   Tel: 020-8348 0918

STEINBERG Micheline ASSOCIATES*
104 Great Portland Street
London W1W 6PE
Website: www.steinplays.com
e-mail: info@steinplays.com   Tel: 020-7631 1310

STEVENS Rochelle & Co*
2 Terretts Place
Upper Street, London N1 1QZ
Fax: 020-7354 5729   Tel: 020-7359 3900

TENNYSON AGENCY The
10 Cleveland Avenue
Merton Park, London SW20 9EW
Website: www.tennysonagency.co.uk
e-mail: agency@tennysonagency.co.uk Tel: 020-8543 5939

THEATRE OF LITERATURE
(c/o Calder Publications)
51 The Cut, London SE1 8LF
e-mail: info@calderbookshop.com
Fax: 020-7928 5930   Tel: 020-7633 0599

THURLEY J M MANAGEMENT
Archery House
33 Archery Square
Walmer, Deal CT14 7AY
e-mail: jmthurley@aol.com
Fax: 01304 371416   Tel: 01304 371721

TYRRELL Julia MANAGEMENT*
57 Greenham Road
London N10 1LN
Website: www.jtmanagement.co.uk
e-mail: info@jtmanagement.co.uk
Fax: 020-8374 5580   Tel: 020-8374 0575

WARE Cecily LITERARY AGENTS*
19C John Spencer Square
London N1 2LZ
e-mail: info@cecilyware.com
Fax: 020-7226 9828   Tel: 020-7359 3787

WEINBERGER Josef Ltd*
12-14 Mortimer Street
London W1T 3JJ
Website: www.josef-weinberger.com
e-mail: general.info@jwmail.co.uk
Fax: 020-7436 9616   Tel: 020-7580 2827

How do I become a Presenter?

There is no easy answer to this question. Some presenters start out as actors and move into presenting work, others may be 'experts' such as chefs, designers or sports people who are taken on in a presenting capacity. Others may have a background in stand-up comedy. All newsreaders are professional journalists with specialist training and experience. Often presenters work their way up through the production side of broadcasting, starting by working as a runner or researcher and then moving to appear in front of the camera. To get this kind of production work you could contact TV and Film Production companies, many of whom are listed in this book. A number of Performing Arts Schools, Colleges and Academies also offer useful part-time training courses for presenters. See the 'Drama Training, Schools and Coaches' section of this book for college / school listings.

How should I use these listings?

The following pages contain contact details for the UK's leading presenter agencies. It is their job to promote their clients to job opportunities and negotiate contracts on their behalf. In return they take commission ranging from 10-15%. Before you approach any agency looking for representation, do some research into their current client list and the areas in which they specialise. Many have websites you can visit. Once you have made a short-list of the ones you think are most appropriate, you should send them your CV with a covering letter and a good quality, recent photograph which is a genuine likeness of you. Showreels can also be a good way of showcasing your talents, but only send these if you have checked with the agency first. Enclosing a stamped-addressed envelope with sufficent postage (SAE) will also give you a better chance of a reply.

Should I pay a Presenter's agent to join their books? Or sign a contract?

As with other types of agencies, Equity does not generally recommend that artists pay an agent to join their client list. Before signing any contract, you should be clear about the terms and commitments involved. Always speak to Equity www.equity.org.uk if you have any concerns or queries.

What is the Spotlight Presenters directory?

Spotlight Presenters is a specialist directory published annually by The Spotlight. It contains photographs and contact details for over seven hundred professional TV and radio presenters and is a great way of promoting yourself for work. It is used by production companies, casting directors, TV and radio stations, advertising agencies and publicists to browse and locate talent for future productions. Entry is available to any presenter with proven professional broadcast experience. Please see www.spotlight.com for more information.

What are voice-over agencies?

These are smaller agencies which specialise in promoting clients specifically for voice-over work, mostly in the commercial and corporate sectors. Some actors and presenters will have both a main agent, representing them for acting / presenting work, and then a voice-over agent who looks after this separate side of their career.

See page 114 for more information

Kate Douglas is an agent at Princess Talent Management, a division of Princess Productions. They represent broadcasters and presenters including Janet Street-Porter, Andy Goldstein, Vicki Butler-Henderson and Dave Berry. Kate has been an agent for six years, prior to which she worked in Production. She offers the following advice to those considering a career as a presenter.

Presenting, like television in general, is a dynamic industry. There are no hard and fast rules and tastes change almost as quickly as in fashion. Don't try to emulate a presenter already on our screens. What is fresh and new one month may not be so popular the next - so the best bet is to try and always be yourself.

Make sure you really want to be a presenter. It is not something that you can 'play at doing' or something to look into because drama school didn't work out. If it is something you want to pursue wholeheartedly, then go at it 110%. Breaking into presenting and securing an agent can be a long, demoralising and often tiresome process.

Remember that TV is a visual entity: looks are important. However, whereas models get turned down simply for their looks, be prepared to be turned down for not only the way you look, but also the way you talk, and your personality! So, everyone who thinks how easy and fun presenting looks - please take note!

As a general rule, TV is a good world to work in - not as glamorous as most people imagine, but fun nonetheless. But, as any 'jobbing' presenter will tell you, it is hard work, and unless you are fortunate enough to get offered a ground-breaking two year deal with a terrestrial channel at your first screen-test or meeting (unlikely!), it is at times a frustrating and difficult job.

Deal with others as you would like to be treated yourself. After all, a runner or a receptionist today could be a producer, director or presenter in five years time (it wasn't that long ago that Dermot O'Leary was booking audiences here at Princess!). It's important to keep your feet on the ground.

If and when you do secure an agent, make sure that you like, respect and have faith in each other. Agents are not comedy clichéd characters, we don't all look alike, work alike or speak like Jerry Maguire, Joey's agent Estelle in *Friends*, or Stephen Merchant from *Extras*. It is an intense relationship and one which has no real comparison in the 'outside world'. We are here to help you along your journey - but we cannot make something happen from nothing. We have relationships within the industry to 'get you in' and will develop these to push you in the right direction. What we cannot do (although doubtless some have tried!) is to present the TV shows for you - or for that matter make the Channel opt for a 23 year old girl (you) instead of the 45 year old male news reporter they asked for!

Ultimately we work for you, the talent, but you do need to work with us too. You need a great deal of patience, a willingness to learn and take advice (criticism!), and know how and when to help yourselves. It is a two-way relationship and you will need to learn to accept the rough with the smooth.

When you are sending out your reel to agents, bear in mind we receive hundreds each month, so make sure it is simple, has variety (of presenting not of programme genres - you cannot be everything to everyone) but fundamentally that it tells us what you are about and indicates to us the type of presenting you want to do. Only then can we work out if we are right for you - as well as the other way round - and determine if we can help try to make it happen for you.

So, if you're prepared to put in the hard work, the presenting world could be your oyster. When everything goes to plan, and with a little luck, it can be hugely rewarding - here's to an exciting future together. We'll be right behind you.

For more information about Princess Talent Management visit www.princesstv.com/talent

ALEXANDER PERSONAL MANAGEMENT Ltd
Pinewood Studios, Pinewood Road
Iver Heath, Bucks SL0 0NH
Website: www.apmassociates.net
e-mail: lindafrench@apmassociates.net
Fax: 01753 639205   Tel: 01753 639204

A.P.M. (Linda French)
(See ALEXANDER PERSONAL MANAGEMENT Ltd)

ARLINGTON ENTERPRISES Ltd
1-3 Charlotte Street
London W1T 1RD
Website: www.arlingtonenterprises.co.uk
e-mail: info@arlington-enterprises.co.uk
Fax: 020-7580 4994   Tel: 020-7580 0702

BLACKBURN SACHS ASSOCIATES
2-4 Noel Street
London W1F 8GB
Website: www.blackburnsachsassociates.com
e-mail: presenters@blackburnsachsassociates.com
Fax: 020-7292 7576   Tel: 020-7292 7555

CAMERON Sara MANAGEMENT
(See TAKE THREE MANAGEMENT)

CANTOR WISE REPRESENTATION
(See TAKE THREE MANAGEMENT)

CHASE PERSONAL MANAGEMENT
Celebrity Division of Modelplan
1st Floor, 18-22 Lloyd Street
Manchester M2 5WA
e-mail: sue@sammon.fsnet.co.uk
Mobile: 00 33 6 11 09 01 40   Tel: 0161-819 1162

CINEL GABRAN MANAGEMENT
PO Box 5163, Cardiff CF5 9BJ
Website: www.cinelgabran.co.uk
e-mail: info@cinelgabran.co.uk
Fax: 0845 0666601   Tel: 0845 0666605

CRAWFORDS
PO Box 44394, London SW20 0YP
Website: www.crawfords.tv
e-mail: cr@wfords.com
Fax: 020-3258 5037   Tel: 020-8947 9999

CURTIS BROWN GROUP Ltd
Haymarket House
28-29 Haymarket, London SW1Y 4SP
e-mail: presenters@curtisbrown.co.uk
Fax: 020-7393 4401   Tel: 020-7393 4460

DAVID ANTHONY PROMOTIONS
PO Box 286, Warrington, Cheshire WA2 8GA
Website: www.davewarwick.co.uk
e-mail: dave@davewarwick.co.uk
Fax: 01925 416589   Tel: 01925 632496

DOWNES PRESENTERS AGENCY
96 Broadway, Bexleyheath, Kent DA6 7DE
Website: www.presentersagency.com
e-mail: downes@presentersagency.com   Tel: 020-8304 0541

DUDDRIDGE Paul MANAGEMENT
32 Rathbone Place, London W1T 1JJ
Website: www.paulduddridge.com
e-mail: mail@paulduddridge.com
Fax: 020-7580 3480   Tel: 020-7580 3580

EVANS Jacque MANAGEMENT Ltd
Top Floor Suite
14 Holmesley Road, London SE23 1PJ
e-mail: jacque@jemltd.demon.co.uk
Fax: 020-8699 5192   Tel: 020-8699 1202

EXCELLENT TALENT COMPANY The
19-21 Tavistock Street
London WC2E 7PA
Website: www.excellentvoice.co.uk
e-mail: viv@excellentvoice.co.uk   Tel: 020-7520 5656

FBI AGENCY Ltd The
PO Box 250, Leeds LS1 2AZ
Website: www.fbi-agency.ltd.uk
e-mail: casting@fbi-agency.ltd.uk
Fax: 0113-279 7270   Tel/Fax: 07050 222747

FIRST ARTIST ENTERTAINMENT Ltd
(Incorporating NCI Management)
3 Tenterden Street, London W1S 1TD
Website: www.firstnci.com
e-mail: info@firstnci.com
Fax: 020-3205 2140   Tel: 020-7096 9999

FLETCHER ASSOCIATES
(Broadcast & Media)
25 Parkway, London N20 0XN
Fax: 020-8361 8866   Tel: 020-8361 8061

**FORD-CRUSH PERSONAL MANAGEMENT &
REPRESENTATION**
PO Box 57948, London W4 2UJ
Website: www.junefordcrush.com
e-mail: june@junefordcrush.com
Mobile: 07711 764160   Tel/Fax: 020-8742 7724

GAY Noel
19 Denmark Street
London WC2H 8NA
Website: www.noelgay.com
Fax: 020-7287 1816   Tel: 020-7836 3941

GLORIOUS TALENT
Lower Ground Floor
79 Noel Road, London N1 8HE
e-mail: lisa@glorioustalent.co.uk   Tel: 020-7704 6555

GRANT James MANAGEMENT
94 Strand on The Green
London W4 3NN
Website: www.jamesgrant.co.uk
e-mail: enquiries@jamesgrant.co.uk
Fax: 020-8742 4951   Tel: 020-8742 4950

GURNETT J. PERSONAL MANAGEMENT Ltd
12 Newburgh Street, London W1F 7RP
Website: www.jgpm.co.uk
e-mail: mail@jgpm.co.uk
Fax: 020-7287 9642   Tel: 020-7440 1850

HICKS Jeremy ASSOCIATES
114-115 Tottenham Court Road
London W1T 5AH
Website: www.jeremyhicks.com
e-mail: info@jeremyhicks.com
Fax: 020-7383 2777   Tel: 020-7383 2000

HOBBS Liz GROUP Ltd
65 London Road
Newark, Notts NG24 1RZ
Website: www.lizhobbsgroup.com
e-mail: casting@lizhobbsgroup.com
Fax: 0870 3337009   Tel: 08700 702702

HOBSON'S PRESENTERS
62 Chiswick High Road
London W4 1SY
Website: www.hobsons-international.com
e-mail: presenters@hobsons-international.com
Fax: 020-8996 5350   Tel: 020-8995 3628

INTERNATIONAL ARTISTES Ltd
4th Floor, Holborn Hall
193-197 High Holborn
London WC1V 7BD
e-mail: reception@internationalartistes.com
Fax: 020-7404 9865   Tel: 020-7025 0600

IVELAW-CHAPMAN Julie
51 Aylesbury Road
Aston Clinton, Bucks HP22 5AQ
e-mail: jivelawchapman@gmail.com   Mobile: 07850 080626

JLA (Jeremy Lee Associates Ltd)
(Supplies celebrities and after dinner speakers)
4 Stratford Place, London W1C 1AT
e-mail: talk@jla.co.uk
Fax: 020-7907 2801   Tel: 020-7907 2800

KBJ MANAGEMENT Ltd
(TV Presenters)
7 Soho Street, London W1D 3DQ
e-mail: general@kbjmgt.co.uk
Fax: 020-7287 1191   Tel: 020-7434 6767

KNIGHT AYTON MANAGEMENT
114 St Martin's Lane
London WC2N 4BE
Website: www.knightayton.co.uk
e-mail: info@knightayton.co.uk
Fax: 020-7836 8333   Tel: 020-7836 5333

KNIGHT Hilary MANAGEMENT Ltd
Grange Farm, Church Lane
Old, Northampton NN6 9QZ
Website: www.hkmanagement.co.uk
e-mail: hilary@hkmanagement.co.uk   Tel: 01604 781818

LEIGH Mike ASSOCIATES
37 Marylebone Lane, London W1U 2NW
Website: www.mikeleighassoc.com
Fax: 020-7486 5886   Tel: 020-7935 5500

LYTE Seamus MANAGEMENT Ltd
Apartment 5, Oswald Building
Chelsea Bridge Wharf
374 Queenstown Road, London SW8 4NU
e-mail: seamus@seamuslyte.com   Mobile: 07930 391401

MACFARLANE CHARD ASSOCIATES Ltd
33 Percy Street, London W1T 2DF
Website: www.macfarlane-chard.co.uk
e-mail: enquiries@macfarlane-chard.co.uk
Fax: 020-7636 7751   Tel: 020-7636 7750

MARKS PRODUCTIONS Ltd
2 Gloucester Gate Mews, London NW1 4AD
Fax: 020-7486 2165   Tel: 020-7486 2001

MARSH Billy ASSOCIATES Ltd
76A Grove End Road
St Johns Wood, London NW8 9ND
Website: www.billymarsh.co.uk
e-mail: talent@billymarsh.co.uk
Fax: 020-7449 6933   Tel: 020-7449 6930

MEDIA PEOPLE
13 Montagu Mews South, London W1H 7ER
Website: www.celebrity.co.uk
e-mail: info@celebrity.co.uk   Tel: 0871 2501234

MILES John ORGANISATION
Cadbury Camp Lane
Clapton-in-Gordano, Bristol BS20 7SB
e-mail: john@johnmiles.org.uk
Fax: 01275 810186   Tel: 01275 854675

MONDI ASSOCIATES Ltd
Unit 3 O, Cooper House
2 Michael Road, London SW6 2AD
Website: www.mondiassociates.com
e-mail: michelle@mondiassociates.com
    Mobile: 07817 133349

MPC ENTERTAINMENT
MPC House, 15-16 Maple Mews, London NW6 5UZ
Website: www.mpce.com
e-mail: mpc@mpce.com
Fax: 020-7624 4220   Tel: 020-7624 1184

MTC (UK) Ltd
20 York Street, London W1U 6PU
Website: www.mtc-uk.com
e-mail: natasha@mtc-uk.com
Fax: 020-7935 8066   Tel: 020-7935 8000

NOEL John MANAGEMENT
2nd Floor, 10A Belmont Street, London NW1 8HH
Website: www.johnnoel.com
e-mail: john@johnnoel.com
Fax: 020-7428 8401   Tel: 020-7428 8400

OFF THE KERB PRODUCTIONS
(Comedy Presenters & Comedians)
3rd Floor, Hammer House
113-117 Wardour Street, London W1F 0UN
Website: www.offthekerb.co.uk
e-mail: westend@offthekerb.co.uk
Fax: 020-7437 0647   Tel: 020-7437 0607

PHOTOGRAPHY
angela large
020 8521 7654
07931 537 363
angela@artshot.co.uk
www.artshot.co.uk

Helen White   Helen Rynne   Alec Walters   David Kennedy   Sergio Pizzorno

OFF THE KERB PRODUCTIONS
22 Thornhill Crescent, London N1 1BJ
Website: www.offthekerb.co.uk
e-mail: info@offthekerb.co.uk
Fax: 020-7700 4646   Tel: 020-7700 4477

PANMEDIA UK Ltd
18 Montrose Crescent, London N12 0ED
e-mail: v.panagi@btinternet.com   Tel: 020-8446 9662

PHA ACTORS MANAGEMENT
Tanzaro House
Ardwick Green North, Manchester M12 6FZ
Website: www.pha-agency.co.uk
e-mail: casting@pha-agency.co.uk
Fax: 0161-273 4567   Tel: 0161-273 4444

PRINCESS TALENT MANAGEMENT
Princess Studios, Whiteleys Centre
151 Queensway, London W2 4YN
Website: www.princesstv.com
e-mail: talent@princesstv.com
Fax: 020-7985 1989   Tel: 020-7985 1985

PVA MANAGEMENT Ltd
Hallow Park, Hallow, Worcester WR2 6PG
e-mail: clients@pva.co.uk
Fax: 01905 641842   Tel: 01905 640663

RAZZAMATAZZ MANAGEMENT
Mulberry Cottage, Park Farm
Haxted Road, Lingfield RH7 6DE
e-mail: razzamatazzmanagement@btconnect.com
                          Tel/Fax: 01342 835359

RDF MANAGEMENT
3-6 Kenrick Place, London W1U 6HD
e-mail: debi.allen@rdfmanagement.com
Fax: 020-7317 2245   Tel: 020-7317 2251

RED CANYON MANAGEMENT
Website: www.redcanyon.co.uk
e-mail: info@redcanyon.co.uk
Mobile: 07939 365578   Mobile: 07931 381696

RHINO PERSONAL MANAGEMENT
Studio House, Delamare Road
Cheshunt, Hertfordshire EN8 9SH
Website: www.rhino-management.co.uk
e-mail: info@rhino-management.co.uk
Fax: 0845 3625457   Tel: 0845 3625456

ROSEMAN ORGANISATION The
51 Queen Anne Street
London W1G 9HS
Website: www.therosemanorganisation.co.uk
e-mail: info@therosemanorganisation.co.uk
Fax: 020-7486 4600   Tel: 020-7486 4500

SINGER Sandra ASSOCIATES
21 Cotswold Road
Westcliff-on-Sea, Essex SS0 8AA
Website: www.sandrasinger.com
e-mail: sandrasingeruk@aol.com
Fax: 01702 339393   Tel: 01702 331616

SOMETHIN' ELSE
20-26 Brunswick Place
London N1 6DZ
Website: www.somethinelse.com
e-mail: info@somethinelse.com
Fax: 020-7250 0937   Tel: 020-7250 5500

SPEAK-EASY Ltd
PO Box 648, Harrington
Northampton, NN6 9XT
Website: www.speak-easy.co.uk
e-mail: enquiries@speak-easy.co.uk   Tel: 0870 0135126

STAR MANAGEMENT Ltd
16A Winton Drive
Glasgow G12 0QA
Website: www.starmanagement.co.uk
e-mail: star@starmanagement.co.uk   Tel: 0870 2422276

TAKE THREE MANAGEMENT
110 Gloucester Avenue
Primrose Hill
London NW1 8HX
Website: www.take3management.co.uk
e-mail: info@take3management.com
Fax: 020-7209 3770   Tel: 020-7209 3777

TALENT4MEDIA Ltd
Power Road Studios
114 Power Road, London W4 5PY
Website: www.unique-management.co.uk
e-mail: jc@uniquemgt.co.uk
Fax: 020-8987 6401   Tel: 020-8987 6400

TROIKA
3rd Floor, 74 Clerkenwell Road
London EC1M 5QA
Fax: 020-7490 7642   Tel: 020-7336 7868

V R M
1st Floor, 100 Talbot Road
Old Trafford
Manchester M16 0PG
Fax: 0161-888 2242   Tel: 0161-874 5741

WILLCOCKS John MEDIA AGENCY Ltd
34 Carisbrook Close
Enfield, Middlesex EN1 3NB
e-mail: john.willcocks@blueyonder.co.uk
Fax: 020-8366 5285   Tel: 020-8364 4556

WWW.PEOPLEMATTER.TV
(Tony Fitzpatrick)
40 Bowling Green Lane
Clerkenwell
London EC1R ONE
Website: www.peoplematter.tv
e-mail: tony@peoplematter.tv
Fax: 020-7415 7074   Tel: 07000 300707

ZWICKLER Marlene & ASSOCIATES
1 Belgrave Crescent Lane
Edinburgh EH4 3AG
Website: www.mza-artists.com   Tel/Fax: 0131-343 3030

ACCENT BANK
420 Falcon Wharf
34 Lombard Road
London SW11 3RF
Website: www.accentbank.co.uk
e-mail: info@accentbank.co.uk   Tel: 020-7223 5160

AD VOICE
Oxford House
76 Oxford Street
London W1D 1BS
Website: www.advoice.co.uk
e-mail: info@advoice.co.uk
Fax: 020-7323 0101   Tel: 020-7323 2345

AMERICAN AGENCY VOICES The
14 Bonny Street
London NW1 9PG
Website: www.americanagency.tv
e-mail: americanagency@btconnect.com
Fax: 020-7482 4666   Tel: 020-7485 8883

ANOTHER TONGUE VOICES Ltd
The Basement
10-11 D'Arblay Street
London W1F 8DS
Website: www.anothertongue.com
e-mail: info@anothertongue.com
Fax: 020-7494 7080   Tel: 020-7494 0300

ASQUITH & HORNER
(Write with SAE)
The Studio
14 College Road
Bromley
Kent BR1 3NS
Fax: 020-8313 0443   Tel: 020-8466 5580

BIG MOUTH COMPANY Ltd The
PO Box 619 CT14 9YA
Website: www.thebigmouthcompany.com
e-mail: info@thebigmouthcompany.com
Tel/Fax: 0871 7500075

BURNETT GRANGER CROWTHER ASSOCIATES Ltd
3 Clifford Street, London W1S 2LF
Website: www.bgcltd.org
e-mail: voiceovers@bgcltd.org
Fax: 020-7287 3239   Tel: 020-7437 8029

CALYPSO VOICES
25-26 Poland Street
London W1F 8QN
Website: www.calypsovoices.com
e-mail: calypso@calypsovoices.com
Fax: 020-7437 0410   Tel: 020-7734 6415

CASTAWAY
Suite 3
15 Broad Court
London WC2B 5QN
Website: www.castaway.org.uk
e-mail: sheila@castaway.org.uk
Fax: 020-7240 2772   Tel: 020-7240 2345

CINEL GABRAN MANAGEMENT
PO Box 5163
Cardiff CF5 9BJ
Website: www.cinelgabran.co.uk
e-mail: info@cinelgabran.co.uk
Fax: 0845 0666601   Tel: 0845 0666605

CONWAY VAN GELDER GRANT Ltd
3rd Floor
18-21 Jermyn Street
London SW1Y 6HP
Website: www.conwayvangelder.com
e-mail: kate@conwayvg.co.uk
Fax: 020-7287 1940   Tel: 020-7287 1070

CUT GLASS VOICES
7 Crouch Hall Road
Crouch End
London N8 8HT
Website: www.cutglassproductions.com
e-mail: info@cutglassproductions.com
Tel/Fax: 020-8374 4701

do you know how to judge a professional voiceover showreel?

*Very high quality.
I've always been impressed*
Sheila Britten - Castaway Voice Agency

*Consistently produce showreels
of the highest Standard*
David Hodge - Hobson's Voices

*A professional and high
quality showreel*
Penny Brown - Voicecall

*Professional, sharp,
well presented quality demos*
Ben Romer Lee – Vocal Point

*Unfailingly produce
exceptional showreels*
Vicky Crompton - Talking Heads

Definitely the best showreels
Leigh Matty - The Just Voices Agency

Outstanding quality reels
Alex Lynch White - Earache Voice Agency

*Consistently the best
produced audio reels we receive*
Victoria Braverman & Sean Bolger – Voicebookers.com

*Professional and unique showreels, 2 very
important aspects for a top quality demo*
Jennifer & Clair - Shining Management Ltd

the voice agencies do.

Register now for one of our voiceover workshops

Today's voiceover industry is a competitive one and it requires skill, dedication, persistence and hard work if you are to succeed.
It can also be incredibly rewarding. The fact that you are reading this advert is a good sign that you are interested in voiceovers. Maybe you know someone who does them for a living, or maybe you're looking for another skill to add to your "toolbox". Whatever your reason, we can help you get started, and hopefully enjoy a long and successful voice career.

"No voiceover artist plans to fail, they fail to plan"

To get started in this industry, you will need a "calling card", your voice showreel. This is the audio equivalent of an actor's headshot and in about a minute and a half, any potential agent or client should be able to gain a clear picture of your vocal range, age and ability. You are competing with working professionals that have great voice showreels and yours must sound just as professional if you are to succeed.

"You only get one chance to get it right"

You need to discover your creative range and vocal abilities before you record anything. It is a waste of time and money to record a "bad" voice showreel, showing only a few poorly

developed vocal styles and deliveries.

"It's not how you sound, it's how you make the listener feel"

Seventeen years of solid experience "behind the glass" has taught us that what separates the successful from the rest is knowledge.
Our voiceover workshops will introduce you to the knowledge you need to succeed in this competitive but potentially lucrative industry.

Introductory Voiceover Workshop
Length 3 hours - Cost £65
If you're thinking about "breaking into" voiceovers but have no idea where to start, then this workshop is definitely for you. It explains everything you need to know about how the voiceover industry works and what you need to know to succeed in it. This is your chance to get behind the microphone and find out once and for all if voiceover work is for you.

"...I learnt more in 3 hours than I could've picked up in weeks of voice over work - most importantly the pitfalls to avoid and how NOT to look like a beginner... I got a voice over agent from my new showreel immediately."
Beth Cordingly - London

1 Day Voiceover Workshop
Length 8 hours - Cost £125
This workshop is perfect for those of you who have had previous acting or broadcast experience. We will help you build on the skills you've previously learnt before you record your final showreel with us.

"...This is an excellent and informative workshop... On discussion throughout the industry, the name that comes up time after time is The Showreel."
Mike Newbold - Nottingham

Voice Showreel Packages

Agent Pack	£350
Spotlight Pack	£85
Radio Drama Pack	£350
Update Pack	£235

(All prices include VAT)

" ...The Showreel went on to provide me with a first class demo, as a result of which I got a voiceover agent, which is no mean feat in today's voiceover business."
Matthew Field - Forest Hill

Call 020 7043 8660 to find out more about our workshops and showreel packages or visit our website at www.theshowreel.com

theShowreel.com
trust us to get it right

Knightsbridge House, 229 Acton Lane, Chiswick, London W4 5DD   email info@theshowreel.com

DIAMOND MANAGEMENT
31 Percy Street, London W1T 2DD
e-mail: hj@diman.co.uk
Fax: 020-7631 0500   Tel: 020-7631 0400

DREW Bryan Ltd
Mezzanine, Quadrant House
80-82 Regent Street
London W1B 5AU
e-mail: bryan@bryandrewltd.com
Fax: 020-7437 0561   Tel: 020-7437 2293

EARACHE VOICES
177 Wardour Street
London W1F 8WX
Website: www.earachevoices.com
e-mail: alex@earachevoices.com
Fax: 020-7287 2288   Tel: 020-7287 2291

EVANS O'BRIEN
115 Humber Road
London SE3 7LW
Website: www.evansobrien.co.uk
e-mail: info@evansobrien.co.uk
Fax: 020-8293 7066   Tel: 020-8293 7077

EXCELLENT VOICE COMPANY
19-21 Tavistock Street
London WC2E 7PA
Website: www.excellentvoice.co.uk
e-mail: info@excellentvoice.co.uk
Fax: 020-7240 9344   Tel: 020-7520 5656

FOREIGN LEGION
1 Kensal Road, London NW10 1JH
Website: www.foreignlegion.co.uk
e-mail: voices@foreignlegion.co.uk   Tel: 020-8450 4451

FOREIGN VERSIONS Ltd
(Translation)
60 Blandford Street
London W1U 7JD
Website: www.foreignversions.com
e-mail: info@foreignversions.co.uk
Fax: 020-7935 0507   Tel: 020-7935 0993

GAY Noel
19 Denmark Street
London WC2H 8NA
Website: www.noelgay.com
Fax: 020-7287 1816   Tel: 020-7836 3941

GORDON & FRENCH
(Write)
12-13 Poland Street, London W1F 8QB
Website: www.gordonandfrench.co.uk
e-mail: voices@gordonandfrench.net
Fax: 020-7734 4832   Tel: 020-7734 4818

HAMILTON HODELL Ltd
5th Floor, 66-68 Margaret Street
London W1W 8SR
Website: www.hamiltonhodell.co.uk
e-mail: louise@hamiltonhodell.co.uk
Fax: 020-7636 1226   Tel: 020-7636 1221

HARVEY VOICES
(No unsolicited mail or e-mails)
54-55 Margaret Street
London W1W 8SH
Website: www.harveyvoices.co.uk   Tel: 020-7952 4361

HOBSON'S SINGERS
62 Chiswick High Road
London W4 1SY
Website: www.hobsons-international.com
e-mail: singers@hobsons-international.com
Fax: 020-8996 5350   Tel: 020-8995 3628

HOBSON'S VOICES
62 Chiswick High Road
London W4 1SY
Website: www.hobsons-international.com
e-mail: voices@hobsons-international.com
Fax: 020-8996 5350   Tel: 020-8995 3628

HOPE Sally ASSOCIATES
108 Leonard Street, London EC2A 4XS
Website: www.sallyhope.biz
e-mail: casting@sallyhope.biz
Fax: 020-7613 4848   Tel: 020-7613 5353

HOWARD Amanda ASSOCIATES
(See JONESES The)

J H A VOICE
114-115 Tottenham Court Road
London W1T 5AH
Fax: 020-7383 2777   Tel: 020-7383 2000

JONESES The
21 Berwick Street
London W1F 0PZ
Website: www.meetthejoneses.co.uk
e-mail: mail@meetthejoneses.co.uk
Fax: 020-7287 7785   Tel: 020-7287 9666

JUST VOICES AGENCY The
140 Buckingham Palace Road
London SW1W 9SA
Website: www.justvoicesagency.com
e-mail: info@justvoicesagency.com
Fax: 020-7881 2501   Tel: 020-7881 2567

KIDZTALK Ltd
(Children's Voices aged 4-24 yrs)
Website: www.kidztalk.com
e-mail: studio@kidztalk.com
Fax: 01737 352456   Tel: 01737 350808

LIP SERVICE CASTING Ltd
60-66 Wardour Street
London W1F 0TA
Website: www.lipservice.co.uk
e-mail: bookings@lipservice.co.uk
Fax: 020-7734 3373   Tel: 020-7734 3393

MANSON Andrew
(Genuine Americans only)
288 Munster Road
London SW6 6BQ
Website: www.andrewmanson.com
e-mail: post@andrewmanson.com
Fax: 020-7381 8874   Tel: 020-7386 9158

MARKHAM & FROGGATT Ltd
4 Windmill Street
London W1T 2HZ
Website: www.markhamfroggatt.com
e-mail: millie@markhamfroggatt.co.uk
Fax: 020-7637 5233   Tel: 020-7636 4412

MBA
2 Futura House
169 Grange Road, London SE1 3BN
e-mail: info@braidman.com
Fax: 020-7231 4634   Tel: 020-7237 3523

McREDDIE Ken ASSOCIATES Ltd
36-40 Glasshouse Street
London W1B 5DL
Fax: 020-7734 6530   Tel: 020-7439 1456

NOEL John MANAGEMENT
2nd Floor
10A Belmont Street
London NW1 8HH
Website: www.johnnoel.com
e-mail: john@johnnoel.com
Fax: 020-7428 8401   Tel: 020-7428 8400

The voice agency of Amanda Howard Associates

www.meetthejoneses.co.uk +44 (0)20 7287 9666

NUTOPIA VOICES
(Ferris Entertainment)
Number 8
132 Charing Cross Road
London WC2H 0LA
Website: www.ferrisentertainment.com
Mobile: 07801 493133

PEMBERTON VOICES
193 Wardour Street
London W1F 8ZF
Website: www.pembertonassociates.com
e-mail: general@pembertonassociates.com
Fax: 020-7734 2522   Tel: 020-7734 4144

Express Networks
1 George Leigh Street
Manchester M4 5DL
Fax: 0161-235 8442   Tel: 0161-235 8440

PFD
Drury House, 34-43 Russell Street
London WC2B 5HA
Website: www.pfd.co.uk
e-mail: postmaster@pfd.co.uk
Fax: 020-7836 9544   Tel: 020-7344 1010

QVOICE
4th Floor, Holborn Hall
193-197 High Holborn
London WC1V 7BD
Website: www.qvoice.co.uk
e-mail: info@qvoice.co.uk
Fax: 020-7025 0659   Tel: 020-7025 0660

RABBIT VOCAL MANAGEMENT
2nd Floor, 18 Broadwick Street
London W1F 8HS
Website: www.rabbit.uk.net
e-mail: info@rabbit.uk.net
Fax: 020-7287 6566   Tel: 020-7287 6466

RED CANYON MANAGEMENT
Website: www.redcanyon.co.uk
e-mail: info@redcanyon.co.uk
Mobile: 07939 365578   Mobile: 07931 381696

RHINO PERSONAL MANAGEMENT
Studio House
Delamare Road
Cheshunt, Hertfordshire EN8 9SH
Website: www.rhino-management.co.uk
e-mail: info@rhino-management.co.uk
Fax: 0845 3625457   Tel: 0845 3625456

RHUBARB VOICES
1st Floor
1A Devonshire Road
London W4 2EU
Website: www.rhubarbvoices.co.uk
e-mail: enquiries@rhubarbvoices.co.uk
Fax: 020-8742 8693   Tel: 020-8742 8683

RICHARD STONE PARTNERSHIP
(See STONE Richard PARTNERSHIP The)

SHINING MANAGEMENT Ltd
12 D'Arblay Street
London W1F 8DU
Website: www.shiningvoices.com
e-mail: info@shiningvoices.com
Fax: 020-7734 2528   Tel: 020-7734 1981

SPEAK-EASY Ltd
PO Box 648
Harrington
Northampton NN6 9XT
Website: www.speak-easy.co.uk
e-mail: enquiries@speak-easy.co.uk   Tel: 0870 0135126

STONE Richard PARTNERSHIP The
2 Henrietta Street, London WC2E 8PS
Website: www.thersp.com
e-mail: all@thersp.com
Fax: 020-7497 0869   Tel: 020-7497 0849

TALKING HEADS
2-4 Noel Street
London W1F 8GB
Website: www.talkingheadsvoices.com
e-mail: voices@talkingheadsvoices.com
Fax: 020-7292 7576   Tel: 020-7292 7575

TERRY Sue VOICES Ltd
3rd Floor
18 Broadwick Street
London W1F 8HS
Website: www.sueterryvoices.co.uk
e-mail: sue@sueterryvoices.co.uk
Fax: 020-7434 2042   Tel: 020-7434 2040

TONGUE & GROOVE
4th Floor, Manchester House
84-86 Princess Street
Manchester M1 6NG
Website: www.tongueandgroove.co.uk
e-mail: info@tongueandgroove.co.uk
Fax: 0161-237 1809   Tel: 0161-228 2469

VACCA Roxane VOICES
73 Beak Street
London W1F 9SR
Website: www.roxanevaccamanagement.com
Fax: 020-7734 8086   Tel: 020-7734 8085

VOCAL POINT
25 Denmark Street
London WC2H 8NJ
Website: www.vocalpoint.net
e-mail: enquiries@vocalpoint.net
Fax: 020-7419 0699   Tel: 020-7419 0700

VOICE BANK Ltd
1st Floor, 100 Talbot Road
Old Trafford
Manchester M16 0PG
Website: www.thevoicebankltd.co.uk
Fax: 0161-888 2242   Tel: 0161-874 5741

Silver~Tongued Productions

Specialising in the recording and production of voice reels and production tracks

We will guide you through the whole process of recording your voice reel. From choosing your scripts to directing you during the recording session, making it as simple and as easy as possible.

Call us for a brochure and free sample CD, 'Silver~Tongued Examples'

t: 020 8309 0659 ~ **e:** contactus@silver-tongued.co.uk ~ **w:** www.silver-tongued.co.uk

(For Production Tracks please visit: www.productiontracks.co.uk)

VOICE MASTER STUDIO
(Specialising in Foreign Language Voice-Overs)
88 Erskine Hill
London NW11 6HR
Website: www.voicemaster.co.uk
e-mail: stevehudson@voicemaster.co.uk   Tel: 020-8455 2211

VOICE SHOP
First Floor, Thomas Place
1A Devonshire Road, London W4 2EU
Website: www.voice-shop.co.uk
e-mail: info@voice-shop.co.uk
Fax: 020-8742 7011   Tel: 020-8742 7077

VOICE SQUAD
1 Kendal Road, London NW10 1JH
Website: www.voicesquad.com
e-mail: voices@voicesquad.com   Tel: 020-8450 4451

VOICEBANK, THE IRISH VOICE-OVER AGENCY
The Barracks
76 Irishtown Road
Dublin 4, Ireland
Website: www.voicebank.ie
e-mail: voicebank@voicebank.ie
Fax: 00 353 1 6607850   Tel: 00 353 1 6687234

VOICECALL
67A Gondar Gardens
London NW6 1EP
e-mail: voices@voicecall-online.co.uk   Tel: 020-7209 1064

VOICEOVER GALLERY The
PO Box 213, Chorlton
Manchester M21 9ZA
Website: www.thevoiceovergallery.co.uk
e-mail: info@thevoiceovergallery.co.uk
Fax: 0161-881 8951   Tel: 0161-881 8844

VOICEOVERS.CO.UK
Ford Park House
24 Ford Park Road
Plymouth PL4 6RD
Website: www.voiceovers.co.uk
e-mail: info@voiceovers.co.uk
Fax: 01752 661595   Tel: 0871 3096653

VSI - VOICE & SCRIPT INTERNATIONAL
(Foreign Language Specialists)
132 Cleveland Street
London W1T 6AB
Website: www.vsi.tv
e-mail: info@vsi.tv
Fax: 020-7692 7711   Tel: 020-7692 7700

WILLIAMSON & HOLMES
9 Hop Gardens, St. Martin's Lane, London WC2N 4EH
e-mail: info@williamsonandholmes.co.uk
Fax: 020-7240 0408   Tel: 020-7240 0407

WOOTTON Suzy VOICES
72 Towcester Road
Far Cotton, Northampton NN4 8LQ
Website: www.suzywoottonvoices.com
e-mail: suzy@suzywoottonvoices.com
Fax: 0870 7659668   Tel: 0870 7659660

YAKETY YAK
7A Bloomsbury Square, London WC1A 2LP
Website: www.yaketyyak.co.uk
e-mail: info@yaketyyak.co.uk
Fax: 020-7404 6109   Tel: 020-7430 2600

Voice Overs
Translations
Script Adaptation
Foreign Copywriting
Studio Production
Subtitles

Contact: Margaret Davies, Annie Geary or Bérangère Capelle

On 020 7935 0993

Foreign Versions Ltd
60 Blandford Street
London W1U 7JD

e-mail: info@foreignversions.co.uk
www.foreignversions.com

AVENUE ARTISTES LTD
The South's most efficient casting service

ACTORS, SUPPORTING ARTISTES, EXTRAS & WALK ONS AVAILABLE FOR TELEVISION, FILMS, COMMERCIALS, ADVERTISING etc

8 Winn Road, Southampton (023) 8055 1000 Fax No. (023) 8090 5703

EMAIL: info@avenueartistes.com WEBSITE: www.avenueartistes.com

10 TWENTY TWO CASTING ■
PO Box 1022, Liverpool L69 5WZ
Website: www.10twentytwo.com
e-mail: contact@10twentytwo.com
Fax: 0151-207 4230   Tel: 0870 8501022

2020 CASTING Ltd ■
2020 Hopgood Street, London W12 7JU
Website: www.2020casting.com
e-mail: info@2020casting.com
Fax: 020-8735 2727   Tel: 020-8746 2020

ALLSORTS AGENCY
(Modelling)
Suite 1 & 2 Marlborough Business Centre
96 George Lane, London E18 1AD
Website: www.allsortsagency.com
e-mail: bookings@allsortsagency.com
Fax: 020-8989 5600   Tel: 020-8989 0500

ARTIST MANAGEMENT UK Ltd
PO Box 96, Liverpool L9 8WY
Website: www.artistmanagementuk.com
e-mail: chris@artistmanagementuk.com Tel: 0151-523 6222

AVENUE ARTISTES Ltd
8 Winn Road, Southampton SO17 1EN
Website: www.avenueartistes.com
e-mail: info@avenueartistes.com   Tel: 023-8055 1000

AWA - ANDREA WILDER AGENCY
23 Cambrian Drive, Colwyn Bay, Conwy LL28 4SL
Website: www.awagency.co.uk
e-mail: casting@awagency.co.uk
Fax: 07092 249314   Mobile: 07919 202401

BALDIES CASTING AGENCY
(The only agency purely for bald people)
6 Marlott Road, Poole, Dorset BH15 3DX
Mobile: 07860 290437   Tel: 01202 666001

BIRMINGHAM CENTRAL CASTING
PO Box 145, Inkberrow, Worcestershire WR7 4EL
Website: www.bccasting.co.uk
e-mail: info@mouthpieceuk.co.uk   Tel: 08700 427587

BLUE WAND MANAGEMENT
2nd Floor, 12 Weljte Road, Hammersmith, London W6 9TG
e-mail: bluewand@btinternet.com   Tel: 020-8741 2038

BODENS ADVANCED
Bodens Studios & Agency
99 East Barnet Road, New Barnet, Herts EN4 8RF
Website: www.bodensagency.com
e-mail: info@bodensagency.com
Fax: 020-8449 5212   Tel: 020-8447 1226

BRISTOL EXTRA SERVICE TEAM (B.E.S.T.)
(Ernest Jones) (Film & TV Actors, Extras, Speciality Artists)
21 Ellesmere, Thornbury
Near Bristol BS35 2ER
Website: www.best-agency.co.uk
e-mail: ejj.best@blueyonder.co.uk
Mobile: 07951 955759   Tel/Fax: 01454 411628

BROADCASTING AGENCY
Unit 36, Pall Mall Deposit
124-128 Barlby Road, London W10 6BL
Website: www.broadcastingagency.co.uk
e-mail: info@broadcastingagency.co.uk Tel: 020-8960 5020

BROOK Dolly CASTING AGENCY
PO Box 5436, Dunmow CM6 1WW
e-mail: dollybrookcasting@btinternet.com
Fax: 01371 875996   Tel: 01371 875767

CAIRNS AGENCY The
(Maureen Cairns)
1st Floor, 84 Miller Street, Glasgow G1 1DT
Website: www.west-endmgt.com
Fax: 0141-226 8983   Tel: 0141-226 8941

Who are Walk-on and Supporting Artists?

Sometimes known as 'Extras', walk-on and supporting artists appear in the background of TV and film scenes in order to add a sense of realism, character or atmosphere. They do not have individual speaking roles, unless required to make background / ambient noise. Working as a walk-on or supporting artist does not require any specific 'look', training or experience as such; however it does involve more effort than people think. Artists are often required to start very early in the morning (6am is not uncommon), and days can be long with lots of waiting around, sometimes in tough conditions on location. It is certainly not glamorous, nor is it a way to become a TV or film star! Artists must be reliable and available at very short notice, which can make it difficult to juggle with other work or family commitments. Requirements vary from production to production and, as with mainstream acting work, there are no guarantees that you will get regular work, let alone be able to earn a living as a walk-on.

How should I use these listings?

If you are serious about working as a walk-on artist, you will need to register with an agency in order to be put forward for jobs. In return for finding you work, you can expect an agency to take between 10-15% in commission. The following pages contain contact details of many walk-on and supporting artist agencies. Some will specialise in certain areas, so make sure you research the different companies carefully to see if they are appropriate for you. Many have websites you can visit. It is also worth asking questions about how long an agency has existed, and about their recent production credits. When approaching an agency for representation, you should send them your CV with a covering letter and a recent photograph which is a genuine, natural likeness of you. Enclosing a stamped-addressed envelope with sufficient postage (SAE) will give you a better chance of a reply.

Should I pay a Walk-on Agent to join their books? Or sign a contract?

As with other types of agencies, Equity does not generally recommend that artists pay an agent to join their client list. Before signing any contract, you should be clear about the terms and commitments involved. Always speak to Equity www.equity.org.uk or BECTU www.bectu.org.uk if you have any concerns or queries.

Where can I find more information?

The website www.hiddenextra.com is an invaluable source of information for anyone thinking about working a walk-on or supporting artist. You may also find it useful to contact the Film Artists Association, part of BECTU www.bectu.org.uk or the National Association of Supporting Artistes Agents www.nasaa.org.uk. NASAA members are shown by the symbol ■ in this book. Within Equity, the actors' trade union, there is a committee which represents walk-on and supporting artists. As a general rule, walk-on artists can join Equity if they have proof of at least six days' paid work over a period of twelve consecutive months undertaken on an Equity agreement.

For more information visit www.equity.org.uk

Ray Knight Casting was founded in 1988 and is an Agency specialising in the supply of walk-on and supporting artists for Film, Television and Commercials. They have a main workforce of approximately 1800 artists on their books. Ray Knight offers the following advice to budding supporting artists:

Supporting artist work is not for everybody. You need to have endless patience, a very compliant and tolerant attitude, and the ability to get on with other people in close and often awkward circumstances. The vast majority of employment is handled by agencies specialising in this field of work. I have been such an agent since 1988 and like to think I have done a good job for both artist and client, building a reputation for fairness and reliability.

When seeking an agent to represent you, please bear the following useful pointers in mind. There are unfortunately some real cowboys in the field. Do not part with any money in advance of receiving any viable work, whatever the explanation you are given. Be it for registration, photographs, advertising or promotional material or for any other reason, do not pay *anything* 'up-front'. Honest agencies will make a nominal charge for promotional material they produce on behalf of their artists, but this will always be taken from fees earned from work supplied. It will be a one-off annual charge and by law, only based on an estimate of cost basis.

A good agent will want to see you before he or she will offer to put you forward for employment, be keen to make an appointment. This will give you an opportunity to check that the agent has proper premises and is operating in a viable fashion. Get to know as much as you can about your agent, both before and after you join. Check to see if they are members of the trade association NASAA www.nasaa.org.uk

Supporting artist work does not lead to stardom. If you want to be an actor, go to drama school. It is essentially a part-time occupation for those who have a good level of availability, often at short notice, and find it both rewarding and interesting. Much depends on types and age groups. Over the years it has been my perception that 60% of work goes to men and 40% to women, with the greatest demand being for men aged between 25 and 45, and women between 20 and 40. This does not mean that there is no work for those outside those rough parameters, but just that it is likely to be more erratic than for those in the categories for which there is a concentration of demand. It also helps to be of average size and measurements.

Please remember that leading artists are carrying the burden of scripted lines, close up action and focusing on their work. They may not welcome chatting to the supporting artists, even though at other times they would be very approachable. Do not bother them unless they invite you to socialise with them, give them space and respect their need for concentration.

The best supporting artists are the ones who turn up on time, wearing the right clothes where appropriate, only need telling once, are quick to re-position, and are amenable to all they work with be it fellow artist or crew. Do not adopt a high profile - people who try to get noticed are only seen as irritating. There is enough ego on a film set already, it is not a good idea for supporting artists to add to it.

Having said all of this, supporting artists can have an interesting, rewarding and enjoyable time with the right attitude and approach. I have been fortunate to represent some lovely people whom I have very much enjoyed having on my books. I hope they have thought as well of me as I of them.

For more information about Ray Knight Casting please visit www.rayknight.co.uk

Bill Gerard

Northern Professionals Casting Co.

Licence No. L1299.....

Casting - Supporting/Principal Artistes
Action Safety Consultant
Diving support teams - Boat Hire - Diving Equipment Hire

Office: 0191 257 8635 Mob: 07860 186978 Fax: 0191 296 3243
21 Cresswell Avenue, North Shields, Near Tyne & Wear NE29 9BQ
www.northernprocasting.co.uk

CAMCAST ■
Laragain, Upper Banavie
Fort William, Inverness-shire PH33 7PB
Website: www.camcast.co.uk   e-mail: anne@camcast.co.uk
Fax: 01397 772456   Tel: 01397 772523

CASTING COLLECTIVE Ltd The ■
Olympic House, 317-321 Latimer Road, London W10 6RA
Website: www.castingcollective.co.uk
e-mail: enquiries@castingcollective.co.uk
Fax: 020-8962 0333   Tel: 020-8962 0099

CASTING NETWORK Ltd The ■
2nd Floor, 10 Claremont Road, Surbiton, Surrey KT6 4QU
Website: www.thecastingnetwork.co.uk
e-mail: casting-network@talk21.com
Fax: 020-8390 0605   Tel: 020-8339 9090

CASTING STUDIO The
PO Box 167, Middleton, Manchester M24 5WY
Website: www.thecastingstudio.co.uk
e-mail: info@thecastingstudio.co.uk   Tel/Fax: 0161-643 6266

CELEX CASTING Ltd ■
(Children available)
PO Box 7317, Derby DE1 0GS   e-mail: anne@celex.co.uk
Fax: 01332 232115   Tel: 01332 232445

CENTRAL CASTING Ltd
(See also KNIGHT Ray CASTING)
21A Lambolle Place, Belsize Park, London NW3 4PG
Website: www.rayknight.co.uk
e-mail: casting@rayknight.co.uk
Fax: 020-7722 2322   Tel: 020-7722 1551

CORNWALL FILM AGENCY
Higher Leyonne, Golant, Fowey, Cornwall PL23 1LA
Website: www.cornwallfilmagency.co.uk
e-mail: info.cfa@btconnect.com
Mobile: 07918 648330   Tel/Fax: 01726 833004

DAVID AGENCY The ■
26-28 Hammersmith Grove, London W6 7BA
Website: www.davidagency.net
e-mail: casting@davidagency.net   Tel: 020-7967 7001

DOE John ASSOCIATES
26 Noko, 3/6 Banister Road, London W10 4AR
Website: www.johndoeassociates.com
e-mail: info@johndoeassociates.com
Mobile: 07979 558594   Tel: 020-8960 2848

ELITE CASTING AGENCY
(Film & TV Extras)
77 Widmore Road, Bromley, Kent BR1 3AA
Website: www.elitecasting.co.uk
e-mail: admin@elitecasting.co.uk   Tel/Fax: 0871 3103438

ELLIOTT AGENCY Ltd The ■
10 High Street, Shoreham-by-Sea BN43 5DA
Website: www.elliottagency.co.uk
e-mail: elliottagency@btconnect.com   Tel: 01273 454111

EUROKIDS & ADULTS INTERNATIONAL CASTING & MODEL AGENCY
The Warehouse Studios, Glaziers Lane
Culcheth, Warrington, Cheshire WA3 4AQ
Website: www.eka-agency.com
e-mail: castings@eka-agency.com
Fax: 01925 767563   Tel: 01925 761088

FACES CASTING AGENCY ■
15A Cambridge Grove, Hove, East Sussex BN3 3ED
Website: www.faces-casting.co.uk
e-mail: nick@faces-casting.co.uk
Fax: 01273 719165   Tel: 01273 329436

FBI AGENCY Ltd The ■
PO Box 250, Leeds LS1 2AZ
e-mail: casting@fbi-agency.ltd.uk
Fax: 0113-279 7270   Mobile: 07050 222747

SÉVA DHALIVAAL M: 07956 553879

Janet Howe Casting Agency
• Extras, Walk-ons, Crowd • Fashion and Photographic
• Also Representing Talented Actors

The Pie Factory
101 Broadway, Salford Quays
Manchester M50 2EQ
Tel/Fax: 0161 263 0633

The Works Media Centre
36 White House Street
Hunslet, Leeds, LS10 1AD
Tel/Fax: 0113 242 5225

56 Ironmarket, N-U-L
Staffordshire ST5 1PE
Tel/Fax: 01782 661777
Mobile: 07801 942178   info@janethowe.com

Sykes Family
Pizza Hut
Commercial '07

FRESH AGENTS Ltd
Suite 5, Saks House, 19 Ship Street, Brighton BN1 1AD
Website: www.freshagents.com
e-mail: info@freshagents.com   Tel: 0848 4080998

FTS CASTING AGENCY
55 Pullan Avenue, Eccleshill, Bradford BD2 3RP
e-mail: helen@footsteps.fslife.co.uk
Fax: 01274 637429   Tel: 01274 636036

G2 ■
15 Lexham Mews, London W8 6JW
Website: www.g2casting.com   e-mail: email@g2casting.com
Fax: 020-7376 2416   Tel: 020-7376 2133

GUYS & DOLLS CASTING ■
Trafalgar House, Grenville Place
Mill Hill, London NW7 3SA
Fax: 020-8381 0080   Tel: 020-8906 4144

HOWE Janet CASTING & MODELLING AGENCY
The Pie Factory, 101 Broadway
Salford Quays, Manchester M50 2EQ
Mobile: 07801 942178   Tel/Fax: 0161-263 0633
e-mail: info@janethowe.com
The Works Media Centre, 36 White House Street
Hunslet, Leeds LS10 1AD   Tel/Fax: 0113-242 5225
56 The Ironmarket, Newcastle-Under-Lyme
Staffordshire ST5 1PE   Tel/Fax: 01782 661777

INDUSTRY CASTING
Suite 332, Royal Exchange, Manchester M2 7BR
Website: www.industrycasting.co.uk
e-mail: mark@industrypeople.co.uk
Fax: 0161-839 1661   Tel: 0161-839 1551

JACLYN AGENCY ■
52 Bessemer Road, Norwich, Norfolk NR4 6DQ
Website: www.jaclyncastingagency.co.uk
e-mail: info@jaclynagency.co.uk
Fax: 01603 612532   Tel: 01603 622027

JB AGENCY ONLINE Ltd ■
Chelsea Business Centre
73-77 Brittania Road, London SW6 2JR
Website: www.jb-agency.com   e-mail: info@jb-agency.com
Mobile: 07962 434111   Tel/Fax: 020-7751 0910

JPM EXTRAS
(A Division of Janet Plater Management Ltd)
D Floor, Milburn House
Dean Street, Newcastle upon Tyne NE1 1LF
Website: www.janetplatermanagement.co.uk
e-mail: magpie@tynebridge.demon.co.uk
Fax: 0191-233 1709   Tel: 0191-221 2491

J .R. FILM ARTISTES
1100 Parkway, Solent Business Centre, Whiteley PO15 7AB
e-mail: info@jrfilmextras.co.uk   Tel: 023-8044 5977

KNIGHT Ray CASTING ■
(See also CENTRAL CASTING Ltd)
21A Lambolle Place, Belsize Park, London NW3 4PG
Website: www.rayknight.co.uk   e-mail: casting@rayknight.co.uk
Fax: 020-7722 2322   Tel: 020-7722 4111

KREATE PRODUCTIONS
Unit 232, 30 Great Guildford Street, London SE1 0HS
Website: www.kreatepromotions.co.uk
e-mail: enquiries@kreatepromotions.co.uk
Fax: 020-7401 3003   Tel: 020-7401 9007

nidges
casting agency

arguably the north of england's most established casting agency
we have a comprehensive selection of experienced, quality Equity & non-Equity
supporting artistes available for work in any sphere of the theatre,
television, film, video & advertising industries

Half Moon Chambers   Chapel Walks   Manchester M2 1HN

Tel: **0161 832 8259** Fax: **0161 832 5219** **www.nidgescasting.co.uk**

LEE'S PEOPLE: RAPID TALENT Ltd ■
90 Long Acre, London WC2E 9RZ
Website: www.rapidtalent.co.uk   Tel: 020-7734 5775
LEMON CASTING Ltd
The Pie Factory, 101 Broadway
Salford Quays, Manchester M50 2EQ
e-mail: lemon.tv@btconnect.com
Mobile: 07723 317489   Tel: 0161-876 0088
LINTON MANAGEMENT
3 The Rock, Bury BL9 0JP   e-mail: carol@linton.tv
Fax: 0161-761 1999   Tel: 0161-761 2020
MAD DOG CASTING Ltd ■
Third Floor
15 Leighton Place, London NW5 2QL
e-mail: info@maddogcasting.com
Fax: 020-7284 2689   Tel: 020-7482 4703
M.E.P. MANAGEMENT
1 Malvern Avenue
Highams Park, London E4 9NP
Website: www.global-theatre-company.net
e-mail: mep@btclick.com   Tel/Fax: 020-8523 3540
NEMESIS AGENCY Ltd
Nemesis House, 1 Oxford Court
Bishopsgate, Manchester M2 3WQ
Website: www.nemesisagency.co.uk
e-mail: sheila@nmsmanagement.co.uk
Fax: 0161-228 6727   Tel: 0161-228 6404
NE REPRESENTATION
(Models, Photographers, Hair & make-up artists, Stylists
and Film Extras)
38 Coniscliffe Road, Darlington DL3 7RG
Website: www.nerepresentation.co.uk
e-mail: info@nerepresentation.co.uk
Fax: 01325 488390   Tel: 01325 488385

NIDGES CASTING AGENCY
Half Moon Chambers, Chapel Walks, Manchester M2 1HN
e-mail: kirstie@nidgescasting.co.uk
Fax: 0161-832 5219   Tel: 0161-832 8259
NORTHERN PROFESSIONALS CASTING COMPANY
21 Cresswell Avenue, North Shields, Tyne & Wear NE29 9BQ
Website: www.northernprocasting.co.uk
e-mail: bill@northernprocasting.co.uk
Fax: 0191-296 3243   Tel: 0191-257 8635
ORIENTAL CASTING AGENCY Ltd (Peggy Sirr) ■
(Afro/Asian Artists)
1 Wyatt Park Road
Streatham Hill, London SW2 3TN
Website: www.orientalcasting.com
e-mail: peggy.sirr@btconnect.com
Fax: 020-8674 9303   Tel: 020-8671 8538
PAN ARTISTS AGENCY Ltd
Cornerways, 34 Woodhouse Lane, Sale, Cheshire M33 4JX
Website: www.panartists.co.uk
e-mail: panartists@btconnect.com
Mobile: 07952 018175   Tel: 0800 6349147
PC THEATRICAL & MODEL AGENCY
12 Carlisle Road, Colindale, London NW9 0HL
Website: www.twinagency.com   e-mail: twinagy@aol.com
Fax: 020-8933 3418   Tel: 020-8381 2229
PERFORMERS LEAGUE AGENCY The
Unit F18, Birch House, Birch Walk
Off Fraizer Road, Erith, Kent DA8 1QX
Website: www.tpla.co.uk   e-mail: info@tpla.co.uk
Mobile: 07886 319807   Tel: 020-8854 4576
PHA ACTORS MANAGEMENT
Tanzaro House, Ardwick Green North, Manchester M12 6FZ
Website: www.pha-agency.co.uk
e-mail: casting@pha-agency.co.uk
Fax: 0161-273 4567   Tel: 0161-273 4444

PHOENIX CASTING AGENCY ■
PO Box 387, Bristol BS99 3JZ
Website: www.phoenixagency.biz
e-mail: info@phoenixagency.biz
Fax: 0117-973 4160   Tel: 0117-973 1100

POLICE-ACTION
59 Sylvan Avenue, Wood Green, London N22 5JA
Website: www.police-action.co.uk
e-mail: police-action@hotmail.co.uk   Tel/Fax: 020-8889 6540

POWER MODEL MANAGEMENT CASTING AGENCY
PO Box 1198, Salhouse, Norwich NR13 6WD
Website: www.powermodel.co.uk
e-mail: info@powermodel.co.uk   Tel: 01603 721287

PRAETORIAN ASSOCIATES
(Specialist Action Extras)
Room 501, 2 Old Brompton Road, London SW7 3DG
Website: www.praetorianasc.com
e-mail: info@praetorianasc.com   Tel/Fax: 020-7096 1827

RAY'S NORTHERN CASTING AGENCY
7 Wince Close, Alkrington, Middleton, Manchester M24 1UJ
e-mail: rayscasting@yahoo.co.uk   Tel/Fax: 0161-643 6745

REGENCY AGENCY
25 Carr Road, Calverley
Pudsey, West Yorks LS28 5NE   Tel: 0113-255 8980

REYNOLDS Sandra AGENCY
Shakespeare House, 168 Lavender Hill, London SW11 5TF
Website: www.sandrareynolds.co.uk
e-mail: info@sandrareynolds.co.uk
Fax: 020-7387 5848   Tel: 020-7387 5858
Bacon House, 35 St Georges Street, Norwich NR3 1DA
Fax: 01603 219825   Tel: 01603 623842

RHODES AGENCY
5 Dymoke Road, Hornchurch, Essex RM11 1AA
e-mail: rhodesarts@hotmail.com
Fax: 01708 730431   Tel: 01708 747013

SA19 - THE UNIFORMED ARTISTE AGENCY ■
2020 Hopgood Street, Shepherds Bush, London W12 7JU
Website: www.sa19.co.uk
e-mail: info@sa19.co.uk
Fax: 020-8735 2727   Tel: 020-8746 2523

SAPPHIRES MODEL MANAGEMENT
The Makers Dozen, Studio 11
8 Wulfruna Street, Wolverhampton WV1 1LW
Website: www.sapphiresmodel.com
e-mail: contact@sapphiresmodel.com
Fax: 0870 9127563   Tel: 0870 2245484

SCREAM MANAGEMENT
The Red Door
32 Clifton Street, Blackpool, Lancs FY1 1JP
Website: www.screammanagement.com
e-mail: info@screammanagement.com
Fax: 01253 750829   Tel: 01253 750820

SCREENLITE AGENCY ■
Shepperton Film Studios, Shepperton, Middlesex TW17 0QD
Website: www.screenliteagency.co.uk
e-mail: kerry@screenliteagency.co.uk
Fax: 01932 592507   Tel: 01932 566977

SOLOMON ARTISTES
30 Clarence Street
Southend-on-Sea, Essex SS1 1BD
Website: www.solomon-artistes.co.uk
e-mail: info@solomon-artistes.co.uk
Fax: 01702 392385   Tel: 01702 437118

STAV'S CASTING AGENCY
82 Station Crescent, Tottenham, London N15 5BD
e-mail: stavscast@yahoo.co.uk   Mobile: 07757 720406

SUMMERS Mark MANAGEMENT
(Formerly Extras Unlimited)
137 Freston Road, London W10 6TH
Website: www.marksummers.com
e-mail: info@marksummers.com
Fax: 020-7243 1987   Tel: 020-7229 8413

TK EXTRAS WALK-ON MODEL AGENCY
51 Ashford Square, Eastbourne BN21 3TX
Website: www.tkextras.co.uk
e-mail: tk@tkextras.co.uk   Tel/Fax: 01323 643068

TO BE SEEN Ltd
Website: www.tobeseen.co.uk
e-mail: info@tobeseen.co.uk   Tel: 020-7288 0191

TUESDAYS CHILD Ltd
(Children & Adults)
Oakfield House, Springwood Way
Macclesfield SK10 2XA
Website: www.tuesdayschildagency.co.uk
e-mail: info@tuesdayschildagency.co.uk
Tel/Fax: 01625 501765

UGLY ENTERPRISES Ltd
Tigris House
256 Edgware Road, London W2 1DS
Website: www.ugly.org   e-mail: info@ugly.org
Fax: 020-7402 0507   Tel: 020-7402 5564

UNI-VERSAL EXTRAS
118-120 Kenton Road, Harrow HA3 8AL
Website: www.universalextrascasting.co.uk
e-mail: wayne.berko@universalextras.co.uk
Tel: 0845 0090344

UNIVERSAL MODEL MANAGEMENT Ltd
PO Box 127, Northampton NN1 3XU
Website: www.universalmodels.tv
e-mail: enquiries@universalmodels.tv   Tel/Fax: 0844 890111

A-Z ANIMALS Ltd
The Bell House, Bell Lane, Fetcham, Surrey KT22 9ND
e-mail: info@a-zanimals.com
Fax: 01372 377666   Tel: 01372 377111

A1 ANIMALS
(Farm, Domestic & Exotic Animals)
9 The Drive, Enstone, Oxon OX7 4NQ
Website: www.a1animals.co.uk
e-mail: info@a1animals.freeserve.co.uk   Tel/Fax: 01608 677348

ABBIE@JANIMALS Ltd
T/A Abbie's Animals, Greystones
Spirit Hill, Calne, Wilts SN11 9HW
Website: www.abbiesanimals.co.uk
e-mail: info@abbiesanimals.co.uk
Mobile: 07900 494028   Mobile: 07914 607778

ABNALLS HORSES
Abnalls Farm, Cross in Hand Lane
Lichfield, Staffs WS13 8DZ
e-mail: carolynsj@dial.pipex.com
Fax: 01543 417226   Tel: 01543 417075

ACTION STUNT DOGS
3 The Chestnuts, Clifton, Deddington, Oxon OX15 OPE
e-mail: gill@stuntdogs.net   Tel/Fax: 01869 338546

ALTERNATIVE ANIMALS
(Animatronics/Taxidermy)
19 Greaves Road, High Wycombe, Bucks HP13 7JU
Website: www.animalworld.org.uk
e-mail: animalworld@bushinternet.com
Fax: 01494 441385   Tel: 01494 448710

ANIMAL ACTING
(Animals, Stunts, Prop, Horse-Drawn Vehicles)
7 Dovedale Court, Windermere Road
Middleton, Manchester M24 5QT
Website: www.animalacting.com
e-mail: information@animalacting.com
Mobile: 07831 800567   Tel: 0161-655 3700

ANIMAL ACTORS
(Animals, Birds, Reptiles)
95 Ditchling Road
Brighton, Sussex BN1 4ST   Tel: 020-8654 0450

ANIMAL AMBASSADORS
Old Forest, Hampstead Norreys Road
Hermitage, Berks RG18 9SA
Website: www.animalambassadors.co.uk
e-mail: kayweston@tiscali.co.uk
Mobile: 07831 558594   Tel/Fax: 01635 200900

ANIMAL ARK
(Animals & Animal Prop Shop)
Studio, 29 Somerset Road, Brentford, Middlesex TW8 8BT
Website: www.animal-ark.co.uk
e-mail: info@animal-ark.co.uk
Fax: 020-8560 5762   Tel: 020-8560 3029

ANIMAL ARRANGERS
(Animal Suppliers & Co-ordinators)
28 Greaves Road, High Wycombe, Bucks HP13 7JU
e-mail: trevorsmith@bushinternet.com
Mobile: 07956 564715   Tel: 01494 448710

ANIMAL CASTING
119 Magdalen Road, London SW18 3ES
e-mail: silcresta@aol.com
Mobile: 07956 246450   Tel: 020-8874 9530

ANIMALS GALORE Ltd
208 Smallfield Road, Horley, Surrey RH6 9LS
Website: www.animals-galore.co.uk
Fax: 01342 841546   Tel: 01342 842400

ANIMALS O KAY
16 Queen Street, Chipperfield
Kings Langley, Herts WD4 9BT
Website: www.animalsokay.com
e-mail: kay@animalsokay.com
Fax: 01923 269076   Tel: 01923 291277

ANIMAL WELFARE FILMING FEDERATION
28 Greaves Road, High Wycombe, Bucks HP13 7JU
e-mail: animalworld@bushinternet.com
Fax: 01494 441385   Mobile: 07770 666088

ANIMAL WORK WITH ANIMAL WORLD
(Trevor Smith)
19 Greaves Road, High Wycombe, Bucks HP13 7JU
Website: www.animalworld.org.uk
e-mail: trevorsmith@bushinternet.com
Fax: 01494 441385   Tel: 01494 442750

CANINE FILM ACADEMY The
57C Cheapside Road, Ascot, Berks SL5 7QR
Website: www.thecaninefilmacademy.com
e-mail: katie.cfa@virgin.net
Mobile: 07767 341424   Tel: 01344 291465

CHEESEMAN Virginia
21 Willow Close, Flackwell Heath
High Wycombe, Bucks HP10 9LH
Website: www.virginiacheeseman.co.uk
e-mail: virginia@virginiacheeseman.co.uk Tel: 01628 522632

COTSWOLD FARM PARK
(Rare Breed Farm Animals)
Guiting Power, Cheltenham, Gloucestershire GL54 5UG
e-mail: info@cotswoldfarmpark.co.uk
Fax: 01451 850423   Tel: 01451 850307

CREATURE FEATURE
(Animal Agent)
Gubhill Farm, Ae, Dumfries, Scotland DG1 1RL
Website: www.creaturefeature.co.uk
e-mail: david@creaturefeature.co.uk
Mobile: 07770 774866   Tel/Fax: 01387 860648

DOG EXTRAS
33 Harold Avenue, Belvedere, Kent DA17 5NN
Website: www.dog-extras.co.uk
e-mail: info@dog-extras.co.uk   Tel: 01322 448272

DOLBADARN FILM HORSES
Dolbadarn Hotel, High Street
Llanberis, Gwynedd, North Wales LL55 4SU
Website: www.filmhorses.co.uk
e-mail: info@filmhorses.co.uk
Mobile: 07710 461341   Tel/Fax: 01286 870277

DUDLEY Yvonne LRPS
(Glamour Dogs)
55 Cambridge Park, Wanstead
London E11 2PR   Tel: 020-8989 1528

EAST NOLTON RIDING STABLES
Nolton, Nr Newgale, Haverfordwest
Pembrokeshire SA62 3NW
Website: www.noltonstables.com
e-mail: noltonstables@aol.com
Fax: 01437 710967   Tel: 01437 710360

FILM HORSES
(Horses, Saddlery, Equestrian Centre)
Free Range Farm, Oakleigh Green Road
Windsor, Berks SL4 4GW
Website: www.filmhorses.com
e-mail: janetrogers@whsmithnet.co.uk
Mobile: 07831 629662   Tel/Fax: 01628 675105

FREE ANIMAL CONSULTANT SERVICES
28 Greaves Road, High Wycombe, Bucks HP13 7JU
Fax: 01494 441385   Tel: 08000 749383

GET STUFFED
(Taxidermy)
105 Essex Road, London N1 2SL
Website: www.thegetstuffed.co.uk
e-mail: taxidermy@thegetstuffed.co.uk
Fax: 020-7359 8253   Tel: 020-7226 1364

GRAY Robin COMMENTARIES
(Equestrian Equipment)
Comptons, Isington
Alton, Hants GU34 4PL
e-mail: gray@isington.fsnet.co.uk
Mobile: 07831 828424   Tel: 01420 23347

HILTON HORSES
(Samantha Jones)
478 London Road
Ashford, Middlesex TW15 3PL
Website: www.hilton-horses.com
e-mail: samantha@hilton-horses.com   Mobile: 07958 292222

KNIGHTS OF ARKLEY The
Glyn Sylen Farm, Five Roads, Llanelli SA15 5BJ
Website: www.knightsofarkley.com
e-mail: penny@knightsofarkley.fsnet.co.uk
                                         Tel/Fax: 01269 861001

MILLENNIUM BUGS
(Live Insects)
28 Greaves Road, High Wycombe, Bucks HP13 7JU
e-mail: animalworld@bushinternet.com
Fax: 01494 441385   Tel: 01494 448710

MORTON Geoff
(Shire Horse & Equipment)
Hasholme Carr Farm
Holme on Spalding Moor
York YO43 4BD   Tel: 01430 860393

OTTERS
(Tame Otters) (Daphne & Martin Neville)
Baker's Mill, Frampton Mansell
Stroud, Glos GL6 8JH
e-mail: martin_neville_bakers_mill@yahoo.co.uk
                                         Tel: 01285 760234

PETMUNCH
114 Mill Lane, West Hampstead, London NW6 1NF
e-mail: info@petmunch.com   Tel/Fax: 020-7813 2644

PROP FARM Ltd
(Pat Ward)
Grange Farm, Elmton, Nr Creswell
North Derbyshire S80 4LX
e-mail: pat/les@propfarm.co.uk
Fax: 01909 721465   Tel: 01909 723100

ROCKWOOD ANIMALS ON FILM
Lewis Terrace, Llanbradach, Caerphilly CF83 3JZ
Website: www.rockwoodanimals.com
e-mail: martin@rockwoodanimals.com
Mobile: 07973 930983   Tel: 029-2088 5420

SCHOOL OF NATIONAL EQUITATION Ltd
(Sam Humphrey)
Bunny Hill Top, Costock
Loughborough, Leicestershire LE12 6XE
Website: www.bunnyhill.co.uk   e-mail: sam@bunnyhill.co.uk
Fax: 01509 856067   Tel: 01509 852366

TATE'S Nigel DOGSTARS
4 Hoads Wood Gardens
Ashford, Kent TN25 4QB
Website: www.dogstars.co.uk
e-mail: animals@dogstars.co.uk
Fax: 07092 031929   Tel: 01233 635439

TATE Olive
(Trained Dogs & Cats)
49 Upton Road, Bexleyheath, Kent DA6 8LW
Mobile: 07731 781892   Tel/Fax: 020-8303 0683

THORNE'S OF WINDSOR
(Beekeeping & Other Insect Suppliers)
Oakley Green Farm, Oakley Green
Windsor, Berks SL4 4PZ   Tel: 01753 830256

WHITE DOVES COMPANY Ltd The
(Provision of up to 150 Doves for Release)
Suite 210 Sterling House, Langston Road
Loughton, Essex IG10 3TS
Website: www.thewhitedovecompany.co.uk
e-mail: thewhitedovecompany@lineone.net
Fax: 020-8502 2461   Tel: 020-8508 1414

WOLF SPECIALISTS The
The UK Wolf Conservation Trust, UK Wolf Centre
Butlers Farm, Beenham, Berks RG7 5NT
Website: www.ukwolf.org
e-mail: ukwct@ukwolf.org   Tel: 0118-971 3330

WOODS Sue
(Animal Promotions, Specialising in Dogs, Domestic Cats, Rodents, Poultry & Farm Stock)
White Rocks Farm, Underriver, Sevenoaks, Kent TN15 0SL
Website: www.animalpromotions.co.uk
e-mail: happyhoundschool@yahoo.co.uk
Fax: 01732 763767   Tel: 01732 762913

ALDERSHOT
West End Centre, Queens Road
Aldershot, Hants GU11 3JD
Website: www.westendcentre.co.uk
BO: 01252 330040   Admin: 01252 408040

BANGOR
Theatr Gwynedd, Ffordd Deiniol
Bangor, Gwynedd LL57 2TL
Website: www.theatrgwynedd.co.uk
e-mail: theatr@theatrgwynedd.co.uk
BO: 01248 351708   Admin: 01248 351707

BILLERICAY
Billericay Arts Association
The Fold, 72 Laindon Road
Billericay, Essex CM12 9LD
Secretary: Edmond Philpott   Tel: 01277 659286

BINGLEY
Bingley Arts Centre
Main Street, Bingley
West Yorkshire BD16 2LZ   Tel: 01274 431576

BIRMINGHAM
The Custard Factory
Gibb Street, Digbeth, Birmingham B9 4AA
Website: www.custardfactory.co.uk
e-mail: post@custardfactory.co.uk
Fax: 0121-604 8888   Tel: 0121-693 7777

BIRMINGHAM
Midlands Arts Centre
Cannon Hill Park, Birmingham B12 9QH
Website: www.macarts.co.uk
Director: Dorothy Wilson
BO: 0121-440 3838   Admin: 0121-440 4221

BOSTON
Blackfriars Arts Centre
Spain Lane, Boston
Lincolnshire PE21 6HP
Website: www.blackfriars.uk.com
e-mail: director@blackfriars.uk.com
Contact: Tony Hill
Fax: 01205 358855   Tel: 01205 363108

BRACKNELL
South Hill Park Arts Centre, Ringmead
Bracknell, Berkshire RG12 7PA
Chief Executive: Ron McAllister
Fax: 01344 411427
BO: 01344 484123   Admin: 01344 484858

BRADFORD
Theatre in The Mill, University of Bradford
Shearbridge Road, Bradford
West Yorkshire BD7 1DP
e-mail: theatre@bradford.ac.uk
BO: 01274 233200   Tel: 01274 233185

BRAINTREE
The Town Hall Centre, Market Square
Braintree, Essex CM7 3YG
General Manager: Jean Grice   Tel: 01376 557776

BRENTFORD
Watermans, 40 High Street
Brentford TW8 0DS
Fax: 020-8232 1030
BO: 020-8232 1010   Admin: 020-8232 1020

BRIDGWATER
Bridgwater Arts Centre
11-13 Castle Street
Bridgwater, Somerset TA6 3DD
Website: www.bridgwaterartscentre.co.uk
e-mail: info@bridgwaterartscentre.co.uk   Tel: 01278 422700

BRISTOL
Arnolfini, 16 Narrow Quay
Bristol BS1 4QA
e-mail: development@arnolfini.org.uk
Fax: 0117-917 2303   Tel: 0117-917 2313

BUILTH WELLS
Wyeside Arts Centre, Castle Street
Builth Wells, Powys LD2 3BN
Fax: 01982 553995   Tel: 01982 553668

BURY
The Met, Market Street, Bury, Lancs BL9 0BW
e-mail: post@themet.biz
Director: David Agnew
Fax: 0870 0520297
BO: 0161-761 2216   Admin: 0161-761 7107

CANNOCK
Prince of Wales Centre
Church Sreet, Cannock, Staffs WS11 1DE
e-mail: princeofwales@cannockchasedc.gov.uk
General Manager: Richard Kay
Fax: 01543 574439
BO: 01543 578672   Tel: 01543 466453

CARDIFF
Chapter Arts Centre
Market Road, Canton
Cardiff CF5 1QE
Theatre Programmer: James Tyson
BO: 029-2030 4400   Admin: 029-2031 1050

CHIPPING NORTON
The Theatre, 2 Spring Street
Chipping Norton
Oxon OX7 5NL
Website: www.chippingnortontheatre.com
e-mail: admin@chippingnortontheatre.com
Director: Caroline Sharman
General Manager: Chris Durham
Fax: 01608 642324
BO: 01608 642350   Admin: 01608 642349

CHRISTCHURCH
The Regent Centre
51 High Street, Christchurch, Dorset BH23 1AS
Website: www.regentcentre.co.uk
e-mail: info@regentcentre.co.uk
General Manager: Keith Lancing   Admin: 01202 499199

CIRENCESTER
Brewery Arts
Brewery Court
Cirencester, Glos GL7 1JH
Website: www.breweryarts.org.uk
e-mail: admin@breweryarts.org.uk
Fax: 01285 644060   Admin: 01285 657181

COLCHESTER
Colchester Arts Centre, Church Street
Colchester, Essex CO1 1NF
Website: www.colchesterartscentre.com
e-mail: info@colchesterartscentre.com
Director: Anthony Roberts   Tel: 01206 500900

COVENTRY
Warwick Arts Centre
University of Warwick, Coventry CV4 7AL
Website: www.warwickartscentre.co.uk
e-mail: arts.centre@warwick.ac.uk
Director: Alan Rivett
BO: 024-7652 4524   Admin: 024-7652 3734

CUMBERNAULD
Cumbernauld Theatre
Kildrum, Cumbernauld G67 2BN
Artistic Director: Ed Robson
Fax: 01236 738408
BO: 01236 732887   Admin: 01236 737235

DARLINGTON
Darlington Arts Centre
Vane Terrace, Darlington, County Durham DL3 7AX
Website: www.darlingtonarts.co.uk
BO: 01325 486555   Admin: 01325 348843

DORSET
The Coade Hall Theatre
Blandford Forum, Dorset DT11 0PX
e-mail: clt@bryanston.co.uk
Administrator: Claire Topping
Artistic Director: Jane Quan
Fax: 01258 484506   Tel: 01258 484623

EDINBURGH
Scottish Storytelling Centre, The Netherbow
43-45 High Street, Edinburgh EH1 1SR
Website: www.scottishstorytellingcentre.co.uk
e-mail: reception@scottishstorytellingcentre.com
Director: Dr Donald Smith   Tel: 0131-556 9579

EDINBURGH
Theatre Workshop, 34 Hamilton Place, Edinburgh EH3 5AX
Website: www.theatre-workshop.com
Director: Robert Rae
Fax: 0131-220 0112   Tel: 0131-225 7942

EPSOM
Playhouse, Ashley Avenue, Epsom, Surrey KT18 5AL
Website: www.epsomplayhouse.co.uk
e-mail: tmitchell@epsom-ewell.gov.uk
Playhouse Manager: Trevor Mitchell
Fax: 01372 726228
BO: 01372 742555   Admin: 01372 742226

EXETER
Exeter Phoenix
Bradninch Place, Gandy Street, Exeter, Devon EX4 3LS
Website: www.exeterphoenix.org.uk
e-mail: admin@exeterphoenix.org.uk
Director: Patrick Cunningham
Fax: 01392 667599
BO: 01392 667080   Admin: 01392 667060

FAREHAM
Ashcroft Arts Centre
Osborn Road, Fareham, Hants PO16 7DX
Website: www.ashcroft.org.uk
e-mail: info@ashcroft.org.uk
Director/Programmer: Annabel Cook
Fax: 01329 825661
BO: 01329 223100   Tel: 01329 235161

FROME
Merlin Theatre, Bath Road, Frome
Somerset BA11 2HG
Website: www.merlintheatre.co.uk
BO: 01373 465949   Admin: 01373 461360

GAINSBOROUGH
Trinity Arts Centre
Trinity Street, Gainsborough
Lincolnshire DN21 2AL
Fax: 01427 811198   BO/Admin: 01427 676655

GREAT TORRINGTON
The Plough Arts Centre
9-11 Fore Street
Great Torrington, Devon EX38 8HQ
Website: www.plough-arts.org
BO: 01805 624624   Admin: 01805 622552

HARLECH
Theatr Ardudwy, Harlech, Gwynedd LL46 2PU
Theatre Director: Clare Williams   BO: 01766 780667

HAVANT
Havant Arts Centre
East Street, Havant, Hants PO9 1BS
Website: www.havantartscentre.co.uk
e-mail: info@havantartsactive.co.uk
Director: Amanda O'Reilly
BO: 023-9247 2700   Admin: 023-9248 0113

HELMSLEY
Helmsley Arts Centre
Meeting House Court
Helmsley, York YO62 5DW
Website: www.helmsleyarts.co.uk
e-mail: davidgoodwinhac@yahoo.co.uk
Development Manager: David Goodwin
BO: 01439 771700   Tel: 01439 772112

HEMEL HEMPSTEAD
Old Town Hall Arts Centre
High Street
Hemel Hempstead, Herts HP1 3AE
Website: www.oldtownhall.co.uk
e-mail: othadmin@dacorum.gov.uk
Art & Entertainment Manager: Sara Railson
BO: 01442 228091   Admin: 01442 228095

HEXHAM
Queens Hall Arts
Beaumont Street, Hexham, Northumberland NE46 3LS
Website: www.queenshall.co.uk
e-mail: boxoffice@queenshall.co.uk
Artistic Director: Geof Keys
Fax: 01434 652478
BO: 01434 652477   Admin: 01434 652476

HORSHAM
The Capitol
North Street, Horsham
West Sussex RH12 1RG
Website: www.thecapitolhorsham.com
General Manager: Michael Gattrell
Fax: 01403 756092   Tel: 01403 756080

HUDDERSFIELD
Kirklees (various venues)
Kirklees Culture & Leisure Services
Red Doles Lane, , Huddersfield HD2 1YF
BO: 01484 223200   Admin: 01484 226300

INVERNESS
Eden Court, Bishop's Road, Inverness IV3 5SA
e-mail: admin@eden-court.co.uk
Director: Colin Marr
BO: 01463 234234   Admin: 01463 239841

JERSEY
Jersey Arts Centre
Phillips Street, St Helier, Jersey JE2 4SW
Website: www.artscentre.je
Director: Daniel Austin
Deputy Directors: Steven Edwards, Graeme Humphries
Fax: 01534 726788
BO: 01534 700444   Admin: 01534 700400

KENDAL
Brewery Arts Centre
Highgate, Kendal, Cumbria LA9 4HE
Website: www.breweryarts.co.uk
e-mail: admin@breweryarts.co.uk
Chief Executive: Sam Mason
BO: 01539 725133   Admin: 01539 722833

KING'S LYNN
King's Lynn Arts Centre, 27 King's Street
King's Lynn, Norfolk PE30 1HA
Website: www.kingslynnarts.co.uk
Fax: 01553 762141
BO: 01553 764864   Tel: 01553 765565

LEICESTER
Phoenix Arts Centre
21 Upper Brown Street, Leicester LE1 5TE
e-mail: erika@phoenix.org.uk
BO: 0116-255 4854   Admin: 0116-224 7700

LICHFIELD
Lichfield District Arts Association
Donegal House, Bore Street, Lichfield WS13 6LU
Website: www.lichfieldarts.org.uk
e-mail: info@lichfieldarts.org.uk
Director: Brian Pretty
Fax: 01543 308211   Tel: 01543 262223

LISKEARD
Sterts Theatre & Arts Centre
Upton Cross, Liskeard, Cornwall PL14 5AZ
Tel/Fax: 01579 362382   Tel/Fax: 01579 362962

LONDON
Artsdepot
5 Nether Street, Tally Ho Corner
North Finchley, London N12 0GA
Website: www.artsdepot.co.uk
e-mail: info@artsdepot.co.uk
BO: 020-8369 5454

LONDON
BAC
Lavender Hill, Battersea, London SW11 5TN
Website: www.bac.org.uk
e-mail: mailbox@bac.org.uk
Fax: 020-7978 5207
BO: 020-7223 2223   Admin: 020-7223 6557

LONDON
Chats Palace
42-44 Brooksby's Walk, Hackney, London E9 6DF
Website: www.chatspalace.com
e-mail: info@chatspalace.com
Administrator: Nick Reed   BO/Admin: 020-8533 0227

LONDON
Cockpit Theatre
Gateforth Street, London NW8 8EH
Website: www.cockpittheatre.org.uk
e-mail: dave.wybrow@cwc.ac.uk
Fax: 020-7258 2921
BO: 020-7258 2925   Admin: 020-7258 2920

LONDON
The Drill Hall, 16 Chenies Street, London WC1E 7EX
Website: www.drillhall.co.uk
e-mail: admin@drillhall.co.uk
Fax: 020-7307 5062   Tel: 020-7307 5061

LONDON
Hoxton Hall Arts Centre
130 Hoxton Street, London N1 6SH
Website: www.hoxtonhall.co.uk
e-mail: info@hoxtonhall.co.uk
Venue Manager: Mark Hone
Fax: 020-7729 3815   Admin: 020-7684 0060

LONDON
Institute of Contemporary Arts
(No in-house productions or castings)
The Mall, London SW1Y 5AH
Website: www.ica.org.uk
Live & Media Arts Director: Emma Quinn
Fax: 020-7306 0122
BO: 020-7930 3647   Admin: 020-7930 0493

LONDON
Islington Arts Factory
2 Parkhurst Road, London N7 0SF
e-mail: iaf@islingtonartsfactory.fsnet.co.uk
Fax: 020-7700 7229   Tel: 020-7607 0561

LONDON
Jacksons Lane
269A Archway Road, London N6 5AA
Website: www.jacksonslane.org.uk
e-mail: mail@jacksonslane.org.uk
Fax: 020-8348 2424
BO: 020-8341 4421   Admin: 020-8340 5226

LONDON
Menier Chocolate Factory
53 Southwark Street, London SE1 1RU
Website: www.menierchocolatefactory.com
e-mail: office@menierchocolatefactory.com
Artistic Director: David Babani
Fax: 020-7378 1713   Admin: 020-7378 1712

LONDON
The Nettlefold
West Norwood Library Centre
1 Norwood High Street, London SE27 9JX
Centre Development Officers: Joanne Johnson,
Mark Sheehan   Admin/BO: 020-7926 8070

LONDON
October Gallery
24 Old Gloucester Street, London WC1N 3AL
Website: www.octobergallery.co.uk
e-mail: rentals@octobergallery.co.uk
Contact: Charlotte Ferguson
Fax: 020-7405 1851   Tel: 020-7831 1618

LONDON
Oval House Theatre
52-54 Kennington Oval, London SE11 5SW
Website: www.ovalhouse.com
e-mail: info@ovalhouse.com
Programmer: Ben Evans
Director: Deborah Bestwick   Tel: 020-7582 0080

LONDON
Polish Social & Cultural Association
238-246 King Street, London W6 0RF   Tel: 020-8741 1940

LONDON
Riverside Studios
Crisp Road, Hammersmith, London W6 9RL
Website: www.riversidestudios.co.uk
e-mail: admin@riversidestudios.co.uk
Fax: 020-8237 1001
BO: 020-8237 1111   Tel: 020-8237 1000

LONDON
The Stables Gallery & Arts Centre
Gladstone Park
Dollis Hill Lane, London NW2 6HT   Tel: 020-8452 8655

MAIDENHEAD
Norden Farm Centre for The Arts
Altwood Road, Maidenhead SL6 4PF
Website: www.nordenfarm.org
e-mail: admin@nordenfarm.org
Director: Annabel Turpin
Fax: 01628 682525
BO: 01628 788997   Admin: 01628 682555

MAIDSTONE
Corn Exchange Complex/Hazlitt Theatre
Earl Street, Maidstone, Kent ME14 1PL
Theatre & Events Manager: Mandy Hare
Fax: 01622 602194
BO: 01622 758611   Admin: 01622 753922

MANCHESTER
Green Room
54-56 Whitworth Street West
Manchester M1 5WW
Website: www.greenroomarts.org
e-mail: info@greenroomarts.org
Artistic Director: Garfield Allen
Fax: 0161-615 0516
BO: 0161-615 0500   Admin: 0161-615 0515

MANCHESTER
The Lowry
Pier 8, Salford Quays M50 3AZ
Website: www.thelowry.com
e-mail: info@thelowry.com
Theatre Production Bookings: Louise Ormerod
Fax: 0161-876 2021
BO: 0870 1112000   Admin: 0870 1112020

MILFORD HAVEN
Torch Theatre, St Peter's Road
Milford Haven
Pembrokeshire SA73 2BU
Website: www.torchtheatre.org
e-mail: info@torchtheatre.co.uk
Artistic Director: Peter Doran
Fax: 01646 698919
BO: 01646 695267   Admin: 01646 694192

NEWCASTLE UPON TYNE
The Round
34 Lime Street, Ouseburn
Newcastle Upon Tyne NE1 2PQ
Website: www.the-round.com
e-mail: info@the-round.com
Theatre Manager: Ben Fletcher-Watson   Tel: 0191-260 5605

NEWPORT (Isle of Wight)
Quay Arts
Sea Street
Newport Harbour
Isle of Wight PO30 5BD
Website: www.quayarts.org
Fax: 01983 526606   Tel: 01983 822490

NORWICH
Norwich Arts Centre
St Benedicts Street
Norwich, Norfolk NR2 4PG
Website: www.norwichartscentre.co.uk
e-mail: stuarthobday@norwichartscentre.co.uk
BO: 01603 660352   Admin: 01603 660387

NUNEATON
Abbey Theatre & Arts Centre
Pool Bank Street
Nuneaton, Warks CV11 5DB
Website: www.abbeytheatre.co.uk
e-mail: admin@abbeytheatre.co.uk
Chairman: Tony Deeming
Tel: 024-7632 7359   BO: 024-7635 4090

PLYMOUTH
Plymouth Arts Centre
38 Looe Street
Plymouth, Devon PL4 0EB
Website: www.plymouthac.org.uk
e-mail: arts@plymouthac.org.uk
Director: Ian Hutchinson
Fax: 01752 206118   Tel: 01752 206114

POOLE
Lighthouse Poole Centre for The Arts
Kingland Road
Poole, Dorset BH15 1UG
Website: www.lighthousepoole.co.uk
BO/Admin: 08700 668701

RADLETT
The Radlett Centre
1 Aldenham Avenue
Radlett, Herts WD7 8HL
Website: www.radlettcentre.co.uk
Fax: 01923 857592   Tel: 01923 857546

ROTHERHAM
Rotherham Theatres
Walker Place, Rotherham, South Yorkshire S65 1JH
Website: www.rotherham.gov.uk
Strategic Leader Culture/Leisure/
Lifelong Learning: Phil Rodgers
BO: 01709 823621   Admin: 01709 823641

SALISBURY
Salisbury Arts Centre
Bedwin Street, Salisbury, Wiltshire SP1 3UT
e-mail: info@salisburyarts.co.uk
Fax: 01722 343030   BO: 01722 321744

SHREWSBURY
Shrewsbury & District Arts Association
The Gateway, Chester Street
Shrewsbury, Shropshire SY1 1NB
e-mail: gateway.centre@shropshire-cc.gov.uk
                                    Tel: 01743 355159

SOUTHPORT
Southport Arts Centre
Lord Street, Southport, Merseyside PR8 1DB
Website: www.seftonarts.co.uk
e-mail: artsops@seftonarts.co.uk
BO: 01704 540011   Admin: 0151-934 2131

STAMFORD
Stamford Arts Centre
27 St Mary's Street, Stamford, Lincolnshire PE9 2DL
Website: www.stamfordartscentre.co.uk
General Manager: David Popple
Fax: 01780 766690
BO: 01780 763203   Admin: 01780 480846

STIRLING
MacRobert
University of Stirling, Stirling FK9 4LA
Website: www.macrobert.org
Director: Liz Moran
BO: 01786 466666   Admin: 01786 467155

SWANSEA
Taliesin Arts Centre
University of Wales Swansea
Singleton Park, Swansea SA2 8PZ
Website: www.taliesinartscentre.co.uk
e-mail: s.e.crouch@swansea.ac.uk
Head of Cultural Services: Sybil Crouch   Tel: 01792 295238

SWINDON
Wyvern Theatre
Theatre Square, Swindon, Wiltshire SN1 1QN
BO: 01793 524481   Admin: 01793 535534

TAUNTON
Brewhouse Theatre & Arts Centre
Coal Orchard, Taunton, Somerset TA1 1JL
Website: www.thebrewhouse.net
e-mail: info@thebrewhouse.net
Director: Robert Miles
BO: 01823 283244   Admin: 01823 274608

TOTNES
Dartington Arts
The Barn, Dartington Hall, Totnes, Devon TQ9 6DE
e-mail: info@dartingtonarts.org.uk
BO: 01803 847070   Admin: 01803 847074

TUNBRIDGE WELLS
Trinity Theatre, Church Road
Tunbridge Wells, Kent TN1 1JP
Director: Jonathan Salisbury
BO: 01892 678678   Admin: 01892 678670

ULEY
Prema
South Street, Uley, Nr Dursley, Glos GL11 5SS
Website: www.prema.demon.co.uk
e-mail: info@prema.demon.co.uk
Director: Gordon Scott   Tel: 01453 860703

VALE OF GLAMORGAN
St Donats Arts Centre
St Donats Castle, The Vale of Glamorgan CF61 1WF
e-mail: janetsmith@stdonats.com
General Manager: Janet Smith
Fax: 01446 799101
BO: 01446 799100   Tel: 01446 799099

WAKEFIELD
Wakefield Arts Centre
Wakefield College
Thornes Park Centre
Thornes Park, Horbury Road
Wakefield WF2 8QZ
Website: www.theatreroyalwakefield.co.uk
BO: 01924 211311   Admin: 01924 215531

WALLSEND
Buddle Arts Centre
258B Station Road, Wallsend, Tyne & Wear NE28 8RG
Contact: Geoffrey A Perkins
Fax: 0191-200 7142   Tel: 0191-200 7132

WASHINGTON
The Arts Centre Washington
Biddick Lane, Fatfield
Washington, Tyne & Wear NE38 8AB
Fax: 0191-219 3458   Tel: 0191-219 3455

WELLINGBOROUGH
The Castle, Castle Way
Wellingborough, Northants NN8 1XA
Website: www.thecastle.org.uk
e-mail: info@thecastle.org.uk
Executive Director: Gail Arnott
Fax: 01933 229888   Tel: 01933 229022

WIMBORNE
Layard Theatre
Canford School, Canford Magna
Wimborne, Dorset BH21 3AD
e-mail: layardtheatre@canford.com
Director of Drama: Stephen Hattersley
Administrator: Christine Haynes
BO/Fax: 01202 847525   Admin: 01202 847529

WINCHESTER
Tower Arts Centre
Romsey Road, Winchester, Hampshire SO22 5PW
Website: www.towerarts.co.uk
Director: John Tellett   Tel: 01962 867986

WINDSOR
Windsor Arts Centre
St Leonard's Road, Windsor, Berks SL4 3BL
Website: www.windsorartscentre.org
e-mail: admin@windsorartscentre.org
General Manager: Graham Steel
Fax: 01753 621527
BO: 01753 859336   Admin: 01753 859421

WREXHAM
Wrexham Arts Centre
Rhosddu Road, Wrexham LL11 1AU
e-mail: arts.centre@wrexham.gov.uk
Fax: 01978 292611   Tel: 01978 292093

ARTS COUNCIL ENGLAND, EAST
(Norfolk, Suffolk, Bedfordshire, Cambridgeshire, Essex, Hertfordshire and the unitary authorities of Luton, Peterborough, Southend-on-Sea and Thurrock)

Eden House, 48-49 Bateman Street
Cambridge CB2 1LR
Website: www.artscouncil.org.uk
Fax: 0870 2421271   Tel: 0845 3006200

ARTS COUNCIL ENGLAND, EAST MIDLANDS
(Derbyshire, Leicestershire, Lincolnshire excluding North and North East Lincolnshire, Northamptonshire, Nottinghamshire and the unitary authorities of Derby, Leicester, Nottingham and Rutland)

St Nicholas Court, 25-27 Castle Gate
Nottingham NG1 7AR
Website: www.artscouncil.org.uk
Fax: 0115-950 2467   Tel: 0845 3006200

ARTS COUNCIL ENGLAND, LONDON
(Greater London)

2 Pear Tree Court, London EC1R 0DS
Website: www.artscouncil.org.uk
Fax: 020-7608 4100   Tel: 0845 3006200

ARTS COUNCIL ENGLAND, NORTH EAST
(Durham, Northumberland, Metropolitan authorities of Gateshead, Newcastle upon Tyne, North Tyneside, South Tyneside, Sunderland and the unitary authorities of Darlington, Hartlepool, Middlesborough, Red Car and Cleveland, Stockton-on-Tees)

Central Square, Forth Street
Newcastle upon Tyne NE1 3PJ
Website: www.artscouncil.org.uk
Fax: 0191-230 1020   Tel: 0845 3006200

ARTS COUNCIL ENGLAND, NORTH WEST
(Lancashire, Cheshire, Cumbria and the metropolitan authorities of Bolton, Bury, Knowsley, Liverpool, Manchester, Oldham, Rochdale, St Helens, Salford, Sefton, Stockport, Tameside, Trafford, Wigan, Wirral and the unitary authorities of Blackburn with Darwen, Blackpool, Halton and Warrington)

Manchester House, 22 Bridge Street
Manchester M3 3AB
Website: www.artscouncil.org.uk
Fax: 0161-834 6969   Tel: 0845 3006200

ARTS COUNCIL ENGLAND, SOUTH EAST
(Buckinghamshire, East Sussex, Hampshire, Isle of Wight, Kent, Oxfordshire, Surrey, West Sussex and the unitary authorities of Bracknell Forest. Brighton & Hove, Medway Towns, Milton Keynes, Portsmouth)

Sovereign House, Church Street, Brighton BN1 1RA
Website: www.artscouncil.org.uk
Fax: 0870 2421257   Tel: 0845 3006200

ARTS COUNCIL ENGLAND, SOUTH WEST
(Cornwall, Devon, Dorset, Gloucestershire, Somerset and Wiltshire and the unitary authorities of Bristol, Bath, Bournemouth, Plymouth, Poole, Torbay and Swindon)

Senate Court
Southernhay Gardens
Exeter, Devon EX1 1UG
Website: www.artscouncil.org.uk
Fax: 01392 229229   Tel: 0845 3006200

ARTS COUNCIL ENGLAND, WEST MIDLANDS
(Herefordshire, Worcestershire, Staffordshire, Warwickshire and Shropshire, Stoke-on-Trent, Telford and Wrekin and districts of Birmingham, Coventry, Dudley, Sandwell, Solihull, Walsall & Wolverhampton)

82 Granville Street
Birmingham B1 2LH
Website: www.artscouncil.org.uk
Fax: 0121-643 7239   Tel: 0845 3006200

ARTS COUNCIL ENGLAND, YORKSHIRE
(North Yorkshire, metropolitan authorities of Barnsley, Bradford, Calderdale, Doncaster, Kirklees, Leeds, Rotherham, Sheffield, Wakefield and the unitary authorities of East Riding of Yorkshire, Kingston upon Hull, North Lincolnshire, North East Lincolnshire, York)

21 Bond Street
Dewsbury
West Yorkshire WF13 1AX
Website: www.artscouncil.org.uk
Fax: 01924 466522   Tel: 0845 3006200

ARTS COUNCIL OF WALES, NORTH WALES OFFICE
(Isle of Anglesey, Gwynedd, Conwy, Denbighshire, Flintshire, Wrexham)

36 Prince's Drive, Colwyn Bay
Conwy LL29 8LA
Website: www.artswales.org
Fax: 01492 533677   Tel: 01492 533440

ARTS COUNCIL OF WALES, SOUTH WALES OFFICE
(Vale of Glamorgan, Cardiff, Newport, Monmouthshire, Torfaen, Blaenau Gwent, Caerphilly, Merthyr Tydfil, Rhonda Cynon Taff, Bridgend)

9 Museum Place
Cardiff CF10 3NX
Website: www.artswales.org
Fax: 029-2022 1447   Tel: 029-2037 6525

ARTS COUNCIL OF WALES, MID & WEST WALES OFFICE
(Ceredigion, Carmarthenshire, Pembrokeshire, Powys, Swansea, Neath & Port Talbot)

6 Gardd Llydaw, Jacksons Lane
Carmarthen SA31 1QD
Website: www.artswales.org
Fax: 01267 233084   Tel: 01267 234248

A C A CASTING
(Catherine Arton)
32A Edenvale Street, London SW6 2SF
e-mail: catherine@acacasting.com   Tel/Fax: 020-7384 2635

ADAMSON Jo CDG
c/o Northern Spirit Productions Ltd
4 Pollard Lane
Leeds LS13 1EY
e-mail: jo@joadamson-jacasting.co.uk   Mobile: 07787 311270

c/o International Collective Casting
Golden Cross House
8 Duncannon Street
The Strand, London WC2N 4JF
Website: www.internationalcollective.co.uk
e-mail: casting@castingcollective.co.uk
Fax: 020-7484 5100   Tel: 020-7484 5080

AILION Pippa CDG
3 Towton Road, London SE27 9EE
e-mail: enquiries@pippaailioncasting.co.uk
                                     Tel/Fax: 020-8670 4816

ALL DIRECTIONS OF LONDON
7 Rupert Court
Off Wardour Street
London W1D 6EB   Tel: 020-7437 5879

ANDERSON Jane
e-mail: andersoncasting@yahoo.co.uk

ANDREW Dorothy CASTING
Campus Manor
Childwall Abbey Road
Childwall, Liverpool L16 0JP
Fax: 0151-722 9079   Tel: 0151-737 4044

AP CASTING
(Annelie Powell)
21 Tibberton Square
London N1 8SF
e-mail: apcasting@gmail.com   Mobile: 07821 440422

ASHTON HINKINSON CASTING
1 Charlotte Street, London W1T 1RD
Website: www.ashtonhinkinson.com
e-mail: casting@ahcasting.com
Fax: 020-7636 1657   Tel: 020-7580 6101

BAIG Shaheen CASTING
343B Archway Road, London N6 5AA
e-mail: shaheen.baig@btconnect.com   Tel: 020-8348 2039

BALDIES CASTING AGENCY
(The only agency purely for bald people)
6 Marlott Road
Poole, Dorset BH15 3DX
Mobile: 07860 290437   Tel: 01202 666001

BARNES Derek CDG
BBC DRAMA SERIES CASTING
BBC Elstree, Room N221
Neptune House, Clarendon Road
Borehamwood, Herts WD6 1JF
Fax: 020-8228 8311   Tel: 020-8228 7096

BATH Andrea
85 Brightwell Road
Watford WD18 0HR
e-mail: andreabath@btinternet.com   Tel: 01923 333067

BEARDSALL Sarah CDG
73 Wells Street, London W1T 3QG
e-mail: casting@beardsall.com
Fax: 020-7436 8859   Tel: 020-7323 4040

C

Casting Directors

For information regarding membership of
the Casting Directors' Guild (CDG) please contact

PO Box 34403
London W6 0YG
e-mail: info@thecdg.co.uk
Website: www.thecdg.co.uk

Concert & Exhibition Halls
Concert Promoters & Agents
Consultants
Costumes, Wigs & Make-up
Critics

[CONTACTS 2008]

Chook Sibtain

Photography by

ANGUS DEUCHAR

t. 020 8286 3303
m. 07973 600728

www.ActorsPhotos.co.uk

Peta Lily

BEATTIE Victoria
Scottish Office: Out of The Blue @ The Drill Hall
36 Dalmeny Street, Edinburgh EH6 8RG
e-mail: victoria@victoriabeattie.com   Tel: 0131-553 0559

BECKLEY Rowland
BBC DRAMA SERIES CASTING
BBC Elstree, Room N222, Neptune House
Clarendon Road, Borehamwood, Herts WD6 1JF
Fax: 020-8228 8311   Tel: 020-8228 7130

BERTRAND Leila CASTING
53 Hormead Road, London W9 3NQ
e-mail: leilabcasting@aol.com   Tel/Fax: 020-8964 0683

BEVAN Lucy
c/o Twickenham Studios, St Margaret's
Twickenham TW1 2AW   Tel: 020-8607 8888

BEWICK Maureen CASTING
104A Dartmouth Road, London NW2 4HB

BEXFIELD Glenn
35 Cephas Avenue, London E1 4AT
e-mail: glenn.bexfield@btinternet.com
Mobile: 07803 889218

BILL The
Thames Television Ltd, Talkbackthames Studios
1 Deer Park Road, Merton
London SW19 3TL   Tel: 020-8540 0600

BIRD Sarah CDG
PO Box 32658, London W14 0XA
Fax: 020-7602 8601   Tel: 020-7371 3248

BIRKETT Hannah CASTING
26 Noko, 3/6 Banister Road, London W10 4AR
e-mail: hannah@hbcasting.com
Mobile: 07957 114175   Tel: 020-8960 2848

BRACKE Siobhan CDG
Basement Flat, 22A The Barons
St Margaret's TW1 2AP   Tel: 020-8891 5686

BROAD CASTING COMPANY
(Lesley Beastall & Sophie North)
e-mail: lesley@broad-casting.co.uk
e-mail: sophie@broad-casting.co.uk
Mobile: 07956 516603 (Lesley)   Mobile: 07956 516606 (Sophie)

BROWNING Grace
See CASTING COMPANY (UK) The

BUCKINGHAM Jo
(Entertainment - Comedy)
BBC Television Centre, Wood Lane, London W12 7RJ
Fax: 020-8576 4414   Tel: 020-8225 7585

CANDID CASTING
1st Floor, 32 Great Sutton Street, London EC1V 0NB
e-mail: mail@candidcasting.co.uk
Fax: 020-7490 8966   Tel: 020-7490 8882

CANNON DUDLEY & ASSOCIATES
43A Belsize Square, London NW3 4HN
e-mail: cdacasting@blueyonder.co.uk
Fax: 020-7813 2048   Tel: 020-7433 3393

CANNON John CDG
BBC DRAMA SERIES CASTING
BBC Elstree, Room N222
Neptune House, Clarendon Road
Borehamwood, Herts WD6 1JF
Fax: 020-8228 8311   Tel: 020-8228 7130

CARLING Di CASTING CDG
1st Floor, 49 Frith Street, London W1D 4SG
Fax: 020-7287 6844   Tel: 020-7287 6446

Who are Casting Directors?

Casting directors are employed by directors / production companies to source the best available actors for roles across TV, film, radio, theatre and commercials. They do the ground-work and present a shortlist of artists to the director, who often makes the final selection. Many casting directors work on a freelance basis, others are employed permanently by larger organisations such as the BBC or the National Theatre. Discovering new and emerging talent also plays an important part in their job.

How should I use these listings?

If you are an actor looking for work, you can promote yourself directly to casting directors by sending them your photo and details. They may keep these on file and consider you for future productions. Research the names and companies listed in the following pages so that you can target your letters accordingly. It helps to keep an eye on TV / film / theatre credits so you are familiar with previous productions they have cast. If a casting director has 'CDG' after their name, it means they are a member of the Casting Directors' Guild www.thecdg.co.uk, the professional organisation of casting directors working in the UK. Remember, casting professionals receive hundreds of letters every week, so try to keep them short, concise, professional and free of 'gimmicks'. Make sure your CV is up-to-date and all the information is accurate and spelt correctly. Never lie: the chances are you will be found out and it may damage your reputation. Your photo should be as recent as possible and an accurate likeness: you are wasting everyone's time if you turn up to an audition looking nothing like it. Remember to label it clearly with your name. Only send a showreel if you have checked with the casting director first. It helps to have a focus to your letter, such as inviting the casting director to see you in a current performance or showcase.

How do I prepare for a casting / audition?

Make sure you are fully prepared with accurate information about the audition time, venue, format and the people you will be meeting. Unless it's a last minute casting, you should always read the script in advance and try to have some opinions on it. If you are asked in advance to prepare a piece, always stick to the brief with something suitable and relevant. On the day, allow plenty of time to get there so you are not flustered when you arrive. Try to be positive and enjoy yourself. Remember, the casting director doesn't want to spend several days auditioning - they want you to get the job! Never criticise previous productions you have worked on. And at the end of the casting, remember to take your script away unless you are asked to leave it, otherwise it can look as if you're not interested.

Should I attend a casting in a house or flat?

Professional auditions are rarely held anywhere other than an official casting studio or venue. Be very wary if you are asked to go elsewhere. Trust your instincts. If something doesn't seem right to you, it probably isn't. Always take someone with you if you are in any doubt

How do I become a casting director?

The best way to gain experience in this field is to work as a casting assistant. Vacancies are sometimes advertised in The Stage. You may also find it useful to contact The Casting Directors' Guild www.thecdg.co.uk

the Casting Directors' Guild of Great Britain

If you see CDG after a Casting Director's name, you know he / she is a member of The Casting Directors' Guild and have at least five years' experience. The current CDG Committee has prepared the following advice in the hope it will prove a useful guide to actors.

Casting directors are there to help actors and not to hinder them. We want you to do your best as it reflects back on us. It is a total misconception that we are there to prevent actors getting jobs. Casting directors are answerable to Networks, Studios, Producers and Directors and we are given briefs to CAST. Sometimes, during the casting process, visions and budgets can change ... and that means roles can sometimes change. Sadly we do not have control over this.

Firstly, when asked to attend an interview or audition, an actor should feel confident in asking his/her agent relevant questions about the role. If this is not forthcoming, arrive early and seek information from the casting director or, better still, contact him/her the day before. If it is only possible to speak to the casting director on the day, preferably do so before entering the audition room, rather than in front of the Director / Producer. The casting director will be more than happy to help. If possible, read the entire play / screenplay rather than just the scenes your 'character' appears in, and, ideally, be able to talk about the script as a whole during the interview.

Actors are a fundamental tool of this industry: CDG members are aware of this and aim to put actors at their ease during interviews. It is hoped actors realise that casting directors are only as good as the actors they submit for each role.

There will naturally be disappointment on not getting a role. There are many reasons why one actor will be chosen over another, which explains why even the best audition might not necessarily secure a part. The physical image of the actor comes into play. Is he / she too young, too mature, not fit enough to play a PE instructor or Olympic athlete? There is also the frustrating problem of scripts, and parts, being re-written. A character may have an entirely different physical description in a later draft. Not getting a role should in no way diminish an actor's confidence and determination.

When it comes to contacting casting directors, most are happy to receive letters, updated photos and CVs. Letters should be brief and CVs well laid out, with relevant info e.g. production/director/venue clearly stated. Casting directors rarely like unsolicited DVDs and showreels: you must be aware that we do get inundated. Also be aware that not receiving a response to your letter does not mean it hasn't been read and filed: it is virtually impossible to reply to the volume of mail received from actors.

If work is thin on the ground, getting a temporary / flexible job elsewhere is no bad thing. It will put money in your bank, keep your spirits up, perhaps give you another skill, and generally raise your confidence. It is not in the least demeaning, and casting directors will admire your enterprise!

For more information about the CDG please visit www.thecdg.co.uk

Sally George

RUTH MULHOLLAND
Photographer

07939 516987

www.ruthmulholland.co.uk

Suzanne Maddock

CARROLL Anji CDG
4 Nesfield Drive
Winterley, Cheshire CW11 4NT
e-mail: anjicarrollcdg@yahoo.co.uk   Tel: 01270 250240

CASTING COMPANY (UK) The
(Michelle Guish, Grace Browning)
3rd Floor, 112-114 Wardour Street
London W1F 0TS
Fax: 020-7434 2346   Tel: 020-7734 4954

CASTING CONNECTION The
(Michael Syers)
Dalrossie House, 16 Victoria Grove
Stockport, Cheshire SK4 5BU
Fax: 0161-442 7280   Tel: 0161-432 4122

CASTING COUCH The
(Moira Townsend)
e-mail: moiratownsend@yahoo.co.uk Mobile: 07932 785807

CASTING UK
10 Coptic Street, London WC1A 1NH
Website: www.castinguk.com
e-mail: info@castinguk.com   Tel: 020-7580 3456

CATLIFF Suzy CDG
PO Box 39492, London N10 3YX
e-mail: soose@soose.co.uk   Tel: 020-8442 0749

CELEX CASTING Ltd
PO Box 7317, Derby DE1 0GS
Website: www.celex.co.uk   e-mail: enquiries@celex.co.uk
Fax: 01332 232115   Tel: 01332 232445

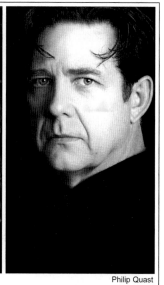

Paul Fox   Helena Blackman   Philip Quast

Nick james

PHOTOGRAPHER

STUDENT RATES   www.nickjamesphotography.co.uk   07961 122030

Valerie Colgan

- For professional actors who need a voice production "MOT"
- Private individual classes
- Valerie Colgan and a consortium of tutors as appropriate.

Ex Head of Drama at the City Lit • **5 Drama Schools** • **The Actors Centre**

Tel: 020 7267 2153 The Green, 17 Herbert Street, London NW5 4HA

CHAND Urvashi CDG
Cinecraft, 115A Kilburn Lane
London W10 4AN
e-mail: urvashi@cinecraft.biz   Tel/Fax: 020-8968 7016

CHARD Alison CDG
23 Groveside Court
4 Lombard Road
Battersea, London SW11 3RQ
e-mail: alisonchard@castingdirector.freeserve.co.uk
Tel/Fax: 020-7223 9125

CHARKHAM CASTING
(Beth Charkham)
Suite 361
14 Tottenham Court Road
London W1T 1JY
e-mail: charkhamcasting@btconnect.com
Mobile: 07956 456630

CLARK Andrea
PO Box 28895, London SW13 0WG
e-mail: andrea@aclarkcasting.com   Tel: 020-8876 6869

CLAYTON Rosalie CDG
e-mail: rosalie@rosalieclayton.com   Tel/Fax: 020-7242 8109

COGAN Ben
BBC DRAMA SERIES CASTING
BBC Elstree, Room N221
Neptune House, Clarendon Road
Borehamwood, Herts WD6 1JF
Fax: 020-8228 8311   Tel: 020-8228 7516

COHEN Abi CASTING
London
e-mail: cohencasting@tinyonline.co.uk   Tel: 020-7687 9002

COHEN Yona
9 Seymour Road
Hampton Wick KT1 4HN

COLLINS Jayne CASTING CDG
4th Floor
20 Bedford Street
London WC2E 9HP
Website: www.jaynecollinscasting.com
e-mail: info@jaynecollinscasting.com
Fax: 020-7422 0015   Tel: 020-7422 0014

COMMERCIALS CASTING UK Ltd
(Michelle Smith)
220 Church Lane, Stockport SK7 1PQ
Fax: 0161-439 0622   Tel: 0161-439 6825

CORDORAY Lin
66 Cardross Street
London W6 0DR

COTTON Irene CDG
25 Druce Road
Dulwich Village
London SE21 7DW
e-mail: irenecotton@btinternet.com
Tel/Fax: 020-8299 2787   Tel: 020-8299 1595

CRAMPSIE Julia
(Casting Executive)
BBC DRAMA SERIES CASTING
BBC Elstree, Room N224
Neptune House
Clarendon Road
Borehamwood, Herts WD6 1JF
Fax: 020-8228 8311   Tel: 020-8228 7170

CRANE Carole CASTING
e-mail: crane.shot@virgin.net   Mobile: 07976 869442

CRAWFORD Kahleen CASTING
Film City Glasgow
4 Summertown Road
Glasgow G51 2LY
Website: www.kahleencrawford.com
e-mail: kahleen@kahleencrawford.com
Mobile: 07950 414164   Tel: 0141-425 1725

CROCODILE CASTING COMPANY The
(Claire Toeman & Tracie Saban)
9 Ashley Close
Hendon, London NW4 1PH
Website: www.crocodilecasting.com
e-mail: croccast@aol.com
Fax: 020-8203 7711   Tel: 020-8203 7009

CROSS Louise
128A North View Road
London N8 7LP   Tel: 020-8341 2200

CROWE Sarah CASTING
75 Amberley Road
London W9 2JL
e-mail: sarah@sarahcrowecasting.co.uk
Fax: 020-7286 5030   Tel: 020-7286 5080

CROWLEY POOLE CASTING
11 Goodwins Court
London WC2N 4LL
Fax: 020-7379 5971   Tel: 020-7379 5965

CROWLEY Suzanne CDG
(See CROWLEY POOLE CASTING)

DAVIES Jane CASTING Ltd
(Jane Davies CDG & John Connor CDG)
PO Box 680, Sutton
Surrey SM1 3ZG
e-mail: info@janedaviescasting.co.uk
Fax: 020-8644 9746   Tel: 020-8715 1036

DAVIS Leo (Miss)
(JUST CASTING)
20th Century Theatre
291 Westbourne Grove
London W11 2QA
Fax: 020-7792 2143   Tel: 020-7229 3471

DAVY Gary CDG
1st Floor, 55-59 Shaftesbury Avenue
London W1D 6LD
Fax: 020-7437 0881   Tel: 020-7437 0880

DAWES Gabrielle CDG
PO Box 52493, London NW3 9DZ
e-mail: gdawescasting@tiscali.co.uk   Tel: 020-7435 3645

DAY Kate CDG
Pound Cottage
27 The Green South
Warborough, Oxon OX10 7DR   Tel/Fax: 01865 858709

DE FREITAS Paul CDG
PO Box 4903, London W1A 7JZ

DENMAN Jack CASTING
Burgess House
Main Street
Farnsfield, Notts NG22 8EF   Tel/Fax: 01623 882272

Simon Bowman

Lindsey Coulson

Martin Freeman

DAVID LAWRENCE PHOTOGRAPHY

Eva Gray

www.davidlawrencephoto.co.uk
david@davidlawrencephoto.co.uk
020 8858 2820

Paul Fox

Stéphan Grégoire
photographer

07869 141510

www.studio-sg.com

Headshots - Production - Publicity

DENNISON Lee ASSOCIATES
(London & New York)
Fushion (London Office)
27 Old Gloucester Street
London WC1N 3XX
Website: www.ukscreen.com/crew/Idennison
e-mail: leedennison@fushion-uk.com
Fax: 08700 111020 Tel: 08700 111100

DICKENS Laura CDG
197 Malpas Road, London SE4 1BH
e-mail: dickenscasting@aol.com Mobile: 07958 665468

DOWD Kate
74 Wells Street, London W1T 3QG
Fax: 020-7580 6688 Tel: 020-7580 8866

DRURY Malcolm CDG
34 Tabor Road, London W6 0BW Tel: 020-8748 9232

DUDLEY Carol CDG
(See CANNON DUDLEY & ASSOCIATES)

DUFF Julia CDG
73 Wells Street, London W1T 3QG
Fax: 020-7436 8859 Tel: 020-7436 8860

DUFF Maureen CDG
PO Box 47340, London NW3 4TY
e-mail: belgrove@dircon.co.uk
Fax: 020-7681 7172 Tel: 020-7586 0532

DUFFY Jennifer CDG
11 Portsea Mews
London W2 2BN Tel: 020-7262 3326

EAST Irene CASTING CDG
40 Brookwood Avenue
Barnes, London SW13 0LR
e-mail: irneast@aol.com Tel: 020-8876 5686

EJ CASTING
150 Tooley Street, London SE1 2TU
e-mail: info@ejcasting.com
Mobile: 07891 632946 Tel: 020-7564 2688

EMMERSON Chloe
96 Portobello Road
London W11 2QG
e-mail: c@ChloeEmmerson.com Tel: 020-7792 8823

ET-NIK-A PRIME MANAGEMENT & CASTINGS Ltd
30 Great Portland Street
London W1W 8QU
Website: www.etnikapmc.com
e-mail: info@etnikapmc.com
Fax: 020-7299 3558 Tel: 020-7299 3555

EVANS Kate CASTING
Basement Museum House
24 Museum Street, London WC1A 1JT
e-mail: kateevanscasting@hotmail.co.uk
Mobile: 07976 252531

EVANS Richard CDG
10 Shirley Road
London W4 1DD
Website: www.evanscasting.co.uk
e-mail: contact@evanscasting.co.uk Tel: 020-8994 6304

EYE CASTING The
51 Hoxton Square
London N1 6PB
Website: www.theeyecasting.com
e-mail: jody@theeyecasting.com
Mobile: 07950 263499 Tel: 020-7729 9705

FEARNLEY Ali
26 Goodge Street, London W1T 2QG
e-mail: cast@alifearnley.com
Fax: 020-7636 8080   Tel: 020-7636 4040

FIGGIS Susie
19 Spencer Rise
London NW5 1AR   Tel: 020-7482 2200

FILDES Bunny CASTING CDG
56 Wigmore Street, London W1   Tel: 020-7935 1254

FINCHER Sally CDG
e-mail: sally.fincher@btinternet.com Tel: 020-8347 5945

FOX CASTING
Pinewood Studios, Pinewood Road
Iver Heath, Bucks SL0 0NH
e-mail: julie.fox@virgin.net   Tel: 01753 656848

FOX Celestia
23 Leppoc Road, London SW4 9LS
e-mail: celestia.fox@virgin.net   Tel: 020-7720 6143

FRAZER Janie CDG
ITV/Granada, London TV Centre
South Bank, London SE1 9LT
e-mail: janie.frazer@granadamedia.com Tel: 020-7261 3848

FRECK Rachel CDG
e-mail: casting@rachelfreck.com   Tel/Fax: 020-8673 2455

FREND Amanda
87 Swindon Road
Horsham, West Sussex RH12 2HF
e-mail: amandafrendcasting@hotmail.co.uk

FRISBY Jane CASTING CDG
51 Ridge Road, London N8 9LJ
e-mail: jane.frisby@tiscali.co.uk   Tel: 020-8341 4747

FUNNELL Caroline CDG
25 Rattray Road, London SW2 1AZ   Tel: 020-7326 4417

GALLIE Joyce
37 Westcroft Square, London W6 0TA   Tel: 020-8741 4009

GANE CASTING
(Natasha Gane)
52 Woodhouse Road, London N12 0RJ
e-mail: natasha@ganecasting.com
Fax: 020-8446 2508   Tel: 020-8446 2551

GB CASTING UK Ltd (Karin Grainger)
65F Rowley Way, Abbey Road, London, NW8 0SJ
e-mail: kggbuk@lineone.net
Mobile: 07901 553075   Tel: 020-7328 8815

GILLHAM Tracey CDG
(Entertainment - Comedy)
BBC Television Centre
Wood Lane, London W12 7RJ
Fax: 020-8576 4414   Tel: 020-8225 8488

GILLON Tamara CASTING
26 Carson Road, London SE21 8HU
e-mail: tamaragillon@yahoo.co.uk
Fax: 020-8265 6330   Tel: 020-8766 0099

GOLD Nina CDG
117 Chevening Road, London NW6 6DU
e-mail: info@ninagold.co.uk
Fax: 020-8968 6777   Tel: 020-8960 6099

GOOCH Miranda CASTING
102 Leighton Gardens
London NW10 3PR
e-mail: mirandagooch@gmail.com
Fax: 020-8962 9579   Tel: 020-8962 9578

GREENE Francesca CASTING
79 Ashworth Mansions
London W9 1LN
e-mail: francesca@francescagreene.co.uk
       Tel: 020-7286 5957

GREEN Jill CASTING CDG
PO Box 56927
London N10 3UR   Tel: 0845 4786343

GRESHAM Marcia CDG
3 Langthorne Street
London SW6 6JT   Tel: 020-7381 2876

GROSVENOR CASTING
(Angela Grosvenor CDG)
27 Rowena Crescent, London SW11 2PT
Fax: 020-7652 6256   Tel: 020-7738 0449

GUISH Michelle
See CASTING COMPANY (UK) The

HALL David CASTING
2 The Shrubbery
2 Lavender Gardens, London SW11 1DL
Mobile: 07950 526599   Tel: 020-7223 4382

HALL Janet
69 Buckstones Road
Shaw, Oldham OL2 8DW
e-mail: stage@hall257.fsbusiness.co.uk
Mobile: 07956 822773   Tel: 01706 291459

HALL Pippa
(Children & Teenagers only)
Rosebank, High Street
Blockley, Glos GL56 9EX
e-mail: pippa@pippahallcasting.com   Tel/Fax: 01386 700227

HAMILTON Des
Website: www.deshamilton.com
e-mail: deshamilton@aol.com   Mobile: 07931 333792

HAMMOND Louis
30-31 Peter Street, London W1F 0AR
Fax: 020-7439 2522   Tel: 020-7734 0626

HANCOCK Gemma CDG
The Rosary, Broad Street
Cuckfield, West Sussex RH17 5DL
e-mail: gemma.hancock@virgin.net   Tel: 01444 441398

HARKIN Julie CDG
154 Vartry Road, London N15 6HA
e-mail: julieharkincasting@googlemail.com
       Tel: 020-8800 4226

Brenda
Fricker

Ortis
Deley

Hannah
Waterman

LYDIA LEONARD

ROB STOTT

JAMEL RODRIGUEZ

STEFAN LACANDLER
PHOTOGRAPHY

Tel: 020 8509 7420
M: 0794 975 7457

Web: www.lacandler.com
Email: stefan@lacandler.com

HARRIS Lisa
290 Coulsdon Road, Old Coulsdon
Surrey CR5 1EB   Mobile: 07956 561247

HAWSER Gillian CASTING
24 Cloncurry Street, London SW6 6DS
e-mail: gillianhawser@btinternet.com
Fax: 020-7731 0738   Tel: 020-7731 5988

HAYFIELD Judi CDG
Judy Hayfield Ltd
6 Richmond Hill Road
Gatley, Cheadle, Stockport SK8 1QG
e-mail: judi.hayfield@hotmail.co.uk   Mobile: 07919 221873

HILL Serena
Sydney Theatre Company
Pier 4, Hickson Road, Walsh Bay, NSW 2000, Australia
e-mail: shill@sydneytheatre.com.au   Tel: 00 612 925 01700

HOOTKINS Polly CDG
PO Box 52480, London NW3 9DH
e-mail: phootkins@clara.net   Tel: 020-7692 1184

HORAN Julia CDG
26 Falkland Road
London NW5 2PX   Tel: 020-7267 5261

HOWE Gary CASTING
34 Orbit Street, Roath
Cardiff CF24 0JX   Tel/Fax: 029-2045 3883

HUBBARD CASTING
(Ros Hubbard, John Hubbard, Dan Hubbard CDG)
14 Rathbone Place, London W1T 1HT
e-mail: email@hubbardcasting.com
Fax: 020-7636 7117   Tel: 020-7631 4944

HUGHES Sarah
BBC Television Centre
Wood Lane, London W12 7RJ
e-mail: shughes.casting@btinternet.com   Tel: 020-8225 8610

HUGHES Sylvia
Casting Suite, The Deanwater
Wilmslow Road,
Woodford, Cheshire SK7 1RJ
e-mail: sylviahughescastingdirector@hotmail.co.uk
Mobile: 07770 520007   Tel/Fax: 01565 653777

INTERNATIONAL COLLECTIVE CASTING
(See ADAMSON Jo CDG)

JACKSON Sue
53 Moseley Wood Walk
Leeds LS16 7HQ   Tel: 0113-267 0819

JAFFA Janis CASTING CDG
67 Starfield Road
London W12 9SN
e-mail: janis@janisjaffacasting.co.uk
Fax: 020-8743 9561   Tel: 020-7565 2877

JAFFREY Jennifer
136 Hicks Avenue
Greenford, Middlesex UB6 8HB
e-mail: jaffreymag@aol.com
Fax: 020-8575 0369   Tel: 020-8578 2899

JAY Jina CASTING CDG
Office 2, Sound Centre
Twickenham Film Studios
The Barons, St Margarets
Twickenham, Middlesex TW1 2AW
Fax: 020-8607 8982   Tel: 020-8607 8888

JELOWICKI Ilenka
(Mad Dog Casting Ltd)
15 Leighton Place, London NW5 2QL
e-mail: ilenka@maddogcasting.com
Fax: 020-7284 2689   Tel: 020-7482 4703

JENKINS Lucy CDG
Royal Shakespeare Company
35 Clapham High Street
London SW4 7TW
e-mail: lucy.jenkins@rsc.org.uk
Fax: 020-7498 0472   Tel: 020-7622 8773

JN PRODUCTION
5A Penton Street, London N1 9PT
e-mail: james@jnproduction.net
Fax: 020-7278 8855   Tel: 020-7278 8800

JOHN Priscilla CDG
PO Box 22477, London W6 0GT
Fax: 020-8741 4005   Tel: 020-8741 4212

JOHNSON Alex CASTING
15 McGregor Road
London W11 1DE
e-mail: alex@alexjon.demon.co.uk
Fax: 020-7229 1665   Tel: 020-7229 8779

JOHNSON Marilyn CDG
1st Floor, 11 Goodwins Court
London WC2N 4LL
e-mail: casting@marilynjohnsoncasting.com
Fax: 020-7497 5530   Tel: 020-7497 5552

JONES Doreen CDG
PO Box 22478, London W6 0WJ
Fax: 020-8748 8533   Tel: 020-8746 3782

JONES Sue CDG
e-mail: casting@suejones.net
Fax: 020-8838 1130   Tel: 020-8838 5153

KENNEDY Anna CASTING
8 Rydal Road
London SW16 1QN
e-mail: anna@kennedycasting.com   Tel: 020-8677 6710

KEOGH Beverley CASTING Ltd
29 Ardwick Green North
Ardwick Green, Manchester M12 6DL
e-mail: beverley@beverleykeogh.tv
Fax: 0161-273 4401   Tel: 0161-273 4400

KESTER Gaby
e-mail: casting@gabykester.com

KIBBEY Leoni CASTING
Website: www.leonikibbey.com
e-mail: casting@leonikibbey.com
Mobile: 07855 313552   Tel: 01727 832423

KNIGHT-SMITH Jerry CDG
Royal Exchange Theatre Company
St Ann's Square, Manchester M2 7DH
Fax: 0161-615 6691   Tel: 0161-615 6761

KOREL Suzy CDG
20 Blenheim Road
London NW8 0LX
e-mail: suzy@korel.org
Fax: 020-7372 3964   Tel: 020-7624 6435

KRUGER Beatrice
(FBI Casting)
46 via della Pelliccia, 00153 Roma, Italy
Website: www.fbicasting.com
e-mail: mail@fbicasting.it
Fax: 00 39 06 23328203   Tel: 00 39 06 58332747

KYLE CASTING Ltd
71B North Worple Way
Mortlake, London SW14 8PR
e-mail: kylecasting@btinternet.com   Tel: 020-8876 6763

LAYTON Claudie CASTING
(Claudie Layton & Alix Charpentier)
Unit 308, Canalot Studios
222 Kensal Road, London W10 5BN
e-mail: casting@claudielayton.com
Fax: 020-8968 1330   Tel: 020-8964 2055

LEVENE Jon
e-mail: jonlevene@mac.com
Mobile: 07977 570899   Tel: 020-7792 8501

ray fearon

jennifer james

john pearson

david james photography

07808 597362

www.davidjamesphotos.com

Actorscv.com
PRINT & WEBSITE SOLUTIONS

LEVINSON Sharon
30 Stratford Villas, London NW1 9SG
e-mail: sharonlev@blueyonder.co.uk   Tel: 020-7485 2057

LINDSAY-STEWART Karen CDG
PO Box 2301, London W1A 1PT
Fax: 020-7439 0548   Tel: 020-7439 0544

LIP SERVICE CASTING Ltd
(Voice-overs only)
60-66 Wardour Street, London W1F 0TA
Website: www.lipservice.co.uk
e-mail: bookings@lipservice.co.uk
Fax: 020-7734 3373   Tel: 020-7734 3393

LUNN Maggie
Unit HG14, Aberdeen Centre
22-24 Highbury Grove, London N5 2EA
e-mail: maggie@maggielunn.co.uk   Tel: 020-7226 7502

MAGSON Kay CDG
PO Box 175, Pudsey, Leeds LS28 7WY
e-mail: kay.magson@btinternet.com   Tel: 0113-236 0251

MANN Andrew
10 Coptic Street, London WC1A 1NH
Website: www.castinguk.com
e-mail: drew@castinguk.com   Tel: 020-7580 0456

MANNING John
4 Holmbury Gardens, Hayes
Middlesex UB3 2LU   Tel: 020-8573 5463

MARCH Heather CASTING
The Aberdeen Centre
22-24 Highbury Grove, London N5 2EA
Website: www.heathermarchcasting.com
e-mail: hm@heathermarchcasting.com
Fax: 020-7704 6085   Tel: 020-7704 6464

McCANN Joan CDG
26 Hereford Road, London W3 9JW
Fax: 020-8992 8715   Tel: 020-8993 1747

McLEOD Carolyn
PO Box 26495, London SE10 0WO
e-mail: carolyn@cmcasting.eclipse.co.uk
Tel/Fax: 07044 001720

McLEOD Thea
e-mail: mcleodcasting@hotmail.com
Mobile: 07941 541314   Tel: 020-8888 8993

McMURRICH Chrissie
16 Spring Vale Avenue
Brentford, Middlesex TW8 9QH   Tel: 020-8568 0137

McSHANE Sooki CDG
8A Piermont Road
East Dulwich, London SE22 0LN   Tel: 020-8693 7411

McWILLIAMS Debbie
e-mail: debbiemcwilliams@hotmail.com   Tel: 020-7493 7953

MEULENBERG Thea
Keizersgracht 116
1015 CW, Amsterdam, The Netherlands
Website: www.theameulenberg.com
e-mail: info@theameulenberg.com
Fax: 00 31 20 622 9894   Tel: 00 31 20 626 5846

MILLER Hannah CDG
Birmingham Repertory Theatre
Centenary Square, Broad Street
Birmingham B1 2EP   Tel: 0121-245 2023

MOISELLE Frank
7 Corrig Avenue, Dun Laoghaire, Co. Dublin, Ireland
Fax: 00 353 1 2803277   Tel: 00 353 1 2802857

MOISELLE Nuala
7 Corrig Avenue, Dun Laoghaire, Co. Dublin, Ireland
Fax: 00 353 1 2803277   Tel: 00 353 1 2802857

MOORE Stephen
BBC DRAMA SERIES CASTING
BBC Elstree, Room N222
Neptune House, Clarendon Road
Borehamwood, Herts WD6 1JF
Fax: 020-8228 8311   Tel: 020-8228 7109

MORGAN Andy CASTING
PO Box 52083, Coach House, London SW2 9DT
e-mail: andymorgancasting@btinternet.com
Tel: 020-8674 5375

MORRISON Melika
12A Rosebank, Holyport Road
London SW6 6LG   Tel/Fax: 020-7381 1571

MUGSHOTS
(Becky Kidd)
153 Buckhurst Avenue
Carshalton, Surrey SM5 1PD
e-mail: becky@mugshots.co.uk
Fax: 020-8296 8056   Tel: 020-8296 0393

NATIONAL THEATRE CASTING DEPARTMENT
(Head of Casting: Wendy Spon CDG, Deputy Head of
Casting: Alastair Coomer, Casting Assistant: Juliet Horsley)
Upper Ground, South Bank, London SE1 9PX
Fax: 020-7452 3340   Tel: 020-7452 3336

SUE JONES ("Nil By Mouth", "Human Traffic", "Ronin") ONE TO ONE TUITION AND CASTING WORKSHOPS
An opportunity to get valuable insight into the casting process from the perspective of an experienced casting director. Examining the difference between a good performance and the successful performance. Demonstrating common pitfalls. The purpose of the workshops is to improve and refine actors' audition, interview and reading/performance technique, identifying and eliminating bad habits. Actors work in pairs on a script which is then directed and shot on camera and reviewed with observation and constructive criticism. To finish, there is a review of the session, general advice and a Q and A on any subject which the actors wish to pursue. One to one tuition, either for a specific important audition or to improve general technique. Available subject to availability. NB. THE WORKSHOPS ARE FOR PROFESSIONALS ONLY. SELECTION BY CV. COMMERCIALS AND EPISODIC TV - 12 ACTORS PER 4 HR SESSION, FEATURES AND TV DRAMA - 10 ACTORS PER 4 HR SESSION EMAIL info@suejones.net FOR FULL DETAILS

STUART**ALLEN**
PHOTOGRAPHER

07776 258829

www.stuartallenphotos.com

Production, Publicity, Portraits

STUDENT DISCOUNTS

Sean Gleeson   Natalie Barrett

NEEDLEMAN Sue
19 Stanhope Gardens, London NW7 2JD
Fax: 020-8959 0225   Tel: 020-8959 1550

NOA PRODUCTIONS
(Casting & Production Services)
40 Brookland Hill, London NW11 6DX
Mobile: 07944 953540   Tel/Fax: 020-8455 3160

NORCLIFFE Belinda
(Belinda Norcliffe & Matt Selby)
23 Brougham Road, London W3 6JD
e-mail: belinda@bncasting.co.uk
Fax: 020-8992 5533   Tel: 020-8992 1333

O'BRIEN Debbie
72 High Street, Ashwell, Nr Baldock, Herts SG7 5NS
Fax: 01462 743110   Tel: 01462 742919

O'CONNOR Orla
Scottish Office: Out of The Blue @ The Drill Hall
36 Dalmeny Street, Edinburgh EH6 8RG
e-mail: victoria@victoriabeattie.com   Tel: 0131-553 0559

O'DONNELL Rory
178A Adelaide Avenue, London SE4 1JN
e-mail: rory@acting4camera.com
Fax: 020-8690 8005   Mobile: 07940 073165

PALMER Helena
(See CANNON DUDLEY & ASSOCIATES)

PARRISS Susie CASTING CDG
PO Box 40, Morden SM4 4WJ
Fax: 020-8543 3327   Tel: 020-8543 3326

PERRYMENT Mandy CASTING
e-mail: mail@mandyperryment.com   Mobile: 07790 605191

PETTS Tree CASTING
125 Hendon Way, London NW2 2NA
e-mail: casting@treepetts.co.uk   Tel: 020-8458 8898

PLANTIN Kate
4 Riverside, Lower Hampton Road
Sunbury on Thames TW16 5PW
e-mail: kateplantin@hotmail.com
Fax: 01932 783235   Tel: 01932 782350

POLENTARUTTI Tania CASTING CDG
Top Floor, 37 Berwick Street, London W1F 8RS
Fax: 020-7734 3549   Tel: 020-7734 1819

POOLE Gilly CDG
(See CROWLEY POOLE CASTING)

PROCTOR Carl CDG
22 Poland Street, London W1F 8QH
Website: www.carlproctor.com
e-mail: carlproctor@btconnect.com
Fax: 020-7287 7261   Tel: 020-7287 2277

PRYOR Andy CDG
Suite 3, 15 Broad Court, London WC2B 5QN
Fax: 020-7836 8299   Tel: 020-7836 8298

RAFTERY Francesca CASTING
51 Purley Vale, Purley, Surrey CR8 2DU
Website: www.francescaraftery.com
e-mail: info@francescaraftery.com   Tel/Fax: 020-8763 0105

REGAN Leigh-Ann
(Welsh Language/English) TV, Film, Commercials & Theatre
Ynylas Uchaf Farm, Blackmill
Brigend CF35 6DW
Fax: 01656 841815   Tel: 01656 841841

- Studio in SW16
- 2 hour session. 70 -120 Digital Images
- FULL SIZE preview 'as we shoot'.
- Friendly, relaxed, fun and best of all you only pay if you want them.
- Online selection & digital contact sheets. Hi-res C.D. and 4 hand prepared *digital* images included.
- Maximise your *Spotlight Portfolio* with a range of shots that really look like you.
- Black & White & Green? - I use: energy efficiency / Renewable power / Carbon offsetting.

www.joncamplingheadshots.com
020 86798671 - 07941 421 101
photo@joncampling.com

REICH Liora
25 Manor Park Road, London N2 0SN   Tel: 020-8444 1686

REYNOLDS Gillian CASTING
14 Rathdown Road, Dublin 7, Ireland
Website: www.gillianreynoldscasting.com

REYNOLDS Simone CDG
60 Hebdon Road, London SW17 7NN
Fax: 020-8767 0280   Tel: 020-8672 5443

RHODES JAMES Kate CDG
Suite 6, 135 High Street, Teddington TW11 8HH
Fax: 020-8977 2624   Tel: 020-8977 1191

RIPLEY Jane
e-mail: janeripley@blueyonder.co.uk   Tel: 020-8342 8216

ROBERTSON Sasha CASTING CDG
19 Wendell Road, London W12 9RS
e-mail: casting@sasharobertson.com
Fax: 020-8740 1396   Tel: 020-8740 0817

ROFFE Danielle
71 Mornington Street
London NW1 7QE   Tel: 020-7388 1898

ROSE Dionne
e-mail: dionnerosecasting@hotmail.co.uk
Mobile: 07772 446627   Tel: 0118-958 3936

ROWAN Amy CASTING
PO Box 10247, Blackrock, Co. Dublin, Ireland
Fax: 00 353 1 2802005   Tel: 00 353 1 2140514

ROYAL SHAKESPEARE COMPANY
Casting Department, c/o RSC Rehearsal Rooms
35 Clapham High Street, London SW4 7TW
Website: www.rsc.org.uk
Fax: 020-7845 0505   Tel: 020-7845 0500

SALBERG Jane
8 Halstow Road, Greenwich, London SE10 0LD
e-mail: janesalberg@aol.com
Mobile: 07931 932103   Tel: 020-8858 1114

SAUNDERS Claire
4 Cavendish Mansions, Mill Lane, London NW6 1TE
e-mail: clairesaunderscasting@yahoo.co.uk

SCHILLER Ginny CDG
180A Graham Road, London E8 1BS
e-mail: ginny.schiller@virgin.net
Fax: 020-8525 1049   Tel: 020-8525 1637

SCOTT Laura CDG
56 Rowena Crescent, London SW11 2PT
Website: www.thecdg.co.uk
e-mail: laurascottcasting@mac.com
Fax: 020-7924 1907   Tel: 020-7978 6336

SEARCHERS The
70 Sylvia Court, Cavendish Street, London N1 7PG
e-mail: waynesearcher@mac.com
Fax: 020-7684 5763   Mobile: 07958 922829

SEECOOMAR Nadira
PO Box 167, Twickenham TW1 2UP
Fax: 020-8744 1274   Tel: 020-8892 8478

SHAW David
(See KEOGH Beverley CASTING Ltd)

SHAW Phil
Suite 476, 2 Old Brompton Road
South Kensington, London SW7 3DQ
e-mail: shawcastlond@aol.com   Tel: 020-8715 8943

SHEPHERD Debbie CASTING
Suite 16, 63 St Martin's Lane, London WC2N 4JS
e-mail: debbie@debbieshepherd.com
Fax: 020-7240 4640   Tel: 020-7240 0400

SID PRODUCTIONS
Suite 84, The London Fruit & Wool Exchange
Brushfield Street, London E1 6EP
Website: www.sidproductions.co.uk
e-mail: casting@sidproductions.co.uk
Fax: 020-7247 8810   Tel: 020-7655 4477

SINGER Sandra ASSOCIATES
21 Cotswold Road, Westcliff-on-Sea, Essex SS0 8AA
Website: www.sandrasinger.com
e-mail: sandrasingeruk@aol.com
Fax: 01702 339393   Tel: 01702 331616

SMITH Michelle CDG
220 Church Lane, Stockport SK7 1PQ
Fax: 0161-439 0622   Tel: 0161-439 6825

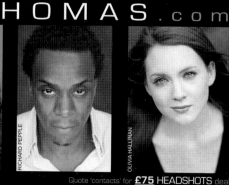

SMITH Suzanne CDG
33 Fitzroy Street, London W1T 6DU
e-mail: zan@dircon.co.uk
Fax: 020-7436 9690   Tel: 020-7436 9255

STAFFORD Emma CASTING
The Royal Exchange
St Ann's Square, Manchester M2 7BR
Website: www.emmastafford.tv
e-mail: info@emmastafford.tv
Fax: 0161-833 4264   Tel: 0161-833 4263

STARK CASTING
e-mail: stark.casting@virgin.net
Mobile: 07956 150689   Tel: 020-8800 0060

STEVENS Gail CASTING CDG
Greenhill House
90-93 Cowcross Street, London EC1M 6BF
Fax: 020-7253 6574   Tel: 020-7253 6532

STEVENSON Sam CDG
e-mail: sam@hancockstevenson.com

STEWART Amanda CASTING
Apartment 1, 35 Fortess Road
London NW5 1AD   Tel: 020-7485 7973

STOLL Liz
BBC DRAMA SERIES CASTING, BBC Elstree
Room N223, Neptune House, Clarendon Road
Borehamwood, Herts WD6 1JF
Fax: 020-8228 8311   Tel: 020-8228 8285

STYLE Emma CDG
7 Chamberlain Cottages
Camberwell Grove, London SE5 8JD   Tel: 020-7701 7750

SUMMERS Mark CASTING
(Formerly CASTING UNLIMITED)
137 Freston Road
London W10 6TH
Website: www.marksummers.com
e-mail: mark@marksummers.com
Fax: 020-7243 1987   Tel: 020-7229 8413

SYERS Michael
(See CASTING CONNECTION The)

SYSON Lucinda CDG
1st Floor
33 Old Compton Street, London W1D 5JT
e-mail: office@lucindasysoncasting.com
Fax: 020-7287 3629   Tel: 020-7287 5327

TABAK Amanda CDG
(See CANDID CASTING)

TEECE Shirley
106 North View Road, London N8 7LP
e-mail: casting@teece.demon.co.uk   Tel: 020-8347 9241

TOPOLSKI Tessa
25 Clifton Hill, London NW8 0QE   Tel: 020-7328 6393

TOPPING Nicci
c/o Topps Casting
The Media Centre
7 Northumberland Street HD1 1RL
e-mail: info@toppscasting.co.uk   Mobile: 07802 684256

TRAMONTANO Luisa
Church Studios, 50 Church Road, London NW10 9PY
Website: www.luisatcasting.co.uk
e-mail: luisa@luisatcasting.co.uk   Mobile: 07767 438787

TREVELLICK Jill CDG
92 Priory Road, London N8 7EY
e-mail: jill@trevellick.force9.co.uk
Fax: 020-8348 7400   Tel: 020-8340 2734

TREVIS Sarah CDG
PO Box 47170, London W6 6BA
e-mail: info@sarahtrevis.com
Fax: 020-7602 8110   Tel: 020-7602 5552

TWIST & FLIC CASTING
(Penny Burrows)
1A Carlton Avenue
Dulwich Village, London SE21 7DE
Website: www.sportsmodels.com
e-mail: info@sportsmodels.com
Mobile: 07973 863263   Tel: 020-8299 8800

VAN OST & MILLINGTON CASTING
(Valerie Van Ost & Andrew Millington)
PO Box 115
Petersfield GU31 5BB   Tel: 01730 821530

VAUGHAN Sally CDG
2 Kennington Park Place
London SE11 4AS   Tel: 020-7735 6539

VITAL PRODUCTIONS
PO Box 26441, London SE10 9GZ
e-mail: mail@vital-productions.co.uk
Fax: 0870 3850168   Tel: 0870 0421276

VOSSER Anne CASTING CDG
3rd Floor, 212 Strand, London WC2R 1AP
e-mail: anne@vosser-casting.co.uk
Mobile: 07968 868712   Tel: 020-7427 5684

WEIR Fiona CDG
c/o Twickenham Studios
St Margaret's
Twickenham TW1 2AW   Tel: 020-8607 8888

WEST June
Granada Television, Quay Street
Manchester M60 9EA
Fax: 0161-827 2853   Tel: 0161-832 7211

WESTERN Matt CASTING
150 Blythe Road, London W14 0HD
e-mail: matt@mattwestern.co.uk   Tel: 020-7602 6646

WHALE Toby CDG
80 Shakespeare Road
London W3 6SN
Website: www.whalecasting.com
e-mail: toby@whalecasting.com
Fax: 020-8993 8096   Tel: 020-8993 2821

WILDMANHALL CASTING
(Vicky Wildman & Buffy Hall)
1 Child's Place, London SW5 9RX
e-mail: wildmanhall@mac.com   Tel: 020-7373 2036

WILLIS Catherine
e-mail: catherine@cwcasting.co.uk Tel: 020-7697 4482

YOUNGSTAR CASTING
(Specialist in Children & Teenagers only)
5 Union Castle House, Canute Road SO14 3FJ
e-mail: info@youngstar.tv

ZIMMERMANN Jeremy CASTING
36 Marshall Street, London W1F 7EY
Fax: 020-7437 4747   Tel: 020-7478 5161

AMADEUS CENTRE The
50 Shirland Road
London W9 2JA
e-mail: info@amadeuscentre.co.uk
Fax: 020-7266 1225   Tel: 020-7286 1686

BAC VENUES
Battersea Arts Centre
Lavender Hill
Battersea, London SW11 5TN
Website: www.bacvenues.org.uk
e-mail: venues@bac.org.uk   Tel: 020-7326 8211

BARBICAN EXHIBITION CENTRE
Barbican
Silk Street
London EC2Y 8DS
e-mail: exhibitions@barbican.org.uk
Fax: 020-7382 7263   Tel: 020-7382 7053

BIRMINGHAM SYMPHONY HALL
Broad Street
Birmingham B1 2EA
Website: www.symphonyhall.co.uk
e-mail: feedback@symphonyhall.co.uk
BO: 0121-780 3333   Admin: 0121-200 2000

BLACKHEATH HALLS
23 Lee Road
Blackheath
London SE3 9RQ
Website: www.blackheathhalls.com
e-mail: mail@blackheathhalls.com
Fax: 020-8852 5154   BO: 020-8463 0100

CENTRAL HALL - WESTMINSTER
Storey's Gate
Westminster
London SW1H 9NH
Website: www.c-h-w.com
e-mail: info@c-h-w.co.uk   Tel: 020-7222 8010

CHICHESTER FESTIVAL THEATRE
Oaklands Park
Chichester
West Sussex PO19 6AP
Website: www.cft.org.uk
e-mail: admin@cft.org.uk
Fax: 01243 787288   Tel: 01243 784437

EC & O VENUES
Warwick Road
London SW5 9TA
Website: www.eco.co.uk
e-mail: marketing@eco.co.uk   Tel: 020-7385 1200

EC & O VENUES - EARL'S COURT
The Brewery
Chiswell Street, London EC1Y 4SD
Website: www.thebrewery.co.uk   Tel: 020-7638 8811

EC & O VENUES - OLYMPIA
Hammersmith Road
London W14 8UX
Website: www.eco.co.uk   Tel: 020-7385 1200

FAIRFIELD HALLS
Park Lane, Croydon CR9 1DG
Website: www.fairfield.co.uk
BO: 020-8688 9291   Tel: 020-8681 0821

FERNEHAM HALL
Osborn Road
Fareham, Hants PO16 7DB
e-mail: boxoffice@fareham.gov.uk   Tel: 01329 824864

GORDON CRAIG THEATRE
Stevenage Arts & Leisure Centre
Lytton Way
Stevenage
Herts SG1 1LZ
Website: www.stevenage-leisure.co.uk
e-mail: gordoncraig@stevenage-leisure.co.uk
BO: 08700 131030   Admin: 01438 242679

HEXAGON The
Queen's Walk
Reading RG1 7UA
Website: www.readingarts.com
e-mail: boxoffice@readingarts.com
Fax: 0118-939 0670   Admin: 0118-939 0390

MINERVA THEATRE
Oaklands Park
Chichester
West Sussex PO19 6AP
Website: www.cft.org.uk
Fax: 01243 787288   Tel: 01243 784437

NATIONAL CONCERT HALL OF WALES The
St David's Hall
The Hayes
Cardiff CF10 1SH
Website: www.stdavidshallcardiff.co.uk
Fax: 029-2087 8599   Tel: 029-2087 8500

OLYMPIA EXHIBITION CENTRES
Hammersmith Road
Kensington
London W14 8UX
Fax: 020-7598 2500   Tel: 020-7385 1200

RIVERSIDE STUDIOS
Crisp Road
London W6 9RL
Website: www.riversidestudios.co.uk
e-mail: online@riversidestudios.co.uk
BO: 020-8237 1111   Tel: 020-8237 1000

ROUND The
34 Lime Street
Ouseburn
Newcastle Upon Tyne NE1 2PQ
Website: www.the-round.com   Tel: 0191-260 5605

ROYAL ALBERT HALL
Kensington Gore
London SW7 2AP
Website: www.royalalberthall.com
e-mail: admin@royalalberthall.com
Fax: 020-7823 7725   Tel: 020-7589 3203

SOUTH BANK CENTRE
(Including The Royal Festival Hall, Queen Elizabeth Hall,
Purcell Room & Hayward Gallery)
Royal Festival Hall
London SE1 8XX
Website: www.rfh.org.uk
BO: 0870 3828000   Tel: 020-7921 0601

ST JOHN'S SMITH SQUARE
London SW1P 3HA
Website: www.sjss.org.uk
Fax: 020-7233 1618   Tel: 020-7222 2168

WIGMORE HALL
36 Wigmore Street
London W1U 2BP
e-mail: info@wigmore-hall.org.uk   BO: 020-7935 2141

ACORN ENTERTAINMENTS Ltd
PO Box 64, Cirencester, Glos GL7 5YD
Website: www.acornents.co.uk
e-mail: info@acornents.co.uk
Fax: 01285 642291 Tel: 01285 644622

ASKONAS HOLT Ltd
(Classical Music)
Lonsdale Chambers, 27 Chancery Lane, London WC2A 1PF
Website: www.askonasholt.co.uk
e-mail: info@askonasholt.co.uk
Fax: 020-7400 1799 Tel: 020-7400 1700

AVALON PROMOTIONS Ltd
4A Exmoor Street, London W10 6BD
Fax: 020-7598 7334 Tel: 020-7598 7333

BARRUCCI LEISURE ENTERPRISES Ltd
(Promoters)
45-47 Cheval Place, London SW7 1EW
e-mail: barrucci@barrucci.com
Fax: 020-7581 2509 Tel: 020-7225 2255

BLOCK Derek ARTISTES AGENCY
70-76 Bell Street, Marylebone, London NW1 6SP
e-mail: derekblock@derekblock.co.uk
Fax: 020-7724 2102 Tel: 020-7724 2101

CITY CONCERT ORGANISATION Ltd The
PO Box 3145, Lichfield WS13 6YN
Website: www.cityconcert.com
e-mail: admin@cityconcert.com Tel/Fax: 01543 262286

FLYING MUSIC
110 Clarendon Road, London W11 2HR
Website: www.flyingmusic.com
e-mail: reception@flyingmusic.com
Fax: 020-7221 5016 Tel: 020-7221 7799

GOLDSMITH Harvey PRODUCTIONS Ltd
(Concert Promotion)
13-14 Margaret Street, London W1W 8RN
Website: www.harveygoldsmith.com
e-mail: mail@harveygoldsmith.com
Fax: 020-7224 0111 Tel: 020-7224 1992

GUBBAY Raymond Ltd
Dickens House
15 Tooks Court, London EC4A 1QH
Website: www.raymondgubbay.co.uk
e-mail: info@raymondgubbay.co.uk
Fax: 020-7025 3751 Tel: 020-7025 3750

HOBBS Liz CONCERTS & EVENTS Ltd
65 London Road
Newark, Nottinghamshire NG24 1RZ
Website: www.lizhobbsgroup.com
e-mail: info@lizhobbsgroup.com
Fax: 0870 3337009 Tel: 08700 702702

HOCHHAUSER Victor
4 Oak Hill Way, London NW3 7LR
e-mail: hochhauser@homechoice.co.uk
Fax: 020-7431 2531 Tel: 020-7794 0987

IMG ARTS & ENTERTAINMENT
Pier House, Strand on the Green
Chiswick, London W4 3NN
Fax: 020-8233 5001 Tel: 020-8233 5000

McINTYRE Phil ENTERTAINMENT
2nd Floor, 35 Soho Square
London W1D 3QX
e-mail: reception@mcintyre-ents.com
Fax: 020-7439 2280 Tel: 020-7439 2270

MEADOW Jeremy Ltd
73 Great Titchfield Street
London W1W 6RD
Website: www.tegproductions.com
e-mail: info@tegproductions.com
Fax: 0870 7627882 Tel: 020-7436 2244

RBM
(Comedy)
3rd Floor, 168 Victoria Street
London SW1E 5LB
Website: www.rbmcomedy.com
e-mail: info@rbmcomedy.com
Fax: 020-7630 6549 Tel: 020-7630 7733

Who are 'Consultants'?

Broadly, this section contains listings for a variety of companies and services which exist to help performers with the day-to-day administration of their working lives. It also includes companies with particular specialisms or who offer niche services.

Performers need to manage their business affairs personally, in ways that those in 'normal' jobs do not. For example, unlike most employees, a performer does not have an accounts department to work out their tax and national insurance, or an HR department to take care of contracts or health insurance on their behalf. On top of which, performers can often be away on tour or on set for many months and unable to attend to these matters themselves.

Areas covered in this section include:

Finance

Dedicated companies exist which can help you look after key financial issues, including national insurance, taxation, benefits, savings and pensions. Specialist mortgage companies also exist for performers and other self-employed workers within the entertainment industry. See overleaf for specific information about accountancy services. If you are a member of Equity you can also ask them for free financial advice, and an Equity pension scheme exists into which the BBC, ITV, PACT, TV companies and West End Theatre producers will pay when you have a main part with one of them. Similar schemes also exist for dancers and other performers.

Insurance

Performers may often need specialist insurance for specific jobs, as well as the standard life and health insurance policies held by most people. A number of specialist insurers are listed in the pages overleaf. Equity also offers a specialist backstage/accident and public liability insurance policy to all of its members.

Legal

There may be times in a performer's career when he/she needs specialist legal advice or representation. Legal advisors and solicitors are listed in this section. In addition, as part of their membership, Equity performers can also obtain free legal advice regarding professional engagements or personal injury claims.

Health & Wellbeing

The unique pressures of working within the entertainment industry can take their toll on performers' physical and psychological wellbeing. Fortunately there are hundreds of specialist practitioners with years of experience in treating performers and understanding the issues which regularly affect them. See the 'Health & Wellbeing' section of this directory for listings. Equity members can also use the British Performing Arts Medicine Trust Helpline to access advice and information on performance-related medical, psychological and dental problems.
www.bpamt.co.uk

How should I use these listings?

As when looking to hire any company or individual, contact a number of different companies and carefully compare the services they offer. Ask others in the industry for recommendations. If you are an Equity member, don't forget to check first that the service isn't already available free of charge, as part of your annual membership.

GORDON LEIGHTON
tel: 020 7831 8300
fax: 020 7831 0500
freephone: 0800 085 1258
email: malcolms@gordonl.com

Are your tax affairs in a mess? If you think they are, Malcolm Somerston FCA, Partner in Gordon Leighton Chartered Accountants, offers some advice to get back on track.

Can you answer 'yes' to all of the following questions?

- Are your tax and national insurance payments completely up-to-date? Are they paid by the required deadlines?
- Are your completed Self-Assessment Tax Forms returned by the required deadlines?
- Do you know what your tax liabilities will be for the next 18 months, enabling you to plan your cashflow?
- When you receive a letter from H M Revenue & Customs marked 'Please Open Immediately', do you open it *immediately?*

If not, then please reconsider your approach.

Self Assessment for Tax (with us for some ten years now) is a major advantage for those in the Entertainment Industry who are self-employed or whose earnings fluctuate. With a little effort, it is possible to accurately predict in advance tax payments which are generally payable only twice a year and can thus be planned for properly, and paid on time.

Such compliance with the Revenue's requests can also avoid expensive and worrying enquiries. Like bank managers, the one thing your average Revenue official hates is to be ignored and, like it or not, he has a breathtaking array of weapons at his disposal to whip you into line.

So what if you don't complete a Tax Return on time or, worse still, fail to declare income or gains? Well, the repercussions fall into 4 categories:

Interest. The Revenue will charge you interest on any tax paid late. And make no mistake, they *will* charge it!
Surcharges. They will also hit you with one-off charges of 5% of the tax outstanding.
Penalties. This is where it starts to get really serious. The Revenue has the power (in the most serious of cases) to charge a penalty of up to 100% of the tax and interest outstanding.
Enquiries. There is the additional worry caused by having the Revenue ask all sorts of questions about your financial affairs with the attendant cost in terms of fees.

Here's my simple three-point guide to keeping the taxman from your door.

1. Use an accountant with expertise in proactive personal and business tax-saving. (You'd expect me to say that, wouldn't you?). If your financial affairs are kept in order, the fees will be a fraction of the cost should the worst happen. Remember: accountant's fees are tax-deductible. And, as well as giving you peace of mind and keeping you on the straight and narrow, a good accountant can suggest many ways to improve your finances.

2. Open all correspondence from the Revenue and deal with it in a timely fashion. Don't just ignore it. If this means quickly redirecting it to your accountant, all well and good - that's what you pay them for.

3. Keep rudimentary records of all your income and expenses. Half an hour with your accountant will clarify what you need to do and will stand you in good stead in the years to come.

And what to do if the Revenue are already at your door? Don't panic! Consult your accountant with a view to providing the Revenue with the information they need and reaching a settlement. Deal with it early and any penalties will be modest. Leave it, and it will just get worse.

For more information please visit www.gordonl.co.uk

ACTOR'S ONE-STOP SHOP The
(Showreels for Performing Artists)
First Floor, Above The Gate Pub
Station Road, London N22 7SS
Website: www.actorsonestopshop.com
e-mail: info@actorsonestopshop.com   Tel: 020-8888 7006

AGENTFILE
(Software for Agents)
Website: www.agentfile.com
e-mail: admin@agentfile.com   Mobile: 07050 683662

ANDREW JENKINS Ltd
St Martin's House, 59 St Martin's Lane
London WC2N 4JS
Website: www.andrewjenkinsltd.com
e-mail: info@andrewjenkinsltd.com
Fax: 020-7240 0710   Tel: 020-7240 0607

AON Ltd (Trading as AON/ALBERT G. RUBEN)
(Insurance Brokers)
Pinewood Studios, Pinewood Road
Iver, Bucks SL0 0NH
Website: www.aon.co.uk
Fax: 01753 785861   Tel: 01753 785859

ARIAS Enrique
(Subtitles, Translations & Voice Overs)
21 Middleton Road, London NW11 7NR
Website: www.nwlondon.com/eag
e-mail: enriqueag@gmail.com   Mobile: 07956 261568

ARTS VA The
(Bronwyn Robertson) (Experienced PA and Admin Support)
PO Box 2911, CV37 1WU
Website: www.theartsva.com
e-mail: bronwyn@theartsva.com
Fax: 01789 552818   Tel: 01789 552559

ATKINS Chris & COMPANY
(Accountants & Business Consultants)
Astra House, Arklow Road, London SE14 6EB
e-mail: info@chrisatkins.co.uk   Tel: 020-8691 4100

BIG PICTURE
(Casual Work in IT Field Marketing)
13 Netherwood Road, London W14 0BL
Website: www.ebigpicture.co.uk
e-mail: info@ebigpicture.co.uk   Tel: 020-7371 4455

BLACKMORE Lawrence
(Production Accountant)
Suite 5, 26 Charing Cross Road
London WC2H 0DG
Fax: 020-7836 3156   Tel: 020-7240 1817

BLAKE LAPTHORNE TARLO LYONS
(Solicitors)
Watchmaker Court
33 St John's Lane, London EC1M 4DB
Website: www.bllan.com
e-mail: info@bllan.com
Fax: 020-7814 9421   Tel: 020-7405 2000

BLUE SKY ENTERTAINMENT
(Corporate, Open Air & Specialist Entertainment)
8 Adelaide Grove
London W12 0JJ
Website: www.blueskyentertainment.co.uk
e-mail: info@blueskyentertainment.co.uk
Mobile: 07702 474430   Tel: 020-8723 2127

BOWKER ORFORD
(Chartered Accountants)
15-19 Cavendish Place, London W1G 0DD
e-mail: rparmar@bowkerorford.com
Fax: 020-7580 3909   Tel: 020-7636 6391

BREBNERS
(Chartered Accountants)
180 Wardour Street, London W1F 8LB
Website: www.brebners.com
e-mail: partners@brebners.com
Fax: 020-7287 5315   Tel: 020-7734 2244

BRECKMAN & COMPANY
(Chartered Certified Accountants)
49 South Molton Street
London W1K 5LH
Website: www.breckmanandcompany.co.uk
Tel: 020-7499 2292

BRITISH ASSOCIATION OF DRAMA THERAPISTS The
Waverley, Battledown Approach
Cheltenham, Glos GL52 6RE
Website: www.badth.org.uk
e-mail: badth1@aol.com   Tel/Fax: 01242 235515

BYFORD Simon PRODUCTION MANAGEMENT SERVICES
(Production & Event Management)
22 Freshfield Place
Brighton, East Sussex BN2 0BN
e-mail: simon@simonbyfordpms.com
Fax: 01273 606402   Tel: 01273 623972

BYRNE John
(The Stage's Agony Uncle)
71 Amina Way, London SE16 3UH
Website: www.showbusiness-success.com
e-mail: dearjohn@thestage.co.uk   Tel: 020-7231 4907

CAP PRODUCTION SOLUTIONS Ltd
(Technical Production Services)
20 Merton Industrial Park
Jubilee Way
Wimbledon, London SW19 3WL
e-mail: leigh@leighporter.com
Fax: 07970 763480   Tel: 020-8544 8668

CARR Mark & Co Ltd
(Chartered Accountants)
Garrick House
26-27 Southampton Street
Covent Garden
London WC2E 7RS
Website: www.markcarr.co.uk
e-mail: mark@markcarr.co.uk   Tel: 020-7717 8474

CASTLE MAGICAL SERVICES
(Magical Consultants) (Michael Shepherd)
Broompark, 131 Tadcaster Road
Dringhouses, York YO24 1QJ
e-mail: info@castlemagicalservices.co.uk
Tel/Fax: 01904 709500

CAULKETT Robin Dip SM, MIIRSM
(Abseiling, Rope Work)
3 Churchill Way, Mitchell Dean
Glos GL17 0AZ   Mobile: 07970 442003

CELEBRITIES WORLDWIDE Ltd
(Celebrity on-line Media Database)
39-41 New Oxford Street
London WC1A 1BN
Website: www.celebritiesworldwide.com
e-mail: info@celebritiesworldwide.com
Fax: 020-7836 7701   Tel: 020-7836 7702

CHAPERONE AGENCY The
Website: www.chaperoneagency.com   Mobile: 07960 075928

CIRCUS MANIACS
(Circus, Theatre, Dance, Choreography, Extreme Sports)
Office 8A
The Kingswood Foundation
Britannia Road
Kingswood, Bristol BS15 8DB
Website: www.circusmaniacsagency.com
e-mail: agency@circusmaniacs.com
Mobile: 07977 247287   Tel/Fax: 0117-947 7042

CLASS - CARLINE LUNDON ASSOCIATES
25 Falkner Square, Liverpool L8 7NZ
Website: www.stagescreenandbroadcast.co.uk
e-mail: carline.lundon@ukonline.co.uk
Mobile: 07935 117038   Tel/Fax: 0151-703 0600

COBO MEDIA Ltd
(Performing Arts, Entertainment & Leisure Marketing)
43A Garthorne Road, London SE23 1EP
Website: www.theatrenet.com
e-mail: admin@cobomedia.com
Fax: 020-8291 4969   Tel: 020-8291 7079

COLCLOUGH John
(Practical Independent Guidance for Actors and Actresses)
Website: www.johncolclough.co.uk
e-mail: john@johncolclough.org.uk   Tel: 020-8873 1763

COOPER Margaret
(Executive Producer)
Wind Ltd, 75/1 Old College Street
Sleima SLM08, Malta
e-mail: mediacorp1@yahoo.com   Mobile: 00 44 7884 074315

COUNT AND SEE Ltd
(Tax, Accountancy & Book-keeping Services)
219 Macmillan Way
London SW17 6AW
Website: www.countandsee.com
e-mail: info@countandsee.com
Fax: 0845 004 3454   Tel: 020-8767 7882

CREATIVE INDUSTRIES DEVELOPMENT AGENCY (CIDA)
(Professional Development & Business Support for Artists
& Creative Businesses)
Media Centre, Northumberland Street
Huddersfield, West Yorkshire HD1 1RL
Website: www.cida.org
e-mail: info@cida.org
Fax: 01484 483150   Tel: 01484 483140

CROFTS Andrew
(Book Writing Services)
Westlands Grange
West Grinstead
Horsham, West Sussex RH13 8LZ
Website: www.andrewcrofts.com   Tel/Fax: 01403 864518

DYNAMIC FX Ltd
(Entertainers and Magic Consultants)
Regent House, 291 Kirkdale
London SE26 4QD
e-mail: mail@dynamicfx.co.uk
Fax: 0845 0062443   Tel: 0845 0062442

EARLE Kenneth PERSONAL MANAGEMENT
214 Brixton Road, London SW9 6AP
e-mail: kennethearle@agents-uk.com
Fax: 020-7274 9529   Tel: 020-7274 1219

EQUIP
11 Balmoral Road, Gidea Park
Romford, Essex RM2 5XD
Website: www.equip-u.com
e-mail: sales@equip-u.com   Tel: 01708 479898

EQUITY INSURANCE SERVICES
131-133 New London Road
Chelmsford, Essex CM2 0QZ
Website: www.equity-ins-services.com
e-mail: enquiries@equity-ins-services.com
Fax: 01245 491641   Tel: 01245 357854

FACADE
(Creation & Production of Musicals)
43A Garthorne Road
London SE23 1EP
e-mail: facade@cobomedia.com   Tel: 020-8291 7079

FISHER BERGER & ASSOCIATES
(Chartered Accountants)
57 Elmcroft Crescent, London NW11 9TA
e-mail: mail@fisherberger.com
Fax: 020-8458 9776   Tel: 020-8458 9770

FLAMES MARTIAL ARTS ACADEMY
(Adam Richards)
Unit 2
128 Milton Road Business Park
Gravesend, Kent DA12 2PG
Website: www.kuentao.com
e-mail: arstunts@yahoo.co.uk   Mobile: 07950 396389

FONTAINE Valley
(Broadcast Careers Mentor/Trainer)
Website: www.valleyfontaine.com
e-mail: info@valleyfontaine.com

FORD Jonathan & Co
(Chartered Accountants)
The Coach House
31 View Road
Rainhill, Merseyside L35 0LF
Website: www.jonathanford.co.uk
e-mail: info@jonathanford.co.uk   Tel: 0151-426 4512

FULL EFFECT The
(Live Event Producers including Choreographers)
Exchange Building
16 St Cuthbert's Street, Bedford MK40 3JG
Website: www.thefulleffect.co.uk
e-mail: mark.harrison@tfe.co.uk
Fax: 01234 214445   Tel: 01234 269099

GHOSTWRITER/AUTHOR
(John Parker)
21 Hindsleys Place, London SE23 2NF
e-mail: parkerwrite@aol.com   Tel: 020-8244 5816

GILMOUR Rev/Dr Glenn J. MscD, IMM, SHsc.D, BCMA.Reg
Fully Qualified/International Clairvoyant, Experienced
Healer & Holistic Therapist. (Investigator & Consultant.
Paranormal/Metaphysics/Occult for Radio/TV)
e-mail: drgilmour@3mail.com
Tel: 0114-234 7726   Mobile: 07737 245103

GORDON LEIGHTON
(Chartered Accountants, Business Advisers)
3rd Floor
20-23 Greville Street, London EC1N 8SS
Website: www.gordonl.co.uk
e-mail: malcolms@gordonl.co.uk
Fax: 020-7831 0500   Tel: 020-7831 8300

HANDS UP PUPPETS
c/o Peter Charlesworth & Associates
68 Old Brompton Road, London SW7 3LD
Website: www.handsuppuppets.com
e-mail: enquiries@handsuppuppets.com   Tel: 020-7581 2478

HARLEY PRODUCTIONS
68 New Cavendish Street
London W1G 8TE
e-mail: harleyprods@aol.com
Fax: 020-8202 8863   Tel: 020-7580 3247

HATSTAND CIRCUS
(Specialist in Themed Performances for Events & Promotions)
98 Milligan Street
Westferry, London E14 8AS
Website: www.hatstandcircus.co.uk
e-mail: helenahatstand@btconnect.com
Mobile: 07748 005839   Tel/Fax: 020-7538 3368

HATTON Richard Ltd
29 Roehampton Gate
London SW15 5JR
Fax: 020-8876 8278   Tel: 020-8876 6699

HAYES Susan
(Choreographer/Body Worker)
46 Warrington Crescent, London W9 1EP
e-mail: susan22@btinternet.com   Mobile: 07721 927714

HERITAGE RAILWAY ASSOCIATION
10 Hurdeswell, Long Hanborough
Witney, Oxfordshire OX29 8PH
Website: www.heritagerailways.com   Tel: 01993 883384

HOMEMATCH PROPERTY FINANCE
(Mortgages for Entertainers)
Eagle Place, Pheasant Street
Worcester WR1 2EE
e-mail: chrisjcatchpole@aol.com
Fax: 01905 22121   Tel: 01905 22007

HONRI Peter
(Music Hall Consultant)
1 Evingar Road, Whitchurch
Hants RG28 7EY   Tel: 01256 892162

IMAGE DIGGERS
(Slide/Stills/Audio/Video Library & Theme Research)
618B Finchley Road
London NW11 7RR
Website: www.imagediggers.netfirms.com
e-mail: lambhorn@tiscali.co.uk   Tel: 020-8455 4564

IMPACT AGENCY
(Public Relations)
3 Bloomsbury Place, London WC1A 2QL
e-mail: mail@impactagency.co.uk
Fax: 020-7580 7200   Tel: 020-7580 1770

I R A - INDEPENDENT REVIEWS ARTS SERVICES
(Stories from World of Film/Art/Showbiz)
12 Hemingford Close
London N12 9HF
e-mail: critic@independentradioarts.com
Mobile: 07956 212916   Tel/Fax: 020-8343 7437

JACKSON Kim
(Arts Education Consultancy)
1 Mellor Road, Leicester LE3 6HN
e-mail: jacksongillespie@hotmail.com   Tel: 0116-233 8432

JENKINS Andrew Ltd
(Venue & Production Consultancy, General Management)
63 Kidbrooke Park Road, London SE3 0EE
Website: www.andrewjenkinsltd.com
e-mail: enquiries@andrewjenkinsltd.com
Fax: 020-8856 7106   Tel: 020-8319 3657

JFL SEARCH & SELECTION
(Recruitment Consultants)
27 Beak Street, London W1F 9RU
Website: www.jflrecruit.com
Fax: 020-7734 6501   Tel: 020-7009 3500

JORDAN Richard PRODUCTIONS Ltd
(General Management, UK and International Productions,
Festivals, Production Consultancy)
Mews Studios, 16 Vernon Yard, London W11 2DX
e-mail: richard.jordan@virgin.net
Fax: 020-7313 9667   Tel: 020-7243 9001

JOSHI CLINIC The
57 Wimpole Street, London W1G 8YW
Fax: 020-7486 9622   Tel: 020-7487 5456

KEAN LANYON Ltd
(Graphic Designers, PR & Marketing Consultants)
Rose Cottage, Aberdeen Centre
22 Highbury Grove, London N5 2EA
Website: www.keanlanyon.com
e-mail: iain@keanlanyon.com
Fax: 020-7359 0199   Tel: 020-7354 3362

KELLER Don
(Marketing Consultancy & Project Management)
65 Glenwood Road, Harringay, London N15 3JS
e-mail: info@dakam.org.uk
Fax: 020-8809 6825   Tel: 020-8800 4882

KERR John CHARTERED ACCOUNTANTS
369-375 Eaton Road, West Derby, Liverpool L12 2AH
e-mail: advice@jkca.co.uk
Fax: 0151-228 3792   Tel: 0151-228 8977

KIEVE Paul
(Magical Effects for Theatre & Film)
23 Terrace Road, South Hackney, London E9 7ES
Website: www.stageillusion.com
e-mail: mail@stageillusion.com   Tel/Fax: 020-8985 6188

LAMBOLLE Robert
(Script Evaluation/Editing)
618B Finchley Road, London NW11 7RR
Website: www.readingandrighting.netfirms.com
e-mail: lambhorn@tiscali.co.uk   Tel: 020-8455 4564

LARK INSURANCE BROKING GROUP
(Insurance Brokers)
Wigham House, Wakering Road
Barking, Essex IG11 8PJ
e-mail: mailbox@larkinsurance.co.uk
Fax: 020-8557 2430   Tel: 020-8557 2300

LEEP MARKETING & PR
(Marketing, Press and Publicity)
5 Nassau House
122 Shaftesbury Avenue, London W1D 5ER
e-mail: philip@leep.biz
Fax: 020-7439 8833   Tel: 020-7439 9777

LEO MEDIA & ENTERTAINMENT GROUP The
150 Minories, London EC3N 1LS
Website: www.leomediagroup.com
e-mail: info@leomediagroup.com
Fax: 08701 330258   Tel: 020-8905 5191

LOCATION TUTORS NATIONWIDE
(Fully Qualified/Experienced Teachers working with
Children on Film Sets and Covering all Key Stages of
National Curriculum)
16 Poplar Walk, Herne Hill
London SE24 0BU
Website: www.locationtutors.co.uk
e-mail: locationtutorsnationwide@hotmail.com
Fax: 020-7207 8794   Tel: 020-7978 8898

LONGREACH INTERNATIONAL Ltd
(Specialist Insurance Brokers)
20-21 Tooks Court
London EC4A 1LB
Website: www.longreachint.com/theatre
e-mail: info@longreachint.com
Fax: 020-7421 7550   Tel: 020-7421 7555

LOVE Billie HISTORICAL PHOTOGRAPHS
(Picture Research. Formerly 'Amanda' Theatrical
Portraiture)
3 Winton Street, Ryde
Isle of Wight PO33 2BX
Fax: 01983 616565   Tel: 01983 812572

LUXFACTOR GROUP (UK) The
Fleet Place, 12 Nelson Drive
Petersfield, Hampshire GU31 4SJ
Website: www.luxfactor.co.uk
e-mail: info@luxfactor.co.uk
Fax: 0845 3700588   Tel: 0845 3700589

MAKE IT AMERICA
Suite 04, 1838 El Cerrito Place
Hollywood CA90068
Website: www.makeitamerica.com
e-mail: info@makeitamerica.com
Fax: (323) 436-7561   Tel: (323) 404-1827

MASPALMERAS PRODUCTIONS
(Andrew Empson) (Events Concept & Production)
4th Floor, 80-81 St Martin's Lane
London WC2N 4AA
e-mail: maspalmeras@mac.com   Tel: 020-7240 3270

McCABE Michael
(Marketing Consultant)
32 Linhope Street, Marylebone
London NW1 6HU
Website: www.michaelmccabe.net
e-mail: mailbox@michaelmccabe.net
Fax: 020-7569 8705   Tel: 020-7569 8701

McGEES Ltd
(Accountants)
Third Floor, 15 King Street
Covent Garden, London WC2E 8HN
Website: www.mcgeesltd.co.uk
Fax: 020-7836 8632   Tel: 020-7836 4344

McKENNA Deborah Ltd
(Celebrity Chefs & Lifestyle Presenters)
10 Tideway Yard, 125 Mortlake High Street
London SW14 8SN
Website: www.deborahmckenna.com
e-mail: info@deborahmckenna.com
Fax: 020-8392 2462   Tel: 020-8876 7566

MEDIA LEGAL
(Education Services)
West End House, 83 Clarendon Road
Sevenoaks, Kent TN13 1ET   Tel: 01732 460592

MILDENBERG Vanessa
(Choreographer/Movement Director)
Flat 6, Cameford Court
New Park Road, London SW2 4LH   Mobile: 07796 264828

MILITARY ADVISORY & INSTRUCTION SPECIALISTS
(John Sessions) (Advice on Weapons, Drill, Period to
Present. Ex-Army Instructors)
e-mail: higgins5589@ntlworld.com   Tel: 01904 491198

MINISTRY OF FUN
(Provision of Performers/PR Marketing Campaigns)
Unit 1, Suffolk Studios
127-129 Great Suffolk Street
London SE1 1PP
Website: www.ministryoffun.net
e-mail: james@ministryoffun.net
Fax: 020-7407 5763   Tel: 020-7407 6077

MORGAN Jane ASSOCIATES (JMA)
(Marketing & Media)
3 Heathville Road, London N19 3AJ
e-mail: jma@janemorganassociates.com
Fax: 020-7263 9877   Tel: 020-7263 9867

MOXON Paul
(Arranger & Composer)
c/o Sandra Singer Associates
21 Cotswold Road
Westcliff-on-Sea, Essex SS0 8AA
Website: www.sandrasinger.com
e-mail: sandrasingeruk@aol.com
Fax: 01702 339393   Tel: 01702 331616

MULLEN Julie
(Improvisors/Comedy Consultancy)
The Impro Lab, 34 Watts Lane
Teddington Lock TW11 8HQ   Mobile: 07956 877839

NEATE Rodger PRODUCTION MANAGEMENT
5 Southcote Road, London N19 5BJ
e-mail: rneate@dircon.co.uk
Fax: 020-7697 8237   Tel: 020-7609 9538

NEOVISION
(Location & Production Services)
7 rue Gardiol
1218 Grand-Saconnex
Geneve, Switzerland
Website: www.neovisionprod.com
e-mail: info@neovisionprod.com
Fax: (41 22) 741 1208   Tel: (41 79) 357 5417

NUTOPIA MUSIC
(Music for Film & Television) (Ferris Entertainment)
Number 8, 132 Charing Cross Road
London WC2H 0LA
Website: www.ferrisentertainment.com   Mobile: 07801 493133

NWA-UK HAMMERLOCK
(Wrestling Events, Training & Promotion)
PO Box 282, Ashford
Kent TN23 7ZZ
e-mail: nwauk@hammerlockwrestling.com
Tel/Fax: 01233 663828

NYMAN LIBSON PAUL
(Chartered Accountants)
Regina House
124 Finchley Road, London NW3 5JS
Website: www.nlpca.co.uk
e-mail: entertainment@nlpca.co.uk
Fax: 020-7433 2401   Tel: 020-7433 2400

ORANGE TREE STUDIO Ltd & MUSIC SERVICES
(Original Music/Composition & Production)
PO Box 99
Kings Langley WD4 8FB
Website: www.orangetreestudio.com
e-mail: richard@orangetreestudio.com
Mobile: 07768 146200   Tel: 01923 440550

PB PRODUCTIVE
(Photographers' Agent. Shoot, Production & Event
Management)
2 Netherfield Road
London SW17 8AZ
Website: www.pbproductive.com
e-mail: info@pbproductive.com
Mobile: 07957 424776   Tel/Fax: 020-8767 7237

PLANISPHERES
(Buisness & Legal Affairs)
Sinclair House
2 Sinclair Gardens, London W14 0AT
Website: www.planispheres.com
e-mail: info@planispheres.com   Tel/Fax: 020-7602 2038

POLICE ACTION
(Police Personnel & Tactical Arms Group Inc./Riot Police
with Shields)
59 Sylvan Avenue
Wood Green, London N22 5JA
Website: www.police-action.co.uk
e-mail: police-action@hotmail.com
Mobile: 07757 279891   Tel: 020-8889 6540

PRODUCTIONS & PROMOTIONS Ltd
Apsley Mills Cottage, London Road
Hemel Hempstead, Herts HP3 9QU
Website: www.prodmotions.com
e-mail: reception@prodmotions.com
Fax: 0845 0095540   Tel: 01442 233372

PSYCHOLOGY GROUP The
(Expert Opinion, Assessments, Psychotherapy &
Counselling, Presentation. Nationwide Service)
Website: www.psychologygroup.co.uk
e-mail: info@psychologygroup.co.uk
Fax: 0845 2805243   Tel: 0870 6092445

PUPPET CENTRE TRUST
(Development & Advocacy Agency for Puppetry & Related
Theatre)
BAC Lavender Hill
London SW11 5TN
Website: www.puppetcentre.org.uk
e-mail: pct@puppetcentre.org.uk   Tel: 020-7228 5335

RIPLEY-DUGGAN PARTNERSHIP The
(Tour Booking)
26 Goodge Street, London W1T 2QG
e-mail: info@ripleyduggan.com   Tel: 020-7436 1392

SHAW Bernard
(Specialist in Recording & Directing Voice Tapes)
Horton Manor, Canterbury CT4 7LG
Website: www.bernardshaw.co.uk
e-mail: bernard@bernardshaw.co.uk   Tel/Fax: 01227 730843

SINCLAIR Andy
(Mime)
31 Clissbury Gardens
Worthing
West Sussex BN14 0DY
Website: www.andyjsinclair.co.uk
e-mail: andynebular@hotmail.com   Mobile: 07831 196675

SPENCER Ivor
(Professional Toastmaster, Events Organiser & Principal of
Ivor Spencer International School for Butlers)
12 Little Bornes, Dulwich, London SE21 8SE
Website: www.ivorspencer.com
Fax: 020-8670 0055   Tel: 020-8670 5585

SPORTS WORKSHOP PROMOTIONS Ltd
(Production Advisors, Sport, Stunts, Safety)
PO Box 878
Crystal Palace National Sports Centre
London SE19 2BH
e-mail: info@sportspromotions.co.uk
Fax: 020-8776 7772   Tel: 020-8659 4561

STAGE CRICKET CLUB
(Cricketers & Cricket Grounds)
39-41 Hanover Steps
St George's Fields, Albion Street, London W2 2YG
Website: www.stagecc.co.uk
e-mail: brianjfilm@aol.com
Fax: 020-7262 5736   Tel: 020-7402 7543

STUDIO BOARDMAN Ltd
(Events Organisers)
Unit 7, The Vale Business Centre
203-205 The Vale, Acton, London W3 7QS
Website: www.studioboardman.co.uk
e-mail: info@boardmanbookings.co.uk   Tel: 0845 2581111

STUNT ACTION SPECIALISTS (S.A.S.)
(Corporate & TV Stunt Work)
110 Trafalgar Road, Portslade, East Sussex BN41 1GS
Website: www.stuntactionspecialists.com
e-mail: wayne@stuntactionspecialists.co.uk
Fax: 01273 708699   Tel: 01273 230214

SUMMERS David & COMPANY
(Chartered Accountants)
Argo House, Kilburn Park Road, London NW6 5LF
e-mail: dsummersfca@hotmail.com
Fax: 020-7644 0678   Tel: 020-7644 0478

TECHNICAL ADVISOR
(Spencer Duffy, Weapons Training & Tactical Advice)
e-mail: info@swat-uk.co.uk
Mobile: 07921 954218   Tel: 01634 261703

THEATRE PROJECTS CONSULTANTS
4 Apollo Studios
Charlton Kings Road, London NW5 2SW
Website: www.tpcworld.com
Fax: 020-7284 0636   Tel: 020-7482 4224

TODD Carole
(Director/Choreographer)
c/o Chris Davis Management Ltd
Tenbury House, 36 Teme Street
Tenbury Wells, Worcs WR15 8AA
e-mail: cdavis@cdm-ltd.com
Fax: 01584 819076   Tel: 01584 819005

TODS MURRAY LLP
(Richard Findlay Entertainment Lawyer)
Edinburgh Quay, 133 Fountainbridge, Edinburgh EH3 9AG
e-mail: richard.findlay@todsmurray.com
Fax: 0131-656 2023   Tel: 0131-656 2000

UK THEATRE AVAILABILITY
(Bookings Service for Theatre Producers)
3 Grand Union Walk, Camden Town, London NW1 9LP
Website: www.uktheatreavailability.co.uk
e-mail: info@uktheatreavailability.co.uk   Tel: 020-8455 3278

UNITED KINGDOM COPYRIGHT BUREAU
(Script Services)
110 Trafalgar Road, Portslade, East Sussex BN41 1GS
Website: www.copyrightbureau.co.uk
e-mail: info@copyrightbureau.co.uk
Fax: 01273 705451   Tel: 01273 277333

UPFRONT TELEVISION Ltd
(Celebrity Booking for Events)
39-41 New Oxford Street, London WC1A 1BN
Website: www.celebritiesworldwide.com
e-mail: info@upfronttv.com
Fax: 020-7836 7701   Tel: 020-7836 7702

VANTIS
(Accountants. Business & Tax Advisers)
Torrington House
47 Holywell Hill
St Albans, Hertfordshire AL1 1HD
Website: www.vantisplc.com/stalbanshh
e-mail: stalbans@vantisplc.com
Fax: 01727 861052   Tel: 01727 838255

VERNON Doremy
(Author 'Tiller Girls'/Archivist/Dance Routines Tiller Girl Style)
16 Ouseley Road
London SW12 8EF   Tel/Fax: 020-8767 6944

WELBOURNE Jacqueline
(Circus Trainer, Choreographer, Consultant)
c/o Circus Maniacs Agency, Office 8A
The Kingswood Foundation, Britannia Road
Kingswood, Bristol BS15 8DB
e-mail: jackie@circusmaniacs.com
Mobile: 07977 247287   Tel/Fax: 0117-947 7042

WEST END WORKSHOPS
(Audition Coaching/Arts Workshops)
Website: www.westendworkshops.co.uk
e-mail: info@westendworkshops.co.uk   Mobile: 07989 422808

WHITE Leonard
(Production & Script Consultant)
Highlands
40 Hill Crest Road, Newhaven
Brighton, East Sussex BN9 9EG
e-mail: leoguy.white@virgin.net   Tel: 01273 514473

WIDDOWSON Alexis CHARTERED ACCOUNTANTS
1 High Street
Welford, Northants NN6 6HT
e-mail: alexiswiddowson@aol.com   Tel/Fax: 01858 575734

WILD DREAM CONSULTANCY
(Audition Skills, Public Speaking
Confidence & Personal Development)   Tel: 020-8374 3924

WILKINSON Gavin
(Choreographer/Director/Arts Consultant)
Website: www.westendworkshops.co.uk
e-mail: info@westendworkshops.co.uk   Mobile: 07989 422808

WISE MONKEY FINANCIAL COACHING
(Simonne Gnessen)
14 Eastern Terrace Mews
Brighton BN2 1EP
Website: www.financial-coaching.co.uk
e-mail: simonne@financial-coaching.co.uk   Tel: 01273 691223

YOUNGBLOOD Ltd
(Fight Direction)
Website: www.youngblood.co.uk
e-mail: info@youngblood.co.uk   Tel: 020-7193 3207

Lie of The Mind BAC

Rosemarie Swinfield
m a k e - u p   d e s i g n e r

Rosie's Make-up Box
6 Brewer Street Soho London W1R 3FS
m: 07976-965520 t: 0845 408 2415
e: rosemarie@rosiesmake-up.co.uk

Author of:
* Stage Make-Up Step By Step
* Period Make-Up For The Stage
* Hair And Wigs For The Stage

Also
Courses, Workshops & Seminars

Henry IV LAMDA

ACADEMY COSTUMES
50 Rushworth Street, London SE1 0RB
Website: www.academycostumes.com
e-mail: info@academycostumes.com
Fax: 020-7928 6287   Tel: 020-7620 0771

ACE FEATURE FILM PRODUCTION TEAM
(Margaret Cooper, Costume Designer and
Wardrobe for Film)
Wind Ltd, 111 Sovereign Road
Earlsdon, Coventry CV5 6JB
Website: http://www.myspace.com/mi_six_aqt
e-mail: acefilm1@yahoo.com
Mobile: 07884 074315   Mobile: 00 356 213 42338

AJ COSTUMES Ltd
(Theatrical Costume Hire, Design & Making)
Sullom Lodge, Sullom Side Lane
Barnacre, Garstang PR3 1GH
Website: www.trendsgroup.co.uk
e-mail: info@trendsgroup.co.uk
Fax: 01253 407715   Tel: 0871 2003343

ALL-SEWN-UP
Mechanics Institute
7 Church Street
Heptonstall, West Yorks HX7 7NS
Website: www.allsewnup.org.uk
e-mail: nwheeler_allsewnup@hotmail.com
Fax: 01422 845070   Tel: 01422 843407

ANELLO & DAVIDE
(Handmade Shoes)
15 St Albans Grove, London W8 5BP   Tel: 020-7938 2255

ANGELS
(Fancy Dress & Revue)
119 Shaftesbury Avenue
London WC2H 8AE
Website: www.fancydress.com
e-mail: party@fancydress.com
Fax: 020-7240 9527   Tel: 020-7836 5678

ANGELS THE COSTUMIERS
1 Garrick Road, London NW9 6AA
Website: www.angels.uk.com
e-mail: angels@angels.uk.com
Fax: 020-8202 1820   Tel: 020-8202 2244

ANGELS WIGS
(Wig Hire/Makers, Facial Hair Suppliers)
1 Garrick Road, London NW9 6AA
Website: www.angels.uk.com
e-mail: wigs@angels.uk.com
Fax: 020-8202 1820   Tel: 020-8202 2244

ANTOINETTE COSTUME HIRE
(Stage, Screen and Fancy Dress)
10A Dartmouth Road
London SE23 3XU
Website: www.costumehirelondon.com
e-mail: antoinettehire@aol.com
Fax: 020-8699 1107   Tel: 020-8699 1913

ARMS & ARCHERY
(Armour, Weaponry, Chain Mail, Warrior Costumes, Tents)
The Coach House
London Road
Ware, Herts SG12 9QU
e-mail: armsandarchery@btconnect.com   Tel: 01920 460335

ATTLE Jamie COSTUME MAKER
4 Toynbee Road, Wimbledon
London SW20 8SS
e-mail: aalexiscolby@aol.com   Tel/Fax: 020-8540 3044

BAHADLY R
(Hair & Make-up Specialist, incl. Bald Caps, Ageing &
Casualty)
48 Ivy Meade Road
Macclesfield, Cheshire
Mobile: 07973 553073   Tel: 01625 615878

BBC COSTUME & WIGS
172-178 Victoria Road
North Acton, London W3 6UL
Website: www.bbcresources.co.uk/costumewig
e-mail: costume@bbc.co.uk
Fax: 020-8993 7040   Tel: 020-8576 1761

Derek Easton
Wigs for Television, Film and Theatre

1 Dorothy Avenue   Peacehaven
East Sussex   BN10 8LP

Tel / Fax: 01273 588262
Mobile: 07768 166733
wigs@derekeastonwigs.co.uk
www.derekeastonwigs.co.uk

wigswigswigswigswig

BEJEWELLED STAGE JEWELLERY
23 Glenrise Close, St Mellons
Cardiff CF3 0AS
Website: www.stagejewellery.co.uk
e-mail: info@stagejewellery.co.uk Tel/Fax: 029-2021 6655

BERTRAND Henry
(London Stockhouse for Silk)
52 Holmes Road
London NW5 3AB
Website: www.henrybertrand.co.uk
e-mail: sales@henrybertrand.co.uk
Fax: 020-7424 7001 Tel: 020-7424 7000

BIRMINGHAM COSTUME HIRE
Suites 209-210, Jubilee Centre
130 Pershore Street
Birmingham B5 6ND
e-mail: info@birminghamcostumehire.co.uk
Fax: 0121-622 2758 Tel: 0121-622 3158

BISHOP Kerry
(Hair & Make-up Artist)
Flat 4, 49 Upper Rock Gardens
Brighton, East Sussex BN2 1QF
e-mail: kerrybishop@email.com Mobile: 07759 704394

BRIGGS Ron DESIGN
(Costume Making, Costume Design)
1 Bedford Mews, London N2 9DF
e-mail: costumes@ronbriggs.com Tel: 020-8444 8801

BRYAN PHILIP DAVIES COSTUMES
(Lavish Pantomime, Musical Shows, Opera)
68 Court Road, Lewes
East Sussex BN7 2SA
Website: www.bpdcostumes.co.uk
e-mail: bryan@bpdcostumes.force9.co.uk
Mobile: 07931 249097 Tel: 01273 481004

BURLINGTONS
(Hairdressers)
14 John Princes Street
London W1G 0JS
Website: www.burlingtonsuk.com Tel: 0870 8701299

CALICO FABRICS
(Suppliers of Unbleached Calico & other Fabrics for Stage,
Costumes, Backdrops etc)
3 Ram Passage, High Street
Kingston-upon-Thames
Surrey KT1 1HH
Website: www.calicofabrics.co.uk
e-mail: sales@calicofabrics.co.uk
Fax: 020-8546 7755 Tel: 020-8541 5274

CAPEZIO
(Dance Products)
95 Whiffler Road, Norwich
Norfolk NR3 2AW
Website: www.capeziodance.com
e-mail: eusales@balletmakers.com
Fax: 0870 3500074 Tel: 0870 3500073

CHRISANNE Ltd
(Specialist Fabrics & Accessories)
Chrisanne House, 14 Locks Lane
Mitcham, Surrey CR4 2JX
Website: www.chrisanne.com
e-mail: sales@chrisanne.co.uk
Fax: 020-8640 2106 Tel: 020-8640 5921

ACADEMY COSTUMES
REALIZATION & RENTALS

50 Rushworth Street
London
SE1 0RB
020 7620 0771
info@academycostumes.com
www.academycostumes.com

COLTMAN Mike
(See COSTUME CONSTRUCTION)

COOK Sheila TEXTILES
(Vintage Textiles, Costumes & Accessories for Sale) (By Appointment)
105-107 Portobello Road
London W11 2QB
Website: www.sheilacook.co.uk
e-mail: sheilacook@sheilacook.co.uk   Tel: 020-7792 8001

COSPROP Ltd
(Costumes & Accessories)
469-475 Holloway Road, London N7 6LE
Website: www.cosprop.com
e-mail: enquiries@cosprop.com
Fax: 020-7561 7310   Tel: 020-7561 7300

COSTUME CONSTRUCTION
(Costumes, Masks, Props, Puppets)
Studio 1, Croft Street
Cheltenham GL53 0EE
Website: www.costumeconstruction.co.uk
Tel/Fax: 01242 581847

COSTUME GUIDE The
(Products & Suppliers Directory)
PO Box 54229, London W14 0SE
e-mail: enquiries@thecostumeguide.com   Tel: 020-7602 2857

COSTUME SOLUTIONS
43 Rowan Road, London W6 7DT
Website: www.costumesolutions.co.uk
e-mail: karen@costumesolutions.co.uk   Tel: 020-7603 9035

COSTUME STORE Ltd The
(Costume Accessories)
16 Station Street, Lewes, East Sussex BN7 2DB
Website: www.thecostumestore.co.uk
Fax: 01273 477191   Tel: 01273 479727

COSTUME STUDIO Ltd
(Costumes & Wigs)
Montgomery House
159-161 Balls Pond Road, London N1 4BG
Website: www.costumestudio.co.uk
e-mail: costume.studio@btconnect.com
Tel/Fax: 020-7923 9065   Tel: 020-7275 9614

COSTUMIA
Unit 9, Hockley Goods Yard
Pitsford Street, Hockley
Birmingham B18 6PT
Website: www.costumia.co.uk
e-mail: info@costumia.co.uk   Tel: 0121-551 2710

COUNTY DRAMA WARDROBE
(Costumes & Wigs - Hire only - & Make-up for Sale)
25 Gwydir Street
Cambridge CB1 2LG   Tel: 01223 313423

CRAZY CLOTHES CONNECTION
(1920's-1970's for Sale or Hire)
134 Lancaster Road, Ladbroke Grove
London W11 1QU   Tel: 020-7221 3989

DANCIA INTERNATIONAL
187 Drury Lane, London WC2B 5QD
Website: www.dancia.co.uk
e-mail: dancialondon@btconnect.com   Tel/Fax: 020-7831 9483

DELAMAR ACADEMY
(Make-up Training)
Ealing Studios, Building D, 2nd Floor
Ealing Green, London W5 5EP
Website: www.delamaracademy.co.uk
e-mail: info@delamaracademy.co.uk Tel/Fax: 020-8579 9511

DESIGNER ALTERATIONS
(Restyling & Remodelling of Clothes & Costumes)
220A Queenstown Road
Battersea, London SW8 4LP
Website: www.designeralterations.com
Fax: 020-7622 4148   Tel: 020-7498 4360

EASTON Derek
(Wigs For Theatre, Film & TV)
1 Dorothy Avenue
Peacehaven, East Sussex BN10 8LP
Website: www.derekeastonwigs.co.uk
e-mail: wigs@derekeastonwigs.co.uk
Mobile: 07768 166733   Tel/Fax: 01273 588262

EDA ROSE MILLINERY
(Ladies' Model Hat Design & Manufacture)
Lalique, Mongewell
Wallingford, Oxon OX10 8BP
Website: www.edarosehats.com
Fax: 01491 835909   Tel: 01491 837174

FOX Charles H. Ltd
(Professional Make-up & Wigs)
22 Tavistock Street, London WC2E 7PY
Website: www.charlesfox.co.uk
Fax: 0870 2001369   Tel: 0870 2000369

FREED OF LONDON
(Dancewear & Dance Shoes)
94 St Martin's Lane, London WC2N 4AT
Website: www.freedoflondon.com
e-mail: shop@freed.co.uk
Fax: 020-7240 3061   Tel: 020-7240 0432

FUNN Ltd
(Silk, Cotton Wool Stockings, Opaque Opera Tights & 40's Rayon Stockings)
PO Box 102, Steyning
West Sussex BN44 3EB
e-mail: funn.biz@lycos.com
Fax: 0870 1361780   Tel: 0870 8794430

GAMBA THEATRICAL
(See THEATRICAL FOOTWEAR COMPANY Ltd The)

GAV NICOLA THEATRICAL FOOTWEAR
West Wick, Marshes
Burnham-on-Crouch
Essex CM0 8NE
e-mail: sale@gavnicola.freeserve.co.uk
Mobile: 07961 974278   Tel/Fax: 01621 785623

Stageworks WORLDWIDE PRODUCTIONS COSTUMES

The largest costume wardrobe in the North with a vast stock of costumes. Specialist in show and dance costumes using the finest fabrics. Headdresses, harnesses, feathers, fibre optic costumes, costume characters, bespoke couture

Hire - Made to Order - Design
Also wigs, make up, sets and props
Creative - innovative - professional

Tel **01253 342426/7**   Fax: **01253 342702**
email: info@stageworkswwp.com   www.stageworkswwp.com

GILLHAM Felicite
(Wig Makers for Theatre, Opera & Film)
Trendle Cottage
Trendle Street
Sherborne, Dorset DT9 3NT
e-mail: f.gillham.wigs@gmx.net
Mobile: 07802 955908   Tel: 01935 814328

GREASEPAINT
143 Northfield Avenue
Ealing, London W13 9QT
Website: www.greasepaint.co.uk
e-mail: info@greasepaint.co.uk
Fax: 020-8840 3983   Tel: 020-8840 6000

HAIRAISERS
(Wigs)
9-11 Sunbeam Road, Park Royal
London NW10 6JP
Website: www.hairaisers.com
Fax: 020-8963 1600   Tel: 020-8965 2500

HAND & LOCK
86 Margaret Street
London W1W 8TE
e-mail: enquiries@hand-embroidery.co.uk
Fax: 020-7580 7499   Tel: 020-7580 7488

HARVEYS OF HOVE
(Theatrical Costumes & Military Specialists)
110 Trafalgar Road
Portslade, Sussex BN41 1GS
Website: www.harveysofhove.co.uk
e-mail: harveys.costume@ntlworld.com
Fax: 01273 708699   Tel: 01273 430323

HERALD & HEART HATTERS
(Men's & Women's Hats & Headdresses - Period & Modern)
Church Farm House
East Guildford
Rye, East Sussex TN31 7PA
Website: www.heraldandheart.com
e-mail: enquiries@heraldandheart.com   Tel: 01797 226798

HIREARCHY
(Classic & Contemporary Costume)
45-47 Palmerston Road, Boscombe
Bournemouth, Dorset BH1 4HW
Website: www.hirearchy.co.uk
e-mail: hirearchy1@aol.com   Tel: 01202 394465

HODIN Annabel
(Costume Designer/Stylist)
12 Eton Avenue, London NW3 3EH
e-mail: annabelhodin@aol.com
Mobile: 07836 754079   Tel: 020-7431 8761

INCE Katie
(Wig Maker & Make-up Artist)
15 Birchwood Gardens
Idle Park, Bradford BD10 9EW
e-mail: katieince@gmail.com   Mobile: 07900 250853

INTERNATIONAL COLLECTIVE (CREATIVE)
Golden Cross House
8 Duncannon Street
The Strand, London WC2N 4JF
Website: www.internationalcollective.co.uk
e-mail: enquiries@internationalcollective.co.uk
Fax: 020-7484 5100   Tel: 020-7484 5080

INTERNATIONAL DANCE SUPPLIES/GRISHKO UK Ltd
(Importer & Distributor of Dance Shoes and Dancewear)
64 Butt Lane, Milton, Cambridge CB24 6DG
Website: www.grishko.co.uk
e-mail: info@grishko.co.uk
Fax: 01223 280388   Tel: 01223 861425

JULIETTE DESIGNS
(Diamante Jewellery Manufacturers)
90 Yerbury Road, London N19 4RS
Website: www.stagejewellery.com
Fax: 020-7281 7326   Tel: 020-7263 7878

LANDSFIELD Warren
(Period Legal Wigs)
47 Glenmore Road
London NW3 4DA   Tel: 020-7722 4581

Joan Stribling
BAFTA and D&AD
Film, T.V., Make-up, Hair
07791758480
www.ilfracom.org.uk/stribling

LARGER THAN LIFE STAGEWEAR
(Theatrical Costumes for Hire)
2 Sundridge Parade
Bromley, Kent BR1 4DY
Website: www.largerthanlifestagewear.co.uk
e-mail: info@largerthanlifestagewear.co.uk
Tel/Fax: 020-8466 9010

LEWIS HENRY Ltd
(Dress Makers)
111-113 Great Portland Street
London W1W 6QQ   Tel: 020-7636 6683

LOTTIE
(Childrens' Period Costume Hire)
Unit 10, Omega Works
167 Hermitage Road, London N4 1LZ
Website: www.lottiecostumehire.com
e-mail: info@lottiecostumehire.com   Tel/Fax: 020-8211 8200

MADDERMARKET THEATRE COSTUME HIRE
(Period Clothing, Costume Hire & Wig Hire)
St John's Alley
Norwich NR2 1DR
Website: www.maddermarket.co.uk
e-mail: mmtheatre@btconnect.com
Fax: 01603 661357   Tel: 01603 626292

MASK Kim
(Costume & Make-up Protection masks)
PO Box 532
Isleworth, Middlesex TW7 6XP
Website: www.kimmask.com
e-mail: info@kimmask.com   Tel: 08450 568482

MASON Sophia
(Hair & Make-up Artist)
Website: www.sophiamason.co.uk
e-mail: sophia@facetime.co.uk   Mobile: 07880 720013

MASTER CLEANERS The
(Dry Cleaning of Theatrical Costumes & Antique Garments)
189 Haverstock Hill
London NW3 4QG
e-mail: info@themastercleaners.com   Tel: 020-7431 3725

MEANANDGREEN.COM
17 Lichfield Street
Wolverhampton WV1 1EA
Website: www.meanandgreen.com
e-mail: custserv@meanandgreen.com
Fax: 01902 425564   Tel: 0845 899113

MIDNIGHT
Costume Design & Wardrobe Services (Music, Theatre, Film, Tours)
e-mail: midnight_wardrobe@hotmail.com
Mobile: 07722 882847

MINHA CASA Ltd
51 Chalk Farm Road, London NW1 8AN
Website: www.minha-casa.co.uk
Fax: 020-7428 6901   Tel: 020-7428 6900

NATIONAL THEATRE
(Costume & Furniture Hire)
Chichester House
Kennington Park Estate
1-3 Brixton Road, London SW9 6DE
e-mail: costume_hire@nationaltheatre.org.uk
Tel: 020-7735 4774 (Costume)   Tel: 020-7820 1358 (Props)

NEW ID
(Makeover & Photographic Studios)
Third Floor
17-18 Margaret Street
London W1W 8RP
Website: www.newidstudios.com
e-mail: bookings@newidstudios.co.uk   Tel: 0870 8701299

NORMAN Sam
(Hair & Make-up)
Website: www.samnorman.co.uk
e-mail: sam@samnorman.co.uk   Mobile: 07932 397465

ORIGINAL KNITWEAR
(Inc. Fake Fur) (Gina Pinnick)
Avalon, Tregoney Hill
Mevagissey, Cornwall PL26 6RG
e-mail: okgina@btinternet.com
Mobile: 07957 376855   Tel: 01726 844807

PATEY (LONDON) Ltd
Unit 1, 9 Gowlett Road, London SE15 4HX
Website: www.pateyhats.com
e-mail: pateyhats@aol.com
Fax: 020-7732 9538   Tel: 020-7635 0030

PINK POINTES DANCEWEAR
1A Suttons Lane
Hornchurch, Essex RM12 6RD
e-mail: pink.pointes@btconnect.com   Tel/Fax: 01708 438584

PLAYHOUSE ENTERTAINMENT GROUP
272 Kings Road
Tyseley, Birmingham B11 2AB
Website: www.playhousecostumes.co.uk
e-mail: enquiries@playhousecostumes.co.uk
Tel: 0121-707 9321

POLAND DENTAL STUDIO
(Film/Stage Dentistry)
1 Devonshire Place, London W1G 6HH
e-mail: polandslab@aol.com
Fax: 020-7486 3952   Tel: 020-7935 6919

PORSELLI
9 West Street, Cambridge Circus
London WC2H 9NE
Website: www.porselli.com
e-mail: porselliuk@aol.com
Fax: 020-7836 6171   Tel: 020-7836 2862

PROBLOOD
11 Mount Pleasant, Framlingham
Suffolk IP13 9HQ   Tel/Fax: 01728 723865

PULLON PRODUCTIONS
(Costumiers)
St George's Studio, Wood End Lane
Fillongley, Coventry CV7 8DF
Website: www.pm-productions.co.uk   Tel/Fax: 01676 541390

RAINBOW PRODUCTIONS Ltd
(Manufacture & Handling of Costume Characters)
Rainbow House
56 Windsor Avenue, London SW19 2RR
Website: www.rainbowproductions.co.uk
e-mail: info@rainbowproductions.co.uk
Fax: 020-8545 0777   Tel: 020-8545 0700

REPLICA WAREHOUSE
(Costumiers & Props)
200 Main Road, Goostrey
Cheshire CW4 8PD
Website: www.replicawarehouse.co.uk
e-mail: lesleyedwards@replicawarehouse.co.uk
                Tel/Fax: 01477 534075

ROBBINS Sheila
(Wig Hire)
Broombarn, 7 Ivy Cottages
Hinksey Hill
Oxford OX1 5BQ   Tel/Fax: 01865 735524

ROLANDI Gianluca
(Hair & Make-up)
83 Deroy Lodge
Wicklow Street, London WC1X 3LF
Website: www.gluca.co.uk
e-mail: gluca@gluca.co.uk   Mobile: 07990 637299

ROYAL EXCHANGE THEATRE COSTUME HIRE
(Period Costumes & Accessories)
47-53 Swan Street
Manchester M4 5JY
Website: www.royalexchange.co.uk
e-mail: costume.hire@royalexchange.co.uk
                Tel/Fax: 0161-819 6660

ROYAL LYCEUM THEATRE COMPANY
(Theatrical Costume Hire)
29 Roseburn Street
Edinburgh EH12 5PE
Website: www.lyceum.org.uk
Fax: 0131-346 8072   Tel: 0131-337 1997

ROYAL SHAKESPEARE COMPANY COSTUME HIRE
Timothy's Bridge Road
Stratford-upon-Avon
Warwickshire CV37 9UY   Tel/Fax: 01789 205920

ROYER Hugo INTERNATIONAL Ltd
(Hair & Wig Materials)
10 Lakeside Business Park
Swan Lane, Sandhurst
Berkshire GU47 9DN
Website: www.hugoroyer.com
e-mail: enquiries@royer.co.uk
Fax: 01252 878852   Tel: 01252 878811

RUMBLE Jane
(Masks, Millinery, Helmets Made to Order)
121 Elmstead Avenue, Wembley
Middlesex HA9 8NT   Tel: 020-8904 6462

RUSSELL HOWARTH Ltd
35 Hoxton Square, London N1 6NN
Fax: 020-7729 0107   Tel: 020-7739 6960

SEXTON Sally Ann
(Hair & Make-up Designer)
c/o 52 Forty Avenue
Wembley, Middlesex NW9
e-mail: theharrisagency@btconnect.com
Mobile: 07973 802842   Tel: 020-8908 4451

SIDE EFFECTS
(Custom-made Character/FX Costumes)
92 Fentiman Road, London SW8 1LA
e-mail: sfx@lineone.net
Fax: 020-7207 0062   Tel: 020-7857 1116

SINGER Sandra ASSOCIATES
(Fashion Stylists for TV & Theatre, Costume/Designer)
21 Cotswold Road
Westcliff-on-Sea, Essex SS0 8AA
Website: www.sandrasinger.com
e-mail: sandrasingeruk@aol.com
Fax: 01702 339393   Tel: 01702 331616

SLEIMAN Hilary
(Specialist & Period Knitwear)
72 Godwin Road, London E7 0LG
Website: www.hilarysleiman.co.uk
e-mail: hilary.sleiman@ntlworld.com
Mobile: 07940 555663   Tel: 020-8555 6176

SOFT PROPS
(Costume & Model Makers)
92 Fentiman Road
London SW8 1LA
e-mail: jackie@softprops.co.uk
Fax: 020-7207 0062   Tel: 020-7587 1116

SQUIRES & JOHN'S PRODUCTIONS Ltd
(Theatrical Costume Hire, Design & Making)
Sullom Lodge, Sullom Side Lane
Barnacre, Garstang PR3 1GH
Website: www.trendsgroup.co.uk
e-mail: info@trendsgroup.co.uk
Fax: 01253 407715   Tel: 0871 2003343

STAGEWORKS WORLDWIDE PRODUCTIONS
(Largest Costume Wardrobe in North)
525 Ocean Boulevard
Blackpool FY4 1EZ
Website: www.stageworkswwp.com
e-mail: simon.george@stageworkswwp.com
Fax: 01253 342702   Tel: 01253 342427

STRIBLING Joan
(Film & Television Make-up, Hair & Prosthetic
Designer/Artist, BAFTA. D & AD Awards)
Website: www.ilfracom.org.uk/stribling
e-mail: joanstribling@hotmail.com   Mobile: 07791 758480

SWINFIELD Rosemarie
(Make-up Design & Training)
Rosie's Make-Up Box
6 Brewer Street
Soho, London W1R 3FS
Website: www.rosiesmake-up.co.uk
e-mail: rosemarie@rosiesmake-up.co.uk
Tel: 0845 4082415   Mobile: 07976 965520

TALK TO THE HAND PUPPETS
(Custom Puppets for Television & Theatre)
24 Burstead Close
Brighton BN1 7HT
Website: www.talktothehandproductions.com
e-mail: talktothehandproductions@hotmail.com
Mobile: 07813 682293   Mobile: 07855 421454

THEATREKNITS
102C Belgravia Workshops
157-163 Marlborough Road
London N19 4NF
e-mail: trevorcollins@blueyonder.co.uk
Tel/Fax: 020-7561 0044

THEATRICAL FOOTWEAR COMPANY Ltd The
(Trading as GAMBA Theatrical)
Unit 14, Chingford Industrial Centre
Hall Lane, Chingford
London E4 8DJ
e-mail: gambatheatrical@tiscali.co.uk
Fax: 020-8529 7995   Tel: 020-8529 9195

THEATRICAL SHOEMAKERS Ltd
(Footwear)
Unit 7A, Thames Road Industrial Estate
Thames Road
Silvertown, London E16 2EZ
Website: www.shoemaking.co.uk
e-mail: ts@shoemaking.co.uk
Fax: 020-7476 5220   Tel: 020-7474 0500

THREE KINGS THEATRICAL SUPPLY GROUP
(Make-up, Film Production & Theatrical Services)
84 Queens Road, North Camp
Farnborough, Hampshire GU14 6JR
Website: www.3kmake-up.com
e-mail: info@3kmake-up.com   Tel: 01252 371123

TRYFONOS Mary MASKS
(Designer & Maker of Masks & Costume Properties)
59 Shaftesbury Road, London N19 4QW
e-mail: marytryfonos@aol.com
Mobile: 07764 587433   Tel: 020-7561 9880

VINTAGE SHIRT COMPANY The
2 Mount Place, Lewes, East Sussex BN7 1YH
Website: www.vintageshirt.co.uk
e-mail: info@vintageshirt.co.uk   Tel/Fax: 01273 477699

WEST YORKSHIRE FABRICS Ltd
(Venetian, Crepe, Suiting, Barathea, Stretch Fabrics, Linen,
Cut Lengths)
West Yorkshire House
High Ash Drive, Leeds LS17 8RA
e-mail: info@stroud-brothers.demon.co.uk
Tel/Fax: 0870 4439842

WIG EXPECTATIONS
3 Northernhay Walk
Morden, Surrey SM4 4BS
Website: www.wigexpectations.com
e-mail: wigexpectations@aol.com   Tel: 020-8540 5667

WIG ROOM The
22 Coronation Road, Basingstoke, Hants RG21 4HA
e-mail: wigroom@fsbdial.co.uk   Tel/Fax: 01256 415737

WIG SPECIALITIES Ltd
(Hand Made Wigs & Facial Hair, Hair Extensions etc)
First Floor
173 Seymour Place, London W1H 4PW
Website: www.wigspecialities.co.uk
e-mail: wigspecialities@btconnect.com
Fax: 020-7723 1566   Tel: 020-7262 6565

WILLIAMS Emma
(Costume Designer & Stylist - Film, TV & Theatre)
e-mail: emmacoz@dsl.pipex.com   Mobile: 07710 130345

WILSON Marian WIGS
(Theatrical & Film Wig Maker)
59 Gloucester Street, Faringdon, Oxon SN7 7JA
e-mail: gdwilly60@tiscali.co.uk
Fax: 01367 242438   Tel: 01367 241696

WOOD Kevin PRODUCTIONS
(Costume Hire)
Langdon Abbey, West Langdon, Dover, Kent CT15 5HJ
e-mail: sylviasims@btconnect.com
Fax: 01304 853506   Tel: 01304 853539

WRIGHT Fay
(Freelance Make-up Artist)
37 Veryan, Woking, Surrey GU21 3LL
e-mail: faylin_wright@hotmail.com   Mobile: 07816 128575

DAILY EXPRESS Tel: 0871 4341010
Northern Shell Building
10 Lower Thames Street, London EC3R 6EN
Films: Alan Hunter
Television: Matt Baylis

DAILY MAIL Tel: 020-7938 6000
Northcliffe House
2 Derry Street, Kensington
London W8 5TT
Theatre: Quentin Letts
Films: Chris Tookey

DAILY STAR Tel: 0871 4341010
Northern Shell Building
10 Lower Thames Street, London EC3R 6EN
Show Business & Television: Nigel Pauley, Amy Watts,
Charli McEgan, Leigh Purves
Films & Video: Alan Frank

DAILY TELEGRAPH Tel: 020-7931 2000
111 Buckingham Palace Road
London SW1W 0DT
Theatre: Charles Spencer
Films: Sukhdev Sandhu
Radio: Gillian Reynolds Art: Richard Dorment
Dance: Ismene Brown Music: Geoffrey Norris

FINANCIAL TIMES Tel: 020-7873 3000
1 Southwark Bridge, London SE1 9HL
Theatre: Sarah Hemmings, Ian Shuttleworth
Films: Nigel Andrews
Television: Martin Hoyle, Karl French

GUARDIAN Tel: 020-7278 2332
119 Farringdon Road, London EC1R 3ER
Theatre: Michael Billington
Films: Peter Bradshaw
Television: Nancy Banks-Smith
Radio: Elisabeth Mahoney

INDEPENDENT Tel: 020-7005 2000
191 Marsh Wall
London E14 9RS
Television: Tom Sutcliffe

LONDON EVENING STANDARD Tel: 020-7938 6000
Northcliffe House
2 Derry Street, Kensington, London W8 5EE
Theatre: Nicholas de Jongh, Fiona Mountford,
Kieron Quirke
Films: Derek Malcolm, Opera: Fiona Maddocks
Television: Victor Lewis-Smith
Classical Music: Barry Millington

MAIL ON SUNDAY Tel: 020-7938 6000
(Review Section)
Northcliffe House, 2 Derry Street, London W8 5TS
Theatre: Georgina Brown
Films: Jason Solomons, Matthew Bond
Television: Jaci Stephen
Radio: Simon Garfield

MIRROR Tel: 020-7510 3000
Mirror Group Newspapers Ltd
1 Canada Square, Canary Wharf, London E14 5AP
Films: Dave Edwards
Television: Nicola Methven

MORNING STAR Tel: 020-8510 0815
William Rust House, 52 Beachy Road, London E3 2NS
Theatre & Films: Katie Gilmore

NEWS OF THE WORLD Tel: 020-7782 4000
News International Plc
1 Virginia Street, London E98 1NW
Show Business: Rav Singh
Films: Polly Graham

OBSERVER Tel: 020-7278 2332
3-7 Herbal Hill, London EC1R 5EJ
Theatre: Susanna Clapp
Films: Philip French, Akin Ojumu
Radio: Miranda Sawyer

PEOPLE Tel: 020-7293 3000
1 Canada Square, Canary Wharf, London E14 5AP
Television & Radio: Sarah Moolla
Films: Richard Bacon
Show Business: Alice Walker
Features: Chris Bucktin

SPORT Tel: 0161-238 8151
Sport Newspapers Ltd
19 Great Ancoats Street, Manchester M60 4BT
Showbusiness/Features: Nicky Tabarn

SUN Tel: 020-7782 4000
News International Plc
1 Virginia Street, Wapping, London E98 1SN
Television: Ally Ross

SUNDAY EXPRESS Tel: 0871 4341010
Northern Shell Building
10 Lower Thames Street, London EC3R 6EN
Theatre: Mark Shenton
Films: Henry Fitzherbert
Television: David Stephenson
Radio & Arts: Rachel Jane

SUNDAY MIRROR Tel: 020-7510 3000
Mirror Group
1 Canada Square, Canary Wharf, London E14 5AP
Theatre & Television: Kevin O'Sullivan
Films: Mark Adams
Showbiz: Zoe Griffin

SUNDAY TELEGRAPH Tel: 020-7931 2000
111 Buckingham Palace Road, London SW1W 0DT
Theatre: Tim Walker
Films: Jenny McCartney, Catherine Shoard
Television: John Preston

SUNDAY TIMES Tel: 020-7782 5000
News International Plc
1 Pennington Street, London E98 1ST
Theatre: Christopher Hart
Films: Cosmo Landesman
Television: A. A. Gill
Radio: Paul Donovan

TIMES Tel: 020-7782 5000
News International Plc
1 Pennington Street, London E98 1TT
Theatre: Benedict Nightingale
Films: James Christopher
Television: Andrew Billen
Video: Ed Potton Radio: Chris Campling

D

Dance Companies & Organisations
Dance Training & Professional Classes
Drama Schools (Conference of)
Drama Training, Schools & Coaches

Abbreviations:

SS Stage School for Children
D Dramatic Art (incl Coaching, Audition Technique etc)
DS Full time Drama Training E Elocution Coaching
(incl Correction of Accents, Speech Therapy,
Dialects etc)
S Singing Sp Specialised Training

[CONTACTS 2008]

AKADEMI SOUTH ASIAN DANCE UK
213 Haverstock Hill, Hampstead Town Hall
Haverstock Hill, London NW3 4QP
Website: www.akademi.co.uk
e-mail: info@akademi.co.uk
Fax: 020-7691 3211   Tel: 020-7691 3210

ANJALI DANCE COMPANY
The Mill Arts Centre, Spiceball Park
Banbury, Oxford OX16 5QE
Website: www.anjali.co.uk
e-mail: info@anjali.co.uk   Tel: 01295 251909

ARTSWORLD PRESENTATIONS Ltd
Vicarage House
58-60 Kensington Church Street, London W8 4DB
Website: www.arts-world.co.uk
e-mail: p@triciamurraybett.com
Fax: 020-7368 3338   Tel: 020-7368 3337

BALLROOM - LONDON THEATRE OF
(Artistic Director - Paul Harris)
24 Montana Gardens, Sutton, Surrey SM1 4FP
Website: www.londontheatreofballroom.com
e-mail: office@londontheatreofballroom.com
Mobile: 07958 784462   Tel/Fax: 020-8722 8798

BEDLAM DANCE COMPANY
(Write)
18 St Augustine's Road, London NW1 9RN
Website: www.bedlamdance.com
e-mail: info@bedlamdance.com

BIRMINGHAM ROYAL BALLET
Thorp Street, Birmingham B5 4AU
Website: www.brb.org.uk
e-mail: administrator@brb.org.uk
Fax: 0121-245 3570   Tel: 0121-245 3500

BODY OF PEOPLE
(Jazz Theatre Company)
10 Stayton Road, Sutton, Surrey SM1 1RB
Website: www.bop.org.uk
e-mail: info@bop.org.uk   Tel: 020-8641 6959

BROWN Carole DANCES
(Gwen Van Spijk)
PO Box 563, Banbury OX16 6AQ
Website: www.cueperformance.com
e-mail: gwen@cueperformance.com   Tel: 01869 338458

CANDOCO DANCE COMPANY
2T Leroy House, 436 Essex Road, London N1 3QP
Website: www.candoco.co.uk
e-mail: info@candoco.co.uk
Fax: 020-7704 1645   Tel: 020-7704 6845

CHOLMONDELEYS & FEATHERSTONEHAUGHS The
LF1.1
Lafone House, The Leathermarket
11-13 Leathermarket Street, London SE1 3HN
Website: www.thecholmondeleys.org
e-mail: admin@thecholmondeleys.org
Fax: 020-7378 8810   Tel: 020-7378 8800

COMBINATION DANCE COMPANY
Artists in Residence, Whitton School & Sports College
Percy Road, Twickenham TW2 6JW
Website: www.combinationdance.co.uk
e-mail: info@combinationdance.co.uk
Fax: 020-8894 0690   Tel: 020-8894 4503

COMPANY OF CRANKS
1st Floor, 62 Northfield House
Frensham Street, London SE15 6TN
Website: www.mimeworks.com
e-mail: mimetic16@yahoo.com   Mobile: 07963 617981

How do I become a professional dancer?

Full-time vocational training can start from as young as ten years old. A good starting point for researching the different schools and courses available is CDET (Council for Dance Education & Training) www.cdet.org.uk. There are over sixteen dance colleges offering professional training accredited by CDET, and nearly three hundred university courses which include some form of dance training. It is estimated that over one thousand dancers graduate from vocational training schools or university courses every year, so it is a highly competitive career. Therefore anyone wanting to be a professional dancer must obtain as many years of training and experience as possible, plus go to see plenty of performances spanning different types and genres of dance. If you require further information on vocational dance schools, applying to accredited dance courses, auditions and funding, contact CDET's information line 'Answers for Dancers' on 020 7240 5703.

How should I use these listings?

The following pages will supply you with up-to-date contact details for a wide range of dance companies and organisations, followed by listings for dance training and professional classes. Always research schools and classes thoroughly, obtaining copies of prospectuses where available. Most vocational schools offer two and three year full-time training programmes, many also offer excellent degree programmes. Foundation Courses offer a sound introduction to the profession, but they can never replace a full-time vocational course. Many schools, organisations and studios also offer part-time / evening classes which offer a general understanding of dance and complementary technique or the opportunity to refresh specific dance skills; they will not, however, enable a student to become a professional dancer.

What are dance companies?

There are more than two hundred dance companies in the UK, spanning a variety of dance styles including ballet, contemporary, hip hop and African. A dance company will either be resident in a venue, be a touring company, or a combination of both. Many have websites which you can visit for full information. Most dance companies employ ensemble dancers on short to medium contracts, who may then work on a number of different productions for the same company over a number of months. In addition, the company will also employ principal / leading dancers on a role-by-role basis.

Commercial dance and musical theatre

Dance also plays a role in commercial theatre, musicals, opera, film, television, live music and video, corporate events and many other industries. Dancers wishing to promote themselves to these types of job opportunities should consider joining Spotlight's latest directory for dancers see www.spotlight.com/dancers: a central directory of dancers which is used by dance employers throughout the UK to locate dancers and send out casting or audition information. Dancers may also want to be represented by an agent. A number of specialist dance agencies are listed in the 'Agents – Dance' towards the front of this directory.

Dance organisations

There are numerous organisations which exist to support professional dancers, covering important areas including health and safety, career development, networking and legal and financial aspects. Other organisations (e.g. Regional / National Dance Agencies) exist to promote dance within the wider community.

Other careers in dance

Opportunities also exist to work as a teacher, choreographer, technician or manager. Dance UK www.danceuk.org is a valuable source of information for anyone considering this type of work.

Dance UK is the national voice for dance. It gives the following advice to those embarking on a career in the dance industry:

Dance is a vibrant, creative and boundary-pushing art form. Dance in the UK is more popular than ever, with programmes like *Strictly Come Dancing*, events such as *Big Dance* taking over the country and world-class dancers basing their careers here. The nation is falling in love with dance and it is now the fastest growing art form.

A career in dance demands versatility, elite strength in both mind and body, and a passion and hunger to drive on through different terrains. It is important to know that there is a lot of help and support available, and Dance UK is just one of the support organisations in place.

As the national voice for dance, Dance UK lobbies to raise the profile of dance. It is a membership organisation which champions healthier dancers and a healthier dance economy, facilitates networks for the profession and nurtures career development. In addition, Dance UK hosts the UK Choreographer's Directory, offers cost-effective insurance, and provides information for dance professionals.

I want to be a dancer, what do I do?

- Think about the area of dance you would like to train in, try some classes out locally by contacting your national dance agency. These can be found at www.londondance.com
- Identify what training you will need. The Council for Dance Education and Training www.cdet.org.uk provides information on vocational dance training
- For jobs and auditions, go to www.londondance.com and www.thestage.co.uk, as well as The Place Artist Development www.theplace.org.uk, www.communitydance.org.uk and Dance UK's e-groups
- For information on agencies representing dancers, contact The Knowledge www.theknowledgeonline.com, The Place Artist Development www.theplace.org.uk and Contacts www.spotlight.com
- Throughout your training and career in dance, it is very important to look after your most important instrument: your body and mind. Dance UK's Healthier Dance Programme www.danceuk.org can help you to do so
- Another important area for you to consider is contracts and legal issues. Contact Equity, the Performers' Union www.equity.org.uk, for advice in this area. There is also important financial information for you to be aware of as regards to tax and working freelance, which the HM Revenue & Customs can help you with www.hmrc.gov.uk
- Don't forget your pension - visit www.pensionsforartists.org.uk
- A career in dance develops a large skills base that can be developed or transferred into other areas should you wish to widen your career choices at any time. Dancers' Career Development www.thedcd.org.uk offers support, guidance and financial help to dancers seeking to widen their career options
- For information on teaching dance, useful organisations are the Council for Dance Education and Training www.cdet.org.uk, Foundation for Community Dance www.communitydance.org.uk and the National Dance Teachers Association www.ndta.org.uk
- For information on South Asian arts, contact Sampad www.sampad.org.uk and Akademi www.akademi.co.uk, and to learn about African dance forms contact the Association of Dance of the African Diaspora www.adad.org.uk

  Finally, enjoy your career in dance and all the fantastic opportunities it has to offer!

For more information about Dance UK visit www.danceuk.org

DANCE SOUTH WEST
PO Box 5457, Bournemouth, Dorset BH1 1WU
Website: www.dancesouthwest.org.uk
e-mail: info@dancesouthwest.org.uk   Tel/Fax: 01202 554131

DARKIN ENSEMBLE
c/o Bemove, London House
271-273 King Street, London W6 9LZ
Website: www.writingthebody.co.uk
e-mail: karen@bemove.co.uk   Tel: 020-7149 0250

DAVIES Siobhan DANCE
85 St George's Road, London SE1 6ER
Website: www.siobhandavies.com
e-mail: info@siobhandavies.com
Fax: 020-7091 9669   Tel: 020-7091 9650

DV8 PHYSICAL THEATRE
Arts Admin, Toynbee Studios
28 Commercial Street, London E1 6AB
Website: www.dv8.co.uk
e-mail: dv8@artsadmin.co.uk
Fax: 020-7247 5103   Tel: 020-7655 0977

ENGLISH NATIONAL BALLET Ltd
Markova House, 39 Jay Mews, London SW7 2ES
Website: www.ballet.org.uk
e-mail: feedback@ballet.org.uk
Fax: 020-7225 0827   Tel: 020-7581 1245

ENGLISH YOUTH BALLET
85 Brockley Grove, Brockley, London SE4 1DZ
Website: www.englishyouthballet.co.uk
e-mail: misslewis@englishyouthballet.co.uk
Tel/Fax: 020-8691 2806

GREEN CANDLE DANCE COMPANY
Oxford House, Derbyshire Street
Bethnal Green, London E2 6HG
Website: www.greencandledance.com
e-mail: info@greencandledance.com
Fax: 020-7729 8272   Tel: 020-7739 7722

IJAD
22 Allison Road
London N8 0AT
Website: www.ijad.freeserve.co.uk
e-mail: jouman@ijad.freeserve.co.uk   Mobile: 07930 378639

INDEPENDENT BALLET WALES
30 Glasllwch Crescent, Newport, South Wales NP20 3SE
Website: www.welshballet.co.uk
e-mail: dariusjames@welshballet.co.uk
Fax: 01633 221690   Tel: 01633 253985

JEYASINGH Shobana DANCE COMPANY
Moving Arts Base
34 Liverpool Road, Islington, London N1 1LA
Website: www.shobanajeyasingh.co.uk
e-mail: admin@shobanajeyasingh.co.uk   Tel: 020-7697 4444

KHAN Akram COMPANY
Unit 232a, 35a Britannia Row, London N1 8QH
Website: www.akramkhancompany.net
e-mail: office@akramkhancompany.net
Fax: 020-7354 5554   Tel: 020-7354 4333

KOSH The
(Physical Theatre)
9 Stapleton Hall Road, London N4 3QF
e-mail: info@thekosh.com   Tel/Fax: 020-8374 0407

LUDUS DANCE
Assembly Rooms, King Street, Lancaster LA1 1RE
Website: www.ludusdance.org
e-mail: info@ludusdance.org
Fax: 01524 847744   Tel: 01524 35936

MOVING EAST
St Matthias Church Hall
Wordsworth Road
London N16 8DD
Website: www.movingeast.co.uk
e-mail: admin@movingeast.co.uk   Tel: 020-7503 3101

MUDRALAYA DANCE THEATRE
(Formerly Pushkala Gopal Unnikrishnan & Co)
(Classical Indian Dance-Theatre)
20 Brisbane Road
Ilford, Essex IG1 4SR
e-mail: pushkala.gopal@gmail.com   Tel: 020-8554 4054

NEW ADVENTURES
Sadler's Wells
Rosebery Avenue, London EC1R 4TN
Website: www.new-adventures.net
e-mail: info@new-adventures.net   Tel/Fax: 020-7713 6766

NORTHERN BALLET THEATRE
West Park Centre
Spen Lane, Leeds LS16 5BE
e-mail: administration@northernballettheatre.co.uk
Fax: 0113-220 8007   Tel: 0113-274 5355

OGUIKE Henri DANCE COMPANY
Laban, The Cottages
Office No 2, Creekside, London SE8 3DZ
Website: www.henrioguikedance.co.uk
e-mail: info@henrioguikedance.co.uk
Fax: 020-8694 3669   Tel: 020-8694 7444

PHOENIX DANCE THEATRE
3 St Peter's Buildings
St Peter's Square
Leeds LS9 8AH
Website: www.phoenixdancetheatre.co.uk
e-mail: info@phoenixdancetheatre.co.uk
Fax: 0113-244 4736   Tel: 0113-242 3486

PIPER George DANCES
Sadler's Wells, Rosebery Avenue
Islington, London EC1R 4TN
Website: www.gpdances.com
e-mail: contact@gpdances.com
Fax: 020-7278 5684   Tel: 020-7278 5508

PLACE The
Robin Howard Dance Theatre
17 Duke's Road
London WC1H 9BY
Website: www.theplace.org.uk
e-mail: info@theplace.org.uk
Fax: 020-7121 1142   Tel: 020-7121 1000

RAMBERT DANCE COMPANY
94 Chiswick High Road, London W4 1SH
Website: www.rambert.org.uk
e-mail: rdc@rambert.org.uk
Fax: 020-8747 8323   Tel: 020-8630 0600

ROTIE Marie-Gabrielle PRODUCTIONS
7 Trinity Rise, London SW2 2QP
Website: www.rotieproductions.com
e-mail: rotiemanager@aol.com   Tel: 020-8674 1518

ROYAL BALLET The
Royal Opera House
Covent Garden, London WC2E 9DD
Fax: 020-7212 9121   Tel: 020-7240 1200 ext 712

RUSS Claire ENSEMBLE
(Choreography, Contemporary/Commercial/Corporate)
4 Heatham Park, Twickenham TW2 7SF
Website: www.clairerussensemble.com
e-mail: info@clairerussensemble.com   Mobile: 07932 680224

SCOTTISH BALLET
261 West Princes Street, Glasgow G4 9EE
Website: www.scottishballet.co.uk
e-mail: sb@scottishballet.co.uk
Fax: 0141-331 2629   Tel: 0141-331 2931

SCOTTISH DANCE THEATRE
Dundee Repertory Theatre
Tay Square, Dundee DD1 1PB
Website: www.scottishdancetheatre.com
e-mail: achinn@dundeereptheatre.co.uk
Fax: 01382 228609   Tel: 01382 342600

SKY BLUE PINK
Website: www.skybluepinkproductions.com
Mobile: 07779 866439   Tel: 020-8715 5007

SMALLPETIT KLEIN DANCE COMPANY
20 Parkleigh Road, London SW19 3BU
Website: www.smallpetitklein.com
e-mail: info@smallpetitklein.com   Mobile: 07792 652672

SPRINGS DANCE COMPANY
Jamaica Road
Bermondsey, London SE1
Website: www.springsdancecompany.org.uk
e-mail: springsdc@aol.com   Mobile: 07775 628442

STOP GAP DANCE COMPANY
Farnham Maltings, Bridge Square
Farnham, Surrey GU9 7QR
Website: www.stopgap.uk.com
e-mail: admin@stopgap.uk.com   Tel: 01252 718664

SURAYA HILAL DANCE COMPANY
2/76 Priory Road, London NW6 3NT
Website: www.hilaldance.co.uk
e-mail: info@hilaldance.co.uk   Tel/Fax: 020-7624 2549

TRANSITIONS DANCE COMPANY
Creekside, London SE8 3DZ
e-mail: info@laban.org   Tel: 020-8691 8600

TWITCH
5 Breakspears Mews
Brockley, London SE4 1PY
Website: www.twitch.uk.com
e-mail: info@twitch.uk.com
Mobile: 07932 656358   Mobile: 07747 770816

UNION DANCE
Top Floor, 6 Charing Cross Road, London WC2H 0HG
Website: www.uniondance.co.uk
e-mail: info@uniondance.co.uk
Fax: 020-7836 7847   Tel: 020-7836 7837

ACCELERATE Ltd
374 Ley Street, Ilford, Essex IG1 4AE
Website: www.accelerate-productions.co.uk
e-mail: info@accelerate-productions.co.uk
Fax: 020-8518 4018   Tel: 020-8514 4796

ADAD
Urdang, Finsbury Town Hall
Rosebery Avenue, London EC1R 4QT
Website: www.adad.org.uk
e-mail: info@adad.org.uk
Fax: 020-7833 2363   Tel: 020-7713 0730

AKADEMI SOUTH ASIAN DANCE UK
213 Haverstock Hill
Hampstead Town Hall, London NW3 4QP
Website: www.akademi.co.uk
e-mail: info@akademi.co.uk
Fax: 020-7691 3211   Tel: 020-7691 3210

ALLIED DANCING ASSOCIATION
137 Greenhill Road, Mossley Hill
Liverpool L18 7HQ   Tel: 0151-724 1829

BLUE EYED SOUL DANCE COMPANY
The Lantern, Meadow Farm Drive, Shrewsbury SY1 4NG
Website: www.blueeyedsouldance.com
e-mail: admin@blueeyedsouldance.com   Tel: 01743 210830

BRITISH ARTS The
12 Deveron Way, Rise Park
Romford RM1 4UL
Website: www.britisharts.org
Tel: 01708 756263

BRITISH ASSOCIATION OF TEACHERS OF DANCING
23 Marywood Square, Glasgow G41 2BP
Website: www.batd.co.uk
e-mail: katrina.allan@batd.co.uk   Tel: 0141-423 4029

BRITISH BALLET ORGANISATION
(Dance Examining Society & Teacher Training)
Woolborough House
39 Lonsdale Road
Barnes, London SW13 9JP
Website: www.bbo.org.uk
e-mail: info@bbo.org.uk   Tel: 020-8748 1241

BRITISH THEATRE DANCE ASSOCIATION
Garden Street, Leicester LE1 3UA
Website: www.btda.org.uk
e-mail: info@btda.org.uk
Fax: 0845 1662189   Tel: 0845 1662179

CHISENHALE DANCE SPACE
64-84 Chisenhale Road
Bow, London E3 5QZ
Website: www.chisenhaledancespace.co.uk
e-mail: mail@chisenhaledancespace.co.uk
Fax: 020-8980 9323   Tel: 020-8981 6617

COUNCIL FOR DANCE EDUCATION & TRAINING
Old Brewer's Yard, 17-19 Neal Street
Covent Garden, London WC2H 9UY
Website: www.cdet.org.uk
e-mail: info@cdet.org.uk
Fax: 020-7240 2547   Tel: 020-7240 5703

DANCE 4
(National Dance Agency)
3-9 Hockley, Nottingham NG1 1FH
Website: www.dance4.co.uk
e-mail: info@dance4.co.uk
Fax: 0115-941 0776   Tel: 0115- 941 0773

DANCE BASE NATIONAL CENTRE FOR DANCE
14-16 Grassmarket, Edinburgh EH1 2JU
Website: www.dancebase.co.uk
e-mail: dance@dancebase.co.uk
Fax: 0131-225 5234   Tel: 0131-225 5525

DANCE CITY
(National Dance Agency)
Temple Street
Newcastle-upon-Tyne NE1 4BR
Website: www.dancecity.co.uk
e-mail: info@dancecity.co.uk   Tel: 0191-261 0505

DANCE EAST
(National Dance Agency)
Northgate Arts Centre
Sidegate Lane West
Ipswich IP4 3DF
Website: www.danceeast.co.uk
e-mail: info@danceeast.co.uk
Fax: 01473 639236   Tel: 01473 639230

DANCE HOUSE The
20 St Andrew's Street, Glasgow G1 5PD
Website: www.dancehouse.org
e-mail: info@dancehouse.org   Tel: 0141-552 2442

DANCE IN DEVON
(County Dance Agency)
Exeter Phoenix, Bradnich Place
Gandy Street, Exeter EX4 3LS
Website: www.dancesouthwest.org.uk/devon
e-mail: info@danceindevon.co.uk
Fax: 01392 667599   Tel: 01392 667050

DANCE INITIATIVE GREATER MANCHESTER
Zion Arts Centre, Stretford Road
Hulme, Manchester M15 5ZA
Website: www.digm.org
e-mail: info@digm.org.uk
Fax: 0161-232 7483   Tel: 0161-232 7179

DANCERS' CAREER DEVELOPMENT
220-221 Africa House
64 Kingsway, London WC2B 6BG
Website: www.thedcd.org.uk
e-mail: linda@thedcd.org.uk
Fax: 020-7424 3331   Tel: 020-7404 6141

DANCE SOUTH WEST
PO Box 5457
Bournemouth, Dorset BH1 1WU
Website: www.dancesouthwest.org.uk
e-mail: info@dancesouthwest.org.uk   Tel/Fax: 01202 554131

DANCE UK
(Including the Healthier Dancer Programme)
2nd Floor, Finsbury Town Hall
Rosebery Avenue, London EC1R 4QT
Website: www.danceuk.org
e-mail: info@danceuk.org
Fax: 020-7833 2363   Tel: 020-7713 0730

DANCE UMBRELLA
20 Chancellors Street
London W6 9RN
Website: www.danceumbrella.co.uk
e-mail: mail@danceumbrella.co.uk
Fax: 020-8741 7902   Tel: 020-8741 4040

DANCEXCHANGE
(National Dance Agency)
Birmingham Hippodrome
Thorp Street, Birmingham B5 4TB
Website: www.dancexchange.org.uk
e-mail: info@dancexchange.org.uk   Tel: 0121-689 3170

DAVIES Siobhan DANCE
(Make & Tour the work of Siobhan Davies, dance
professional development & education)
85 St George's Road, London SE1 6ER
Website: www.siobhandavies.com
e-mail: info@siobhandavies.com
Fax: 020-7091 9669   Tel: 020-7091 9650

EAST LONDON DANCE
Stratford Circus, Theatre Square, London E15 1BX
Website: www.eastlondondance.org
e-mail: office@eastlondondance.org
Fax: 020-8279 1054   Tel: 020-8279 1050

ESSEXDANCE
78 Broomfield Road, Chelmsford, Essex CM1 1SS
Website: www.essexdance.co.uk
e-mail: info@essexdance.co.uk   Tel: 01245 346036

FOUNDATION FOR COMMUNITY DANCE
LCB Depot, 31 Rutland Street, Leicester LE1 1RE
Website: www.communitydance.org.uk
e-mail: info@communitydance.org.uk
Fax: 0116-261 6801   Tel: 0116-253 3453

GREENWICH DANCE AGENCY
The Borough Hall, Royal Hill, London SE10 8RE
Website: www.greenwichdance.org.uk
e-mail: info@greenwichdance.org.uk   Tel: 020-8293 9741

IDTA (INTERNATIONAL DANCE TEACHERS' ASSOCIATION)
International House, 76 Bennett Road
Brighton, East Sussex BN2 5JL
Website: www.idta.co.uk
e-mail: info@idta.co.uk
Fax: 01273 674388   Tel: 01273 685652

ISLE OF WIGHT DANCE PROJECT
The Guildhall, High Street
Newport, Isle of Wight PO30 1TY
Website: www.isleofwight-arts.co.uk
e-mail: jane.bridle@iow.gov.uk   Tel: 01983 823813

LANGUAGE OF DANCE CENTRE The
4th Floor, Charles House
375 Kensington High Street, London W14 8QH
Website: www.lodc.org
e-mail: info@lodc.org   Tel: 020-7603 8500

LONDON CONTEMPORARY DANCE SCHOOL
The Place, 17 Duke's Road, London WC1H 9PY
Website: www.theplace.org.uk
e-mail: lcds@theplace.org.uk
Fax: 020-7121 1142   Tel: 020-7121 1111

LUDUS DANCE
The Assembly Rooms, Kings Street, Lancaster LA1 1RE
Website: www.ludusdance.org
e-mail: info@ludusdance.org
Fax: 01524 847744   Tel: 01524 35936

MERSEYSIDE DANCE INITIATIVE
(National Dance Agency)
24 Hope Street, Liverpool L1 9BQ
Website: www.merseysidedance.co.uk
e-mail: info@mdi.org.uk
Fax: 0151-707 0600   Tel: 0151-708 8810

MIDLAND INTERNATIONAL DANCE ARTS ASSOCIATION
29A Sycamore Road
Birmingham B23 5QP
Website: www.midaa.co.uk
e-mail: midaa.hq@hotmail.com
Fax: 0121-694 0013   Tel: 0121-694 0012

NATIONAL RESOURCE CENTRE FOR DANCE
University of Surrey, Guildford GU2 7XH
Website: www.surrey.ac.uk/nrcd
e-mail: nrcd@surrey.ac.uk
Fax: 01483 689500   Tel: 01483 689316

PLACE The
(National Dance Agency)
Robin Howard Dance Theatre
17 Duke's Road, London WC1H 9BY
Website: www.theplace.org.uk
e-mail: info@theplace.org.uk
Fax: 020-7121 1142   Tel: 020-7121 1000

PROFESSIONAL TEACHERS OF DANCING
St Georges House
4A Uplyme Road Business Park
Lentells 1st Floor, Lyme Regis, Dorset DT7 3LS
Website: www.ptdance.com
e-mail: ptd@soton96.freeserve.co.uk   Tel: 01297 678565

SOUTH-EAST DANCE
(National Dance Agency)
28 Kensington Street, Brighton BN1 4AJ
Website: www.southeastdance.org.uk
e-mail: info@southeastdance.org.uk
Fax: 01273 697212   Tel: 01273 696844

SURREY ARTS DANCE
Westfield School, Bonsey Lane
Woking, Surey GU22 9PR
Website: www.surreycountyarts.org.uk
e-mail: gail.brown@surreycc.gov.uk   Tel: 01483 776128

SWINDON DANCE
(National Dance Agency)
Town Hall Studios
Regent Circus, Swindon SN1 1QF
Website: www.swindondance.org.uk
e-mail: info@swindondance.org.uk   Tel: 01793 601700

TURTLE KEY ARTS
Ladbroke Hall, 79 Barlby Road, London W10 6AZ
Website: www.turtlekeyarts.org.uk
e-mail: shaun@turtlekeyarts.org.uk
Fax: 020-8964 4080   Tel: 020-8964 5060

TWITCH
5 Breakspears Mews
Brockley, London SE4 1PY
Website: www.twitch.uk.com
e-mail: info@twitch.uk.com
Mobile: 07932 656358   Mobile: 07747 770816

WELSH INDEPENDENT DANCE
Chapter, Market Road, Canton, Cardiff CF5 1QE
Website: www.welshindance.co.uk
e-mail: welshindance@btconnect.com   Tel: 029-2038 7314

YORKSHIRE DANCE
(National Dance Agency)
3 St Peters Buildings
St Peters Square, Leeds LS9 8AH
Website: www.everybodydances.com
e-mail: admin@everybodydances.com
Fax: 0113-259 5700   Tel: 0113-243 9867

PAUL HARRIS 07958-784462 www.paulharris.uk.com

Choreographer: "The Other Boleyn Girl" "Harry Potter 5" (Wand Combat)
Choreography and Coaching in Vintage and Contemporary Social Dance
* Swing * Waltz * Salsa * Tango * Charleston * Quadrille *etc.*

ACADEMY FOR THEATRE ARTS The
1 Vale View, Porthill
Newcastle under Lyme
Staffs ST5 0AF   Tel: 01782 751900

ARTS EDUCATIONAL SCHOOLS, LONDON
Cone Ripman House, 14 Bath Road
Chiswick, London W4 1LY
Website: www.artsed.co.uk
e-mail: reception@artsed.co.uk   Tel: 020-8987 6666

AVIV DANCE STUDIOS
Wren House, 1st Floor
19-23 Exchange Road
Watford WD18 0JD
Website: www.avivdance.com
e-mail: nikkiavron@btconnect.com   Tel/Fax: 01923 250000

BALLROOM - LONDON THEATRE OF
(Artistic Director - Paul Harris, Mentor "Faking It")
24 Montana Gardens
Sutton, Surrey SM1 4FP
Website: www.londontheatreofballroom.com
e-mail: office@londontheatreofballroom.com
Mobile: 07958 784462   Tel/Fax: 020-8722 8798

BENESH INSTITUTE The
36 Battersea Square
London SW11 3RA
Website: www.rad.org.uk
e-mail: marketing@rad.org.uk   Tel: 020-7326 8000

BHAVAN CENTRE
4A Castletown Road, London W14 9HE
Website: www.bhavan.net
e-mail: info@bhavan.net   Tel: 020-7381 3086

BIRD COLLEGE DANCE & THEATRE PERFORMANCE
(Dance & Theatre Performance Diploma/BA (Hons) Degree
Course)
Birkbeck Centre, Birkbeck Road
Sidcup, Kent DA14 4DE
Website: www.birdcollege.co.uk
Fax: 020-8308 1370   Tel: 020-8300 6004

BODENS STUDIOS
(Performing Arts Classes)
Bodens Studios & Agency
99 East Barnet Road
New Barnet, Herts EN4 8RF
Website: www.bodenstudios.com
e-mail: info@bodensagency.com
Fax: 020-8449 5212   Tel: 020-8449 0982

BRIGHTON DANCE DIVERSION
93 Sea Lane
Rustington, West Sussex BN16 2RS
Website: www.brightondancediversion.com
e-mail: info@brightondancediversion.com   Tel: 01903 770304

CAMBRIDGE PERFORMING ARTS AT BODYWORK
Bodywork Company Dance Studios
25-29 Glisson Road
Cambridge CB1 2HA   Tel: 01223 314461

CANDOCO DANCE COMPANY
2T Leroy House
436 Essex Road, London N1 3QP
Website: www.candoco.co.uk
e-mail: foundationcourse@candoco.co.uk   Tel: 020-7704 6845

CENTRAL SCHOOL OF BALLET
(Full Time Vocational Training, Open Classes
Beginner/Professional Level)
10 Herbal Hill
Clerkenwell Road, London EC1R 5EG
Website: www.centralschoolofballet.co.uk
e-mail: info@csbschool.co.uk
Fax: 020-7833 5571   Tel: 020-7837 6332

CENTRE - PERFORMING ARTS COLLEGE The
Building 62, Level 4
37 Bowater Road
Charlton, London SE18 5TF
Website: www.thecentrepac.com
e-mail: dance@thecentrepac.com
Fax: 020-8855 6662   Tel: 020-8855 6661

COLLECTIVE DANCE & DRAMA
The Studio, Rectory Lane
Rickmansworth
Herts WD3 1FD   Tel/Fax: 020-8428 0037

CONTI Italia ACADEMY OF THEATRE ARTS
(Full-time 3 year Musical Theatre Course)
Italia Conti House
23 Goswell Road, London EC1M 7AJ
e-mail: admin@italiaconti.co.uk
Fax: 020-7253 1430   Tel: 020-7608 0044

COUNCIL FOR DANCE EDUCATION & TRAINING (CDET) The
Old Brewer's Yard, 17-19 Neal Street
Covent Garden, London WC2H 9UY
Website: www.cdet.org.uk
e-mail: info@cdet.org.uk
Fax: 020-7240 2547   Tel: 020-7240 5703

CPA COLLEGE
The Studios, 219B North Street, Romford RM1 4QA
Website: www.colinsperformingarts.co.uk
e-mail: admin@colinsperformingarts.co.uk
Fax: 01708 766077 Tel: 01708 766007

CUSTARD FACTORY
(Professional Dance Classes & Dance Studio Hire)
Gibb Street, Digbeth, Birmingham B9 4AA
e-mail: post@custardfactory.com
Fax: 0121-604 8888 Tel: 0121-224 7777

D & B SCHOOL OF PERFORMING ARTS
Central Studios, 470 Bromley Road, Bromley, Kent BR1 4PN
Website: www.dandbperformingarts.co.uk
e-mail: bonnie@dandbmanagement.com
Fax: 020-8697 8100 Tel: 020-8698 8880

DANCE BASE NATIONAL CENTRE FOR DANCE
14-16 Grassmarket, Edinburgh EH1 2JU
Website: www.dancebase.co.uk
e-mail: dance@dancebase.co.uk
Fax: 0131-225 5234 Tel: 0131-225 5525

DANCE HOUSE The
20 St Andrew's Street, Glasgow G1 5PD
Website: www.dancehouse.org
e-mail: info@dancehouse.org Tel: 0141-552 2442

DANCE RESEARCH COMMITTEE - IMPERIAL SOCIETY OF TEACHERS OF DANCING
(Training in Historical Dance)
c/o Ludwell House
Charing, Kent TN27 0LS
Website: www.istd.org
e-mail: n.gainesarmitage@tiscali.co.uk
Fax: 01233 712768 Tel: 01233 712469

DANCEWORKS
(Also Fitness, Yoga & Martial Arts Classes)
16 Balderton Street
London W1K 6TN Tel: 020-7629 6183

DAVIES Siobhan STUDIOS
(Daily Professional Classes, open classes for wider community)
85 St George's Road
London SE1 6ER
Website: www.siobhandavies.com
e-mail: info@siobhandavies.com
Fax: 020-7091 9669 Tel: 020-7091 9650

D M AGENCY The
The Studios
Briggate, Shipley
Bradford, West Yorks BD17 7BT
Website: www.dmacademy.co.uk
e-mail: info@dmacademy.co.uk
Fax: 01274 592502 Tel: 01274 585317

DUFFILL Drusilla THEATRE SCHOOL
Grove Lodge, Oakwood Road
Burgess Hill
West Sussex RH15 0HZ
Website: www.drusilladuffilltheatreschool.co.uk
e-mail: drusilladschool@btclick.com
Fax: 01444 232680 Tel: 01444 232672

EAST LONDON DANCE
Stratford Circus
Theatre Square, London E15 1BX
Website: www.eastlondondance.org
e-mail: kdavidson@newvic.ac.uk
Fax: 020-8279 1054 Tel: 020-8279 1050

EDINBURGH'S TELFORD COLLEGE
350 West Granton Road
Edinburgh EH5 1QE
Website: www.ed-coll.ac.uk
e-mail: mail@ed-coll.ac.uk
Fax: 0131-559 4411 Tel: 0131-559 4000

ELIE Mark DANCE FOUNDATION
The Tabernacle
Powis Square, London W11 2AY
Website: www.markelie-dancefoundation.co.uk
e-mail: markeliedancefoundation@uk2.net
Mobile: 07947 484021

ELMHURST - SCHOOL FOR DANCE
249 Bristol Road
Edgbaston
Birmingham B5 7UH
Website: www.elmhurstdance.co.uk
e-mail: enquiries@elmhurstdance.co.uk
Fax: 0121-472 6654 Tel: 0121-472 6655

ENGLISH NATIONAL BALLET SCHOOL
Carlyle Building
Hortensia Road, London SW10 0QS
Website: www.enbschool.org.uk
e-mail: info@enbschool.org.uk
Fax: 020-7376 3404 Tel: 020-7376 7076

EXCEL SCHOOL OF PERFORMING ARTS
KT Summit House
100 Hanger Lane
Ealing, London W5 1EZ
Website: www.ktioe-excel.org
e-mail: excel@kt.org Tel: 020-8799 6166

eric
r ichmond
PHOTOGRAPHY

T: 0208 8806909
M: 07866 766240
E: eric@ericrichmond.net
W: www.ericrichmond.net

EXPRESSIONS ACADEMY OF PERFORMING ARTS
3 Newgate Lane
Mansfield
Nottingham NG18 2LB
Website: www.expressions-uk.com
e-mail: expressions-uk@btconnect.com
Fax: 01623 647337   Tel: 01623 424334

GREASEPAINT ANONYMOUS
4 Gallus Close
Winchmore Hill
London N21 1JR
e-mail: info@greasepaintanonymous.co.uk
Fax: 020-8882 9189   Tel: 020-8886 2263

HAMMOND SCHOOL The
Hoole Bank
Mannings Lane
Chester CH2 4ES
Website: www.thehammondschool.co.uk
e-mail: info@thehammondschool.co.uk
Fax: 01244 305351   Tel: 01244 305350

HARRIS Paul
(Movement for Actors, Choreography, Tuition in Traditional
& Contemporary Social Dance)
24 Montana Gardens
Sutton
Surrey SM1 4FP
Website: www.paulharris.uk.com
e-mail: office@paulharris.uk.com
Mobile: 07958 784462   Tel: 020-8771 4274

ISLINGTON ARTS FACTORY
2 Parkhurst Road
London N7 0SF
e-mail: iaf@islingtonartsfactory.fsnet.co.uk
Fax: 020-7700 7229   Tel: 020-7607 0561

LABAN
Creekside, London SE8 3DZ
Website: www.laban.org
e-mail: info@laban.org
Tel: 020-8691 8600   Fax: 020-8691 8400

LAINE THEATRE ARTS
The Studios
East Street
Epsom, Surrey KT17 1HH
Website: www.laine-theatre-arts.co.uk
e-mail: webmaster@laine-theatre-arts.co.uk
Fax: 01372 723775   Tel: 01372 724648

LEE Lynn THEATRE SCHOOL The
(Office)
126 Church Road
Benfleet, Essex SS7 4EP
e-mail: lynn@leetheatre.fsnet.co.uk   Tel: 01268 795863

LIVERPOOL THEATRE SCHOOL
(Musical Theatre & Professional Classes)
19 Aigburth Road
Liverpool
Merseyside L17 4JR
Website: www.liverpooltheatreschool.co.uk
e-mail: info@liverpooltheatreschool.co.uk
Fax: 0151-728 9852   Tel: 0151-728 7800

LONDON CONTEMPORARY DANCE SCHOOL
(Full-time Vocational Training at Degree, Certificate &
Postgraduate Level)
The Place, 17 Duke's Road
London WC1H 9PY
Website: www.theplace.org.uk
e-mail: lcds@theplace.org.uk
Fax: 020-7121 1145   Tel: 020-7121 1111

LONDON STUDIO CENTRE
42-50 York Way, London N1 9AB
Website: www.london-studio-centre.co.uk
e-mail: info@london-studio-centre.co.uk
Fax: 020-7837 3248   Tel: 020-7837 7741

MANN Stella COLLEGE
(Professional Training Course for Performers & Teachers)
10 Linden Road
Bedford, Beds MK40 2DA
Website: www.stellamanncollege.co.uk
e-mail: info@stellamanncollege.co.uk
Fax: 01234 217284   Tel: 01234 213331

MIDLANDS ACADEMY OF DANCE & DRAMA
Century House, Building B
428 Carlton Hill
Nottingham NG4 1QA
Website: www.maddcollege.co.uk
e-mail: admin@maddcollege.supanet.com
                                     Tel/Fax: 0115-911 0401

MILLENNIUM DANCE 2000 Ltd
Hampstead Town Hall Centre
213 Haverstock Hill
London NW3 4QP
Website: www.md2000.co.uk
e-mail: md2000hampstead@aol.com   Tel/Fax: 020-7916 9335

MOVING EAST
St Matthias Church Hall
Wordsworth Road, London N16 8DD
Website: www.movingeast.co.uk
e-mail: admin@movingeast.co.uk   Tel: 020-7503 3101

NLPAC
(Performing Arts Classes 3-19 years/All Dance Styles, GCSE
Course, RAD & ISTD Exams)
76 St James Lane
Muswell Hill, London N10 3DF
Website: www.nlpac.co.uk
e-mail: nlpac@aol.com
Fax: 020-8444 4040   Tel: 020-8444 4544

NORTH LONDON DANCE STUDIO
843-845 Green Lanes
Winchmore Hill, London N21 2RX
e-mail: thedancestudio@btopenworld.com
Fax: 020-8364 2009   Tel: 020-8360 5700

NORTHERN ACADEMY OF PERFORMING ARTS
Anlaby Road, Hull HU1 2PD
Website: www.northernacademy.org.uk
e-mail: napa@northernacademy.org.uk
Fax: 01482 212280 Tel: 01482 310690

NORTHERN BALLET SCHOOL
The Dancehouse
10 Oxford Road, Manchester M1 5QA
Website: www.northernballetschool.co.uk
e-mail: enquiries@northernballetschool.co.uk
Fax: 0161-237 1408 Tel: 0161-237 1406

NORTHERN SCHOOL OF CONTEMPORARY DANCE The
98 Chapeltown Road, Leeds LS7 4BH
Website: www.nscd.ac.uk
e-mail: info@nscd.ac.uk Tel: 0113-219 3000

PAUL'S THEATRE SCHOOL
Fairkytes Arts Centre, 51 Billet Lane
Hornchurch, Essex RM11 1AX
Website: www.paulstheatreschool.co.uk
e-mail: info@paulstheatreschool.co.uk
Fax: 01708 475286 Tel: 01708 447123

PERFORMERS COLLEGE
Southend Road
Corringham, Essex SS17 8JT
Website: www.performerscollege.co.uk
e-mail: pdc@dircon.co.uk
Fax: 01375 672353 Tel: 01375 672053

PINEAPPLE DANCE STUDIOS
7 Langley Street, London WC2H 9JA
Website: www.pineapple.uk.com
e-mail: studios@pineapple.uk.com
Fax: 020-7836 0803 Tel: 020-7836 4004

PLACE The
Robin Howard Dance Theatre
17 Duke's Road, London WC1H 9BY
Website: www.theplace.org.uk
e-mail: info@theplace.org.uk
Fax: 020-7121 1142 Tel: 020-7121 1000

POLECATS Ltd
(Sarah Davis) (Fitness Classes)
e-mail: sarah@pole-cats.co.uk Tel: 0870 0852288

PROFESSIONAL TEACHERS OF DANCING
St Georges House
4A Uplyme Road Business Park
Lentells, 1st Floor, Lyme Regis, Dorset DT7 3LS
Website: www.ptdance.com
e-mail: ptd@soton96.freeserve.co.uk Tel: 01297 678565

RAMBERT SCHOOL OF BALLET & CONTEMPORARY DANCE
Clifton Lodge, St. Margaret's Drive
Twickenham, Middlesex TW1 1QN
Website: www.rambertschool.org.uk
e-mail: info@rambertschool.org.uk
Fax: 020-8892 8090 Tel: 020-8892 9960

REFLECTIONS PERFORMING ARTS AGENCY
9 Weavers Terrace, Fulham, London SW6 1QE
Website: www.reflectionsperfarts.tripod.com
e-mail: reflectionspa@yahoo.co.uk
Mobile: 07709 429354 Tel/Fax: 01322 410003

RIDGEWAY STUDIOS PERFORMING ARTS COLLEGE
Fairley House, Andrews Lane, Cheshunt, Herts EN7 6LB
Website: www.ridgewaystudios.co.uk
e-mail: info@ridgewaystudios.co.uk
Fax: 01992 633844 Tel: 01992 633775

ROEBUCK Gavin
(Classical Ballet)
51 Earls Court Square
London SW5 9DG   Tel: 020-7370 7324

ROJO Y NEGRO
(Argentine Tango School of Dance)
52 Lloyd Baker Street
Clerkenwell, London WC1X 9AA
Website: www.rojoynegroclub.com
e-mail: bianca@rojoynegroclub.com   Tel: 020-8520 2726

ROTIE BUTOH Marie-Gabrielle UK
7 Trinity Rise, London SW2 2QP
Website: www.rotieproductions.com
e-mail: rotiemanager@aol.com   Tel: 020-8674 1518

ROYAL ACADEMY OF DANCE
36 Battersea Square, London SW11 3RA
Website: www.rad.org.uk
e-mail: info@rad.org.uk
Fax: 020-7924 2311   Tel: 020-7326 8000

SAFREY ACADEMY OF PERFORMING ARTS
10 St Julians Close
London SW16 2RY
Website: www.mbkonline.co.uk/safrey
e-mail: info@safreyarts.co.uk
Fax: 020-8488 9121   Tel: 020-8664 6676

SOLE CENTRAL PERFORMING ARTS
Finsbury Town Hall
Rosebery Avenue, London EC1
Website: www.solecentral.org
e-mail: amm.solecentral@btinternet.com   Tel: 01895 810939

TIFFANY THEATRE COLLEGE
969-973 London Road
Leigh on Sea
Essex SS9 3LB
Website: www.tiffanytheatrecollege.com
e-mail: info@tiffanytheatrecollege.com
Fax: 01702 715645   Tel: 01702 710069

URDANG ACADEMY The
Finsbury Town Hall
Rosebery Avenue, London EC1
Website: www.theurdangacademy.com
e-mail: info@theurdangacademy.com
Fax: 020-7278 6727   Tel: 020-7713 7710

VALLÉ ACADEMY OF PERFORMING ARTS
The Vallé Academy Studios
Wilton House, Delamare Road
Cheshunt, Herts EN8 9SG
Website: www.valleacademy.co.uk
e-mail: enquiries@valleacademy.co.uk
Fax: 01992 622868   Tel: 01992 622862

WHITEHALL PERFORMING ARTS CENTRE
Rayleigh Road, Leigh-on-Sea
Essex SS9 5UU   Tel/Fax: 01702 529290

YOUNG Sylvia THEATRE SCHOOL
Rossmore Road
Marylebone
London NW1 6NJ
Website: www.sylviayoungtheatreschool.co.uk
e-mail: sylvia@sylviayoungtheatreschool.co.uk
Fax: 020-7723 1040   Tel: 020-7402 0673

The Council for Dance Education and Training is the national standards body of the professional dance industry. It accredits programmes of training in vocational dance schools and holds the Register of Dance Awarding Bodies - the directory of teaching societies whose syllabuses have been inspected and approved by the Council. It is the body of advocacy of the dance education and training communities and offers a free and comprehensive information service - *Answers for Dancers* - on all aspects of vocational dance provision to students, parents, teachers dance artists and employers.

The Conference of Professional Dance Schools (CPDS) is a committee of the Council and provides a forum in which representatives from vocational dance training institutions may discuss policy and recommend action in relation to vocational dance training.

- Arts Educational School, Tring
- ArtsEd London
- Bird College
- Cambridge Performing Arts
- Elmhurst School for Dance
- Hammond School
- Italia Conti Academy of Theatre Arts Ltd
- LABAN
- Laine Theatre Arts
- Liverpool Theatre School and College
- London Contemporary Dance School
- London Studio Centre
- Northern Ballet School
- Performers College
- Stella Mann College
- Urdang Academy

For more info on the CPDS and CDET:

Contact:

Council for Dance Education & Training

Old Brewer's Yard

17-19 Neal Street

Covent Garden, London WC2H 9UY

Tel: 020 7240 5703

Email: info@cdet.org.uk

Website: www.cdet.org.uk

ALRA (ACADEMY OF LIVE AND RECORDED ARTS)
Studio One, The Royal Victoria Patriotic Building
Fitzhugh Grove, Trinity Road
London SW18 3SX
Website: www.alra.co.uk
e-mail: enquiries@alra.co.uk
Fax: 020-8875 0789   Tel: 020-8870 6475

ARTS EDUCATIONAL SCHOOLS LONDON
14 Bath Road, London W4 1LY
Website: www.artsed.co.uk
e-mail: drama@artsed.co.uk
Fax: 020-8987 6699   Tel: 020-8987 6666

BIRMINGHAM SCHOOL OF ACTING
Millennium Point, Curzon Street
Birmingham B4 7XG
Website: www.bsa.uce.ac.uk
e-mail: info@bsa.uce.ac.uk
Fax: 0121-331 7221   Tel: 0121-331 7200

BRISTOL OLD VIC THEATRE SCHOOL
2 Downside Road
Clifton, Bristol BS8 2XF
Website: www.oldvic.ac.uk
e-mail: enquiries@oldvic.ac.uk
Fax: 0117-923 9371   Tel: 0117-973 3535

CENTRAL SCHOOL OF SPEECH & DRAMA
Embassy Theatre, 64 Eton Avenue
Swiss Cottage, London NW3 3HY
Website: www.cssd.ac.uk
e-mail: enquiries@cssd.ac.uk   Tel: 020-7722 8183

CONTI Italia ACADEMY OF THEATRE ARTS
Avondale, 72 Landor Road
London SW9 9PH
Website: www.italiaconti-acting.co.uk
e-mail: acting@lsbu.ac.uk
Fax: 020-7737 2728   Tel: 020-7733 3210

CYGNET TRAINING THEATRE
New Theatre, Friars Gate
Exeter, Devon EX2 4AZ
e-mail: cygnetarts@btconnect.com   Tel/Fax: 01392 277189

DRAMA CENTRE LONDON
Central Saint Martins College of Art & Design
Saffron House, 10 Back Hill
London EC1R 5EN
Website: www.csm.arts.ac.uk/drama
e-mail: drama@arts.ac.uk
Fax: 020-7514 8777   Tel: 020-7514 8778

DRAMA STUDIO LONDON
Grange Court
1 Grange Road, London W5 5QN
Website: www.dramastudiolondon.co.uk
e-mail: registrar@dramastudiolondon.co.uk
Fax: 020-8566 2035   Tel: 020-8579 3897

EAST 15 ACTING SCHOOL
The University of Essex
Hatfields & Corbett Theatre
Rectory Lane, Loughton, Essex IG10 3RY
Website: www.east15.ac.uk
e-mail: east15@essex.ac.uk
Fax: 020-8508 7521   Tel: 020-8508 5983

GSA CONSERVATOIRE
Millmead Terrace
Guildford, Surrey GU2 4YT
Website: www.conservatoire.org
e-mail: enquiries@conservatoire.org   Tel: 01483 560701

GUILDHALL SCHOOL OF MUSIC & DRAMA
Silk Street, Barbican, London EC2Y 8DT
Website: www.gsmd.ac.uk
e-mail: info@gsmd.ac.uk
Fax: 020-7256 9438   Tel: 020-7628 2571

LAMDA
155 Talgarth Road, London W14 9DA
Website: www.lamda.org.uk
e-mail: enquiries@lamda.org.uk
Fax: 020-8834 0501   Tel: 020-8834 0500

LIVERPOOL INSTITUTE FOR PERFORMING ARTS The
Mount Street, Liverpool L1 9HF
Website: www.lipa.ac.uk
e-mail: reception@lipa.ac.uk
Fax: 0151-330 3131   Tel: 0151-330 3000

**MANCHESTER METROPOLITAN UNIVERSITY SCHOOL OF
THEATRE**
The Mabel Tylecote Building
Cavendish Street
Manchester M15 6BG
Website: www.capitoltheatre.co.uk   Tel: 0161-247 1305

MOUNTVIEW
Academy of Theatre Arts
Ralph Richardson Memorial Studios
Clarendon Road
London N22 6XF
Website: www.mountview.ac.uk
e-mail: enquiries@mountview.ac.uk
Fax: 020-8829 0034   Tel: 020-8881 2201

OXFORD SCHOOL OF DRAMA The
Sansomes Farm Studios
Woodstock, Oxford OX20 1ER
Website: www.oxforddrama.ac.uk
e-mail: info@oxforddrama.ac.uk
Fax: 01993 811220   Tel: 01993 812883

QUEEN MARGARET UNIVERSITY
Queen Margaret University Drive
Musselburgh, East Lothian EH21 6UU
Website: www.qmu.ac.uk
e-mail: admissions@qmu.ac.uk
Fax: 0131-474 0001   Tel: 0131-474 0000

ROSE BRUFORD COLLEGE
Lamorbey Park, Burnt Oak Lane
Sidcup, Kent DA15 9DF
Website: www.bruford.ac.uk
Fax: 020-8308 0542   Tel: 020-8308 2600

ROYAL ACADEMY OF DRAMATIC ART
62-64 Gower Street
London WC1E 6ED
Website: www.rada.org
e-mail: enquiries@rada.ac.uk
Fax: 020-7323 3865   Tel: 020-7636 7076

ROYAL SCOTTISH ACADEMY OF MUSIC & DRAMA
100 Renfrew Street
Glasgow G2 3DB
Website: www.rsamd.ac.uk
e-mail: registry@rsamd.ac.uk   Tel: 0141-332 4101

ROYAL WELSH COLLEGE OF MUSIC & DRAMA
Drama Department
Castle Grounds
Cathays Park, Cardiff CF10 3ER
Website: www.rwcmd.ac.uk
e-mail: drama.admissions@rwcmd.ac.uk
Fax: 029-2039 1302   Tel: 029-2039 1327

THE CONFERENCE OF DRAMA SCHOOLS

The Conference of Drama Schools comprises Britain's 22 leading Drama Schools. CDS exists to set and maintain the highest standards of training within the vocational drama sector and to make it easier for prospective students to understand the range of courses on offer and the application process. CDS member schools offer courses in Acting, Musical Theatre, Directing and Technical Theatre training.

CDS members offer courses which are:
Professional – you will be trained to work in the theatre by staff with professional experience and by visiting professionals.
Intensive – courses are full-time
Work Orientated – you are being trained to do a job – these courses are practical training for work.

CDS publishes *The Conference of Drama Schools – Guide to Professional Training in Drama* and

Technical Theatre 2008 and *The CDS Guide to Careers Backstage*.

For links to CDS schools please visit the website at **www.drama.ac.uk**

The full texts of both guides are available on the website – if you would like a hard copy please contact French's Theatre Bookshop, by phone on 020 7255 4300 or by emailing **theatre@samuelfrench-london.co.uk** or by visiting the shop at 52 Fitzroy Street, London, W1T 5JR. Single copies will be sent free of charge to UK addresses.
To contact CDS please visit the website or write to the Executive Secretary, CDS Ltd, P.O. Box 34252, London NW5 1XJ.

in association with

Gloria Lytton

Former Actress
Qualified Speech Therapist
Teacher at R.A.D.A. 1972-1986

Remedial Voice and Speech Work
Speaking with Confidence
Public Speaking
Audition Coaching

For people from all backgrounds
and walks of life

Tel: 020-8441 3118

A & J THEATRE WORKSHOP
The Trinity Church
Beaumont Road, London SW19
Website: www.ajmanagement.co.uk
e-mail: info@ajmanagement.co.uk
Fax: 020-8342 0842   Tel: 020-8342 0542

A B ACADEMY THEATRE SCHOOL
Act Out Ltd, 22 Greek Street
Stockport, Cheshire SK3 8AB
e-mail: ab22actout@aol.com   Tel/Fax: 0161-429 7413

ABOMELI TUTORING
(Stage & Screen Acting Technique,
Characterisation Coach)
Website: www.charlesabomeli.com
e-mail: charlesabm@aol.com   Mobile: 07981 066185

ACADEMY OF CREATIVE TRAINING
8-10 Rock Place, Brighton
East Sussex BN2 1PF
Website: www.actedu.org.uk
e-mail: info@actedu.org.uk   Tel: 01273 818266

ACADEMY OF THE SCIENCE OF ACTING AND DIRECTING The
67-83 Seven Sisters Road, London N7 6BU
Website: www.asad.org.uk
e-mail: info@asad.org.uk
Fax: 020-7272 0026   Tel: 020-7272 0027

ACADEMY SCHOOL OF PERFORMING ARTS The
(Drama, Singing, Dance)
PO Box 432, Oldham, Lancashire OL9 8ZS
Website: www.academy-sopa.co.uk
e-mail: theacademy@ntlworld.com   Tel: 0161-287 9700

ACE ACCOMPANIST
S (Coaching/Accompanist)
165 Gunnersbury Lane
London W3 8LJ   Tel: 020-8993 2111

ACKERLEY STUDIOS OF SPEECH, DRAMA & PUBLIC SPEAKING
Sp D Margaret Christina Parsons (Principal)
5th Floor, Hanover House, Hanover Street
Liverpool L1 3DZ   Tel: 0151-709 5995

ACT @ SCHOOL
(Drama for Children & Young People)
Part of APM Training Group
PO Box 834, Hemel Hempstead HP3 9ZP
Website: www.apmtraining.co.uk
e-mail: info@apmtraining.co.uk
Fax: 01442 241099   Tel: 01442 252907

ACT ONE DRAMA STUDIO
31 Dobbin Hill, Sheffield S11 7JA
Website: www.actonedrama.co.uk
e-mail: casting@actonedrama.co.uk
Fax: 0870 7058322   Tel: 0114-266 7209

ACT UP
(Acting Classes for Everyone)
Unit 88, Battersea Business Centre
99-109 Lavender Hill, London SW11 5QL
Website: www.act-up.co.uk
e-mail: info@act-up.co.uk
Fax: 020-7924 6606   Tel: 020-7924 7701

ACTING & AUDITION SUCCESS
(Philip Rosch, Association of Guildhall Teachers FVCM,
LGSM, LALAM, ATCL, ANEA, BA Hons)
(Audition Speeches/Effective Sight Reading & Career
Guidance, RADA Acting Exams)
53 West Heath Court, North End Road
London NW11 7RG   Tel: 020-8731 6686

ACTION LAB
(Part-time Acting Courses/Private Coaching,
Miranda French & Peter Irving)
18 Lansdowne Road, London W11 3LL
Mobile: 07979 623987   Tel: 020-7727 3474

ACTORS STUDIO
Pinewood Film Studios
Pinewood Road, Iver Heath
Bucks SL0 0NH
Website: www.actorsstudio.co.uk
e-mail: info@actorsstudio.co.uk
Fax: 01753 655622   Tel: 01753 650951

CAROLE ANN FORD

Audition Techniques

Advanced diploma voice studies
Central School of Speech & Drama

Coaching in
Effective, Healthy, Voice Use
For
T.V. - Films - Theatre
Presentation Skills for Business People etc.

Dialects-R.P.

020 8444 5365/020 8815 1832

TOM RADCLIFFE

ARTISTIC DIRECTOR, ACTORS' TEMPLE PRODUCTIONS

Classes & Private lessons in the most modern
& effective acting technique available today.

Tom trained extensively with SANFORD MEISNER
and is one of only three actors personally
approved by Sanford Meisner to teach the
MEISNER TECHNIQUE independently.

- Professional Actor: Stage, TV, Film
- Central School of Speech & Drama graduate

Contact: tom@bagend.net

Why do I need drama training?

The entertainment industry is an extremely competitive one, with thousands of performers competing for a small number of jobs. In such a crowded market, professional training will increase an actor's chances of success, and professionally trained artists are also more likely to be represented by agencies. Drama training can begin at any age and should continue throughout an actor's career.

What kind of training is available?

For the under 18's, stage schools provide specialist training in acting, singing and dancing. They offer a variety of full and part-time courses. After 18, students can attend drama school. The standard route is to take a three-year, full-time course, in the same way you would take a University degree. Some schools also offer one or two year courses. Full information will be available in each school's prospectus or on their website. Even after drama school, ongoing training is also vital for actors so that they can continue to develop acting techniques, or to prepare for a specific role.

How should I use these listings?

For ease of use, listings are classified with the following abbreviations:

Stage School for Children = SS
Dramatic Art, e.g. Coaching, Audition Technique, etc. = D
Full time Drama Training (includes every school listed in the Conference of Drama Schools section) = DS
Elocution Coaching e.g. Correction of Accents, Speech Therapy, Dialects, etc = E
Singing = S
Specialised Training = Sp

Many listings also include a brief description regarding their areas of expertise.

What is the Conference of Drama Schools (CDS)?

The Conference of Drama Schools was founded in 1969 and comprises Britain's twenty two leading Drama Schools. It exists in order to strengthen the voice of the member schools, to set and maintain the highest standards of training within the vocational drama sector, and to make it easier for prospective students to understand the range of courses on offer and the application process. The twenty two member schools listed in the section 'Drama Schools (Conference Of)' offer courses in Acting, Musical Theatre, Directing and Technical Theatre training. For more information you can visit their website www.drama.ac.uk

What is NCDT?

The National Council for Drama Training was established in 1976 and is a unique collaborative partnership of employers in the theatre, broadcast and media industry, employee representatives and training providers. Its aim is to champion and support professional drama training and education working to safeguard the highest standards and quality assurance through accreditation for vocational drama courses in the UK. This provides students with the confidence that the courses they choose are recognised by the drama profession as being relevant to the purposes of their employment For more information please see www.ncdt.co.uk

Christopher Denys is a director and writer and has just retired as Principal of the Bristol Old Vic Theatre School. He offers the following advice about training to be a performer:

Whether you are just starting out as a performer or technician, or whether you are looking to update or broaden your skills in line with changing practices, you will find the contacts you are looking for in the following section: ranging from full-time drama schools to evening and weekend classes, or one-to-one tuition.

Be warned: training is expensive and demanding in time, energy and total commitment - but then the working life of a performer is all that and more. Do you *really* want to do this for a living? You *can* just go on doing it for fun and live like a real person.

If you are starting out (and taking 'talent' for granted), two or three years at a good drama school should provide you with the knowledge, understanding and the physical and vocal (or technical) skills to see you, given a favourable wind and a huge amount of personal effort, into your early working years. But it shouldn't stop there. Training is a lifelong process.

First, you need to be sure that the course is concerned with actually 'doing it' rather than reading and/or writing about it. There's a big difference between *vocational* training to *work* and studying drama as an academic subject. Now that the majority of vocational courses also offer a BA or a Diploma, it's harder to tell which is which. The CDS 'Official Guide to Vocational Courses for Drama and Technical Training' will help you in this and, if a course is accredited by the NCDT, you will know that it provides full-time vocational preparation for whichever field of work you wish to enter. Also, schools vary greatly in ethos, practice and (for want of a better word) philosophy. You want to be sure that the course is the right one for you - so use the following pages to do as much detective work as you can.

You are looking to enter - or to broaden your field of work in - a huge industry. The UK's Arts and Entertainment Industry represents 8% of GNP, is consistently among the top three export earners, and employs around a million talented and highly-skilled people. This Industry is also, of course - on a good night - an Art. It isn't for anybody else to tell you what 'Art' is. 'Art' is whatever excites and stimulates you at that particular moment in your career and personal development. The trouble is that 'Art' doesn't usually pay very well. In fact, sometimes, it actually costs you money to do - but then it's probably what made you want to join this profession in the first place. So it's essential to be very good at the Industry, if you're going to create a reasonable financial base to survive and still be there when the chance to do something which really excites you comes along.

The Industry is currently enjoying an unprecedented period of growth, expansion and change and there is a need for even experienced practitioners to be constantly 'retooling', updating and broadening their range of skills to cope with accelerated production practices and new technologies. The diversification resulting from these new technologies has created more (and many new) employment opportunities, but these require the acquisition of completely new skills and the modification of traditional ones.

Again, the new technologies have made 'faster' possible. Faster is cheaper so the employers like faster. But faster makes huge demands on performers and technicians, so regular updating, re-training and learning new tricks is more and more essential for a successful and sustainable career.

Eileen Benskin
Dialect/Dialogue Coach
R.A.D.A. dip., C.P.E.P. University College London

FILMS • TELEVISION • THEATRE

Specialist in Standard British English (R.P.)
and American, British & Foreign Accents & Dialects

Tel/Fax: 020-8455 9750 *or* **The Spotlight 020-7437 7631**   **Mobile 07785 791715**

ACTOR'S TEMPLE The
13 Warren Street, London W1T 5LG
Website: www.actorstemple.com
e-mail: info@actorstemple.com
Mobile: 07771 734670   Tel: 020-7383 3535

ACTORS' THEATRE SCHOOL
(Foundation Course)
32 Exeter Road, London NW2 4SB
Website: www.theactorstheatreschool.co.uk
e-mail: info@theactorstheatreschool.co.uk
Fax: 020-8450 1057   Tel: 020-8450 0371

ACTOR WORKS The
1 Knighten Street
Wapping, London E1W 1PH
Website: www.theactorworks.co.uk   Tel: 020-7702 0909

ACTORSPACE.CO.UK
D E Sp (Auditions, Improvisation, Voice & Text, Roleplay
and Acting in Business)
6 Chandos Court
The Green, Southgate, London N14 7AA
Website: www.actorspace.co.uk
e-mail: drama@london.com
Fax: 0870 1342719   Tel: 020-8886 8870

ACTS
(Ayres-Clark Theatre School)
12 Gatward Close, Winchmore Hill
London N21 1AS   Tel: 020-8360 0352

ADNAN Samia
(Language/Dialect Coach, English-Arabic Translator,
Ex-SOAS)
e-mail: samiaadnan@hotmail.com   Mobile: 07710 897432

ALEXANDER Helen
(Audition Technique/Drama School Entry)
14 Chestnut Road, Raynes Park
London SW20 8EB   Tel: 020-8543 4085

ALLSORTS - DRAMA FOR CHILDREN
(Part-time Courses - Kensington,
Notting Hill, Hampstead, Fulham ages 3-18 yrs)
34 Pember Road, London NW10 5LS
Website: www.allsortsdrama.com
e-mail: info@allsortsdrama.com   Tel/Fax: 020-8969 3249

ALRA (ACADEMY OF LIVE & RECORDED ARTS)
See DRAMA SCHOOLS (Conference of)

AMERICAN VOICES
(Lynn Bains) (American Accent/Dialect Coach, Acting
Teacher & Director)
20 Craighall Crescent, Edinburgh EH6 4RZ
e-mail: mail@lynnbains.com   Mobile: 07875 148755

AMERSHAM & WYCOMBE COLLEGE
Dual Campuses: Amersham & Chesham
Website: www.amersham.ac.uk
e-mail: info@amersham.ac.uk   Tel: 0800 614016

AND ALL THAT JAZZ
(Eileen Hughes - Accompanist & Vocal Coaching)
165 Gunnersbury Lane, Acton Town
London W3 8LJ   Tel: 020-8993 2111

ARDEN SCHOOL OF THEATRE The
City Campus, Whitworth Street
Manchester M1 3HB
e-mail: ast@ccm.ac.uk
Fax: 0161-272 7645   Tel: 0161-279 7257

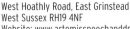

ARTEMIS SCHOOL OF SPEECH & DRAMA
Peredur Centre of The Arts
West Hoathly Road, East Grinstead
West Sussex RH19 4NF
Website: www.artemisspeechanddrama.org.uk
e-mail: office@artemisspeechanddrama.org.uk
Tel/Fax: 01342 321330

ARTEMIS STUDIOS
30 Charles Square, Bracknell
Berkshire RG12 1AY
Website: www.artemis-studios.co.uk
e-mail: info@artemis-studios.co.uk   Tel: 01344 429403

ARTS EDUCATIONAL SCHOOL
(Dance, Drama & Musical Theatre Training School
for 8-18 yrs)
Tring Park, Tring, Herts HP23 5LX
Website: www.aes-tring.com
e-mail: info@aes-tring.com   Tel: 01442 824255

ARTS EDUCATIONAL SCHOOLS LONDON
See DRAMA SCHOOLS (Conference of)

ASHCROFT ACADEMY OF DRAMATIC ART The
(Drama LAMDA, Dance ISTD, Singing, Age 4-18 yrs)
Malcolm Primary School
Malcolm Road, Penge, London SE20 8RH
Website: www.ashcroftacademy.com
e-mail: geraldi.gillma@btconnect.com
Mobile: 07799 791586   Tel/Fax: 01634 856900

ASHFORD Clare BSc, PGCE, LLAM, ALAM (Recital), ALAM (Acting)
D E
20 The Chase, Coulsdon, Surrey CR5 2EG
e-mail: clareashford@handbag.com   Tel: 020-8660 9609

AUDITION COACH
245 Broadfield Road, Manchester M14 7JT
Website: www.auditioncoach.co.uk
e-mail: info@auditioncoach.co.uk   Tel: 0161-226 8788

AUDITION CONSULTANT The
Website: www.auditionconsultancy.co.uk
e-mail: annemarielthomas@aol.com

BAC
(Young People's Theatre Workshops & Performance
Projects, 12-25 yrs)
Lavender Hill, London SW11 5TN
e-mail: bacypt@bac.org.uk
Fax: 020-7978 5207   Tel: 020-7223 6557

BARNES Barbara
(Feldenkrais Practitioner & Voice Coach)
The Studio, Church Road
Ashmanhaugh, Norwich NR12 8YL
Website: www.barbarabarnesvoiceovers.co.uk
e-mail: barbara.barnes@feldenkrais.co.uk
Mobile: 07770 375339   Tel: 01603 781281

BATE Richard MA (Theatre) LGSM (TD), PGCE (FE), Equity
D E
Apt 1, Broom Hall, High Street
Broom, Biggleswade
Bedfordshire SG18 9ND   Mobile: 07940 589295

BATES Esme
(Speech & Drama Coach, LAMDA Exam Specialist)
2 Barons Court
52-54 Western Elmes Avenue, Reading RG30 2BP
e-mail: esmebates@btinternet.com
Mobile: 07941 700941   Tel: 0118-958 9330

BECK Eirene
D E (Specialising in Voice & Audition Pieces)
23 Rayne House, 170 Delaware Road
London W9 2LW   Tel: 020-7286 0588

BELCANTO LONDON ACADEMY Ltd
(Stage School & Agency)
Performance House, 20 Passey Place
Eltham, London SE9 5DQ
e-mail: bla@dircon.co.uk
Fax: 020-8850 9944   Tel: 020-8850 9888

BENCH Paul MEd, LGSM, ALAM, FRSA, LJBA (Hons), PGCE, ACP (Lings) (Hons), MASC (Ph), MIFA (Reg)
D E
Whitehall Terrace
Shrewsbury, Shropshire SY2 5AA
e-mail: pfbench@aol.com   Tel/Fax: 01743 233164

BENSKIN Eileen
(Dialect Coach)   Tel: 020-8455 9750

BERKERY Barbara
Dialogue/Dialect Coach for
Film & Television)   Tel: 020-7281 3139

BEST THEATRE ARTS
PO Box 749, St Albans AL1 4YW
Website: www.besttheatrearts.com
e-mail: bestarts@aol.com   Tel: 01727 759634

BIG LITTLE THEATRE SCHOOL
Unit 305, Green Zone, Maycrete Road, Industrial Park West
Bournemouth Airport, Bournemouth BH23 6NW
Website: www.biglittletheatreschool.co.uk
e-mail: info@biglittletheatreschool.co.uk   Tel: 01202 574422

BIRD COLLEGE
(Drama/Musical Theatre College)
Birkbeck Centre, Birkbeck Road, Sidcup, Kent DA14 4DE
Website: www.birdcollege.co.uk
e-mail: admin@birdcollege.co.uk
Fax: 020-8308 1370   Tel: 020-8300 6004

BIRMINGHAM SCHOOL OF ACTING
See DRAMA SCHOOLS (Conference of)

BIRMINGHAM THEATRE SCHOOL
The Old Rep Theatre
Station Street, Birmingham B5 4DY
Website: www.birminghamtheatreschool.co.uk
e-mail: info@birminghamtheatreschool.co.uk
                                 Tel: 0121-643 3300

BODENS STUDIOS
A S E SS DS
Bodens Studio & Agency
99 East Barnet Road
New Barnet, Herts EN4 8RF
Website: www.bodenstudios.com
e-mail: info@bodenstudios.com
Fax: 020-8449 5212   Tel: 020-8449 0982

BORLAND Denise MA Voice (Perf), LRAM, PG Dip RAM, Perf Dip GSMD, ALCM
(Singing, Acting & Voice Coach)
5 Frogston Road West, Edinburgh EH10 7AB
Website: www.dbsvoicedevelopment.com
e-mail: deniseborland@hotmail.com   Tel: 0131-445 7491

BOWES Sara
(Child Acting Coach for Film)
3 John Aird Court, London W2 1UY
e-mail: sara@sarabowes.com
Mobile: 07830 375389   Tel: 020-7262 3543

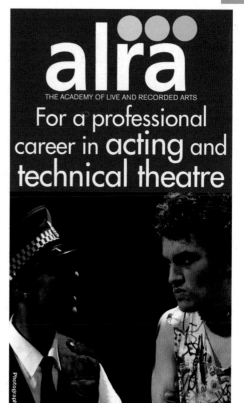

Photograph by Richard Andersen

For a professional career in **acting** and technical theatre

BA (Hons) Acting
Validated by The University of Greenwich
and Trinity College London. NCDT Accredited.

One Year/Post-Graduate Acting Course
National Certificate in Professional Acting.
Validated by Trinity College London. NCDT Accredited.

Stage Management & Technical Theatre Foundation Degree
Validated by The University of Greenwich.

Access Courses
Dance and Drama Awards available

www.alra.co.uk
enquiries@alra.co.uk
tel: 020 8870 6475 fax: 020 8875 0789

UNIVERSITY of GREENWICH   TRINITY COLLEGE LONDON   CDS   >lsc

Principal: Pat Trueman
ALRA is committed to an Equal Opportunities policy.
Company Number: 4306353 Charity Number: 1090724 Registered in England.

BOYD Beth
D S
10 Prospect Road, Long Ditton
Surbiton, Surrey KT6 5PY   Tel: 020-8398 6768

BRADSHAW Irene
(Private Coach. Voice & Audition Preparation)
Flat F, Welbeck Mansions, Inglewood Road
West Hampstead, London NW6 1QX
Website: www.voicepowerworks.com   Tel: 020-7794 5721

BRAITHWAITE'S ACROBATIC SCHOOL
8 Brookshill Avenue
Harrow Weald, Middlesex   Tel: 020-8954 5638

BRANSTON Dale
(Singing Coach)
Ground Floor Flat, 16 Fernwood Avenue
Streatham, London SW16 1RD
e-mail: branpickle@yahoo.co.uk   Tel: 020-8696 9958

BRIDGE THEATRE TRAINING COMPANY The
Cecil Sharp House, 2 Regent's Park Road, London NW1 7AY
Website: www.thebridge-ttc.org
Fax: 020-7424 9118   Tel: 020-7424 0860

BRIGHTON PERFORMERZONE
(William Pool ARCM, Singing Tuition & Workshops)
33A Osmond Road, Hove
East Sussex BN3 1TD
Website: www.performerzone.co.uk
e-mail: info@performerzone.co.uk   Mobile: 07973 518643

BRIGHTON SCHOOL OF MUSIC & DRAMA
96 Claremont Road, Seaford
East Sussex BN25 2QA   Tel: 01323 492918

BRISTOL ACADEMY OF PERFORMING ARTS
The Academy Theatre, Market Place
Shepton Mallet, Somerset BA4 5AZ
Website: www.academytheatre.co.uk
e-mail: info@academytheatre.co.uk   Tel: 01749 347984

BRISTOL OLD VIC THEATRE SCHOOL
See DRAMA SCHOOLS (Conference of)

BRITISH AMERICAN DRAMA ACADEMY
14 Gloucester Gate, Regent's Park, London NW1 4HG
Website: www.badaonline.com
Fax: 020-7487 0731   Tel: 020-7487 0730

B.R.I.T. SCHOOL FOR PERFORMING ARTS & TECHNOLOGY The
60 The Crescent, Croydon CR0 2HN
Website: www.brit.croydon.sch.uk
e-mail: admin@brit.croydon.sch.uk
Fax: 020-8665 8676   Tel: 020-8665 5242

BURTON Gwendolen MA, PG Dip (Performance) AOTOS
(Singing Teacher)
London N1
e-mail: singing@symbolic.net   Mobile: 07771 65726

CALE Bart TRAINING
Bristol
e-mail: bart.cale@virgin.net   Tel: 0117-969 2224

CAMERON BROWN Jo PGDVS
(Dialect and Voice)
6 The Bow Brook, Gathorne Street, London E2 0PW
Agent: Representation Upson Edwards 020-8888 2525
e-mail: sarahupson@hotmail.com
Mobile: 07970 026621   Tel: 020-8981 100

SCREEN ACTING
STEFAN GRYFF (DGGB) (LLB)

"I believe that for film and TV an actors quality is more important than their level of talent."

I will provide:
- Individual or group tuition in camera acting
- Preparation of show reels for Casting Directors and Agents
- Special training for beginners and artists unused to camera acting
- Rehearsal & workshops for experienced actors currently employed in TV or film

MARBLE ARCH STUDIO TEL: 020 7723-8181

CAMPBELL Kenneth
S E D
Parkhills, 6 Clevelands Park
Northam, Bideford
North Devon EX39 3QH
e-mail: campbell870@btinternet.com   Tel: 01237 425217

CAMPBELL Ross ARCM, Dip RCM (Perf)
(Singing Coach, Accompanist & Music Director)
17 Oldwood Chase
Farnborough, Hants GU14 0QS
e-mail: rosscampbell@ntlworld.com   Tel: 01252 510228

CAPITAL ARTS THEATRE SCHOOL
(Kathleen Shanks)
Wyllyotts Centre, Darkes Lane
Potters Bar, Herts EN6 2HN
e-mail: capitalarts@btconnect.com
Mobile: 07885 232414   Tel/Fax: 020-8449 2342

CARSHALTON COLLEGE
DS
Nightingale Road
Carshalton, Surrey SM5 2EJ
Website: www.carshalton.ac.uk
e-mail: cs@carshalton.ac.uk
Fax: 020-8544 4440   Tel: 020-8544 4444

CARTEURS THEATRICAL AGENCY
170A Church Road
Hove, East Sussex BN3 2DJ
Website: www.stonelandsschool.co.uk
e-mail: dianacarteur@stonelandsschool.co.uk
Fax: 01273 770404   Tel: 01273 770445

CELEBRATION THEATRE COMPANY FOR THE YOUNG
SS D E S Sp, 48 Chiswick Staithe
London W4 3TP
Website: www.speakwell.co.uk
e-mail: nevillewortman@beeb.net
Mobile: 07976 805976   Tel: 020-8994 8886

CENTRAL SCHOOL OF SPEECH & DRAMA
See DRAMA SCHOOLS (Conference of)

CENTRE STAGE SCHOOL OF PERFORMING ARTS
(Students 4-18 yrs) (North London)
The Croft, 7 Cannon Road
Southgate
London N14 7HJ
Website: www.centrestageuk.com
Fax: 020-8886 7555   Tel: 020-8886 4264

CENTRESTAGE SCHOOL OF PERFORMING ARTS
(All Day Saturday Classes, Summer Courses, Private
Coaching for Professionals & Drama School Auditions)
Centrestage House
117 Canfield Gardens
London NW6 3DY
Website: www.centrestageschool.co.uk
e-mail: vickiwoolf@centrestageschool.co.uk
Tel: 020-7328 0788

CHARD Verona LRAM, Dip RAM (Musical Theatre)
(Singing Tutor) (Teacher at Central School of
Speech & Drama)
Ealing House
33 Hanger Lane, London W5 3HJ
e-mail: veronachardmusic@aol.com   Tel: 020-8992 1571

CHARRINGTON Tim
E D
54 Topmast Point
Strafford Street
London E14 8SN
e-mail: tim.charrington@lycos.co.uk
Mobile: 07967 418236   Tel: 020-7987 3028

CHASE Stephan PRODUCTIONS Ltd
(Private Coach for Acting Auditions & Public Speaking)
The Studio, 22 York Avenue
London SW14 7LG
Website: www.stephanchase.com
e-mail: coaching@stephanchase.com   Tel: 020-8878 911.

CHEKHOV Michael CENTRE
Website: www.michaelchekhov.org.uk
e-mail: admin@michaelchekhov.org.uk   Tel: 01273 73823

SCHOOL OF MUSICAL THEATRE

Director Ian Watt-Smith
Tel 020 8987 6677 Fax 020 8987 6680
email mts@artsed.co.uk

BA (Hons) Musical Theatre

A CDET Accredited Course. Validated by City University.

A full-time 3 yr course (18+). A fully integrated approach providing outstanding training in dance, acting and singing by leading professionals. Training the Complete Performer with excellent employment opportunities for graduates.

SCHOOL OF ACTING

Director Jane Harrison
Associate Director Adrian James
Tel 020 8987 6655
Fax 020 8987 6656
email drama@artsed.co.uk

BA (Hons) Acting

3 Year Acting Course. An NCDT Accredited Course. Validated by City University.

A 3 yr course offering the full range of acting skills to adult students aged 18 or over. The emphasis is on the actor in performance and the relationship with an audience. Classes and tutorial work include: a range of textual, psychological and physical acting techniques, screen acting and broadcasting, voice and speech, movement and dance, mask and theatre history.

MA Acting

1 Year Course. An NCDT Accredited Course. Validated by City University.

An intensive 1 yr post-graduate acting course offering a fully integrated ensemble training for mature students (aged 21 or over) with a degree or equivalent professional experience. Emphasis is on the pro-active contemporary performer.

Post Diploma BA (Hons) Performance Studies

Validated by City University.

One-year part-time degree conversion course for anyone who has graduated since 1995 from a NCDT/CDET accredited 3 yr acting or musical theatre course: or for those who can offer appropriate professional experience.

Latest Government Inspection rated ArtsEd "outstanding". Government funded Dance and Drama Awards available.

www.artsed.co.uk

The Arts Educational Schools
14 Bath Road, Chiswick W4 1LY

Member of the Conference of Drama Schools

CHRISKA STAGE SCHOOL
37-39 Whitby Road, Ellesmere Port
Cheshire L64 8AA   Tel: 01928 739166

CHRYSTEL ARTS THEATRE SCHOOL
Edgware Parish Hall, Rectory Lane
Edgware, Middlesex HA8 7LG
e-mail: chrystelarts@beeb.net   Tel/Fax: 01494 773336

CHURCHER Mel MA
(Acting & Vocal Coach)
Website: www.melchurcher.com
e-mail: melchurcher@hotmail.com   Mobile: 07778 773019

CHURCHER Teresa
London & Milton Keynes
Website: www.teresachurcher.co.uk
e-mail: info@teresachurcher.co.uk   Mobile: 07966 228395

CIRCOMEDIA
(Centre for Contemporary Circus & Physical Performance)
Britannia Road, Kingswood
Bristol BS15 8DB
Website: www.circomedia.com
e-mail: info@circomedia.com   Tel/Fax: 0117-947 7288

CIRCUS MANIACS SCHOOL OF CIRCUS ARTS
(Full & Part-time Courses, One-to-One Act Development &
Production Support)
Office 8A
The Kingswood Foundation
Britannia Road, Kingswood, Bristol BS15 8DB
Website: www.circusmaniacs.com
e-mail: info@circusmaniacs.com
Mobile: 07977 247287   Tel/Fax: 0117-947 7042

CITY LIT The
(Part-time Day & Evening)
Keeley Street, Covent Garden
London WC2B 4BA
Website: www.citylit.ac.uk
e-mail: drama@citylit.ac.uk   Tel: 020-7492 2542

CLEMENTS Anne MA, LGSM, FRSA
(Drama/Speech/Auditions/Coaching)
Hampstead, London NW3
e-mail: anne@cityphotography.freeserve.co.uk
Mobile: 07963 818845

COLDIRON M J
(Private Coaching, Audition Preparation &
Presentation Skills)
54 Millfields Road, London E5 0SB
e-mail: jiggs@blueyonder.co.uk   Tel: 020-8533 1506

COLGAN Valerie
The Green, 17 Herbert Street
London NW5 4HA   Tel: 020-7267 2153

COMBER Sharrone BA Hons MAVS (CSSD)
D E Sp (Voice & Speech, Text, Auditions)
8 Pinelands Close, St John's Park
Blackheath, London SE3 7TF
e-mail: sharronecomber@hotmail.com   Mobile: 07752 029422

COMEDY COACH - Jack Milner
(Jack Milner)
43 Church Street, Chesham, Buckinghamshire HP5 1HU
Website: www.jackmilner.com
e-mail: jack@jackmilner.com   Tel: 01494 772908

**COMPLETE WORKS CREATIVE TRAINING
COMPANY Ltd The**
The Old Truman Brewery
91 Brick Lane, London E1 6QL
Website: www.tcw.org.uk
e-mail: info@tcw.org.uk
Fax: 0870 1431979   Tel: 0870 1431969

CONTI Dizi
D Sp E
4 Brentmead Place
London NW11 9LH   Tel: 020-8458 5535

CONTI Italia ACADEMY OF THEATRE ARTS
SS
Italia Conti House, 23 Goswell Road, London EC1M 7AJ
e-mail: info@italiaconti.co.uk
Fax: 020-7253 1430   Tel: 020-7608 0044

CONTI Italia ACADEMY OF THEATRE ARTS
See DRAMA SCHOOLS (Conference of)

CORNER Clive AGSM LRAM
(Qualified Teacher, Private Coaching & Audition Training)
3 Bainbridge Close, Ham, Middlesex TW10 5JJ
e-mail: cornerassociates@aol.com   Tel/Fax: 020-8332 1910

COURT THEATRE TRAINING COMPANY
55 East Road, London N1 6AH
Website: www.thecourtyard.org.uk
e-mail: info@thecourtyard.org.uk   Tel/Fax: 020-7251 6018

CPA COLLEGE
(Full-time 3 yr Performing Arts College)
The Studios, 219B North Street, Romford, Essex RM1 4QA
Website: www.colinsperformingarts.co.uk
e-mail: college@colinsperformingarts.co.uk
Fax: 01708 766077   Tel: 01708 766007

www.zoenathenson.com

ZOË NATHENSON SCHOOL OF FILM ACTING

• **FILM ACTING, AUDITION TECHNIQUE & SIGHT READING**

• **GROUP WORKSHOPS AND INTENSIVE COURSES AVAILABLE**

Zoe Nathenson School of Film Acting
55 St James' Lane, London N10 3DA
Mobile: 07956 833 850 Tel: 020 8883 7554
Email: zoe.act@btinternet.com

CREATIVE PERFORMANCE
(Mobile Workshop in Circus Skills & Drama TIE. Events Management for Communities)
20 Pembroke Road
North Wembley, Middlesex HA9 7PD
e-mail: mjennymayers@aol.com   Tel/Fax: 020-8908 0502

CROWE Ben
(Acting/Audition Tuition, Accent Coach)
23 John Aird Court
London W2 1UY
e-mail: bencrowe@hotmail.co.uk
Mobile: 07952 784911   Tel: 020-7262 3543

CYGNET TRAINING THEATRE
See DRAMA SCHOOLS (Conference of)

D & B SCHOOL OF PERFORMING ARTS
Central Studios
470 Bromley Road, Bromley BR1 4PN
Website: www.dandbperformingarts.co.uk
e-mail: bonnie@dandbmanagement.com
Fax: 020-8697 8100   Tel: 020-8698 8880

DALLA VECCHIA Sara
(Italian Teacher)
13 Fauconberg Road
London W4 3JZ   Mobile: 07877 404743

DAVIDSON Clare
D E
30 Highgate West Hill
London N6 6NP
Website: www.csf.edu
e-mail: cdavidson@csf.edu   Tel: 020-8348 0132

DEBUT THEATRE SCHOOL OF PERFORMING ARTS
14 Titania Close, Cottingley
Bingley, West Yorkshire BD16 1WE
Website: www.debuttheatreschool.co.uk
Fax: 01274 564448   Tel: 01274 532347

DE COURCY Bridget
S (Singing Teacher)
19 Muswell Road, London N10   Tel: 020-8883 8397

De FLOREZ Jane LGSM PG Dip
(Singing Teacher - Auditions, Musical Theatre, Jazz, Classical)
70 Ipsden Buildings
Windmill Walk
Waterloo, London SE1 8LT
Website: www.session-singer.archangel-promotions.co.uk
Tel: 020-7803 0835

DIGNAN Tess PDVS
(Audition, Text & Voice Coach)
004 Oregon Building
Deals Gateway
Lewisham SE13 7RR
e-mail: tessdignan60@tiscali.co.uk   Tel: 020-8691 4275

DI LACCIO Gabriela
S (Singing Teacher & Coach)
165 Gunnersbury Lane
London W3 8LJ   Tel: 020-8993 2111

DIRECTIONS THEATRE ARTS (CHESTERFIELD) Ltd
Office: 76 Rupert Street
Lower Pilsley
Chesterfield S45 8DR
Website: www.directionstheatrearts.org
e-mail: geoffrey.cox@btconnect.com
Mobile: 07973 768201   Tel/Fax: 01246 854455

DOGGETT Antonia MA
Flat 2/2
131 Queen Margaret Drive, Glasgow G20 8PD
e-mail: antonia.doggett@googlemail.com
Mobile: 07814 155090

DONNELLY Elaine
(Children's Acting Coach)
Sangwin Associates
8-30 Galena Road, Hammersmith
London W6 0LT   Tel: 020-8748 8698

DRAGON DRAMA
(Drama for Children)
347 Hanworth Road
Hampton TW12 3EJ
Website: www.dragondrama.co.uk
e-mail: info@dragondrama.co.uk   Tel/Fax: 020-8255 8356

DRAMA ASSOCIATION OF WALES
(Summer Courses for Amateur Actors & Directors)
The Old Library, Singleton Road
Splott, Cardiff CF24 2ET
e-mail: aled.daw@virgin.net
Fax: 029-2045 2277   Tel: 029-2045 2200

DRAMA CENTRE LONDON
See DRAMA SCHOOLS (Conference of)

DRAMA STUDIO EDINBURGH The
(Children's weekly drama workshops)
19 Belmont Road
Edinburgh EH14 5DZ
Website: www.thedramastudio.co.uk
e-mail: thedra@thedramastudio.co.uk
Fax: 0131-453 3108   Tel: 0131-453 3284

Drama Studio London

* One year full time ACTING Course

Established 1966 (Accredited by NCDT)

* One year full time DIRECTING Course

Established 1978

* Excellent graduate employment record

* For postgraduate and mature students

* Comprehensive training includes regular productions of classical and modern texts, TV acting and employment classes

Drama Studio London,

Grange Court, Grange Road, London W5 5QN

Tel: 020 8579 3897 Fax: 020 8566 2035

e-mail: registrar@dramastudiolondon.co.uk

www.dramastudiolondon.co.uk

DSL is supported by Friends of Drama Studio London
a registered charity: no 1051375 - President Dame Judi Dench

DRAMA STUDIO LONDON
See DRAMA SCHOOL (Conference of)

DREAM FACTORY The
(Accredited Professional Creative Arts Training Facility
Located within a UK Prison - Open to Offenders,
Ex-offenders & the Wider Community)
PO Box 31855
London SE17 3XP
Website: www.londonshakespeare.org.uk
e-mail: londonswo@hotmail.com　　　Tel: 020-7793 9755

DULIEU John
(Acting Coach, Audition Preparation)
16 Fernwood Avenue
Streatham, London SW16 1RD
e-mail: john_dulieu@yahoo.com
Mobile: 07803 289599　　　Tel: 020-8696 9958

DUNMORE Simon
(Acting & Audition Tuition)
Website: www.simon.dunmore.btinternet.co.uk
e-mail: simon.dunmore@btinternet.com

DURRENT Peter
(Audition & Rehearsal Pianist & Vocal Coach)
Blacksmiths Cottage
Bures Road
Little Cornard
Sudbury, Suffolk CO10 0NR　　　Tel: 01787 373483

DYSON Kate LRAM
(Audition Coaching - Drama)
39 Arundel Street
Kemptown BN2 5TH
Tel: 01273 607490　　　Mobile: 07812 949875

HERTFORDSHIRE

THEATRE SCHOOL LIMITED

THREE YEAR ACTING & MUSICAL THEATRE COURSE &
ONE YEAR COURSE FOR POSTGRADUATES & TEACHERS

Applications now being accepted for the academic year commencing Sept. 2008
from the U.K. and abroad. Please apply for prospectus and audition details from
The Registrar, Hertfordshire Theatre School, 40 Queen Street, Hitchin, Herts SG4 9TS
or phone 01462 421416. Email: info@htstheatreschool.co.uk Website: www.htstheatreschool.co.uk

---

MEL CHURCHER Voice & Acting Coach

R.S.C., Regent's Park, Royal Court, Young Vic.

'Eragon,' 'Unleashed', 'The Count Of Monte Cristo', 'Incendiary', 'The Fifth Element', 'Lara Croft, Tomb Raider'.

'Acting for Film: Truth 24 Times a Second' Virgin Books 2003.

Mobile: 07778 773019   Email: melchurcher@hotmail.com   www.melchurcher.com

---

EARNSHAW Susi THEATRE SCHOOL
SS
68 High Street
Barnet, London EN5 5SJ
Website: www.susiearnshaw.co.uk
e-mail: casting@susiearnshaw.co.uk
Fax: 020-8364 9618   Tel: 020-8441 5010

EAST 15 ACTING SCHOOL
See DRAMA SCHOOLS (Conference of)

ECOLE INTERNATIONALE DE THEATRE JACQUES LECOQ
57 rue du Faubourg Saint-Denis
75010 Paris
Website: www.ecole-jacqueslecoq.com
e-mail: contact@ecole-jacqueslecoq.com
Fax: 00 331 45 23 40 14   Tel: 00 331 47 70 44 78

ELLIOTT CLARKE THEATRE SCHOOL & COLLEGE
(Full time vocational training 2008, Saturday &
evening classes)
132 Bold Street, Liverpool L1 4EZ   Tel: 0151-709 3323

EXCEL SCHOOL OF PERFORMING ARTS
KT Summit House
100 Hanger Lane, Ealing W5 1EZ
Website: www.ktioe-excel.org
e-mail: excel@kt.org   Tel: 020-8799 6166

EXPRESSIONS ACADEMY OF PERFORMING ARTS
3 Newgate Lane
Mansfield, Notts NG18 2LB
Website: www.expressions-uk.com
e-mail: expressions-uk@btconnect.com
Fax: 01623 647337   Tel: 01623 424334

FAIRBROTHER Victoria MA, CSSD, LAMDA Dip
15A Devenport Road
Shepherd's Bush
London W12 8NZ
e-mail: victoriafairbrother1@hotmail.com
Mobile: 07877 228990   Tel: 020-8749 1253

FAITH Gordon BA, IPA Dip, REM Sp, MCHC (UK), LRAM
Sp
1 Wavel Mews, Priory Road
London NW6 3AB   Tel: 020-7328 0446

FBI AGENCY Ltd
(Acting Classes for Everyone)
PO Box 250
Leeds LS1 2AZ
e-mail: j.spencer@fbi-agency.ltd.uk Tel/Fax: 07050 222747

FERRIS Anna MA (Voice Studies, CSSD)
D E
Gil'cup Leaze, Hilton
Blandford Forum
Dorset DT11 0DB   Tel: 01258 881098

FINBURGH Nina
D Sp
1 Buckingham Mansions
West End Lane, London NW6 1LR
e-mail: ninafinburgh@aol.com   Tel: 020-7435 9484

FOOTSTEPS THEATRE SCHOOL
(Dance, Drama & Singing Training)
145 Bolton Lane
Bradford BD2 4AT
e-mail: helen@footsteps.fslife.co.uk Tel/Fax: 01274 626353

FORD Carole Ann ADVS
E D Sp (Acting Training & Communication Skills for
Business)
N10 2AL
Fax: 020-8365 3248   Tel: 020-8815 1832

FORREST Dee
(Voice/Dialects, Film & TV) (London & Brighton. Deputy
Head of Voice, Mountview)
Basement Flat 1A
43 Brunswick Road, Brighton BN3 1DH
Website: www.deeforrest4voice.com
e-mail: dee_forrest@yahoo.com
Mobile: 07957 211065   Tel: 01273 204779

FOX Betty STAGE SCHOOL
Slade Road, Erdington
Birmingham B23 7PX
e-mail: bettyfox.school@virgin.net
Mobile: 07703 436045   Tel/Fax: 0121-327 1020

FRANKLIN Michael
(Meisner Technique)
Correspondence: c/o The Spotlight
7 Leicester Place
London WC2H 7RJ   Tel/Fax: 020-8979 9185

FRANKLYN Susan
(Audition Speeches, Interview Technique, Sight Readings,
Presentation, Confidence)
Mobile: 07780 742891   Tel: 01306 884913

FRIEZE Sandra
D E Sp (English & Foreign Actors)
London Area NW3/NW6   Mobile: 07802 865305

TIM CHARRINGTON

Dip. C.S.S.D., A.D.V.S., ACTOR & TEACHER

ACCENT & DIALECTS T: 020 7987 3028 M: 07967 418 236

FUSHION ACADEMY OF PERFORMING ARTS
Parkshot House
5 Kew Road, Richmond
Surrey TW9 2PR
Website: www.fushionacademy.co.uk
e-mail: info@fushionacademy.co.uk
Fax: 020-8334 8100   Tel: 020-8334 8800

GARLON Yolanda
Queen Alexandra's House, Bremner Road
Kensington Gore, London SW7 2QT
e-mail: yolanda_sangareau@hotmail.com
                                    Mobile: 07904 146314

GAUNT Julia, ALCM, TD-Musical Theatre
(Singing Teacher)
116 Nottingham Road, Selston, Nottinghamshire
e-mail: joolsmusicbiz@aol.com   Mobile: 07712 624083

GETTING THE PART
(Audition and Drama School Coaching)
7 Union Street, High Barnet
London EN5 4HY
Website: www.gettingthepart.com
e-mail: info@gettingthepart.com
Mobile: 07722 168366   Tel: 020-8449 1885

GLASGOW ACTING ACADEMY
1st Floor, 84 Miller Street, Glasgow G1 1DT
e-mail: info@west-endmgt.com
Fax: 0141-226 8983   Tel: 0141-222 2942

GLYNNE Frances THEATRE STUDENTS
Flat 9, Elmwood, 6 The Avenue
Hatch End, Middlesex HA5 4EP
e-mail: franandmo@googlemail.com   Mobile: 07950 918355

VOICE CONSULTANT & COACH
Jessica Higgs
Tel/Fax: 020-7359 7848   Mobile: 079-4019 3631
Basic vocal technique - text and acting -
Consultancy in all areas of voice use.

GMA TELEVISION AND PRESENTER TRAINING
86 Beverley Gardens
Maidenhead
Berks SL6 6SW
e-mail: geoff@geoffmotley.co.uk   Tel: 01628 673078

GO FOR IT THEATRE SCHOOL
47 North Lane, Teddington
Middlesex TW11 0HU
Website: www.goforitts.com
e-mail: agency@goforitts.com   Tel: 020-8943 1120

GRAYSON John
(Coaching for Drama Auditions)
West Midlands
e-mail: jgbizzybee@btinternet.com   Mobile: 07702 188031

GREASEPAINT ANONYMOUS
(Youth Theatre & Training Company)
4 Gallus Close, Winchmore Hill
London N21 1JR
e-mail: info@greasepaintanonymous.co.uk
Fax: 020-8882 9189   Tel: 020-8886 2263

GREGORY Lynda SCHOOL OF SPEECH & DRAMA
(Speech and Drama Classes, All Ages)
23 High Ash Avenue
Leeds LS17 8RS   Tel: 0113-268 4519

GREGORY Paul
(RSC & RNT Actor/Drama Coach)
133 Kenilworth Court
Lower Richmond Road
Putney, London SW15 1HB
Mobile: 07878 757814   Tel: 020-8789 5726

GREVILLE Jeannine THEATRE SCHOOL
Melody House, Gillott's Corner
Henley-on-Thames, Oxon RG9 1QU   Tel: 01491 572000

GROUT Philip
(Theatre Director, Drama Coaching)
81 Clarence Road
London N22 8PG
e-mail: philipgrout@hotmail.com   Tel: 020-8881 1800

Voice and Elocution Coach
Bart Cale
www.english-elocution.com
Tel Bristol 0117 9692224

GSA CONSERVATOIRE
See DRAMA SCHOOLS (Conference of)

GUILDHALL SCHOOL OF MUSIC & DRAMA
See DRAMA SCHOOLS (Conference of)

HALL Michael THEATRE SCHOOL & CASTING AGENCY
Performing Arts Centre
19 Preston Old Road
Blackpool, Lancs FY3 9PR
e-mail: frances@thehalls.force9.co.uk   Tel: 01253 696990

HANCOCK Allison LLAM
D E (Dramatic Art, Acting, Voice, Audition Coaching,
Elocution, Speech Correction etc)
38 Eve Road
Isleworth
Middlesex TW7 7HS   Tel/Fax: 020-8891 1073

HARLEQUIN STUDIOS PERFORMING ARTS SCHOOL
(Drama & Dance Training)
122A Phyllis Avenue
Peacehaven
East Sussex BN10 7RQ   Tel: 01273 581742

**HARRIS Sharon NCSD, LRAM, LAM, STSD, IPA Dip DA
(London Univ)**
The Harris Drama School
52 Forty Avenue
Wembley, Middlesex HA9 8LQ
e-mail: theharrisagency@btconnect.com
Fax: 020-8908 4455   Tel: 020-8908 4451

HEALING VOICES
London, Paris
Los Angeles, Athens
e-mail: healing.voices@yahoo.com   Mobile: 07939 143721

HERTFORDSHIRE THEATRE SCHOOL
40 Queen Street
Hitchin, Herts SG4 9TS
Website: www.htstheatreschool.co.uk
e-mail: info@htstheatreschool.co.uk   Tel: 01462 421416

HESTER John LLCM (TD)
D E (Member of The Society of Teachers of Speech &
Drama)
105 Stoneleigh Park Road
Epsom, Surrey KT19 0RF
e-mail: hjohnhester@aol.com   Tel: 020-8393 5705

HIGGS Jessica
(Voice)
41A Barnsbury Street
London N1 1PW
Mobile: 07940 193631   Tel/Fax: 020-7359 7848

H. J. A. (HERBERT JUSTICE ACADEMY)
PO Box 253, Beckenham
Kent BR3 3WH
Website: www.hjaworld.com
e-mail: mail@hjaworld.com
Fax: 020-8249 2616   Tel: 020-8249 3299

HOFFMANN-GILL Daniel
(Acting & Audition Tuition)
Flat 4, 131 Evering Road, London N16 7BU
e-mail: danielhg@gmail.com   Mobile: 07946 433903

HONEYBORNE Jack
S (Accompanist & Coach)
The Studio, 165 Gunnersbury Lane
London W3 8LJ   Tel: 020-8993 2111

HOPE STREET Ltd
DS Sp (Physical & Multi-Media Perfomance, Training for Actors, Designers, Directors & Participatory Arts Workers)
13A Hope Street, Liverpool L1 9BQ
Website: www.hope-street.org
e-mail: arts@hope-street.org
Fax: 0151-709 3242   Tel: 0151-708 8007

HOPNER Ernest LLAM
E D Public Speaking
70 Banks Road
West Kirby CH48 ORD   Tel: 0151-625 5641

HOUSEMAN Barbara
(Ex-RSC Voice Dept, Associate Director Young Vic, Voice/Text/Acting/Confidence)
e-mail: barbarahouseman@hotmail.com
          Mobile: 07767 843737

HOWARD Ashley BA MA
(Vocal Coach)
16 Aisthorpe
Caple St Mary, Suffolk IP9 2HT
Website: www.vocalcoach.uk.com
e-mail: info@vocalcoach.uk.com   Mobile: 07821 213752

JACK WALTZER *ACTING WORKSHOPS*

*Excerpt from **Dustin Hoffman's** letter of recommendation:*
*"After knowing **Jack Waltzer** for many years as a professional actor & teacher and having attended his acting classes in New York City numerous times, I chose his class to appear in my film "**Tootsie**" because his work represented for me the best of American acting techniques. I feel it would be most valuable for any professional actor to have the opportunity to study and work with **Jack Waltzer**".*

*Excerpt from **Sigourney Weaver's** letter of recommendation:*
"Jack's *script breakdown techniques and his innovative exercises have completely revolutionized the way I prepare for a film. **Jack** is the best teacher I have ever known. He is inspiring, practical and discreet. I cannot recommend **Jack Waltzer** more highly. He is "**The Man**".*

*Excerpt from **Roman Polanski's** letter of recommendation:*
*"I used **Jack Waltzer's** expertise on several motion pictures and plays I directed. He helped me immensely coaching the beginners as well as the experienced and accomplished actors. **Jack Waltzer** is the only no-nonsense acting teacher I know and recommend. His classes are fascinating. I like to pop in as a sort of "guest student" just to learn some more. In preparing an actor for a performance he knows how to build a character."*

MR. WALTZER *trained extensively as an actor for many years with America's foremost teachers and directors of the **Stanislavsky** system. These include: **Stella Adler**, **Sandford Meisner**, **Lee Strasberg**, **Robert Lewis**, **Uta Hagen** and **Elia Kazan**. Acting credits include: Lifetime member of the **Actors Studio**. Elia Kazan's and **Arthur Miller's** New York Lincoln Center Repertory Company. Students who have studied and coached with **Jack Waltzer** include: **Jon Voight**, **David Soul**, **Geena Davis**, **Sharon Stone**, **Teri Garr** and **Sigourney Weaver** among others. In **France**, he has taught and coached many well known actors and actresses. He has also assisted **Roman Polanski** as a drama coach in filming of both "**Bitter Moon**" and "**Death and the Maiden**"-*

Paris 00331 48.03.14.82   London 07847 126318   New York 001 (212) 840-1234
e-mail: jackwaltzer@hotmail.com   Website: www.jackwaltzer.com

HUDDERSFIELD TECHNICAL COLLEGE
(BTec, GCE and HNC Courses in Acting, Dance & Musical Theatre)
Highfields Annexe, New North Road
Huddersfield HD1 5NN
e-mail: info@huddcoll.ac.uk   Tel: 01484 437047

HUGHES-D'AETH Charlie
(Voice Coach)
22 Osborne Road, Brighton BN1 6LQ
e-mail: chdaeth@aol.com   Mobile: 07811 010963

HUGHES Dewi
(Voice, Accents, Bodywork, Text, Auditions)
Flat 2, 4 Fielding Road, London W14 0LL
e-mail: dewih@onetel.com   Mobile: 07836 545717

IMPULSE COMPANY The
PO Box 158, Twickenham TW1 3WG
e-mail: info@impulsecompany.co.uk   Tel/Fax: 020-8892 7292

INDEPENDENT THEATRE WORKSHOP The
2 Mornington Road, Ranelagh, Dublin 6, Ireland
Website: www.independent-theatre-workshop.com
e-mail: info@independent-theatre-workshop.com
Tel/Fax: 00 353 1 4968808

INTERACT
19 Raven Lane, Billericay, Essex CM12 0JB
Website: www.laurenbigby.me.uk
e-mail: renbigby@hotmail.com
Mobile: 07961 982198   Tel: 01277 625517

INTERNATIONAL SCHOOL OF SCREEN ACTING
3 Mills Studios, Unit 3
24 Sugar House Lane, London E15 2QS
Website: www.screenacting.co.uk
e-mail: office@screenacting.demon.co.uk   Tel: 020-8555 5775

JACK Andrew
(Dialect Coach)
Vrouwe Johanna, 24 The Moorings
Willows Riverside, Windsor, Berks SL4 5TG
Website: www.andrewjack.com   Mobile: 07836 615839

JACK Paula
(Dialect Coach & Language Specialist)
Vrouwe Johanna
24 The Moorings, Willows Riverside
Windsor, Berks SL4 5TG   Mobile: 07836 615839

JACOBSEN Anja
(German Tutor)
54 Higham Hill Road
London E17 6ER   Mobile: 07811 911002

JAMES Linda RAM Dip Ed, IPD, LRAM
(Dialect Coach)
25 Clifden Road
Brentford
Middlesex TW8 0PB   Tel: 020-8568 2390

JIGSAW PERFORMING ARTS SCHOOL
64-66 High Street
Barnet, Herts EN5 5SJ
e-mail: admin@jigsaw-arts.co.uk   Tel: 020-8447 4530

JONES Desmond
(Mime & Physical Theatre, Master Classes & Short Courses, Freelance Choreographer, Director, Teacher, Coach)
20 Thornton Avenue
London W4 1QG
Website: www.desmondjones.co.uk
e-mail: enquiries@desmondjones.co.uk
Tel/Fax: 020-8747 3537

JUDE'S DRAMA ACADEMY & MANAGEMENT
Manor House, Oldham Road
Springhead, Oldham OL4 4QJ
Website: www.judesdrama.co.uk
e-mail: judesdrama@yahoo.co.uk   Tel: 0161-624 5378

KASTKIDZ
40 Sunnybank Road
Unsworth, Bury BL9 8HF
Website: www.kastkidz.com
e-mail: kastkidz@ntlworld.com
Fax: 0161-796 7073   Mobile: 07905 646832

KENT YOUTH THEATRE
(School & Agency)
Mulberry Croft, Mulberry Hill
Chilham CT4 8AJ
Website: www.kentyouththeatre.co.uk
e-mail: richard@kyt.org.uk
Mobile: 07787 531569   Tel/Fax: 01227 730177

KERR Louise
(Voice Coach)
20A Rectory Road
London E17 3BQ
Website: www.resonancevoice.com
e-mail: louise@louisekerr.com
Mobile: 07780 708102   Tel: 020-8509 2767

KERSLAKE Kelli
1 Southgate Grove
London N1 5BT
e-mail: kellicolaco@gmail.com   Mobile: 07833 694743

KIDS AHEAD STAGE SCHOOL OF TOTTENHAM
Johnston & Mathers Associates Ltd
PO Box 3167
Barnet EN5 2WA
e-mail: joinkidsahead@aol.com
Fax: 020-8449 2386   Tel: 020-8449 4968

KNYVETTE Sally
52 Burnfoot Avenue
London SW6 5EA
e-mail: salkny@aol.co.uk   Tel/Fax: 020-7731 0639

KRIMPAS Titania
The Garden Flat
23 Lambolle Road, London NW3 4HS
e-mail: titania@krimpas.freeserve.co.uk Mobile: 07957 303958

LAINE THEATRE ARTS
(Betty Laine)
The Studios, East Street
Epsom, Surrey KT17 1HH
Website: www.laine-theatre-arts.co.uk
e-mail: info@laine-theatre-arts.co.uk
Fax: 01372 723775   Tel: 01372 724648

LAMDA
See DRAMA SCHOOLS (Conference of)

LAMONT DRAMA SCHOOL & CASTING AGENCY
2 Harewood Avenue
Ainsdale, Merseyside PR8 2PH
Website: www.lamontcasting.co.uk
e-mail: diane@lamontcasting.co.uk   Mobile: 07736 387543

LAURIE Rona
(Coach for Auditions & Voice & Speech Technique)
Flat 1, 21 New Quebec Street
London W1H 7SA Tel: 020-7262 4909

LEAN David Lawson BA Hons, PGCE
(Acting Tuition for Children, LAMDA Exams,
Licensed Chaperone)
72 Shaw Drive, Walton-on-Thames
Surrey KT12 2LS Tel: 01932 230273

LEE STAGE SCHOOL The
(Office)
126 Church Road
Benfleet, Essex SS7 4EP
e-mail: lynn@leetheatre.fsnet.co.uk Tel: 01268 795863

LESLIE Maeve
(Singing, Voice Production, Presentation,
Classical & Musicals)
60 Warwick Square
London SW1V 2AL Tel: 020-7834 4912

LEVENTON Patricia BA Hons
D E Sp (Audition & Dialect Coach)
113 Broadhurst Gardens
West Hampstead
London NW6 3BJ
e-mail: patricia@lites2000.com
Mobile: 07703 341062 Tel: 020-7624 5661

LIPTON Rick
14 Lock Road, Richmond
Surrey TW10 7LH
e-mail: ricklipton@gmail.com Mobile: 07961 445247

LIVERPOOL INSTITUTE FOR PERFORMING ARTS The
See DRAMA SCHOOLS (Conference of)

LIVINGSTON Dione LRAM, FETC
Sp E D
7 St Luke's Street
Cambridge CB4 3DA Tel: 01223 365970

LOCATION TUTORS NATIONWIDE
(Fully Qualified/Experienced Teachers Working with
Children on Film Sets & Covering all Key Stages of National
Curriculum)
16 Poplar Walk
Herne Hill SE24 0BU
Website: www.locationtutors.co.uk
e-mail: locationtutorsnationwide@hotmail.com
Fax: 020-7207 8794 Tel: 020-7978 8898

LONDON ACTORS WORKSHOP
124D Lavender Hill
Battersea, London SW11 5RB
Website: www.londonactorsworkshop.co.uk
e-mail: info@londonactorsworkshop.co.uk
Mobile: 07748 846294

LONDON DRAMA SCHOOL
(Acting, Speech Training, Singing)
30 Brondesbury Park
London NW6 7DN
Website: www.startek-uk.com
e-mail: enquiries@startek-uk.com
Fax: 020-8830 4992 Tel: 020-8830 0074

**LONDON INTERNATIONAL SCHOOL OF PERFORMING
ARTS**
Unit 8, Latimer Road, London W10 6RQ
Website: www.lispa.co.uk
e-mail: welcome@lispa.co.uk
Fax: 020-8964 9562 Tel: 020-8969 7004

LONDON REPERTORY COMPANY
27 Old Gloucester Street, London WC1N 3XX
Website: www.londonrepertorycompany.com
e-mail: academy@londonrepertorycompany.com
Tel/Fax: 020-7258 1944

LONDON SCHOOL OF DRAMATIC ART
4 Bute Street
South Kensington, London SW7 3EX
Website: www.lsda-acting.com
e-mail: enquiries@lsda-acting.com Tel: 020-7581 6100

LONDON SCHOOL OF MUSICAL THEATRE
83 Borough Road, London SE1 1DN
e-mail: enquiries@lsmt.co.uk Tel/Fax: 020-7407 4455

LONDON STUDIO CENTRE
42-50 York Way, London N1 9AB
Website: www.london-studio-centre.co.uk
e-mail: info@london-studio-centre.co.uk
Fax: 020-7837 3248 Tel: 020-7837 7741

MACKINNON Alison
London SE6
e-mail: alison.mackinnon@tesco.net Mobile: 07973 562132

MADDERMARKET THEATRE
(Education Officer)
Education Department, St John's Alley, Norwich NR2 1DR
Website: www.maddermarket.co.uk
e-mail: mmtedu@btconnect.com
Fax: 01603 661357 Tel: 01603 628600

The Actors Company

Auditioning now for October 2008

Photograph courtesy of Marilyn Kingwill

Not a drama school…but an acclaimed company in training

The Actors Company is a one year programme for mature graduates – 25 to 70. The Company offers intensive vocational training (40 hours per week) and a six week repertory season at the Jermyn Street Theatre in the West End of London. The course is 48 weeks in length – 36 of which are arranged so that Company members support themselves in employment during training.

Much Ado About Nothing
Jermyn Street,
Repertory Season

★★★★
What's On

"Pure Magic"
Paul Vale, The Stage

Some recent successful graduates

Bill Ward
Charlie Stubbs
Coronation Street

Houda Echouafni
Waking the Dead
2006/7

Christopher Terry
The Skin Game
Orange Tree

Mark Extance
Peter Hall Company

Phillip Edgerley
Gone Too Far!
The Royal Court

LONDON CENTRE FOR THEATRE STUDIES

For a prospectus contact:
London Centre for Theatre Studies, 12–18 Hoxton Street, London N1 6NG
Telephone: 020 7739 5866 / Email: ldncts@aol.com

MANCHESTER METROPOLITAN UNIVERSITY SCHOOL OF THEATRE
See DRAMA SCHOOLS (Conference of)

MANCHESTER SCHOOL OF ACTING
29 Ardwick Green North
Manchester M12 6DL
Website: www.manchesterschoolofacting.co.uk
e-mail: actorclass@aol.com   Tel/Fax: 0161-273 4738

MARLOW Jean LGSM
D E
32 Exeter Road
London NW2 4SB   Tel: 020-8450 0371

MARTIN Liza GRSM ARMCM (Singing), ARMCM (Piano)
(Singing Tuition,
Sounds Sensational)   Tel: 020-8348 0346

MASTERS PERFORMING ARTS COLLEGE Ltd
(Musical Theatre/Dance Course)
Arterial Road, Rayleigh
Essex SS6 7UQ   Tel: 01268 777351

McCRACKEN Jenny
First Floor Flat, 316A Chiswick High Road
London W4 5TA   Tel: 020-8747 6724

McDAID Marj
1 Chesholm Road
Stoke Newington, London N16 0DP
Website: www.voicings.co.uk
e-mail: marjmcdaid@hotmail.com
Fax: 020-7502 0412   Tel: 020-7923 4929

McKEAND Ian
(Audition Technique/Drama School Entry)
12 Linnet Close
Birchwood, Lincoln LN6 0JQ
Website: http://homepage.ntlworld.com/ian.mckeand1
e-mail: ian.mckeand@ntlworld.com   Tel: 01522 805966

McKELLAN Martin
62A Neal Street, London WC2H 9PA
e-mail: mckellan@macunlimited.net   Tel: 020-7240 0145

MELLECK Lydia
S (Pianist & Coach for Auditions & Repertoire - RADA)
10 Burgess Park Mansions
London NW6 1DP   Tel: 020-7794 8845

METHOD ACTING
84 Union Road, London SW4 6JU
Website: www.methodacting.co.uk
e-mail: samson@methodacting.co.uk   Tel: 020-7622 9742

METHOD STUDIO, LONDON The
Conway Hall, 25 Red Lion Square
London WC1R 4RL
Website: www.themethodstudio.com
e-mail: info@themethodstudio.com
Fax: 020-7831 8319   Tel: 020-7831 7335

MICALLEF Marianne
(Voice Coach, Accents, Text 4 Business Voice)
15 Lido House
Northfield Avenue
London W13 9LD
e-mail: mariannemicallef@hotmail.com   Mobile: 07974 203001

MICHEL Hilary ARCM
(Singing Teacher, Vocal Coaching, Accompanist, Auditions, Technique)
82 Greenway, Totteridge
London N20 8EJ
Mobile: 07775 780182   Tel: 020-8343 7243

MONTAGE THEATRE ARTS
(Dance, Drama, Singing - Children & Adults)
(Artistic Director Judy Gordon)
The Albany, Douglas Way
London SE8 4AG
Website: www.montagetheatre.com
e-mail: office@montagetheatre.com   Tel: 020-8692 7007

MOORE Stefanie BA Hons LLAM
(Audition Preparation, Public Speaking, Voice and Text)
119 Francis Road, London E10 6PL
Website: www.tinbobbin.com
e-mail: stef@tinbobbin.com   Mobile: 07751 564223

MORLEY ADULT EDUCATION COLLEGE
(Day & Evening LOCN Accredited, Acting School Programme)
61 Westminster Bridge Road, London SE1 7HT
Website: www.morleycollege.ac.uk
e-mail: dominic.grant@morleycollege.ac.uk
Fax: 020-7928 4074   Tel: 020-7450 1832

MORRISON Elspeth
27 Oakworth Road, London W10 6DF
e-mail: elsp.morrison@talk21.com   Mobile: 07790 919870

MORRISON Stuart MA Voice Studies (CSSD)
(Voice & Speech Coach)
24 Deans Walk, Coulsdon
Surrey CR5 1HR
e-mail: stuartvoicecoach@yahoo.co.uk Mobile: 07867 808648

MOUNTVIEW
See DRAMA SCHOOLS (Conference of)

MRS WORTHINGTON'S WORKSHOPS
SS S Md (Part-time Performing Arts for Children 6-16 yrs)
16 Ouseley Road, London SW12 8EF   Tel: 020-8767 6944

MURRAY Barbara LGSM, LALAM
129 Northwood Way, Northwood
Middlesex HA6 1RF   Tel: 01923 823182

NATHENSON Zoe
(Film Acting, Audition Technique & Sight Reading)
55 St James's Lane, London N10 3DA
Website: www.zoenathenson.com
e-mail: zoe.act@btinternet.com   Mobile: 07956 833850

NATIONAL PERFORMING ARTS SCHOOL & AGENCY The
NPAS The Factory
35A Barrow Street, Dublin 4, Ireland
e-mail: info@npas.ie   Tel/Fax: 00 353 1 6684035

NEIL Andrew
2 Howley Place, London W2 1XA
e-mail: andrewneil@talktalk.net
Mobile: 07979 843984   Tel/Fax: 020-7262 9521

NEW PRODUCERS ALLIANCE
Unit 7.03, The Tea Building
56 Shoreditch High Street E1 6JJ
Website: www.npa.org.uk
e-mail: queries@npa.org.uk
Fax: 020-7729 1852   Tel: 020-7613 0440

NEWNHAM Caryll
(Singing Teacher)
35 Selwyn Crescent, Hatfield, Herts AL10 9NL
e-mail: caryll@ntlworld.com
Mobile: 07976 635745   Tel: 01707 267700

NLPAC
(Performing Arts Classes 3-19 yrs, Dance, Drama, Music.
GCSE Courses, LAMDA, ISTD & RAD)
76 St James Lane, Muswell Hill, London N10 3DF
Website: www.nlpac.co.uk
e-mail: nlpac@aol.com
Fax: 020-8444 4040   Tel: 020-8444 4544

NORTHERN ACADEMY OF PERFORMING ARTS
Anlaby Road, Hull HU1 2PD
Website: www.northernacademy.org.uk
e-mail: napa@northernacademy.org.uk
Fax: 01482 212280   Tel: 01482 310690

NORTHERN FILM & DRAMA
PO Box 76, Leeds LS25 9AG
Website: www.northernfilmanddrama.com
e-mail: info@northernfilmanddrama.com
                             Tel/Fax: 01977 681949

NUTOPIA ACTORS STUDIO
(Ferris Entertainment)
(Camera Acting & Presenting Courses)
Number 8
132 Charing Cross Road, London WC2H 0LA
Website: www.ferrisentertainment.com   Mobile: 07801 493133

O'FARRELL STAGE & THEATRE SCHOOL
(Dance, Drama, Singing)
36 Shirley Street, Canning Town
London E16 1HU   Tel/Fax: 020-7511 9444

OLLERENSHAW Maggie BA (Hons), Dip Ed
D Sp (TV & Theatre Coaching, Career Guidance)
151D Shirland Road, London W9 2EP
e-mail: maggieoll@aol.com   Tel: 020-7286 1126

OLSON Lise
(American Accents, Practical Voice, Working with Text)
Midlands Based
c/o BSA Millennium Point, Curzon Street
Birmingham B4 7XG
e-mail: lise.olson@uce.ac.uk   Mobile: 07790 877145

OMOBONI Lino
Sp
2nd Floor, 12 Weltje Road
London W6 9TG
e-mail: bluewand@btinternet.com
Mobile: 07885 528743   Tel/Fax: 020-8741 2038

OPEN VOICE
(Consultancy, Auditions, Personal Presentation - Catherine Owen)
9 Bellsmains, Gorebridge
Near Edinburgh EH23 4QD   Tel: 01875 820175

OPPOSITE LEG Ltd
132 Bethwin Road, London SE5 0YY
Website: www.oppositeleg.co.uk
e-mail: davidwindle@aol.com   Mobile: 07950 824123

ORAM Daron
(Voice Training, Speech & Accent, Audition preparation)
11A Devonshire Road, London W4 2EU
e-mail: darono@yahoo.com   Mobile: 07905 332497

ORTON Leslie LRAM, ALAM, ANEA
E D Sp
141 Ladybrook Lane, Mansfield
Notts NG18 5JH   Tel: 01623 626082

OSBORNE HUGHES John
(Spiritual Psychology of Acting)
Miracle Tree Productions Training Department
51 Church Road, London SE19 2TE
Website: www.spiritualpsychologyofacting.com
e-mail: johughes@miracletreeproductions.com
Mobile: 07801 950916   Tel: 020-8653 7735

OSCARS COLLEGE OF PERFORMANCE ARTS Ltd
103 Fitzwilliam Street
Huddersfield HD1 5PS
e-mail: oscars.college@virgin.net
Fax: 01484 545036   Tel: 01484 545519

OVERSBY William
(Singing & Vocal Projection)
Petersfield, Hants
e-mail: billo363@msn.com
Mobile: 07811 946663   Tel: 01420 538549

OXFORD SCHOOL OF DRAMA The
See DRAMA SCHOOLS (Conference of)

PALMER Jackie STAGE SCHOOL
30 Daws Hill Lane
High Wycombe, Bucks HP11 1PW
Website: www.jackiepalmer.co.uk
e-mail: jackie.palmer@btinternet.com
Fax: 01494 510479   Tel: 01494 510597

PARKES Frances MA, AGSM
(Voice & Acting Coach)
451A Kingston Road
London SW20 8JP
Website: www.makethemostofyourvoice.com
e-mail: frances25@blueyonder.co.uk
          Tel/Fax: 020-8542 2777

PAUL'S THEATRE SCHOOL
Fairkytes Arts Centre
51 Billet Lane
Hornchurch, Essex RM11 1AX
Website: www.paulstheatreschool.co.uk
e-mail: info@paulstheatreschool.co.uk
Fax: 01708 475286   Tel: 01708 447123

PERFORM
SS
66 Churchway, London NW1 1LT
Website: www.perform.org.uk
e-mail: enquiries@perform.org.uk
Fax: 020-7691 4822   Tel: 0845 4004000

PERFORMANCE BUSINESS The
78 Oatlands Drive
Weybridge, Surrey KT13 9HT
Website: www.theperformance.biz
e-mail: michael@theperformance.biz   Tel: 01932 888885

PERFORMERS COLLEGE
(Brian Rogers - Susan Stephens)
Southend Road
Corringham, Essex SS17 8JT
Website: www.performerscollege.co.uk
e-mail: pdc@dircon.co.uk
Fax: 01375 672353   Tel: 01375 672053

PERFORMERS THEATRE SCHOOL
Hope Street
Liverpool & Royal Victoria Patriotic Buildings
London L18 4QJ
Website: www.performerstheatre.co.uk
e-mail: info@performerstheatre.co.uk
Tel: 0151-708 4000   Tel: 020-8479 3000

Offering top class training and individual attention in a glorious setting

THE OXFORD SCHOOL OF DRAMA

Three Year Diploma in Acting
One Year Acting Course

- Accredited by The National Council for Drama Training

- Financial support available through the Government Dance and Drama Awards Scheme

- Chosen by the BBC as one of the top five drama schools in the UK

Six Month Foundation Course

For a prospectus or further information please contact:

The Administrator
The Oxford School of Drama
Sansomes Farm Studios
Woodstock, Oxford OX20 1ER

Tel: **01993 812883**
Fax: **01993 811220**
Email: **info@oxforddrama.ac.uk**

www.oxforddrama.ac.uk
Prospectus and enrolment form
available to download online

Member of the Conference of Drama Schools
The Oxford School of Drama
is a registered charity.

PHELPS Neil
D Sp (Private Coaching for Auditions, Schools, Showbiz, etc)
51 Parkview Court, London SW6 3LL
e-mail: nphelps@usa.com   Tel: 020-7731 3419

PILATES INTERNATIONAL Ltd
(Physical Coaching, Stage, Film & Dance)
Unit 1, Broadbent Close
20-22 Highgate High Street
London N6 5JG
Website: www.pilatesinternational.co.uk
    Tel/Fax: 020-8348 1442

PLAIN SPEAKING
54 Ferry Road, Sudbourne
Woodbridge, Suffolk IP12 2BJ
Website: www.plainspeaking.co.uk
e-mail: enquiries@plainspeaking.co.uk
    Tel/Fax: 01394 450265

POLLYANNA CHILDREN'S TRAINING THEATRE
Knighten Street
Wapping, London E1W 1PH
Website: www.pollyannatheatre.co.uk
e-mail: pollyanna_mgmt@btinternet.com
Fax: 020-7480 6761   Tel: 020-7481 1911

POOR SCHOOL
242 Pentonville Road, London N1 9JY
Website: www.thepoorschool.com
e-mail: acting@thepoorschool.com
Fax: 020-7837 5330   Tel: 020-7837 6030

PRECINCT THEATRE The
Units 2/3 The Precinct
Packington Square, London N1 7UP
Website: www.breakalegman.com
e-mail: theatre@breakalegman.com
Fax: 020-7359 3660   Tel: 020-7359 3594

QUEEN MARGARET UNIVERSITY COLLEGE
See DRAMA SCHOOLS (Conference of)

QUESTORS THEATRE EALING The
12 Mattock Lane, London W5 5BQ
Website: www.questors.org.uk
e-mail: admin@questors.org.uk
Fax: 020-8567 2275   Admin: 020-8567 0011

RADCLIFFE Tom
(Artistic Director at The Actor's Temple)
(Sanford Meisner Technique/Actor Training)
13-14 Warren Street, London W1T 5LG
e-mail: info@actorstemple.com   Tel: 020-7383 3535

Michael Vivian Actor ▮ Director ▮ Writer

Productions at Arts Ed., Mountview, Guildford
Also QDOS, UK Productions & various reps.
Voice Speech & Drama, Audition Coaching, Private Tuition

Tel: 020-8876 2073 Mob: 07958-903911

RAVENSCOURT THEATRE SCHOOL Ltd
8-30 Galena Road
Hammersmith, London W6 OLT
Website: www.ravenscourt.net
e-mail: info@ravenscourt.net
Fax: 020-8741 1786   Tel: 020-8741 0707

RAW TALENT PRODUCTIONS
(Helen Raw)
PO Box 17344, Edinburgh EH12 1DH
Website: www.rawtalentproductions.co.uk
e-mail: info@rawtalentproductions.co.uk
                              Mobile: 07775 592604

RC-ANNIE Ltd
(For Dramatic Fight Services & Theatrical Blood Supplies)
34 Pullman Place, London SE9 6EG
Website: www.rc-annie.com
e-mail: info@rc-annie.com   Tel: 020-8123 5936

**REBEL SCHOOL OF THEATRE ARTS AND CASTING
AGENCY**
46 North Park Avenue
Roundhay, Leeds LS8 1EJ
e-mail: rebeltheatre@aol.com
Mobile: 07808 803637   Tel: 0113-305 3796

RED ONION PERFORMING ARTS CENTRE
(Drama, Dance & Vocal Training, Age 8 yrs to Adult)
26-28 Hatherley Mews, London E17 4QP
Website: www.redonion.uk.com
e-mail: info@redonion.uk.com
Fax: 020-8521 6646   Tel: 020-8520 3975

REDROOFS THEATRE SCHOOL
DS SS D S Sp
Harlequin House, 26 Bath Road
Maidenhead, Berks SL6 4JT
Website: www.redroofs.co.uk
e-mail: sam@redroofs.co.uk
Fax: 01628 822461   Tel: 01628 822982

REFLECTIONS AGENCY
9 Weavers Terrace
Fulham, London SW6 1QE
Website: www.reflectionsperfarts.tripod.com
e-mail: refections pa@yahoo.co.uk
Mobile: 07951 191468   Tel/Fax: 01322 410003

REP COLLEGE The
17 St Mary's Avenue
Purley on Thames, Berks RG8 8BJ
Website: www.repcollege.com
e-mail: tudor@repcollege.co.uk   Tel: 0118-942 1144

REYNOLDS Sandra COLLEGE
(Modelling & Grooming School)
35 St Georges Street, Norwich NR3 1DA
Website: www.sandrareynolds.co.uk
e-mail: recruitment@sandrareynolds.co.uk
Fax: 01603 219825   Tel: 01603 623842

RICHMOND DRAMA SCHOOL
DS (1 & 2 Year Courses)
Parkshot Centre, Parkshot
Richmond, Surrey TW9 2RE
e-mail: mark.woolgar@racc.ac.uk Tel: 020-8891 5907 ext 4022

RIDGEWAY STUDIOS PERFORMING ARTS COLLEGE
Fairley House, Andrews Lane
Cheshunt, Herts EN7 6LB
Website: www.ridgewaystudios.co.uk
e-mail: info@ridgewaystudios.co.uk
Fax: 01992 633844   Tel: 01992 633775

RISING STARS DRAMA SCHOOL
PO Box 6281, Dorchester, Dorset DT1 9BB
Website: www.risingstarsdramaschool.co.uk
e-mail: info@risingstarsdramaschool.co.uk   Tel: 0845 2570127

ROFFE Danielle
71 Mornington Street
London NW1 7QE   Tel: 020-7388 1898

ROSCH Philip
(Association of Guildhall Teachers, FVCM, LALAM, ATCL,
LGSM, ANEA, BA Hons) (Audition Speeches/Effective
Sight-reading, Career Guidance, RADA Acting Exams)
53 West Heath Court
London NW11 7RG   Tel: 020-8731 6686

ROSE BRUFORD COLLEGE
See DRAMA SCHOOLS (Conference of)

ROSSENDALE DANCE & DRAMA CENTRE
52 Bridleway, Waterfoot
Rossendale, Lancs BB4 9DS
e-mail: rddc@btinternet.com   Tel: 01706 211161

ROYAL ACADEMY OF DRAMATIC ART
See DRAMA SCHOOLS (Conference of)

ROYAL ACADEMY OF MUSIC
Marylebone Road, London NW1 5HT
Website: www.ram.ac.uk   Tel: 020-7873 7373

ROYAL SCOTTISH ACADEMY OF MUSIC & DRAMA
See DRAMA SCHOOLS (Conference of)

ROYAL WELSH COLLEGE OF MUSIC & DRAMA
See DRAMA SCHOOLS (Conference of)

RYDER Richard
(Voice & Speech Coach)
15A Worlingham Road
East Dulwich, London SE22 9HD
e-mail: richard_j_ryder@hotmail.com   Mobile: 07967 352551

SCALA SCHOOL OF PERFORMING ARTS
Office: 42 Rufford Avenue
Yeadon, Leeds LS19 7QR
Website: www.scalakids.com
e-mail: office@scalakids.com
Fax: 0113-250 8806   Tel: 0113-250 6823

SHAW Phil
(Actors' Consultancy Service)
(Audition Technique/Voice Coaching)
Suite 476, 2 Old Brompton Road
South Kensington, London SW7 3DQ
e-mail: shawcastlond@aol.com   Tel: 020-8715 8943

SHENEL Helena
(Singing Teacher)
80 Falkirk House, 165 Maida Vale
London W9 1QX   Tel: 020-7328 2921

SIMPKIN Heather
Morriston, Fairmile
Henley-on-Thames, Oxon RG9 2JX
e-mail: heathersimpkin@btinternet.com   Tel: 01491 574349

SINGER Sandra ASSOCIATES
21 Cotswold Road
Westcliff-on-Sea, Essex SS0 8AA
Website: www.sandrasinger.com
e-mail: sandrasingeruk@aol.com
Fax: 01702 339393   Tel: 01702 331616

SINGER STAGE SCHOOL
(School & Summer School)
21 Cotswold Road
Westcliff-on-Sea, Essex SS0 8AA
Website: www.sandrasinger.com
e-mail: sandrasingeruk@aol.com
Fax: 01702 339393   Tel: 01702 331616

SOCIETY OF TEACHERS OF SPEECH & DRAMA The
The Registered Office:
73 Berry Hill Road
Mansfield, Notts NG18 4RU
Website: www.stsd.org.uk
e-mail: ann.k.jones@btinternet.com   Tel: 01623 627636

SPEAKE Barbara STAGE SCHOOL
East Acton Lane, London W3 7EG
e-mail: speakekids3@aol.com   Tel/Fax: 020-8743 1306

SPEED Anne-Marie Hon ARAM, MA (Voice Studies), CSSD, ADVS, BA
(Vocal Technique, Coaching, Auditions, Accents)
PO Box 235
19-21 Crawford Street
London W1H 1PJ
Website: www.thevoiceexplained.com
e-mail: anne-marie.speed@virgin.net
Mobile: 07957 272554   Tel: 020-7644 5947

SPIRITUAL PSYCHOLOGY OF ACTING The
51 Church Road
London SE19 2TE
Website: www.spiritualpsychologyofacting.com
e-mail: info@miracletreeproductions.com   Tel: 020-8653 7735

HOLLY WILSON
LLAM. Actor. Teacher-London Drama Schools.
Voice, Speech & Drama, Audition coaching. Private tuition.
Tel: 020-8878 0015

SPONTANEITY SHOP The
85-87 Bayham Street
London NW1 0AG
Website: www.the-spontaneity-shop.com
e-mail: info@the-spontaneity-shop.com   Tel: 020-7788 4080

STAGE 84 YORKSHIRE SCHOOL OF PERFORMING ARTS
(Evening & Weekend Classes & Summer Schools)
Old Bell Chapel, Town Lane
Idle, West Yorks BD10 8PR
e-mail: valeriejackson@stage84.com
Mobile: 07785 244984   Tel: 01274 569197

**STAGECOACH TRAINING CENTRES FOR THE
PERFORMING ARTS**
The Courthouse, Elm Grove
Walton-on-Thames, Surrey KT12 1LZ
Website: www.stagecoach.co.uk
e-mail: mail@stagecoach.co.uk
Fax: 01932 222894   Tel: 01932 254333

STAGEFIGHT
138 Wilden Lane
Stourport-on-Severn
Worcestershire DY13 9LP
Website: www.stagefight.co.uk
e-mail: raph@stagefight.co.uk   Mobile: 07813 308672

STAR-BRIGHT DRAMA WORKSHOPS
Royal Exchange, St Ann's Square
Manchester M2 7BR
Website: www.emmastafford.tv
e-mail: workshops@emmastafford.tv
Fax: 0161-833 4264   Tel: 0161-833 4263

STE. CROIX Felicitas
(Sense Memories, Meisner, Meyerhold & Audition
Preparation)
London & Los Angeles
e-mail: felicitasstecroix@yahoo.com   Mobile: 07939 143721

STEPHENSON Sarah
(Vocal Coach, Pianist, Musical Director)
8A Edgington Road
Streatham, London SW16 5BS
e-mail: sarahjanestephenson@tiscali.co.uk
Mobile: 07957 477642   Tel: 020-8425 1225

STEWART Carola LRAM NCSD LUD
13 Church Lane
East Finchley, London N2 8DX
e-mail: carolastewart@msn.com   Tel: 020-8444 5994

STIRLING ACADEMY
128 Bradshawgate
Bolton, Lanchashire BL2 1AY
Website: www.stirlingacademy.co.uk
e-mail: admin@stirlingacademy.co.uk
Fax: 0844 4128689   Tel: 0845 0176500

STOCKTON RIVERSIDE COLLEGE
(Education & Training)
Harvard Avenue
Thornaby, Stockton TS17 6FB
Website: www.stockton.ac.uk   Tel: 01642 865400

STOMP! THE SCHOOL OF PERFORMING ARTS
Holcombe House
The Ridgeway, Mill Hill
London NW7 4HY
Website: www.stompschool.com
e-mail: stompschoolnw7@aol.com   Tel/Fax: 020-8959 5353

STONELANDS SCHOOL
(Full-time Training in Ballet & Theatre Arts)
170A Church Road
Hove BN3 2DJ
e-mail: dianacarteur@stonelandsschool.co.uk
Fax: 01273 770444   Tel: 01273 770445

STREETON Jane
(Singing Teacher - RADA)
24 Richmond Road, Leytonstone
London E11 4BA   Tel: 020-8556 9297

SUPPORT ACT SERVICES
(Ian McCracken) (Services for Actors including Stage
Combat Instruction)
243A Lynmouth Avenue
Morden, Surrey SM4 4RX
Website: www.supportact.co.uk
e-mail: info@supportact.co.uk   Tel: 0845 0940796

SWINDON YOUNG ACTORS
65 Stafford Street
Old Town, Swindon, Wiltshire SN1 3PF
e-mail: young.actorsfile@tiscali.co.uk   Tel: 01793 423688

SWINFIELD Rosemarie
(Make-Up Design & Training)
Rosie's Make-Up Box, 6 Brewer Street
Soho, London W1R 3FS
Website: www.rosiesmake-up.co.uk
e-mail: rosemarie@rosiesmake-up.co.uk
Mobile: 07976 965520   Tel: 0845 4082415

BRIGHTON PERFORMERZONE - INSPIRATIONAL SINGING TUITION
YOUTH THEATRE TRAINING
William Pool ARCM. Private Singing Lessons in London and Brighton

All Styles of Singing - Drama - Dance

Brighton Young Performers Drama School (5 years upwards), Performerzone (14-25 years), Group Singing Classes, Summer Schools, Shows. William Pool is an experienced performer who also trains students at Mountview, ArtsEd and Laine Theatre Arts Academies with many pupils in West End Shows.

e: info@performerzone.co.uk **07973 518643** www.performerzone.co.uk

TALENTED KIDS PERFORMING ARTS SCHOOL & AGENCY
(Drama, Singing, Musical Theatre, Dance Classes For All Ages)
23 Burrow Manor
Calverstown
Kilcullen, Co. Kildare, Ireland
e-mail: talentedkids@hotmail.com
Mobile: 00 353 872480348   Tel/Fax: 00 353 45 485464

TEAM ACTIVATE
(Auditions & Presentation Skills)
38 Highbury Hill, London N5 1AL
Website: www.teamactivate.com
e-mail: teamactivate@fastmail.fm   Mobile: 07837 712323

THAT'S A WRAP PERFORMING ARTS SCHOOL
The Actors Studio
Pinewood Studios, Pinewood Road
Iver Heath, Bucks SL0 0NH
Website: www.actorsstudio.co.uk
e-mail: info@actorsstudio.co.uk   Tel: 01753 650951

THEATRETRAIN
(6-18 yrs, Annual West End Productions Involving all Pupils)
121 Theydon Grove, Epping CM16 4QB
Website: www.theatretrain.co.uk
e-mail: info@theatretrain.co.uk   Tel: 01992 577977

TIP TOE STAGE SCHOOL
(Dance, Drama, Singing & Performing Arts Part-time Training)
For correspondence only:
45 Viola Close
South Ockendon, Essex RM15 6JF
Website: www.tiptoestageschool1.piczo.com
e-mail: julieecarter@aol.com   Mobile: 07969 909284

TO BE OR NOT TO BE
(TV/Film Acting Techniques, Showreels, Theatre/Audition pieces, LAMDA Exams) (Anthony Barnett)
40 Grayton Road
King's Lynn
Norfolk PE30 4EL
Website: www.showreels.org.uk
e-mail: tony@tobeornottobe.org.uk
Mobile: 07958 996227   Tel/Fax: 01553 776995

TODD Paul
(Singing Lessons)
3 Rosehart Mews, London W11 3JN
e-mail: paultodd@talk21.com   Tel: 020-7229 9776

TOMORROW'S TALENT THEATRE ARTS
(Theatre Training for students 6-16 years)
Website: www.tomorrowstalent.co.uk
e-mail: info@tomorrowstalent.co.uk   Mobile: 07989 422808

TOP HAT STAGE SCHOOL
(Herts Based) (Part-time Theatre Arts Training for 4-17 years old. Weekend Classes in Potters Bar, Welwyn, Stevenage, St Albans, Hertford & Watford)
PO Box 860, St Albans, Herts AL1 9BR
Website: www.tophatstageschool.co.uk   Tel/Fax: 01727 812666

TOP TV ACADEMY
(Presenter Training)
309 Kentish Town Road, London NW5 2TJ
Website: www.toptvacademy.co.uk
e-mail: admin@toptvacademy.co.uk
Fax: 020-7485 7536   Tel: 020-7267 3530

CTTC
Court Theatre Training Company

"Train for life in the theatre by working in the theatre"

BA (HONS) ACTING
Three year acting course

A comprehensive training for actors in a professional theatre environment focusing on the development of the creative imagination.

POSTGRADUATE DIPLOMA IN PERFORMANCE:
One year full time diploma course

- Acting • Directing
- Theatre Design
- Stage Management
- Musical Theatre

Court Theatre Training Company
The Courtyard, 55 East Road
London N1 6AH
020 7251 6018

info@thecourtyard.org.uk
www.thecourtyard.org.uk

TROTTER William BA, MA, PGDVS
D E Sp
25 Thanet Lodge
Mapesbury Road, London NW2 4JA
Website: www.ukspeech.co.uk
e-mail: william.trotter@ukspeech.co.uk
Tel/Fax: 020-8459 7594

TUCKER John
(Singing Teacher/Voice Couch)
503 Mountjoy House
Barbican, London EC2Y 8BP
Website: www.john-tucker.com
e-mail: mail@john-tucker.com   Mobile: 07903 269409

TV ACTING CLASSES
(Elisabeth Charbonneau)
14 Triangle Place, Clapham, London SW4 7HS
e-mail: ejcharbonneau@aol.com   Mobile: 07885 621061

TWICKENHAM THEATRE WORKSHOP FOR CHILDREN
29 Campbell Road, Twickenham
Middlesex TW2 5BY   Tel: 020-8898 1447

UK DRAMA EDUCATION
2 Baron Court
52-54 Western Elms Avenue
Reading, Berks RG30 2BP
e-mail: esmebates@btinternet.com
Mobile: 07941 700941   Tel: 0118-958 9330

URQUHART Moray
D Sp (Private Coaching for Auditions)
61 Parkview Court
London SW6 3LL
e-mail: nphelps@usa.com   Tel: 020-7731 3604

VALLÉ ACADEMY OF PERFORMING ARTS
The Vallé Academy Studios
Wilton House, Delamare Road
Cheshunt, Herts EN8 9SG
Website: www.valleacademy.co.uk
e-mail: enquiries@valleacademy.co.uk
Fax: 01992 622868   Tel: 01992 622862

VENTURINO Antonio
(Commedia dell'arte, Mask Specialist & Movement Director)
Coup de Masque
97 Moore Road
Mapperley, Nottingham NG3 6EJ
e-mail: a-and-t@coup-de-masque.fsnet.co.uk
Mobile: 07792 827338   Tel/Fax: 0115-985 8409

VERRALL Charles
D
19 Matilda Street
London N1 0LA
Website: www.learntoact.co.uk
e-mail: charles.verrall@virgin.net   Tel: 020-7833 1971

VIVIAN Michael
15 Meredyth Road
Barnes, London SW13 0DS
e-mail: vivcalling@aol.com   Tel: 020-8876 2073

VOCAL CONFIDENCE FOR SPEECH & SINGING
(Alix Longman)
98C Balham Park Road, London SW12 8EA
Website: www.vocalconfidence.com
e-mail: alix@vocalconfidence.com   Tel: 020-8767 6463

VOICE & THE ALEXANDER TECHNIQUE
(Robert Macdonald)
13 Ascot Lane, Greville Place
London NW6 5JD
Website: www.voice.org.uk   Mobile: 07956 852303

VOICE MASTER
(Specialized Training for Voice-Overs & TV Presenters)
88 Erskine Hill, London NW11 6HR
Website: www.voicemaster.co.uk
e-mail: stevehudson@voicemaster.co.uk   Tel: 020-8455 2211

VOICE TAPE SERVICES INTERNATIONAL Ltd
(Professional Voice-Over Direction & CDs)
80 Netherlands Road
New Barnet, Herts EN5 1BS
Website: www.vtsint.co.uk
e-mail: info@vtsint.co.uk
Fax: 020-8441 4828   Tel: 020-8440 4848

VOXTRAINING Ltd
(Voice-Over Training & Demo CDs)
20 Old Compton Street
London W1D 4TW
Website: www.voxtraining.com
e-mail: info@voxtraining.com   Tel: 020-7434 4404

WALLACE Elaine BA
D Sp Voice
249 Goldhurst Terrace, London NW6 3EP
e-mail: im@voicebiz.biz   Tel: 020-7625 4049

WALSH Anne
(Accents, Dialect, Speech)
45B Windsor Road
Willesden Green, London NW2 5DT
Mobile: 07932 440043   Tel: 020-8459 8071

ACCENTS AND DIALECTS

RICK LIPTON

The AMERICAN Coaching
American Accents in the UK

* *Dirty Dancing* the musical
* The Donmar tour of *Guys and Dolls*
* Vertigo Films
* BBC

07961 445 247
ricklipton@gmail.com

ELSPETH MORRISON

British, Irish and Foreign Accents

* Hampstead Theatre
* The Actors Centre
* Faking It
* BBC

07790 919 870
elsp.morrison@talk21.com

WALSH Genevieve
(Acting & Audition Tuition)
87 Kelvedon House
Guildford Road
Stockwell, London SW8 2DN   Tel: 020-7627 0024

WALTZER Jack
(Professional Acting Workshops)
5 Minetta Street Apt 2B
New York NY 10012
Website: www.jackwaltzer.com
e-mail: jackwaltzer@hotmail.com
Tel: 001 (212) 840-1234   Mobile: 07847 126318 (London)

WEBB Bruce
S
Abbots Manor
Kirby Cane, Bungay
Suffolk NR35 2HP   Tel: 01508 518703

WELBOURNE Jacqueline
(Circus Trainer, Choreographer, Consultant)
c/o Circus Maniacs Agency
Office 8A, Britannia Road
The Kingswood Foundation
Kingswood, Bristol BS15 8DB
Website: www.circusmaniacs.com
e-mail: jackie@circusmaniacs.com
Mobile: 07977 247287   Tel/Fax: 0117-947 7042

WEST END WORKSHOPS
(Audition Coaching/Arts Workshops)
Website: www.westendworkshops.co.uk
e-mail: info@westworkshops.co.uk   Tel: 07989 422808

WESTMINSTER KINGSWAY COLLEGE
(Performing Arts)
Regent's Park Centre
Longford Street, London NW1 3HB
Website: www.westking.ac.uk
e-mail: courseinfo@westking.ac.uk
Fax: 020-7391 6400   Tel: 0870 0609800

WHITE Susan
BA TEFL LGSM MA Voice Studies (Distinction).
Voice Coach, Spoken Communication Specialist
42 Bramham Gardens
London SW5 0HG
Website: www.per-sona.com
e-mail: susan@per-sona.com   Tel: 020-7244 0402

WHITEHALL PERFORMING ARTS CENTRE
Rayleigh Road, Leigh-on-Sea
Essex SS9 5UU   Tel: 01702 529290

WHITWORTH Geoffrey LRAM, MA
S (Piano Accompanist)
789 Finchley Road
London NW11 8DP   Tel: 020-8458 4281

WILDER Andrea
D E
23 Cambrian Drive, Colwyn Bay, Conwy LL28 4SL
Website: www.awagency.co.uk
e-mail: andrea@awagency.co.uk
Fax: 07092 249314   Mobile: 07919 202401

WILSON Holly
3 Worple Street, Mortlake
London SW14 8HE   Tel: 020-8878 0015

CHARLES VERRALL

Formerly Co-Director of Anna Scher Theatre

Improvisation based workshops with an emphasis on screen acting technique, for renewal, confidence building and enjoyment: accessible for beginners and suitable for those continuing in training or currently working. 1:1 sessions on voice work, auditions and preparation for drama school entrance.

020 7833 1971

charles.verrall@virgin.net   www.learntoact.co.uk

WIMBUSH Martin Dip GSMD
D E Sp (Audition Coaching)
Flat 4, 289 Trinity Road
Wandsworth Common
London SW18 3SN   Tel: 020-8877 0086

WINDSOR Judith Ph. D
(American Accents/Dialects)
Woodbine
Victoria Road,
Deal, Kent CT14 7AS
e-mail: sarahupson@btconnect.com
Fax: 05600 756516   Tel: 020-8888 2525

WITH PANACHE THEATRE ACADEMY
22 St. David's Close
Maidenhead, Berkshire SL6 3BB
Website: www.withpanache.co.uk
e-mail: info@withpanache.co.uk   Tel: 07881 656575

WOOD Tessa Teach Cert AGSM, CSSD, PGDVS
(Voice Coach)
43 Woodhurst Road
London W3 6SS
e-mail: tessaroswood@aol.com   Tel: 020-8896 2659

WOODHOUSE Alan AGSM ADVS
(Voice & Acting Coach)
33 Burton Road
Kingston upon Thames
Surrey KT2 5TG
Website: www.woodhouse-voice.co.uk
e-mail: alanwoodhouse50@hotmail.com
                            Tel/Fax: 020-8549 1374

WOODHOUSE Nan (Playwright & LAMDA Examiner)
LGSM (Hons Medal)
LLAM, LLCM (TD), ALCM   Mobile: 07812 921625

WORTMAN Neville
(Voice Training & Speech Coach)
48 Chiswick Staithe
London W4 3TP
Website: www.speakwell.co.uk
e-mail: nevillewortman@beeb.net
Mobile: 07976 805976   Tel: 020-8994 8886

WYNN Madeleine
(Director & Acting Coach)
40 Barrie House
Hawksley Court
Albion Road, London N16 0TX
e-mail: madeleine@onetel.com   Tel: 01394 450265

YOUNG ACTORS THEATRE
70-72 Barnsbury Road, London N1 0ES
Website: www.yati.org.uk
e-mail: info@yati.org.uk
Fax: 020-7833 9467   Tel: 020-7278 2101

YOUNG PERFORMERS THEATRE & POP SCHOOL
SS
Unit 3, Ground Floor
Clements Court
Clements Lane
Ilford, Essex IG1 2QY
e-mail: sara@tots-twenties.co.uk
Fax: 020-8553 1880   Tel: 020-8479 3000

YOUNG Sylvia THEATRE SCHOOL
SS
Rossmore Road
Marylebone, London NW1 6NJ
e-mail: info@sylviayoungtheatreschool.co.uk
Fax: 020-7723 1040   Tel: 020-7402 0673

YOUNG VICTORIA The
(Drama Training & Singing)
Correspondence: 35 Thorpes Crescent
Skelmanthorpe
Huddersfield HD8 9DH   Tel: 01484 866401

YOUNGBLOOD EDUCATION Ltd
Website: www.youngblood.co.uk
e-mail: info@youngblood.co.uk   Tel: 020-7193 3207

YOUNGSTAR TELEVISION & FILM ACTING SCHOOL
(Part-time Schools across the UK, 8-20 yrs)
Head Office: 5 Union Castle House
Canute Road, Southampton SO14 3FJ
Website: www.youngstar.tv
e-mail: info@youngstar.tv
Fax: 023-8045 5816   Tel: 023-8033 9322

YOUNGSTARS
(Part-time Children's Theatre School, Age 5-16 yrs, Drama, Singing, Dancing, Voice Over)
4 Haydon Dell
Bushey, Herts WD23 1DD
e-mail: youngstars@bigfoot.com
Fax: 020-8950 5701   Tel: 020-8950 5782

ZANDER Peter
D E SP (German)
22 Romilly Street
London W1D 5AG
e-mail: peterzan.berlin@virgin.net Tel: 020-7437 4767

BELGIUM
ACV/TRANSCOM - CULTUUR
Steenstraat 29
1000 Brussels
Website: www.acvcultuur.be
e-mail: jpvandervurst.transcom@acv-csc.be
Fax: 00 32 2 514 1836   Tel: 00 32 2 289 0830

BELGIUM
CENTRALE GÉNÉRALE DES SERVICES PUBLICS
Place Fontainas 9-11
1000 Brussels
Website: www.cgsp.be
e-mail: mylene.paon@cgsp.be
Fax: 00 32 2 508 5902   Tel: 00 32 2 508 5811

DENMARK
DAF - DANSK ARTIST FORBUND
Vendersgade 24
1363 Copenhagen K
Website: www.artisten.dk
e-mail: artisten@artisten.dk
Fax: 00 45 33 33 73 30   Tel: 00 45 33 32 66 77

DENMARK
DANSK SKUESPILLERFORBUND
Sankt Knuds Vej 26
1903 Frederiksberg C
Website: www.skuespillerforbundet.dk
e-mail: dsf@skuespillerforbundet.dk
Fax: 00 45 33 24 81 59   Tel: 00 45 33 24 22 00

FINLAND
SUOMEN NÄYTTELIJÄLIITTO
Meritullinkatu 33
00170 Helsinki
Finland
Website: www.nayttelijaliitto.fi
e-mail: toimisto@nayttelijaliitto.fi
Fax: 00 358 9 2511 2139   Tel: 00 353 9 2511 2135

FRANCE
SYNDICAT FRANCAIS DES ARTISTES-INTERPRÈTES
1 rue Janssen
75019 Paris
Website: www.sfa-cgt.fr
e-mail: info@sfa-cgt.fr
Fax: 00 33 1 53 25 09 01   Tel: 00 33 1 53 25 09 09

GERMANY
GENOSSENSCHAFT DEUTSCHER BUEHNENANGEHOERIGER
Feldbrunnenstrasse 74, 20148 Hamburg
Website: www.buehnengenossenschaft.de
e-mail: gdba@buehnengenossenschaft.de
Fax: 00 49 40 45 93 52   Tel: 00 49 40 44 51 85

GREECE
HAU - HELLENIC ACTORS' UNION
33 Kaniggos Street
106 82 Athens
Website: www.sei.gr
e-mail: support@sei.gr
Fax: 00 30 210 380 8651   Tel: 00 30 210 383 3742

GREECE
UGS - UNION OF GREEK SINGERS
130 Patission Street
112 57 Athens
Website: www.tragoudistes.gr
e-mail: eratospe@otenet.gr
Fax: 00 30 210 823 8321   Tel: 00 30 210 823 8335

European Trades' & Actor's Unions

For information on the FIA please contact
International Federation of Actors
Guild House, Upper St Martin's Lane
London WC2H GEG
Tel: 020-7379 0900 Fax: 020-7379 8260
e-mail: office@fia-actors.com

[CONTACTS 2008]

IRELAND
IEG- IRISH EQUITY GROUP
SIPTU, Liberty Hall, Dublin 1
Website: www.irishequity.ie
e-mail: equity@siptu.ie
Fax: 00 353 1 874 3691   Tel: 00 353 1 858 6403

ITALY
SINDACATO ATTORI ITALIANI
Via Ofanto 18
00198 Rome
Website: www.cgil.it/sai-slc
e-mail: sai-slc@cgil.it
Fax: 00 39 06 854 6780   Tel: 00 39 06 841 7303

LUXEMBOURG
ONOFHANGEGE GEWERKSCHAFTSBOND LETZEBUERG
19 rue d'Epernay, B.P. 2031, 1020 Luxembourg
Website: www.ogb-l.lu
e-mail: leon.jenal@ogb-l.lu
Fax: 00 352 486 949   Tel: 00 352 496 005

NETHERLANDS
FNV-KUNSTEN INFORMATIE EN MEDIA
Jan Tooropstraat 1, Postbus 9354
1006 AJ Amsterdam
Website: www.fnv.nl/kiem
e-mail: algemeen@fnv-kiem.nl
Fax: 00 31 20 355 3737   Tel: 00 31 20 355 3636

NORWAY
NORSK SKUESPILLERFORBUND
Welhavensgate 3, 0166 Oslo
Website: www.skuespillerforbund.no
e-mail: nsf@skuespillerforbund.no
Fax: 00 47 21 02 71 91   Tel: 00 47 21 02 71 90

PORTUGAL
STE-SINDICATO DOS TRABALHADORES DE ESPECTACULOS
Rua da Fe 23, 2do piso, 1150-149 Lisbon
e-mail: startistas@mail.telepac.pt
Fax: 00 351 21 885 3787   Tel: 00 351 21 885 2728

SPAIN
COMISIONES OBRERAS-COMUNICATIÓN Y TRANSPORTE
Plaza Cristino Martos 4
6a Planta, 28015 Madrid
Website: www.ccoo.es
e-mail: sgeneral@fct.ccoo.es
Fax: 00 34 91 548 1613   Tel: 00 34 91 540 9295

SPAIN
FAEE-FEDERACIÓN DE ARTISTAS DEL ESTADO ESPAÑOL
C/ Montera 34
1ro Piso, 28013 Madrid
Website: www.faee.net
e-mail: faee@wanadoo.es
Fax: 00 34 91 522 6055   Tel: 00 34 91 522 2804

SWEDEN
TF TEATERFÖRBUNDET
Kaplansbacken 2A, Box 12 710, 112 94 Stockholm
Website: www.teaterforbundet.se
e-mail: info@teaterforbundet.se
Fax: 00 46 8 653 9507   Tel: 00 46 8 441 1300

UK
EQUITY
Guild House, Upper St Martin's Lane, London WC2H 9EG
Website: www.equity.org.uk
e-mail: info@equity.org.uk
Fax: 020-7379 7001   Tel: 020-7379 6000

What are performers unions?

The unions listed over the next few pages exist to protect and improve the rights, interests and working conditions of actors and artists working across Europe. They offer very important services to their members, such as advice on pay and conditions, help with contracts and negotiations, legal support and welfare advice. To join a performer's union there is usually a one-off joining fee and then an annual subscription fee calculated in relation to an individual's total yearly earnings. Equity www.equity.org.uk is the main actors' union in the UK. See overleaf for more details.

Do similar organisations exist for other sectors of the entertainment industry?

In addition to representation by trade unions, some skills also have professional bodies and guilds which complement the work of trade unions. These include directors, producers, stage managers, designers and casting directors. Please see the 'Organisations' section of this book for these and other listings.

What is the FIA?

The FIA (International Federation of Actors) www.fia-actors.com is an organisation which represents performers' trades unions, guilds and associations from all around the world. It tackles the same issues as individual actors' unions, but on an international rather than local level.

I'm a professionally trained actor from overseas and I want to work in the UK. How do I get started?

As with all forms of employment, to work as an actor in the UK you will need to have a relevant work permit / working visa. You might want to visit www.workingintheuk.gov.uk for full information. You may also wish to join the UK's actors' union, Equity. For more information please visit their website www.equity.org.uk

What do I do if I am a UK resident and I want to work as an actor abroad?

This will depend on the employment legislation in the country in which you are hoping to work. A good starting point would be to contact the actors' union in that country. Information on actors' unions in Europe can be found over the next few pages, or obtained from the FIA www.fia-actors.com, who in most cases may also be able to advise on what criteria you need to fulfill to be eligible for work.

For example, if you wanted to work in the USA you would either need a Green Card, or to be a member one of the main actors' unions: SAG www.sag.org or AEA www.actorsequity.org. You will not be eligible to join the USA's leading casting directories www.playersdirectory.com or www.breakdownservices.com unless you fulfill these criteria.

LOUISE GRAINGER is the Marketing and Membership Services Manager at Equity, the trade union for the UK entertainment industry.

If you work professionally in the UK as an artist or member of the creative team, you will have been in a workplace where Equity has collectively negotiated the hours you work; the breaks you get; the structure of fees; health and safety; the procedures for dealing with disputes and much more - and you will have been working alongside Equity members.

The best television royalties and residuals structure in the world; contracts and guidelines across the industry; campaigns for an international audiovisual treaty on performers' rights; plans to track your work so you benefit from all the ways in which it is used; theatre funding campaigns; pension schemes; agency regulations; entertainment licensing; television drama production protected by legislation; tax breaks for film - the list goes on and on. Most of this work happens behind the scenes - you may never think about it, but without it, your working life would be riskier and you would be far more open to exploitation.

As the UK trade union Equity genuinely strives to improve the services and support it offers to members and Equity membership gives you access to a range of professional expertise. Non-members do not have this bedrock.

Carrying the Equity card shows you are a professional with a strong support system behind you, no matter where you are working or how your work is used. In return, you are contributing to maintaining the professionalism of the industry.

Equity represents professional artists from across the spectrum of the performing arts and entertainment industry. The membership includes actors, singers, dancers, variety and circus artists, choreographers, stage management, theatre directors and designers, television and radio presenters, walk-on and supporting artists, stunt performers and co-ordinators and theatre fight directors. To obtain an Equity card, applicants must provide proof (contracts, pay slips etc) of professional employment within the entertainment industry.

If you are not yet working professionally but are studying on a full-time course lasting one year or more at HND level or higher, then there is the Student Equity Scheme giving you a lot of information and resources to help you when you start your career.

Equity offices provide all around the UK: London and Isle of Man: 020 7379 6000; South East England: 020 7670 0229; Wales and South West England: 029 2039 7971; Midlands: 02476 553 612; North West England: 0161 832 3183; North East England: 0114 275 9746; Scotland and Northern Ireland: 0141 248 2472

Full information about the work of the union and membership can be found at www.equity.org.uk

ALDEBURGH FESTIVAL OF MUSIC AND THE ARTS
8 - 24 June 2008)
Aldeburgh Music, Snape Maltings Concert Hall
Snape Bridge, Nr Saxmundham, Suffolk IP17 1SP
Website: www.aldeburgh.co.uk
-mail: enquiries@aldeburgh.co.uk   Fax: 01728 687120
BO: 01728 687110   Admin: 01728 687100

ALMEIDA OPERA
July 2008)
Almeida Street, Islington, London N1 1TA
Website: www.almeida.co.uk   e-mail: patrick@almeida.co.uk
Fax: 020-7288 4901
BO: 020-7359 4404   Admin 020-7288 4900

ARUNDEL FRINGE FESTIVAL
24 August - 2 September 2008)
Arundel Town Hall, Arundel, West Sussex BN18 9AP
Director: Kevin Williams   Website: www.arundelfestival.net
e-mail: arundelfringe@aol.com   Tel/Fax: 01903 889821

BARBICAN INTERNATIONAL THEATRE EVENT (BITE)
Year-Round Festival)
Barbican Theatre, Silk Street, London EC2Y 8DS
Website: www.barbican.org.uk
-mail: theatre@barbican.org.uk
Fax: 020-7382 7377   Tel: 020-7382 7372

BATH INTERNATIONAL MUSIC FESTIVAL
16 May - 1 June 2008)
Bath Festivals Trust, Abbey Chambers
Abbey Churchyard, Bath BA1 1NT
Website: www.bathmusicfest.org.uk
e-mail: info@bathfestivals.org.uk   Fax: 01225 445551
BO: 01225 463362   Tel: 01225 462231

BATH LITERATURE FESTIVAL
23 February - 2 March 2008)
Bath Festivals Trust, Abbey Chambers
Abbey Churchyard BA1 1LY
Website: www.bathlitfest.org.uk
e-mail: info@bathfestivals.org.uk
Fax: 01225 445551
BO: 01225 463362   Tel: 01225 462231

BELFAST FESTIVAL AT QUEEN'S
17 October - 1 November 2008)
8 Fitzwilliam Street, Belfast BT9 6AW
Website: www.belfastfestival.com   e-mail: festival@qub.ac.uk
Fax: 028-9097 1336   Tel: 028-9097 1034

BRIGHTON FESTIVAL
3 - 25 May 2008)
12A Pavilion Buildings, Castle Square, Brighton BN1 1EE
Artistic Director: Jane McMorrow
Website: www.brightonfestival.org
e-mail: info@brightonfestival.org
BO: 01273 709709   Admin: 01273 700747

BUXTON FESTIVAL
11 - 27 July 2008)
5 The Square, Buxton, Derbyshire SK17 6AZ
Website: www.buxtonfestival.co.uk
e-mail: info@buxtonfestival.co.uk
BO: 0845 1272190   Admin: 01298 70395

CHESTER MUSIC FESTIVAL
22 June - 23 November 2008)
8 Abbey Square, Chester CH1 2HU
Contact: Carol Griffiths
Website: www.chestersummermusicfestival.co.uk
BO: 01244 304618

CHICHESTER FESTIVITIES
(Not Chichester Festival Theatre)
27 June - 13 July 2008)
Canon Gate Hse, South St, Chichester, W Sussex PO19 1PU
Website: www.chifest.org.uk   e-mail: info@chifest.org.uk
Fax: 01243 528356   Tel: 01243 785718

Festivals
Film & Television Distributors
Film Preview Theatres
Film & Video Facilities
Film, Radio, Television & Video
Production Companies

Key to areas of specialization:
F Films **FF** Feature Films **C** Commercials
CV Corporate Video **D** Drama **Ch** Children's
Entertainment **Co** Comedy & Light Entertainment
Docs Documentaries

Film & Television Schools
Film & Television Studios

[CONTACTS 2008]

THE SUNDAY TIMES

NSDF 08

BRING IT ON

The NSDF is a unique gathering point for those with a dash of theatre running through their veins. If you want to meet the future movers in the entertainment world, come to Scarborough. (Alan Cox – Actor and Visiting Artist **NSDF07**)

The Sunday Times National Student Drama Festival is a week long celebration of theatre and live performance. The festival includes the best student theatre from across the UK, along side workshops from a host of extraordinary professionals. **NSDF07's** Visiting Artists included: Liz Ascroft, Mike Bradwell, Gregory Clarke, Alastair Coomer, Alan Cox, Charlotte Emmerson, Tim Fountain, Colin Grenfell, David Johnson, Nick Moran, Ian Reddington, Indhu Rubasingham, Nabil Shaban and John Wright. **NSDF07** also hosted LAMDA, Mountview, Lyric Hammersmith and Hull Truck who commissioned a student writer.

NSDF08 is the only place to be if you are a student who wants to get involved with theatre. **NSDF08** takes place in Scarborough 15 -21st March 2008 and is open to any student aged sixteen and over and up to a year after graduating.

Thinking about it, I know almost nothing about theatre but I know at least 1300% more than I did exclusively because of NSDF. Its a must-go week. (Tom Ferguson – Winner of the Spotlight Best Actor Award **NSDF07**)

To book a ticket for **NSDF08** or enter a production contact: Holly Kendrick, **NSDF** Director, 19-20 Rheidol Mews, London, N1 8NU T: 020 7354 8070 E:holly@nsdf.org.uk **www.nsdf.org.uk**

Photograph © Allan Titmuss

DANCE UMBRELLA
(October 2008)
Annual Contemporary Dance Festival
20 Chancellors Street, London W6 9RN
Website: www.danceumbrella.co.uk
e-mail: mail@danceumbrella.co.uk
Fax: 020-8741 7902   Tel: 020-8741 404

DUBLIN INTERNATIONAL THEATRE FESTIVAL
(27 September - 14 October 2008)
44 East Essex Street, Temple Bar, Dublin 2, Ireland
Contact: Marcus Barker
Website: www.dublintheatrefestival.com
e-mail: info@dublintheatrefestival.com
Fax: 00 353 1 6797709   Tel: 00 353 1 677843

EDINBURGH FESTIVAL FRINGE
(3 - 25 August 2008)
Festival Fringe Society Ltd
180 High Street, Edinburgh EH1 1QS
Website: www.edfringe.com   e-mail: admin@edfringe.com
Fax: 0131-226 0016
BO: 0131-226 0000   Tel: 0131-226 002

EDINBURGH INTERNATIONAL FESTIVAL
(8 - 31 August 2008)
The Hub, Castlehill, Edinburgh EH1 2NE
Website: www.eif.co.uk   e-mail: eif@eif.co.u
BO: 0131-473 2000   Admin: 0131-473 209

HARROGATE INTERNATIONAL FESTIVAL
(Last week July/First week August 2008)
1 Raglan Hse, Raglan St, Harrogate, North Yorkshire HG1 1LL
Website: www.harrogate-festival.org.uk
e-mail: info@harrogate-festival.org.uk
Fax: 01423 521264   Tel: 01423 56230

KING'S LYNN FESTIVAL
(13 - 26 July 2008)
5 Thoresby College, Queen Street
King's Lynn, Norfolk PE30 1HX
Website: www.kingslynnfestival.org.uk
Fax: 01553 767688   Tel: 01553 76755

LIFT, LONDON INTERNATIONAL FESTIVAL OF THEATRE
(Events Year-round & Biennial Festival)
19-20 Great Sutton Street, London EC1V 0DR
Website: www.liftfest.org.uk   e-mail: info@liftfest.u
Fax: 020-7490 3976   Tel: 020-7490 396

LLANDOVERY THEATRE ARTS FESTIVAL
Llandovery Theatre, Stone Street
Llandovery, Carmarthenshire SA20 0DQ
Artistic Directors: Simon Barnes
Jaqueline Harrison   Tel: 01550 72011

LUDLOW FESTIVAL SOCIETY Ltd
(21 June - 6 July 2008)
Festival Office, Castle Square, Ludlow, Shropshire SY8 1AY
Website: www.ludlowfestival.co.uk
e-mail: rsykes@ludlowfestival.co.uk
Fax: 01584 877673   BO: 01584 872150 Admin: 01584 87507

RE VAMP - READY MADE STREET FESTIVALS
(Complete Touring Festivals)
Ealing House, 33 Hanger Lane, London W5 3HJ
e-mail: verona.chard@vampevents.com   Tel: 020-8997 335

THE 53rd SUNDAY TIMES NATIONAL STUDENT DRAMA FESTIVAL
(15 - 21 March 2008)
19-20 Rheidol Mews, 3 Long Street, London N1 8NU
Director: Holly Kendrick   Website: www.nsdf.org.u
e-mail: admin@nsdf.org.uk   Tel: 020-354 807

WINCHESTER HAT FAIR, FESTIVAL OF STREET THEATRE
(3 - 6 July 2008)
5A Jewry Street, Winchester, Hampshire S23 8RZ
Website: www.hatfair.co.uk
e-mail: info@hatfair.co.uk   Tel: 01962 84984

FILM & TELEVISION DISTRIBUTORS

BLUE DOLPHIN FILM AND VIDEO
(Film Production/Video Distribution)
40 Langham Street
London W1W 7AS
Website: www.bluedolphinfilms.com
e-mail: info@bluedolphinfilms.com
Fax: 020-7580 7670   Tel: 020-7255 2494

CONTEMPORARY FILMS
24 Southwood Lawn Road
London N6 5SF
Website: www.contemporaryfilms.com
e-mail: inquiries@contemporaryfilms.com
Fax: 020-8348 1238   Tel: 020-8340 5715

GUERILLA FILMS Ltd
35 Thornbury Road
Isleworth, Middlesex TW7 4LQ
Website: www.guerilla-films.com
e-mail: david@guerilla-films.com
Fax: 020-8758 9364   Tel: 020-8758 1716

JACKSON Brian FILMS Ltd
39-41 Hanover Steps
St George's Fields
Albion Street, London W2 2YG
Website: www.brianjacksonfilms.com
e-mail: brianjfilm@aol.com
Fax: 020-7262 5736   Tel: 020-7402 7543

NBC UNIVERSAL PICTURES INTERNATIONAL
Oxford House
76 Oxford Street, London W1D 1BS
Fax: 020-7307 1301   Tel: 020-7307 1300

PATHE DISTRIBUTION Ltd
Kent House, 14-17 Market Place
Great Titchfield Street
London W1W 8AR
Website: www.pathe.co.uk
Fax: 020-7631 3568   Tel: 020-7323 5151

SONY PICTURES
25 Golden Square, London W1F 9LU
Fax: 020-7533 1015   Tel: 020-7533 1000

SQUIRREL & SANDS FILMS DISTRIBUTION Ltd
Grice's Wharf
119 Rotherhithe Street
London SE16 4NF
Website: www.sandsfilms.co.uk
Fax: 020-7231 2119   Tel: 020-7231 2209

UIP (UK)
12 Golden Square, London W1A 2JL
Website: www.uip.co.uk
Fax: 020-7534 5202   Tel: 020-7534 5200

UNIVERSAL PICTURES INTERNATIONAL
Oxford House
76 Oxford Street, London W1D 1BS
Fax: 020-7307 1301   Tel: 020-7307 1300

WARNER BROS PICTURES
Warner House
98 Theobald's Road
London WC1X 8WB
Fax: 020-7984 5001   Tel: 020-7984 5000

FILM PREVIEW THEATRES

3 MILLS STUDIOS
Three Mill Lane
London E3 3DU
Website: www.3mills.com
e-mail: info@3mills.com
Fax: 020-8215 3499   Tel: 020-7363 3336

BRITISH ACADEMY OF FILM & TELEVISION ARTS The
195 Piccadilly
London W1J 9LN
Website: www.bafta.org
Fax: 020-7292 5868   Tel: 020-7734 0022

BRITISH FILM INSTITUTE
21 Stephen Street
London W1T 1LN
e-mail: roger.young@bfi.org.uk
Fax: 020-7957 4832   Tel: 020-7957 8976

CENTURY THEATRE
(Twentieth Century Fox)
31 Soho Square
London W1D 3AP
e-mail: projection@fox.com   Tel: 020-7753 7135

DE LANE LEA
75 Dean Street
London W1D 3PU
Website: www.delanelea.com
e-mail: solutions@delanelea.com
Fax: 020-7432 3838   Tel: 020-7432 3800

EXECUTIVE THEATRE
(Twentieth Century Fox)
31 Soho Square
London W1D 3AP
e-mail: projection@fox.com   Tel: 020-7753 7135

MR YOUNG'S PREVIEW THEATRE
(AKA Soho Screening Rooms)
14 D'Arblay Street
London W1F 8DY
Website: www.sohoscreeningroom.co.uk
e-mail: enquiries@sohoscreeningrooms.co.uk
Fax: 020-7734 4520   Tel: 020-7437 1771

NEW PLAYERS THEATRE
The Arches
Off Villiers Street
London WC2N 6NG
Website: www.newplayerstheatre.com
e-mail: info@newplayerstheatre.com
Fax: 0845 6382102   Tel: 020-7930 6601

RSA
(Royal Society of Arts) (Sarah Carr)
8 John Adam Street
London WC2N 6EZ
Website: www.thersa.org.uk/hospitality
e-mail: hospitality@rsa.org.uk
Fax: 020-7321 0271   Tel: 020-7839 5049

TRICYCLE CINEMA
269 Kilburn High Road
London NW6 7JR
Website: www.tricycle.co.uk
e-mail: cinema@tricycle.co.uk   Tel: 020-7328 1000

ACTOR'S ONE-STOP SHOP The
(Showreels for Performing Artists)
First Floor
Above The Gate Pub
Station Road, London N22 7SS
Website: www.actorsonestopshop.com
e-mail: info@actorsonestopshop.com   Tel: 020-8888 7006

ANVIL POST PRODUCTION
(Studio Manager - Mike Anscombe)
Perivale Park
Horsenden Lane South
Perivale UB6 7RL
Website: www.anvilpost.com
e-mail: mike.anscombe@thomson.net   Tel: 020-8799 0555

ARQIVA SATELLITE MEDIA SOLUTIONS Ltd
PO Box 2287, Gerrards Cross
Bucks SL9 8BF
Fax: 01494 876006   Tel: 01494 878585

ARRI MEDIA
3 Highbridge, Oxford Road
Uxbridge
Middlesex UB8 1LX
Website: www.arrimedia.com
e-mail: info@arrimedia.com
Fax: 01895 457101   Tel: 01895 457100

ASCENT MEDIA CAMDEN Ltd
(Post-Production Film Facilities)
13 Hawley Crescent
London NW1 8NP
Website: www.ascentmedia.co.uk
Fax: 020-7284 1018   Tel: 020-7284 7900

ASCENT MEDIA Ltd
(Post-Production Facilities)
Film House
142 Wardour Street,
London W1F 8DD
Website: www.ascentmedia.co.uk
Fax: 020-7878 7800   Tel: 020-7878 0000

AUTOMOTIVE ACTION STUNTS
(Stunt Rigging & Supplies/Camera Tracking Vehicles)
2 Sheffield House
Park Road, Hampton Hill
Middlesex TW12 1HA
Website: www.carstunts.co.uk
e-mail: carstunts@hotmail.co.uk
Mobile: 07974 919589   Tel: 020-8977 6186

AXIS FILMS
(Film Equipment Rental)
Shepperton Studios
Studios Road, Middlesex TW17 0QD
Website: www.axisfilms.co.uk
e-mail: info@axisfilms.co.uk
Fax: 01932 592246   Tel: 01932 592244

CENTRAL FILM FACILITIES
(Camera Tracking Specialists)
c/o The High House
Horderley, Craven Arms
Shropshire SY7 8HT
Website: www.centralfilmfacilities.com
Fax: 0870 7059777   Tel: 0870 7941418

CENTRELINE VIDEO PRODUCTIONS
138 Westwood Road
Tilehurst, Reading RG31 6LL
Website: www.centrelinevideo.com   Tel: 0118-941 0033

CHANNEL 20 20 Ltd
The Clerkenwell Workshops (G15)
27/31 Clerkenwell Close
London EC1R 0AT
Website: www.channel2020.co.uk
e-mail: info@channel2020.co.uk   Tel: 0844 840202

CHANNEL 2020 Ltd
2020 House
26-28 Talbot Lane, Leicester LE1 4LR
Website: www.channel2020.co.uk
e-mail: info@channel2020.co.uk
Fax: 0116-222 1113   Tel: 0116-233 222

CINE TO VIDEO & FOREIGN TAPE CONVERSION & DUPLICATING
(Peter J Snell Enterprises)
Amp House, Grove Road
Rochester, Kent ME2 4BX
e-mail: pjstv@blueyonder.co.uk
Fax: 01634 726000   Tel: 01634 72383

CLICKS
Media Studios, Grove Road
Rochester, Kent ME2 4BX
e-mail: info@clicksstudios.co.uk
Fax: 01634 726000   Tel: 01634 72383

CLUB The
35 Bedfordbury
Covent Garden, London WC2N 4DU
Website: www.theclubpl.co.uk
e-mail: production@theclubpl.co.uk
Fax: 020-7379 5210   Tel: 020-7759 710

CRYSTAL MEDIA
28 Castle Street, Edinburgh EH2 3HT
Website: www.crystal-media.co.uk
e-mail: hello@crystal-media.co.uk
Fax: 0131-240 0989   Tel: 0131-240 098

DE LANE LEA
(Film & TV Sound Dubbing & Editing Suite)
75 Dean Street, London W1D 3PU
Website: www.delanelea.com
e-mail: solutions@delanelea.com
Fax: 020-7432 3838   Tel: 020-7432 380

DENMAN PRODUCTIONS
(3D Computer Animation, Film/Video CD Business Card Showreels)
60 Mallard Place
Strawberry Vale, Twickenham TW1 4SR
Website: www.denman.co.uk
e-mail: info@denman.co.uk   Tel: 020-8891 34

DIVERSE PRODUCTION Ltd
(Pre & Post-Production)
6-12 Gorleston Street, London W14 8XS
Website: www.diverse.tv
e-mail: reception@diverse.tv
Fax: 020-7603 2148   Tel: 020-7603 456

EXECUTIVE AUDIO VISUAL
(Showreels for Actors & TV Presenters)
80 York Street, London W1H 1QW   Tel: 020-7723 448

FARM DIGITAL POST PRODUCTION The
27 Upper Mount Street
Dublin 2, Ireland
Website: www.thefarm.ie
e-mail: info@thefarm.ie
Fax: 00 353 1 676 8816   Tel: 00 353 1 676 881

GREENPARK PRODUCTIONS Ltd
(Film Archives)
Illand, Launceston
Cornwall PL15 7LS
Website: www.greenparkimages.co.uk
e-mail: info@greenparkimages.co.uk
Fax: 01566 782127   Tel: 01566 782107

HARLEQUIN PRODUCTIONS
Suite 5 Woodville Court
31 Sylvan Road, London SE19 2SG
Website: www.harlequinproductions.co.uk
e-mail: neill@harlequinproductions.co.uk   Tel: 020-8653 2333

HUNKY DORY PRODUCTIONS Ltd
(Facilities & Crew, Also Editing: Non-Linear)
57 Alan Drive, Barnet
Herts EN5 2PW
Website: www.hunkydory.tv   Tel: 020-8440 0820

MOVING PICTURE COMPANY The
(Post-Production)
127-133 Wardour Street
London W1F 0NL
Website: www.moving-picture.com
e-mail: mailbox@moving-picture.com
Fax: 020-7287 5187   Tel: 020-7434 3100

OCEAN OPTICS
(Underwater Camera Sales & Operator Rental)
7 & 8 Bush House Arcade
Bush House, Aldwych
London WC2B 4PA
Website: www.oceanoptics.co.uk
e-mail: optics@oceanoptics.co.uk
Fax: 020-7240 7938   Tel: 020-7240 8193

PANAVISION UK
The Metropolitan Centre
Bristol Road, Greenford
Middlesex UB6 8GD
Website: www.panavision.co.uk
Fax: 020-8839 7300   Tel: 020-8839 7333

PEDIGREE PUNKS
(Shooting Crews, Editing, Compositing, Encoding, Mastering
to all formats)
49 Woolstone Road
Forest Hill, London SE23 2TR
Website: www.pedigree-punks.com
e-mail: video@pedigree-punks.com
Fax: 020-8291 5801   Tel: 020-8314 4580

PLACE The
Robin Howard Dance Theatre
17 Duke's Road
London WC1H 9BY
Website: www.theplace.org.uk
e-mail: info@theplace.org.uk
Fax: 020-7121 1142   Tel: 020-7121 1000

PRO-LINK RADIO SYSTEMS Ltd
(Radio Microphones & Communications)
4 Woden Court
Saxon Business Park
Hanbury Road, Bromsgrove
Worcestershire B60 4AD
Website: www.prolink-radio.com
e-mail: service@prolink-radio.com
Fax: 01527 577757   Tel: 01527 577788

SALON Ltd
(Post-Production & Editing Equipment Hire)
12 Swainson Road, London W3 7XB
Website: www.salonrentals.com
e-mail: hire@salonrentals.com   Tel: 020-8746 7611

SOUNDHOUSE The
10th Floor
Ashley House, Quay Street
Manchester M3 4AE
Website: www.thesoundhouse.tv
e-mail: suekeane@thesoundhouse.tv
Fax: 0161-832 7266   Tel: 0161-832 7299

TVMS (SCOTLAND)
(Corporate & Broadcast Facilities)
3rd Floor
420 Sauchiehall Street, Glasgow G2 3JD
e-mail: mail@tvms.wanadoo.co.uk
Fax: 0141-332 9040   Tel: 0141-331 1993

VIDEO INN PRODUCTION
(AV Equipment Hire)
Glebe Farm, Wooton Road
Quinton, Northampton NN7 2EE
Website: www.videoinn.co.uk
e-mail: post@videoinn.co.uk   Tel: 01604 864868

VIDEOSONICS CINEMA SOUND
(Film & Television Dubbing Facilities)
68A Delancey Street
London NW1 7RY
Website: www.videosonics.com
e-mail: info@videosonics.com
Fax: 020-7419 4470   Tel: 020-7209 0209

VSI - VOICE & SCRIPT INTERNATIONAL
(Dubbing, Editing & DVD Encoding & Authoring Facilities)
132 Cleveland Street
London W1T 6AB
Website: www.vsi.tv
e-mail: info@vsi.tv
Fax: 020-7692 7711   Tel: 020-7692 7700

W6 STUDIO
(Video Production & Editing Facilities)
359 Lillie Road
Fulham, London SW6 7PA
Website: www.w6studio.co.uk
Fax: 020-7381 5252   Tel: 020-7385 2272

30 BIRD PRODUCTIONS
24 Wroxton Road, London SE15 2BN
e-mail: thirtybirdproductions@ntlworld.com
Tel: 01223 722112

303 PRODUCTIONS
11 D'Arblay Street, London W1F 8DT
e-mail: anna@303productions.co.uk
Fax: 020-7494 0956   Tel: 020-7494 0955

ACADEMY
16 West Central Street, London WC1A 1JJ
Website: www.academyfilms.com
e-mail: post@academyfilms.com
Fax: 020-7240 0355   Tel: 020-7395 4155

ACTAEON FILMS Ltd
50 Gracefield Gardens, London SW16 2ST
Website: www.actaeonfilms.com
e-mail: info@actaeonfilms.com
Fax: 0870 1347980   Tel: 020-8769 3339

AGILE FILMS
28-30 Coronet Street, London N1 6HD
Website: www.agilefilms.com
Fax: 020-7689 2374   Tel: 020-7689 2373

ALGERNON Ltd
24B Cleveleys Road, London E5 9JN
Website: www.algernonproductions.com
e-mail: info@algernonproductions.com
Fax: 0870 1388516   Mobile: 07092 805026

AN ACQUIRED TASTE TV CORP
51 Croham Road, South Croydon CR2 7HD
e-mail: cbennetttv@aol.com
Fax: 020-8686 5928   Tel: 020-8686 1188

ANGLO IRISH ARTS COLLECTIVE
63 Nicholl House, Woodberry Down
Finsbury Park, London N4 2TQ
e-mail: aiac@btinternet.com   Tel: 020-8800 0640

APT FILMS
Ealing Studios, Ealing Green, London W5 5EP
Website: www.aptfilms.com
e-mail: admin@aptfilms.com
Fax: 020-8280 9111   Tel: 020-8280 9125

APTN
The Interchange, Oval Road
Camden Lock, London NW1 7DZ
Fax: 020-7413 8312   Tel: 020-7482 7400

ARIEL PRODUCTIONS Ltd
46 Melcombe Regis Court
59 Weymouth Street
London W1G 8NT   Tel/Fax: 020-7935 6636

ARLINGTON PRODUCTIONS Ltd
TV D Co
Cippenham Court, Cippenham Lane
Cippenham, Nr Slough, Berkshire SL1 5AU
Fax: 01753 691785   Tel: 01753 516767

ART BOX PRODUCTIONS
10 Heatherway, Crowthorne, Berkshire RG45 6HG
e-mail: artbox@tonyhart.co.uk   Tel/Fax: 01344 773638

ASCENT MEDIA Ltd
Film House
142 Wardour Street, London W1F 8DD
Website: www.ascentmedia.co.uk
Fax: 020-7878 7870   Tel: 020-7878 0000

ASF PRODUCTIONS Ltd
38 Clunbury Court, Manor Street
Berkhamsted, Herts HP4 2FF
e-mail: info@asfproductions.co.uk
Fax: 01442 872536   Tel: 01442 872999

ASHFORD ENTERTAINMENT CORPORATION Ltd The
20 The Chase, Coulsdon, Surrey CR5 2EG
Website: www.ashford-entertainment.co.uk
e-mail: info@ashford-entertainment.co.uk
Tel: 020-8660 9609

ATTICUS TELEVISION Ltd
5 Clare Lawn, London SW14 8BH
e-mail: attwiz@aol.com
Fax: 020-8878 3821   Tel: 020-8487 1173

AVALON TELEVISION Ltd
4A Exmoor Street, London W10 6BD
Fax: 020-7598 7281   Tel: 020-7598 7280

BAILEY Catherine Ltd
110 Gloucester Avenue, Primrose Hill, London NW1 8JA
Fax: 020-7483 2155   Tel: 020-7483 3330

BANANA PARK Ltd
(Animation Production Company)
Banana Park, 6 Cranleigh Mews, London SW11 2QL
Website: www.bananapark.co.uk
e-mail: studio@bananapark.co.uk
Fax: 020-7738 1887   Tel: 020-7228 7136

BARFORD PRODUCTIONS
35 Bedfordbury, London WC2N 4DU
Website: www.barford.co.uk
e-mail: info@barford.co.uk
Fax: 020-7379 5210   Tel: 020-7240 4188

BARRATT Michael
Field House, Ascot Road
Maidenhead, Berkshire SL6 3LD
e-mail: michael@mbarratt.co.uk
Fax: 01628 627737   Tel: 01628 77080C

BBC WORLDWIDE Ltd
Woodlands, 80 Wood Lane, London W12 0TT
Fax: 020-8749 0538   Tel: 020-8433 200C

BHP Ltd
2A Utopia Village, 7 Chalcot Road
London NW1 8LH
Fax: 020-7722 6229   Tel: 020-7722 226'

BIG MOUTH COMPANY Ltd The
PO Box 619 CT14 9YA
Website: www.thebigmouthcompany.com
e-mail: info@thebigmouthcompany.com
Tel/Fax: 0871 7500075

BIG RED BUTTON Ltd
(Write)
91 Brick Lane, London E1 6QL
Website: www.bigredbutton.tv
e-mail: info@bigredbutton.tv

BLACKBIRD PRODUCTIONS
6 Molasses Row, Plantation Wharf
Battersea, London SW11 3UX
e-mail: enquiries@blackbirdproductions.co.uk
Tel: 020-7924 644C

BLUE FISH MEDIA
39 Ratby Close, Lower Earley, Reading RG6 4ER
Website: www.bfmedia.co.uk
e-mail: ideas@bfmedia.co.uk   Tel: 0118-975 027ʒ

BLUE SKY ENTERTAINMENT
(Corporate, Open Air & Specialist Entertainment)
8 Adelaide Grove, London W12 0JJ
Website: www.blueskyentertainment.co.uk
e-mail: info@blueskyentertainment.co.uk
Mobile: 07702 474430   Tel: 020-8723 212'

BLUE WAND PRODUCTIONS Ltd
2nd Floor, 12 Weltje Road, London W6 9TG
e-mail: bluewand@btinternet.com
Mobile: 07885 528743   Tel/Fax: 020-8741 203'

BLUELINE PRODUCTIONS Ltd
16 Five Oaks Close, Woking, Surrey GU21 8TU
e-mail: david@blue-line.tv   Tel: 01483 797002

BOWE John PRODUCTIONS
(Editing & Production)
44 Sotheron Road, Watford
Herts WD17 2QA   Tel: 01923 213008

BRUNSWICK FILMS Ltd
(Formula One Grand Prix Film Library)
26 Macroom Road
Maida Vale, London W9 3HY
Website: www.brunswickfilms.com
e-mail: info@brunswickfilms.com
Fax: 020-8960 4997   Tel: 020-8960 0066

BRYANT WHITTLE Ltd
49 Federation Road
Abbey Wood, London SE2 0JT
Website: www.bryantwhittle.com
e-mail: bryant.whittle@virgin.net
Fax: 020-8311 5827   Tel: 020-8311 8752

BUCKMARK PRODUCTIONS
Commer House, Station Road,
Tadcaster, North Yorkshire LS24 9JF
Website: www.buckmark.com
e-mail: info@buckmark.com
Fax: 01937 835901   Tel: 01937 835900

BUENA VISTA PRODUCTIONS
3 Queen Caroline Street
Hammersmith, London W6 9PE
Fax: 020-8222 2795   Tel: 020-8222 1000

BURDER FILMS
37 Braidley Road, Meyrick Park
Bournemouth BH2 6JY
Website: www.johnburder.co.uk
e-mail: burderfilms@aol.com
    Tel: 01202 295395

CALDERDALE TELEVISION
Dean Clough, Halifax HX3 5AX
e-mail: ctv@calderdaletv.co.uk   Tel: 01422 253100

CAMBRIDGE FILM & TELEVISION PRODUCTIONS Ltd
Building 7200, Cambridge Research Park
Beach Drive, Waterbeach, Cambridge CB25 9TL
Website: www.cftp.co.uk
e-mail: contact@cftp.co.uk
Fax: 01223 815623   Tel: 01223 815613

CARDINAL BROADCAST
Cutting Room 13, Pinewood Studios
Iver Heath, Bucks SL0 0NH   Tel: 01753 639210

CARNIVAL (FILMS & THEATRE) Ltd
47 Marylebone Lane, London W1U 2NT
Website: www.carnival-films.co.uk
Fax: 020-7317 1380   Tel: 020-7317 1370

CELADOR PRODUCTIONS Ltd
39 Long Acre, London WC2E 9LG
Fax: 020-7845 6975   Tel: 020-7240 8101

CELTIC FILMS ENTERTAINMENT Ltd
Lodge House
59 Beaufort Street, London SW3 5AH
Website: www.celticfilms.co.uk
e-mail: info@celticfilms.co.uk
Fax: 0871 2641474   Tel: 020-7351 0909

CENTRAL OFFICE OF INFORMATION
(Television)
Hercules House, Hercules Road, London SE1 7DU
Website: www.coi.gov.uk
e-mail: eileen.newton@coi.gsi.gov.uk
Fax: 020-7261 8776   Tel: 020-7261 8220

CENTRE SCREEN PRODUCTIONS
Eastgate, Castle Street
Castlefield, Manchester M3 4LZ
Website: www.centrescreen.co.uk
e-mail: info@centrescreen.co.uk
Fax: 0161-832 8934   Tel: 0161-832 7151

CHANNEL 2020 Ltd
2020 House, 26-28 Talbot Lane
Leicester LE1 4LR
Website: www.channel2020.co.uk
e-mail: info@channel2020.co.uk
Fax: 0116-222 1113   Tel: 0116-233 2220

CHANNEL TELEVISION PRODUCTION
The Television Centre
La Pouquelaye
St Helier, Jersey JE1 3ZD
e-mail: production@channeltv.co.uk
Fax: 01534 816889   Tel: 01534 816888

CHANNEL X Ltd
2nd Floor, Highgate Business Centre
33 Greenwood Place, London NW5 1LB
e-mail: firstname.lastname@channelx.co.uk
Fax: 020-7428 3998   Tel: 020-7428 3999

CHARISMA FILMS Ltd
Riverbank House
1 Putney Bridge Approach, London SW6 3JD
Fax: 020-7610 6836   Tel: 020-7610 6830

CHILDREN'S FILM & TELEVISION FOUNDATION Ltd
e-mail: annahome@cftf.org.uk   Mobile: 07887 573479

CINEMA VERITY PRODUCTIONS Ltd
F TV D Co
11 Addison Avenue, London W11 4QS
Fax: 020-7371 3329   Tel: 020-7460 2777

Height 5 feet 10 inches   (Equity/M.U.)   Photo: *Stephen Hough*

Peter Durrent

Pianist ~ Accompanist ~ Composer ~ Vocalist
Audition & Rehearsal Pianist ~ Cocktail Pianist

Tel: 01787 373483   Mob: 07810 613 938

or c/o The Spotlight

CLASSIC MEDIA GROUP
Shepperton Studios, Studios Road
Shepperton, Middlesex TW17 0QD
e-mail: lyn.beardsall@classicpictures.co.uk
Fax: 01932 592046   Tel: 01932 592016

COLLINGWOOD O'HARE ENTERTAINMENT Ltd
10-14 Crown Street
Acton, London W3 8SB
e-mail: info@crownstreet.co.uk
Fax: 020-8993 9595   Tel: 020-8993 3666

COMMERCIAL BREAKS
Anglia House, Norwich NR1 3JG
Website: www.commercialbreaks.co.uk
e-mail: commercialbreaks@itv.com
Fax: 01603 752610   Tel: 01603 752600

COMMUNICATOR Ltd
199 Upper Street, London N1 1RQ
e-mail: info@communicator.ltd.uk
Fax: 020-7704 8444   Tel: 020-7704 8333

COMPLETE WORKS The
The Old Truman Brewery
91 Brick Lane, London E1 6QL
Website: www.tcw.org.uk
e-mail: info@tcw.org.uk
Fax: 0870 1431979   Tel: 0870 1431969

COMTEC Ltd
Unit 19, Tait Road, Croydon, Surrey CR0 2DP
Website: www.comtecav.co.uk
e-mail: info@comtecav.co.uk
Fax: 020-8684 6947   Tel: 020-8684 6615

CONVERGENCE PRODUCTIONS Ltd
10-14 Crown Street, Acton, London W3 8SB
e-mail: info@crownstreet.co.uk
Fax: 020-8993 9595   Tel: 020-8993 3666

COURTYARD PRODUCTIONS
TV Production Company
Little Postlings Farmhouse
Four Elms, Kent TN8 6NA
e-mail: courtyard@mac.com   Tel: 01732 700324

CREATE MEDIA VENTURES/CREATE TV & FILM Ltd
52 New Concordia Wharf
Mill Street, London SE1 2BB
Website: www.createtvandfilm.com
e-mail: info@cmventures.co.uk
Fax: 0871 5750720   Tel: 020-7154 6960

CREATIVE PARTNERSHIP The
13 Bateman Street, London W1D 3AF
Website: www.creativepartnership.co.uk
Fax: 020-7437 1467   Tel: 020-7439 7762

CROFT TELEVISION
Croft House, Progress Business Centre
Whittle Parkway, Slough, Berkshire SL1 6DQ
Fax: 01628 668791   Tel: 01628 668735

CROSSROADS FILMS
2nd Floor, 87 Notting Hill Gate, London W11 3JZ
Website: www.crossroadsfilms.com
e-mail: info@crossroadsfilms.co.uk
Fax: 020-7792 0592   Tel: 020-7792 5400

CUTHBERT Tony PRODUCTIONS
Suite 14, 7 Dials Court
3 Shorts Gardens, London WC2H 9AT
Website: www.tonycuthbert.com
e-mail: tonycuthbert@btconnect.com   Tel: 020-7836 3432

DALTON FILMS Ltd
127 Hamilton Terrace, London NW8 9QR
Fax: 020-7624 4420   Tel: 020-7328 6169

DARLOW SMITHSON PRODUCTIONS Ltd
Highgate Studios
53-79 Highgate Road, London NW5 1TL
Website: www.darlowsmithson.com
e-mail: mail@darlowsmithson.com
Fax: 020-7482 7039   Tel: 020-7482 7027

DAWSON FILMS
82 Berwick Street, London W1F 8TP
Website: www.dawsonfilms.com
e-mail: mail@dawsonfilms.com   Tel: 020-7734 1400

DIALOGICS
249-251 Kensal Road, London W10 5DB
e-mail: peter@dialogics.com
Fax: 020-8968 1517   Tel: 020-8960 6069

DLT ENTERTAINMENT UK Ltd
10 Bedford Square, London WC1B 3RA
Fax: 020-7636 4571   Tel: 020-7631 1184

DON PRODUCTIONS Ltd
Unit 2, 44A Shacklewell Lane E8 2EY
Website: www.donproductions.com
e-mail: info@donproductions.com
Fax: 0709 2273283   Tel: 020-7254 0044

DRAMATIS PERSONAE Ltd
(Nathan Silver, Nicolas Kent)
19 Regency Street, London SW1P 4BY
e-mail: ns@nathansilver.com   Tel: 020-7834 9300

DREAMING WILL INITIATIVE The
PO Box 38155, London SE17 3XP
Website: www.londonshakespeare.org.uk/dw.htm
e-mail: lswprison@europe.com   Tel/Fax: 020-7793 9755

DVA
8 Campbell Court, Bramley, Hampshire RG26 5EG
Website: www.dvafacilities.co.uk
e-mail: barrieg@dva.co.uk
Fax: 01256 882024   Tel: 01256 882032

ECOSSE FILMS Ltd
Brigade House, 8 Parsons Green, London SW6 4TN
Website: www.ecossefilms.com
e-mail: info@ecossefilms.com
Fax: 020-7736 3436   Tel: 020-7371 0290

EDGE PICTURE COMPANY Ltd The
7 Langley Street, London WC2H 9JA
Website: www.edgepicture.com
e-mail: ask.us@edgepicture.com
Fax: 020-7836 6949   Tel: 020-7836 6262

EFFINGEE PRODUCTIONS Ltd
13 Colquhoun Avenue
Hillington Park, Glasgow G52 4BN
Website: www.effingee.com
e-mail: info@effingee.com
Fax: 0141-576 1138   Tel: 0141-579 292

ENDEMOL UK Plc
(Including Endemol UK Productions, Initial,
Brighter Pictures, Victoria Real & Hawkshead)
Shepherds Building Central
Charecroft Way, Shepherd's Bush
London W14 0EE
Fax: 0870 3331800   Tel: 0870 333170

ENLIGHTENMENT INTERACTIVE
CV
East End House, 24 Ennerdale, Skelmersdale WN8 6AJ
Website: www.trainingmultimedia.co.uk   Tel: 01695 727555

ENTERTAINMENT RIGHTS Plc
Colet Court
100 Hammersmith Road, London W6 7JP
Fax: 020-8762 6299   Tel: 020-8762 620

EON PRODUCTIONS Ltd
Eon House, 138 Piccadilly, London W1J 7NR
Fax: 020-7408 1236   Tel: 020-7493 7953

EPA INTERNATIONAL MULTIMEDIA Ltd
108 Woodhouse Road, London N12 0RL
Fax: 020-8449 8555   Tel: 020-8446 2233

EYE FILM & TELEVISION
Chamberlain House
2 Dove Street, Norwich NR2 1DE
Website: www.eyefilmandtv.co.uk
e-mail: production@eyefilmandtv.co.uk
Fax: 01603 762420   Tel: 01603 762551

FARNHAM FILM COMPANY The
34 Burnt Hill Road, Lower Bourne, Farnham GU10 3LZ
Website: www.farnfilm.com   e-mail: info@farnfilm.com
Fax: 01252 725855   Tel: 01252 710313

FEELGOOD FICTION Ltd
49 Goldhawk Road, London W12 8QP
Website: www.feelgoodfiction.co.uk
e-mail: feelgood@feelgoodfiction.co.uk
Fax: 020-8740 6177   Tel: 020-8746 2535

FESTIVAL FILM & TELEVISION Ltd
Festival House, Tranquil Passage
Blackheath Village, London SE3 0BJ
Website: www.festivalfilm.com
e-mail: info@festivalfilm.com
Fax: 020-8297 1155   Tel: 020-8297 9999

FILM & GENERAL PRODUCTIONS Ltd
4 Bradbrook House, Studio Place, London SW1X 8EL
Fax: 020-7245 9853   Tel: 020-7235 4495

FILMS OF RECORD Ltd
2 Elgin Avenue, London W9 3QP
e-mail: films@filmsofrecord.com
Fax: 020-7286 0444   Tel: 020-7286 0333

FIRST WRITES RADIO COMPANY
(Radio Drama Company)
Lime Kiln Cottage
High Starlings, Banham, Norfolk NR16 2BS
Website: www.first-writes.co.uk
e-mail: ellen@first-writes.co.uk
Fax: 01953 888974   Tel: 01953 888525

FLASHBACK TELEVISION Ltd
9-11 Bowling Green Lane, London EC1R 0BG
Website: www.flashbacktelevision.com
e-mail: mailbox@flashbacktv.co.uk
Fax: 020-7490 5610   Tel: 020-7490 8996

FLYING DUCKS GROUP
Oakridge, Weston Road, Stafford ST16 3RS
Website: www.flyingducks.biz
e-mail: enquiries@flyingducks.biz
Fax: 01785 252448   Tel: 01785 610966

FLYNN PRODUCTIONS Ltd
Top Floor, Pitfield House
31-35 Pitfield Street, London N1 6HB
Website: www.flynnproductions.com
e-mail: reception@flynnproductions.com
Fax: 020-7251 6272   Tel: 020-7251 6197

FOCUS PRODUCTIONS Ltd
58 Shelley Road, Stratford-upon-Avon
Warwickshire CV37 7JS
Website: www.focusproductions.co.uk
e-mail: maddern@focusproductions.co.uk
Fax: 01789 294845   Tel: 01789 298948

FORSTATER Mark PRODUCTIONS
11 Kerslake Road
London NW6 6DJ   Tel/Fax: 020-8933 5475

FREMANTLEMEDIA TALKBACKTHAMES
1 Stephen Street, London W1T 1AL
Fax: 020-7691 6100   Tel: 020-7691 6000

FULL WORKS The
Dassels House, Dassels, Nr Braughing
Ware, Herts SG11 2RW   Tel: 01763 289905

FULMAR TELEVISION & FILM Ltd
Pascoe House, 54 Bute Street
Cardiff Bay, Cardiff CF10 5AF
Fax: 029-2045 5111   Tel: 029-2045 5000

FUNNY FACE FILMS Ltd
8a Warwick Road
Hampton Wick, Surrey KT1 4DW
Website: www.funnyfacefilms.co.uk
e-mail: steven@funnyfacefilms.co.uk   Mobile: 07951 344602

GALA PRODUCTIONS Ltd
25 Stamford Brook Road, London W6 0XJ
Website: www.galaproductions.co.uk
e-mail: info@galaproductions.co.uk
Fax: 020-8741 2323   Tel: 020-8741 4200

GALLEON FILMS Ltd
Greenwich Playhouse, Station Forecourt
189 Greenwich High Road
London SE10 8JA
Website: www.galleonfilms.co.uk
e-mail: alice@galleontheatre.co.uk   Tel/Fax: 020-8310 7276

GAMMOND Stephen ASSOCIATES
24 Telegraph Lane, Claygate
Surrey KT10 0DU   Tel: 01372 460674

GAY Noel TELEVISION Ltd
TV D Ch Co
Shepperton Studios, Studios Road
Shepperton, Middlesex TW17 0QD
e-mail: charles.armitage@virgin.net
Fax: 01932 592172   Tel: 01932 592569

GHA GROUP
1 Great Chapel Street, London W1F 8FA
Website: www.ghagroup.co.uk
e-mail: sales@ghagroup.co.uk
Fax: 020-7437 5880   Tel: 020-7439 8705

GLASS PAGE Ltd The
15 De Montfort Street
Leicester LE1 7GE
Fax: 0116-249 2188   Tel: 0116-249 2199

GOLDHAWK ESSENTIAL
20 Great Chapel Street, London W1F 8FW
e-mail: enquiries@goldhawk.eu
Fax: 020-7287 3597   Tel: 020-7439 7113

GOOD FILMS
Unit 17, Waterside, 44-48 Wharf Road, London N1 7UX
Fax: 020-7253 1117   Tel: 020-7566 0280

GRADE COMPANY The
23 St Edmonds Terrace
London NW8 7QA   Tel/Fax: 020-7586 2420

GRANT NAYLOR PRODUCTIONS Ltd
Suite 2034-2036, Orson Welles Building
Shepperton Studios, Studios Road
Shepperton, Middlesex TW17 0QD
Fax: 01932 592484   Tel: 01932 592175

GREAT GUNS Ltd
43-45 Camden Road, London NW1 9LR
e-mail: greatguns@greatguns.com
Fax: 020-7692 4422   Tel: 020-7692 4444

GUERILLA FILMS Ltd
35 Thornbury Road, Isleworth, Middlesex TW7 4LQ
Website: www.guerilla-films.com
e-mail: david@guerilla-films.com
Fax: 020-8758 9364   Tel: 020-8758 1716

HAMMERWOOD FILM PRODUCERS
110 Trafalgar Road, Portslade, Sussex BN41 1GS
Website: www.filmangel.co.uk
e-mail: filmangels@freenetname.co.uk
Fax: 01273 705451   Tel: 01273 277333

HARBOUR PICTURES
6 Providence Villas Studios
Brackenbury Road, London W6 0BA
Website: www.harbourpictures.com
e-mail: info@harbourpictures.com
Fax: 020-8740 1937   Tel: 020-8749 4100

HARTSWOOD FILMS
Twickenham Studios, The Barons
St Margaret's, Twickenham, Middlesex TW1 2AW
Fax: 020-8607 8744   Tel: 020-8607 8736

HASAN SHAH FILMS Ltd
153 Burnham Towers, Adelaide Road, London NW3 3JN
Fax: 020-7483 0662   Tel: 020-7722 2419

HAT TRICK PRODUCTIONS Ltd
TV Co
10 Livonia Street, London W1F 8AF
Fax: 020-7287 9791   Tel: 020-7434 2451

HAWK EYE FILMS
82 Kenley Road, St Margarets
Twickenham TW1 1JU   Tel: 020-8241 7089

HEAD Sally PRODUCTIONS
Twickenham Film Studios
The Barons, St Margaret's
Twickenham, Middlesex TW1 2AW
e-mail: admin@shpl.demon.co.uk
Fax: 020-8607 8964   Tel: 020-8607 8730

HEAVY ENTERTAINMENT Ltd
111 Wardour Street, London W1F 0UH
Website: www.heavy-entertainment.com
e-mail: info@heavy-entertainment.com
Fax: 020-7494 1100   Tel: 020-7494 1000

HENSON Jim COMPANY
30 Oval Road, Camden, London NW1 7DE
Website: www.henson.com
Fax: 020-7428 4001   Tel: 020-7428 4000

HIT ENTERTAINMENT Ltd
5th Floor, Maple House
149 Tottenham Court Road, London W1T 7NF
Website: www.hitentertainment.com
e-mail: creative@hitentertainment.com
Fax: 020-7388 9321   Tel: 020-7554 2500

HOLMES ASSOCIATES & OPEN ROAD FILMS
F TV D
The Studio, 37 Redington Road, London NW3 7QY
e-mail: holmesassociates@blueyonder.co.uk
Fax: 020-7813 4334   Tel: 020-7813 4333

HUDSON FILM Ltd
24 St Leonard's Terrace
London SW3 4QG   Tel: 020-7730 0002

HUNGRY MAN Ltd
1-2 Herbal Hill, London EC1R 5EF
Website: www.hungryman.com
e-mail: ukreception@hungryman.com
Fax: 020-7239 4589   Tel: 020-7239 4550

HUNKY DORY PRODUCTIONS Ltd
TV D Co
57 Alan Drive, Barnet, Herts EN5 2PW
Website: www.hunkydory.tv
e-mail: adrian@hunkydory.tv   Mobile: 07973 655510

HURRICANE FILMS Ltd
19 Hope Street, Liverpool L1 9BQ
Website: www.hurricanefilms.net
e-mail: sol@hurricanefilms.co.uk
Fax: 0151-707 9149   Tel: 0151-707 9700

IAMBIC PRODUCTIONS Ltd
89 Whiteladies Road, Clifton, Bristol BS8 2NT
e-mail: admin@iambic.tv
Fax: 0117-923 8343   Tel: 0117-923 7222

ICON FILMS Ltd
1-2 Fitzroy Terrace, Bristol BS6 6TF
Fax: 0117-974 4971   Tel: 0117-973 8755

INFORMATION TRANSFER Ltd
CV (Training Video Packages)
Burleigh House, 15 Newmarket Road, Cambridge CB5 8EG
Fax: 01223 310200   Tel: 01223 312227

ISIS PRODUCTIONS Ltd
387B King Street, London W6 9NJ
Website: www.isisproductions.co.uk
e-mail: isis@isis-productions.com
Fax: 020-8748 7634   Tel: 020-8748 3042

IWC MEDIA
3-6 Kenrick Place, London W1U 6HD
e-mail: info@iwcmedia.co.uk
Fax: 020-7317 2231   Tel: 020-7317 2230

JACKSON Brian FILMS Ltd
F TV Ch
39-41 Hanover Steps
St George's Fields, Albion Street, London W2 2YG
Website: www.brianjacksonfilms.com
e-mail: brianjfilm@aol.com
Fax: 020-7262 5736   Tel: 020-7402 7543

J. I. PRODUCTIONS
10 Linden Grove, Great Linford
Milton Keynes, Bucks MK14 5HF
Website: www.jasonimpey.co.uk
e-mail: jason.impey@freeuk.com
Mobile: 07732 476409   Tel: 01908 676081

JMS GROUP Ltd
Hethersett, Norwich, Norfolk, NR9 3DL
Website: www.jms-group.com
e-mail: info@jms-group.com
Fax: 01603 812255   Tel: 01603 811855

JONES THE FILM
32 Rathbone Place, London W1T 1JJ
Website: www.jonesthefilm.com
e-mail: mail@jonesthefilm.com
Fax: 020-7580 3480   Tel: 020-7580 5007

KELPIE FILMS
227 St Andrews Road, Glasgow G41 1PD
Website: www.kelpiefilms.com
e-mail: info@kelpiefilms.com   Tel: 0871 8740328

KNOWLES Dave FILMS
(Also Multimedia Interactive CD-Roms)
34 Ashleigh Close, Hythe SO45 3QP
Website: www.dkfilms.co.uk
e-mail: mail@dkfilms.co.uk
Fax: 023-8084 1600   Tel: 023-8084 2190

LANDSEER PRODUCTIONS Ltd
140 Royal College Street, London NW1 0TA
Website: www.landseerfilms.com
e-mail: ken@landseerproductions.com   Tel: 020-7485 7333

LIME PICTURES
TV
Campus Manor, Childwall, Abbey Road, Liverpool L16 0JP
Fax: 0151-722 6839   Tel: 0151-722 9122

LITTLE BIRD COMPANY Ltd
9 Grafton Mews, London W1T 5HZ
e-mail: info@littlebird.co.uk
Fax: 020-7380 3981   Tel: 020-7380 3980

LITTLE KING COMMUNICATIONS
The Studio, 2 Newport Road
Barnes, London SW13 9PE
Fax: 020-8653 2742   Tel: 020-8741 7658

LONDON COLLEGE OF COMMUNICATION
(Film & Video Division)
Elephant & Castle, London SE1 6SB
Fax: 020-7514 6843   Tel: 020-7514 6853

LONDON FILMS
71 South Audley Street, London W1K 1JA
Website: www.londonfilms.com
Fax: 020-7499 7994   Tel: 020-7499 7800

LONDON SCIENTIFIC FILMS
Dassels House, Dassels, Braughing
Ware, Herts SG11 2RW   Tel: 01920 444399

LOOKING GLASS FILMS Ltd
103 Brittany Point, Ethelred Estate
Kennington, London SE11 6UH
e-mail: lookingglassfilm@aol.com   Tel/Fax: 020-7735 1363

LOOP COMMUNICATION AGENCY The
Hanover House, Queen Charlotte Street, Bristol BS1 4EX
e-mail: mail@theloopagency.com
Fax: 0117-311 2041   Tel: 0117-311 2040

MAGPIE FILM PRODUCTIONS Ltd
32 Cheapside, Birmingham B5 6AY
Website: www.magpiefilms.co.uk
Fax: 0121-666 6077   Tel: 0121-622 5884

MALLINSON TELEVISION PRODUCTIONS
(TV Commercials)
29 Lynedoch Street, Glasgow G3 6EF
e-mail: shoot@mtp.co.uk
Fax: 0141-332 6190   Tel: 0141-332 0589

MALONE GILL PRODUCTIONS Ltd
27 Campden Hill Road, London W8 7DX
e-mail: malonegill@aol.com
Fax: 020-7460 3750   Tel: 020-7937 0557

MANS Johnny PRODUCTIONS Ltd
PO Box 196, Hoddesdon
Herts EN10 7WG
Website: www.johnnymansproductions.co.uk
e-mail: real@legend.co.uk
Fax: 01992 470516   Tel: 01992 470907

MANSFIELD Mike TELEVISION Ltd/MANSFIELD PRODUCTIONS Ltd
The Gatehouse, 4 Ellerton Road, London SW20 0EP
e-mail: mikemantv@aol.com
Fax: 020-8944 0407   Tel: 020-8947 6884

MARTIN William PRODUCTIONS
The Studio, Tubney Warren Barns
Tubney, Oxfordshire OX13 5QJ
Website: www.wmproductions.co.uk
e-mail: info@wmproductions.co.uk
Fax: 01865 390148   Tel: 01865 390258

MAVERICK MEDIA Ltd
Moray House
23-31 Great Titchfield Street, London W1W 7PA
Website: www.maverickmedia.co.uk
e-mail: info@maverickmedia.co.uk
Fax: 020-7323 4143   Tel: 020-7291 3450

MAVERICK TELEVISION
Progress Works, Heath Mill Lane
Birmingham B9 4AL
Website: www.mavericktv.co.uk
e-mail: mail@mavericktv.co.uk
Fax: 0121-771 1550   Tel: 0121-771 1812

MAX MEDIA
The Lilacs, West End
Woodhurst, Huntingdon, Cambridge PE28 3BH
Website: www.therealmaxmedia.com
e-mail: martin@therealmaxmedia.com
Fax: 01487 825299   Tel: 01487 823608

MBP TV
TV
Saucelands Barn, Coolham
Horsham, West Sussex RH13 8QG
Website: www.mbptv.com
e-mail: info@mbptv.com
Fax: 01403 741641   Tel: 01403 741620

McINTYRE Phil ENTERTAINMENT
2nd Floor, 35 Soho Square, London W1D 3QX
e-mail: reception@mcintyre-ents.com
Fax: 020-7439 2280   Tel: 020-7439 2270

MENTORN
43 Whitfield Street, London W1T 4HA
Fax: 020-7258 6888   Tel: 020-7258 6800

MERCHANT IVORY PRODUCTIONS
46 Lexington Street, London W1F 0LP
Website: www.merchantivory.com
e-mail: miplondon@merchantivory.co.uk
Fax: 020-7734 1579   Tel: 020-7437 1200

MIGHTY MEDIA
Unit M, Bourne End Business Park
Bourne End, Bucks SL8 5AS
Fax: 01628 526530   Tel: 01628 522002

MINAMON FILM
117 Downton Avenue, London SW2 3TX
Website: www.minamonfilm.co.uk
e-mail: min@minamonfilm.co.uk
Fax: 020-8674 1779   Tel: 020-8674 3957

MINISTRY OF VIDEO
(Showreels, Music Video, Casting Shoots)
1533 High Road, Whetstone, London N20 9PP
Website: www.ministryofvideo.co.uk
e-mail: ministryofvideo@yahoo.co.uk   Tel: 020-8369 5956

MISTRAL FILMS Ltd
31 Oval Road, London NW1 7EA
e-mail: info@mistralfilm.co.uk
Fax: 020-7284 0547   Tel: 020-7284 2300

MODUS OPERANDI FILMS
10 Brackenbury Road
London W6 0BA   Tel: 020-7434 1440

MOVE A MOUNTAIN PRODUCTIONS
5 Ashchurch Park Villas, London W12 9SP
Website: www.moveamountain.com
e-mail: mail@moveamountain.com   Tel: 020-8743 3017

MURPHY Patricia FILMS Ltd
Lock Keepers Cottage
Lyme Street, London NW1 0SF
e-mail: office@patriciamurphy.co.uk
Fax: 020-7485 0555   Tel: 020-7267 0007

NEAL STREET PRODUCTIONS Ltd
1st Floor, 26-28 Neal Street, London WC2H 9QQ
e-mail: post@nealstreetproductions.com
Fax: 020-7240 7099   Tel: 020-7240 8890

NEW MOON TELEVISION
8 Ganton Street, London W1F 7QP
Website: www.new-moon.co.uk
e-mail: production@new-moon.co.uk
Fax: 020-7479 7011   Tel: 020-7479 7010

NEXUS PRODUCTIONS Ltd
(Animation for Commercials, Broadcast, Pop Promos & Title
Sequences)
113-114 Shoreditch High Street, London E1 6JN
Website: www.nexusproductions.com
e-mail: info@nexusproductions.com
Fax: 020-7749 7501   Tel: 020-7749 7500

NFD PRODUCTIONS Ltd
PO Box 76, Leeds LS25 9AG
Website: www.nfdproductions.com
e-mail: info@nfdproductions.com
Mobile: 07932 653466   Tel/Fax: 01977 681949

NUTOPIA FILMS
(Ferris Entertainment)
Number 8, 132 Charing Cross Road, London WC2H 0LA
Website: www.ferrisentertainment.com   Mobile: 07801 493133

OLD VIC PRODUCTIONS (FILMS) Plc
The Old Vic Theatre, The Cut, Waterloo, London SE1 8NB
e-mail: ros.povey@oldvictheatre.com
Fax: 020-7981 0946   Tel: 020-7928 2651

OMNI PRODUCTIONS Ltd
Location House, Westside Entrance
5 Dove Lane, Bristol BS2 9HP
Website: www.omniproductions.co.uk
e-mail: info@omniproductions.co.uk   Tel: 0117-954 7170

ON COMMUNICATION
(Work across all Media in Business Communications)
5 East St Helen Street, Abingdon, Oxford OX14 5EG
Website: www.oncommunication.com
e-mail: info@oncommunication.com
Fax: 01235 530581   Tel: 01235 537400

ON SCREEN PRODUCTIONS Ltd
Ashbourne House, 33 Bridge Street
Chepstow, Monmouthshire NP16 5GA
Website: www.onscreenproductions.co.uk
e-mail: action@onscreenproductions.co.uk
Fax: 01291 636301   Tel: 01291 636300

OPEN MIND PRODUCTIONS
3 Waxhouse Gate, St Albans, Herts AL3 4EW
e-mail: production.manager@openmind.co.uk
                                     Tel: 0845 8909192

OPEN SHUTTER PRODUCTIONS Ltd
100 Kings Road, Windsor, Berkshire SL4 2AP
e-mail: jonthebruce@talktalk.net
Mobile: 07753 618875   Tel/Fax: 01753 841309

OPUS PRODUCTIONS Ltd
9A Coverdale Road, Shepherds Bush, London W12 8JJ
Website: www.opusproductions.co.uk
e-mail: claire.bidwell@opusproductions.com
Fax: 020-8749 4537   Tel: 020-8743 3910

ORIGINAL FILM & VIDEO PRODUCTIONS Ltd
84 St Dionis Road, London SW6 4TU
e-mail: original.films@btinternet.com   Tel: 020-7731 0012

OVC MEDIA Ltd
88 Berkeley Court, Baker Street, London NW1 5ND
Website: www.ovcmedia.com
e-mail: eliot@ovcmedia.com
Fax: 020-7723 3064   Tel: 020-7402 9111

PALADIN INVISION
8 Barb Mews, London W6 7PA
Fax: 020-7371 2160   Tel: 020-7348 1950

PAPER MOON PRODUCTIONS
Wychwood House
Burchetts Green Lane, Littlewick Green
Maidenhead, Berkshire SL6 3QW
e-mail: david@paper-moon.co.uk   Tel/Fax: 01628 829819

PARADINE David PRODUCTIONS Ltd
The Penthouse
346 Kensington High Street, London W14 8NS
e-mail: mail@paradine-productions.com
Fax: 020-7602 0411   Tel: 020-7371 3111

PARALLAX EAST Ltd
Victoria Chambers, St Runwald Street
Colchester CO1 1HF   Tel: 01206 574909

PARAMOUNT FILM SERVICES Ltd
UIP House, 45 Beadon Road, London W6 0EG
Fax: 020-8563 4266   Tel: 020-8563 4158

PARK VILLAGE Ltd
1 Park Village East, London NW1 7PX
e-mail: info@parkvillage.co.uk
Fax: 020-7388 3051   Tel: 020-7387 8077

PASSION PICTURES Ltd
(Animation/Documentary/Television)
3rd Floor, 33-34 Rathbone Place, London W1T 1JN
e-mail: info@passion-pictures.com
Fax: 020-7323 9030   Tel: 020-7323 9933

PATHE PICTURES Ltd
Kent House, 14-17 Market Place
Great Titchfield Street, London W1W 8AR
Website: www.pathe.co.uk
Fax: 020-7631 3568   Tel: 020-7323 5151

PCI LIVE DESIGN
(Live Events, Live Design Exhibitions, Film & Video,
2D & 3D Design)
G4 Harbour Yard
Chelsea Harbour, London SW10 0XD
Fax: 020-7352 7906   Tel: 020-7544 7500

PICTURE PALACE FILMS Ltd
13 Egbert Street, London NW1 8LJ
Website: www.picturepalace.com
e-mail: info@picturepalace.com
Fax: 020-7586 9048   Tel: 020-7586 8763

PIER PRODUCTIONS Ltd
Lower Ground Floor, 1 Marlborough Place, Brighton BN1 1UB
e-mail: info@pierproductionsltd.co.uk
Fax: 01273 693658   Tel: 01273 691401

PIEREND PRODUCTIONS
34 Fortis Green, London N2 9EL
e-mail: russell@richardsonassoc.co.uk
Tel/Fax: 020-8444 0138

POKER Ltd
143B Whitehall Court, London SW1A 2EL
e-mail: pokerfilms@yahoo.co.uk   Tel/Fax: 020-7839 6070

POSITIVE IMAGE Ltd
25 Victoria Street
Windsor, Berkshire SL4 1HE
Fax: 01753 830878   Tel: 01753 842248

POTBOILER PRODUCTIONS Ltd
9 Greek Street, London W1D 4DQ
e-mail: edie@potboiler.co.uk
Fax: 020-7287 5228   Tel: 020-7734 7372

POZZITIVE TELEVISION Ltd
Paramount House
162-170 Wardour Street, London W1F 8AB
e-mail: pozzitive@pozzitive.co.uk
Fax: 020-7437 3130   Tel: 020-7734 3258

PRETTY CLEVER PICTURES
Iping Mill, Iping, Midhurst, West Sussex GU29 0PE
e-mail: pcpics@globalnet.co.uk
Mobile: 07836 616981   Tel: 01730 817899

PRISM ENTERTAINMENT
(Television Production & Website Design Company)
The Clockhouse
220 Latimer Road, London W10 6QY
Website: www.prismentertainment.co.uk
e-mail: info@prism-e.com
Fax: 020-8969 1012   Tel: 020-8969 1212

PRODUCERS The
8 Berners Mews, London W1T 3AW
Website: www.theproducersfilms.co.uk
e-mail: info@theproducersfilms.co.uk
Fax: 020-7636 4099   Tel: 020-7636 4226

PRODUCTIONS & PROMOTIONS Ltd
Apsley Mills Cottage, London Road
Hemel Hempstead, Herts HP3 9QU
Website: www.prodmotions.com
e-mail: reception@prodmotions.com
Fax: 0845 0095540   Tel: 01442 233372

PROFESSIONAL MEDICAL COMMUNICATIONS Ltd
Grosvenor House, 1 High Street
Edgware, Middlesex HA8 7TA   Tel: 020-8381 1819

PROMENADE ENTERPRISES Ltd
6 Russell Grove, London SW9 6HS
Website: www.promenadeproductions.com
e-mail: info@promenadeproductions.com   Tel: 020-7582 9354

PSA Ltd
52 The Downs, Altrincham WA14 2QJ
e-mail: info@psafilms.co.uk
Fax: 0161-924 0022   Tel: 0161-924 0011

PVA MANAGEMENT Ltd
Hallow Park, Hallow, Worcs WR2 6PG
e-mail: films@pva.co.uk
Fax: 01905 641842   Tel: 01905 640663

QUADRILLION
The Old Barn, Kings Lane
Cookham Dean, Berkshire SL6 9AY
Website: www.quadrillion.tv
e-mail: enqs@quadrillion.tv
Fax: 01628 487523   Tel: 01628 487522

RAW CHARM MEDIA
Ty Cefn, Rectory Road, Cardiff CF5 1QL
Website: www.rawcharm.tv   e-mail: kate@rawcharm.co.uk
Fax: 029-2066 8220   Tel: 029-2064 1511

READ Rodney
45 Richmond Road, Twickenham, Middlesex TW1 3AW
Website: www.rodney-read.com
e-mail: rodney_read@blueyonder.co.uk
Fax: 020-8744 9603   Tel: 020-8891 2875

RECORDED PICTURE COMPANY Ltd
24 Hanway Street, London W1T 1UH
Fax: 020-7636 2261   Tel: 020-7636 2251

RED KITE ANIMATION
89 Giles Street, Edinburgh EH6 6BZ
Website: www.redkite-animation.com
e-mail: info@redkite-animation.com
Fax: 0131-553 6007   Tel: 0131-554 0060

RED ROSE CHAIN
1 Fore Hamlet, Ipswich IP3 8AA
Website: www.redrosechain.co.uk
e-mail: info@redrosechain.co.uk   Tel: 01473 288886

REDWEATHER PRODUCTIONS
Easton Business Centre, Felix Road, Bristol BS5 0HE
Website: www.redweather.co.uk
e-mail: info@redweather.co.uk
Fax: 0117-941 5851   Tel: 0117-941 5854

REEL THING Ltd The
20 The Chase, Coulsdon, Surrey CR5 2EG
Website: www.reelthing.tv
e-mail: info@reelthing.tv   Tel: 020-8668 8188

REPLAY Ltd
Museum House, 25 Museum Street, London WC1A 1JT
Website: www.replayfilms.co.uk
e-mail: sales@replayfilms.co.uk   Tel: 020-7637 0473

RESOURCE BASE
Fairways House, Mount Pleasant Road
Southampton SO14 0QB
Website: www.resource-base.co.uk
e-mail: jane@resource-base.co.uk
Fax: 023-8023 6816   Tel: 023-8023 6806

REUTERS Ltd
The Reuters Building, South Collonade
Canary Wharf, London E14 5EP   Tel: 020-7250 1122

REVERE ENTERTAINMENT
22 Poland Street, London W1F 8QQ
Fax: 020-7292 7391   Tel: 020-7292 8370

RIVERSIDE TV STUDIOS
Riverside Studios, Crisp Road, London W6 9RL
Website: www.riversidetv.co.uk
e-mail: info@riversidetv.co.uk
Fax: 020-8237 1121   Tel: 020-8237 1123

ROGERS Peter PRODUCTIONS Ltd
Pinewood Studios, Iver Heath
Buckinghamshire SL0 0NH   Tel: 01753 651700

ROOKE Laurence PRODUCTIONS
14 Aspinall House, 155 New Park Road, London SW2 4EY
Mobile: 07765 652058   Tel: 020-8674 3128

ROSE HACKNEY BARBER Ltd
5-6 Kingly Street, London W1B 5PF
Fax: 020-7434 4102   Tel: 020-7380 3435

RSA FILMS
42-44 Beak Street, London W1F 9RH
Fax: 020-7734 4978   Tel: 020-7437 7426

RUSSO Denis ASSOCIATES
F TV Animation
161 Clapham Road, London SW9 0PU
Fax: 020-7582 2725   Tel: 020-7582 9664

SAMUELSON PRODUCTIONS Ltd
13 Manette Street, London W1D 4AW
Fax: 020-7439 4901   Tel: 020-7439 4900

SANDS FILMS
(Squirrel Films Distribution Ltd)
Grice's Wharf, 119 Rotherhithe Street
London SE16 4NF
Website: www.sandsfilms.co.uk
Fax: 020-7231 2119   Tel: 020-7231 2209

SCALA PRODUCTIONS Ltd
4th Floor, Portland House
4 Great Portland Street, London W1W 8QJ
e-mail: scalaprods@aol.com   Tel: 020-7637 5720

SCIMITAR FILMS Ltd
219 Kensington High Street, London W8 6BD
e-mail: winner@ftech.co.uk
Fax: 020-7602 9217   Tel: 020-7734 8385

SCREEN FIRST Ltd
The Studios, Funnells Farm
Down Street
Nutley, East Sussex TN22 3LG
e-mail: paul.madden@virgin.net   Tel: 01825 712034

SCREEN VENTURES
49 Goodge Street, London W1T 1TE
Website: www.screenventures.com
e-mail: info@screenventures.com
Fax: 020-7631 1265   Tel: 020-7580 7448

SEPTEMBER FILMS Ltd
Glen House, 22 Glenthorne Road
Hammersmith, London W6 0NG
Fax: 020-8741 7214   Tel: 020-8563 9393

SEVEN STONES MEDIA Ltd
The Old Butcher's Shop, St Briavels
Gloucestershire GL15 6TA
e-mail: info@sevenstonesmedia.com
Fax: 01594 530094   Tel: 01594 530070

SEVENTH ART PRODUCTIONS
63 Ship Street, Brighton BN1 1AE
Website: www.seventh-art.com
e-mail: info@seventh-art.com
Fax: 01273 323777   Tel: 01273 777678

SHART BROS Ltd
52 Lancaster Road, London N4 4PR
Fax: 020-7436 9233   Tel: 020-7263 4435

SHED PRODUCTIONS
2 Holford Yard, London WC1X 9HD
Website: www.shedproductions.com
e-mail: shed@shedproductions.com
Fax: 020-7239 1011   Tel: 020-7239 1010

SHELL FILM & VIDEO UNIT
F CV Docs
Shell Centre, York Road, London SE1 7NA
Fax: 020-7934 7490   Tel: 020-7934 3310

SHELL LIKE RADIO
Whitfield House, 81 Whitfield Street
London W1T 4HG
Website: www.shelllike.com
e-mail: enquiries@shelllike.com
Fax: 020-7255 5255   Tel: 020-7255 5200

London Academy of Media Film TV

TV Presenter - Acting - Voice - Film - Photography - Make-up - Radio
100 courses Offering an extensive range of full-time, part-time
evening and day courses taught by celebrities and industry professionals.

www.media-courses.com 0871 566 1631

SIGHTLINE
Videos, Commercials, CD-Rom, DVD, Websites)
Dylan House, Town End Street, Godalming, Surrey GU7 1BQ
Website: www.sightline.co.uk
e-mail: action@sightline.co.uk
Fax: 01483 861516   Tel: 01483 861555

SILK SOUND
3 Berwick Street, London W1F 0PW
Website: www.silk.co.uk   e-mail: bookings@silk.co.uk
Fax: 020-7494 1748   Tel: 020-7434 3461

SILVER PRODUCTIONS Ltd
Bridge Farm, Lower Road, Britford
Salisbury, Wiltshire SP5 4DY
Website: www.silver.co.uk
Fax: 01722 336227   Tel: 01722 336221

SINDIBAD FILMS Ltd
9 Knightsbridge, 4th Floor, London SW1X 7RB
Website: www.sindibad.co.uk
e-mail: info@sindibad.co.uk
Fax: 020-7823 9137   Tel: 020-7823 7488

SMITH & WATSON PRODUCTIONS
The Gothic House, Fore Street, Totnes, Devon TQ9 5EH
Website: www.smithandwatson.com
e-mail: info@smithandwatson.com
Fax: 01803 864219   Tel: 01803 863033

SNEEZING TREE FILMS

1st Floor, 37 Great Portland Street, London W1W 8QH
Website: www.sneezingtree.com
e-mail: firstname@sneezingtree.com
Fax: 020-7927 9909   Tel: 020-7927 9900

SONY PICTURES
5 Golden Square, London W1F 9LU
Fax: 020-7533 1015   Tel: 020-7533 1000

SPACE CITY PRODUCTIONS
77 Blythe Road, London W14 0HP
Website: www.spacecity.co.uk
e-mail: info@spacecity.co.uk
Fax: 020-7371 4001   Tel: 020-7371 4000

SPEAKEASY PRODUCTIONS Ltd
Wildwood House, Stanley, Perth PH1 4PX
Website: www.speak.co.uk
e-mail: info@speak.co.uk
Fax: 01738 828419   Tel: 01738 828524

SPECIFIC FILMS Ltd
25 Rathbone Street, London W1T 1NQ
e-mail: info@specificfilms.com
Fax: 020-7636 6886   Tel: 020-7580 7476

SPIRAL PRODUCTIONS Ltd
Aberdeen Studios
22 Highbury Grove, London N5 2EA
Fax: 020-7359 6123   Tel: 020-7354 5492

STAFFORD Jonathan PRODUCTIONS
Shepperton Studios
Studios Road, Shepperton, Middlesex TW17 0QD
e-mail: jon@staffordproductions.com
Fax: 01932 592617   Tel: 01932 562611

STANDFAST FILMS
F TV D
The Studio, 14 College Road
Bromley, Kent BR1 3NS
Fax: 020-8313 0443   Tel: 020-8466 5580

STANTON MEDIA
6 Kendal Close, Aylesbury, Bucks HP21 7HR
Website: www.stantonmedia.com
e-mail: info@stantonmedia.com   Tel/Fax: 01296 489539

STEEL SPYDA Ltd
96-98 Undley, Lakenheath, Suffolk IP27 9BY
Website: www.steelspyda.com
e-mail: kay.hill@steelspyda.com
Fax: 01842 862875   Tel: 01842 862880

STONE PRODUCTIONS CREATIVE Ltd
Lakeside Studio, 62 Mill Street, St Osyth, Essex CO16 8EW
Website: www.stone-productions.co.uk
e-mail: kevin@stone-productions.co.uk
Fax: 01255 822160   Tel: 01255 822172

STUDIO AKA
(Animation)
30 Berwick Street, London W1F 8RH
Website: www.studioaka.co.uk
Fax: 020-7437 2309   Tel: 020-7434 3581

TABARD PRODUCTIONS
Adam House, 7-10 Adam Street, London WC2N 6AA
e-mail: info@tabard.co.uk
Fax: 020-7497 0830   Tel: 020-7497 0850

TABLE TOP PRODUCTIONS
1 The Orchard, Bedford Park, Chiswick, London W4 1JZ
e-mail: berry@tabletopproductions.com
Tel/Fax: 020-8742 0507   Tel: 020-8994 1269

TAKE 3 PRODUCTIONS Ltd
72-73 Margaret Street, London W1W 8ST
Website: www.take3.co.uk   e-mail: mail@take3.co.uk
Fax: 020-7637 4678   Tel: 020-7637 2694

TAKE FIVE PRODUCTIONS
CV Docs
37 Beak Street, London W1F 9RZ
Website: www.takefivestudio.com
e-mail: info@takefivestudio.com
Fax: 020-7287 3035   Tel: 020-7287 2120

TALKBACK THAMES
20-21 Newman Street, London W1T 1PG
Fax: 020-7861 8001   Tel: 020-7861 8000

TALKING PICTURES
Pinewood Studios, Pinewood Road
Iver Heath, Bucks SL0 0NH
Website: www.talkingpictures.co.uk
e-mail: info@talkingpictures.co.uk
Fax: 01753 650048   Tel: 01753 655744

TANDEM TV & FILM Ltd
Charleston House, 13 High Street
Hemel Hempstead, Herts HP1 3AA
Website: www.tandemtv.com
e-mail: info@tandemtv.com
Fax: 01442 219250   Tel: 01442 261576

TAYLOR David ASSOCIATES Ltd
F CV D Ch
83 Westholme Close, Congleton
Cheshire CW12 4FZ   Tel/Fax: 01260 279406

TELEVIRTUAL Ltd
Media Lab, Epic
112 Magdalen Street
Norwich NR3 1JD
Website: www.televirtual.com
e-mail: tim@televirtual.com   Tel: 0845 1210738

THIN MAN FILMS
9 Greek Street, London W1D 4DQ
e-mail: info@thinman.co.uk
Fax: 020-7287 5228   Tel: 020-7734 7372

TIGER ASPECT PRODUCTIONS
7 Soho Street, London W1D 3DQ
Website: www.tigeraspect.co.uk
e-mail: general@tigeraspect.co.uk
Fax: 020-7434 1798   Tel: 020-7434 6700

TKO COMMUNICATIONS Ltd
(A Division of The Kruger Organisation Inc)
PO Box 130, Hove, Sussex BN3 6QU
e-mail: tkoinc@tkogroup.com
Fax: 01273 540969   Tel: 01273 550088

TOP BANANA
The Studio, Stourbridge
West Midlands DY9 0HA
Website: www.top-b.com   e-mail: info@top-b.com
Fax: 01562 700930   Tel: 01562 700404

TOPICAL TELEVISION Ltd
61 Devonshire Road
Southampton SO15 2GR
Fax: 023-8033 9835   Tel: 023-8071 2233

TVE Ltd
(Broadcast Facilities, Non-Linear Editing)
TVE House, Wick Drive
New Milton, Hampshire BH25 6RH
e-mail: enquiries@tvehire.com
Fax: 01425 625021   Tel: 01425 625020

TVF
375 City Road, London EC1V 1NB
Fax: 020-7833 2185   Tel: 020-7837 3000

TVMS (SCOTLAND)
3rd Floor, 420 Sauchiehall Street, Glasgow G2 3JD
e-mail: mail@tvms.wanadoo.co.uk
Fax: 0141-332 9040   Tel: 0141-331 1993

TV PRODUCTION PARTNERSHIP Ltd
4 Fullerton Manor, Fullerton, Hants SP11 7LA
Website: www.tvpp.tv
e-mail: dbj@tvpp.tv   Tel: 01264 861440

TWOFOUR
TwoFour Studios
Estover, Plymouth PL6 7RG
Website: www.twofour.co.uk
e-mail: enq@twofour.co.uk
Fax: 01752 727450   Tel: 01752 727400

TWO SIDES TV Ltd
53A Brewer Street, London W1F 9UH
e-mail: info@2sidestv.co.uk
Fax: 020-7287 2289   Tel: 020-7439 9882

TYBURN FILM PRODUCTIONS Ltd
F
Cippenham Court, Cippenham Lane
Cippenham, Nr Slough, Berkshire SL1 5AU
Fax: 01753 691785   Tel: 01753 516767

UNGER Kurt
112 Portsea Hall, Portsea Place, London W2 2BZ
Fax: 020-7706 4818   Tel: 020-7262 9013

VERA
3rd Floor, 66-68 Margaret Street, London W1W 8SR
e-mail: phoebe@vera.co.uk
Fax: 020-7436 6117   Tel: 020-7436 6116

VERA MEDIA
(Video Production & Training Company)
30-38 Dock Street, Leeds LS10 1JF
e-mail: vera@vera-media.co.uk
Fax: 0113-242 8739   Tel: 0113-242 8646

VIDEO & FILM PRODUCTION
Robin Hill, The Ridge, Lower Basildon, Reading, Berks
Website: www.videoandfilm.co.uk
e-mail: david.fisher@videoandfilm.co.uk
Mobile: 07836 544955   Tel: 0118-984 2488

VIDEO ARTS
6-7 St Cross Street, London EC1N 8UA
e-mail: sales@videoarts.co.uk
Fax: 020-7400 4900   Tel: 020-7400 4800

VIDEO ENTERPRISES
12 Barbers Wood Road
High Wycombe, Buckinghamshire HP12 4EP
Website: www.videoenterprises.co.uk
e-mail: videoenterprises@ntlworld.com
Fax: 01494 534145   Tel: 01494 534144

VIDEOTEL PRODUCTIONS
84 Newman Street, London W1T 3EU
Fax: 020-7299 1818   Tel: 020-7299 1800

VILLAGE PRODUCTIONS
4 Midas Business Centre
Wantz Road, Dagenham, Essex RM10 8PS
e-mail: village000@btclick.com
Fax: 020-8593 0198   Tel: 020-8984 0322

W3KTS Ltd
10 Portland Street, York YO31 7EH
e-mail: chris@w3kts.com   Tel: 01904 647822

W6 STUDIO
359 Lillie Road, Fulham, London SW6 7PA
Website: www.w6studio.co.uk
Fax: 020-7381 5252   Tel: 020-7385 2272

WALKING FORWARD Ltd
Studio 1, 35 Brittania Row, London N1 8QH
Website: www.walkingforward.co.uk
e-mail: info@walkingforward.co.uk
Fax: 020-7359 5091   Tel: 020-7359 5249

WALKOVERS VIDEO
Willow Cottage, Church Lane, Kington Langley
Chippenham, Wiltshire SN15 5NU
e-mail: walkoversvideo@btinternet.com   Tel: 01249 750428

WALNUT MEDIA COMMUNICATIONS Ltd
Crown House, Armley Road, Leeds LS12 2EJ
Website: www.walnutmedia.com
e-mail: mail@walnutmedia.com
Fax: 0870 7427080   Tel: 0870 7427070

WALSH BROS Ltd
24 Redding House, Harlinger Street
King Henry's Wharf, London SE18 5SR
Website: www.walshbros.co.uk
e-mail: info@walshbros.co.uk
Tel/Fax: 020-8854 5557   Tel/Fax: 020-8858 6870

WALSH Steve PRODUCTIONS Ltd
Top Floor, 49 Goodge Street, London W1T 1TE
Website: www.steve-walsh.com
e-mail: info@steve-walsh.com
Fax: 020-7580 6554   Tel: 020-7580 6555

WARNER BROS PRODUCTIONS Ltd
FF
Warner Suite, Leavesden Studios
South Way, Leavesden, Herts WD25 7LT
Fax: 01923 685221   Tel: 01923 685222

WARNER SISTERS PRODUCTIONS Ltd
Ealing Studios
Ealing Green, London W5 5EP
e-mail: ws@warnercini.com
Tel: 020-8567 6655

WEST DIGITAL
(Broadcast Post-Production)
65 Goldhawk Road, London W12 8EG
Fax: 020-8743 2345
Tel: 020-8743 5100

WEST ONE FILM PRODUCERS Ltd
(Cooper Murray)
Tennyson House
159-165 Great Portland Street
London W1W 5PA
e-mail: jocorb@hotmail.com
Tel: 020-8224 8696

WHITEHALL FILMS
10 Lower Common South
London SW15 1BP
e-mail: mwhitehall@msn.com
Fax: 020-8788 2340
Tel: 020-8785 3737

WINNER Michael Ltd
219 Kensington High Street
London W8 6BD
e-mail: winner@ftech.co.uk
Fax: 020-7602 9217
Tel: 020-7734 8385

WORKING TITLE FILMS Ltd
Oxford House
76 Oxford Street, London W1D 1BS
Fax: 020-7307 3001
Tel: 020-7307 3000

WORLD'S END TELEVISION
16-18 Empress Place, London SW6 1TT
Website: www.worldsendproductions.com
e-mail: info@worldsendproductions.com
Fax: 020-7386 4901
Tel: 020-7386 4900

WORLD PRODUCTIONS & WORLD FILM SERVICES Ltd
16 Dufours Place
London W1F 7SP
Website: www.world-productions.com
Fax: 020-7758 7000
Tel: 020-7734 3536

WORLD WIDE PICTURES
21-25 St Anne's Court, London W1F 0BJ
Website: www.worldwidegroup.ltd.uk
e-mail: info@worldwidegroup.ltd.uk
Fax: 020-7734 0619
Tel: 020-7434 1121

WORTHWHILE MOVIE Ltd
(Providing the services of Bruce Pittman as Film Director)
191 Logan Avenue
Toronto, Ontario
Canada M4M 2NT
Tel: 00 1 (416) 4690459

XINGU FILMS
12 Cleveland Row
London SW1A 1DH
Fax: 020-7451 0601
Tel: 020-7451 0600

YOUNGSTAR PRODUCTIONS
(TV Drama)
5 Union Castle House
Canute Road
Southampton SO14 3FJ
e-mail: info@youngstar.tv
Fax: 023-8045 5816
Tel: 023-8033 9322

ZENITH ENTERTAINMENT Ltd
43-45 Dorset Street, London W1U 7NA
Fax: 020-7224 1027
Tel: 020-7224 2440

ZEPHYR FILMS Ltd
33 Percy Street, London W1T 2DF
e-mail: info@zephyrfilms.co.uk
Fax: 020-7255 3777
Tel: 020-7255 3555

BRIGHTON FILM SCHOOL
(Member of the National Association for Higher Education
in the Moving Image (NAHEMI) and the University Film and
Video Association (UFVA). Part-time Day or Evening Film
Directors' Courses includes Screen Writing,
Cinematography etc)
Website: www.brightonfilmschool.org.uk
e-mail: info@brightonfilmschool.org.uk
Fax: 01273 302163   Tel: 01273 302166

LEEDS METROPOLITAN UNIVERSITY
(PG Dip/MA's in Film & Moving Image Production or Fiction
Screenwriting, and BA (Hons) in Film & Moving Image
Production and a BA (Hons) Contemporary Performance)
Cert HE/FdA in Film & Television Production
H505, Calverley Street, Leeds LS1 3HE
Website: www.leedsmet.ac.uk
Fax: 0113-283 8080   Tel: 0113-283 2600

LONDON ACADEMY OF MEDIA
1 Lancing Street, London NW1 1NA
Website: www.media-courses.com
e-mail: daycourses@googlemail.com   Tel: 0871 5661631

LONDON FILM ACADEMY
The Old Church
52A Walham Grove, London SW6 1QR
Website: www.londonfilmacademy.com
e-mail: info@londonfilmacademy.com
Fax: 020-7381 6116   Tel: 020-7386 7711

LONDON FILM SCHOOL The
(2-year MA Course in Film Making, 1-year MA in
Screenwriting)
24 Shelton Street, London WC2H 9UB
Website: www.lfs.org.uk
e-mail: film.school@lfs.org.uk
Fax: 020-7497 3718   Tel: 020-7836 9642

MIDDLESEX UNIVERSITY
(School of Arts)
Cat Hill, Barnet
Herts EN4 8HT
Website: www.mdx.ac.uk   Tel: 020-8411 5555

NATIONAL FILM AND TELEVISION SCHOOL
Diploma Courses: Digital Post Production, Directing Fiction,
Editing for Entertainment Television, Production
Management, Sound Recording, Visual & Special Effects)
Beaconsfield Studios
Station Road
Beaconsfield
Bucks HP9 1LG
Website: www.nfts.co.uk
e-mail: info@nfts.co.uk
Fax: 01494 674042   Tel: 01494 731413

UCCA - FARNHAM
(3-year BA (Hons) Photography, BA (Hons) Journalism, Film
Production, Digital Screen Arts, Arts & Media, Animation)
Falkner Road
Farnham, Surrey GU9 7DS
Website: www.ucreative.ac.uk   Tel: 01252 722441

**UNIVERSITY OF WESTMINSTER SCHOOL OF MEDIA ARTS
& DESIGN**
(Undergraduate courses in Film and Television Production
and Contemporary Media Practice. Postgraduate Courses
in Screenwriting and Producing, Film and Television;
Theory, Culture and Industry)
Admissions & Enquiries:
Watford Road
Northwick Park
Harrow
Middlesex HA1 3TP
Website: www.wmin.ac.uk/filmschool   Tel: 020-7911 5000

3 MILLS STUDIOS
Three Mill Lane, London E3 3DU
Website: www.3mills.com
e-mail: info@3mills.com
Fax: 020-8215 3499   Tel: 020-7363 3336

ARDMORE STUDIOS Ltd
Herbert Road, Bray, Co. Wicklow, Ireland
Website: www.ardmore.ie
e-mail: film@ardmore.ie
Fax: 00 353 1 2861894   Tel: 00 353 1 2862971

BBC TELEVISION
Television Centre, Wood Lane
Shepherds Bush, London W12 7RJ   Tel: 020-8743 8000

BRAY STUDIOS
Down Place, Water Oakley
Windsor Road, Windsor, Berkshire SL4 5UG
Fax: 01628 623000   Tel: 01628 622111

BRIGHTON FILM STUDIOS Ltd
The Brighton Business Centre
95 Ditchling Road, Brighton BN1 4ST
Website: www.brightonfilmstudios.com
e-mail: info@brightonfilmstudios.com
Fax: 01273 302163   Tel: 01273 302166

CAPITAL STUDIOS
Wandsworth Plain, London SW18 1ET
Website: www.capitalstudios.com
e-mail: info@capitalstudios.com
Fax: 020-8877 0234   Tel: 020-8877 1234

CHELTENHAM FILM STUDIOS Ltd
Arle Court, Hatherley Lane, Cheltenham
Gloucestershire GL51 6PN
Website: www.cheltstudio.com
e-mail: info@cheltstudio.com
Fax: 01242 542701   Tel: 01242 542708

EALING STUDIOS
Ealing Green, London W5 5EP
Website: www.ealingstudios.com
e-mail: info@ealingstudios.com
Fax: 020-8758 8658   Tel: 020-8567 6655

ELSTREE FILM & TELEVISION STUDIOS
Shenley Road, Borehamwood, Herts WD6 1JG
Website: www.elstreefilmstudios.co.uk
e-mail: info@elstreefilmstudios.co.uk
Fax: 020-8905 1135   Tel: 020-8953 1600

LONDON STUDIOS The
London Television Centre, Upper Ground, London SE1 9LT
Website: www.londonstudios.co.uk
Fax: 020-7928 8405   Tel: 020-7737 8888

PINEWOOD STUDIOS
Pinewood Road, Iver Heath, Buckinghamshire SL0 0NH
Website: www.pinewoodgroup.com
Fax: 01753 656844   Tel: 01753 651700

REUTERS TELEVISION
The Reuters Building
South Colonnade, Canary Wharf
London E14 5EP   Tel: 020-7250 1122

RIVERSIDE STUDIOS
Crisp Road, London W6 9RL
Website: www.riversidestudios.co.uk
e-mail: online@riversidestudios.co.uk
Fax: 020-8237 1001   Tel: 020-8237 1000

SHEPPERTON STUDIOS
Studios Road, Shepperton, Middlesex TW17 0QD
Website: www.pinewoodgroup.com
Fax: 01932 592555   Tel: 01932 562611

SQUIRREL & SANDS FILMS/ROTHERHITHE STUDIOS
119 Rotherhithe Street
London SE16 4NF
Fax: 020-7231 2119   Tel: 020-7231 2209

TEDDINGTON STUDIOS
Broom Road
Teddington, Middlesex TW11 9NT
Website: www.pinewoodgroup.com
Fax: 020-8943 4050   Tel: 020-8977 3252

TWICKENHAM FILM STUDIOS Ltd
The Barons, St Margaret's
Twickenham, Middlesex TW1 2AW
Fax: 020-8607 8889   Tel: 020-8607 8888

G

Good Digs Guide
Compiled By JANICE CRAMER & DAVID BANKS
This is a list of digs recommended by those who have used
them. To keep the list accurate please send
recommendations for inclusion to GOOD DIGS GUIDE at
The Spotlight. Thanks to all who did so over the last year.
Entries in **Bold** have been paid for by the Digs concerned.

ABERDEEN
Milne, Mrs A
5 Sunnyside Walk
Aberdeen AB24 3NZ   Tel: 01224 638951

Woods, Pat
62 Union Grove
Aberdeen AB10 6RX   Tel: 01224 586324

AYR
Dunn, Sheila
The Dunn-Thing Guest House
13 Park Circus
Ayr KA7 2DJ
Mobile: 07887 928685   Tel: 01292 284531

BATH
Hutton, Mrs Celia
Bath Holiday Homes
Terranova
Shepherds Walk
Bath BA2 5QT
Website: www.bathholidayhomes.co.uk
e-mail: bhh@virgin.net   Tel: 01225 830830

Tapley, Jane
Camden Lodgings
3 Upper Camden Place
Bath BA1 5HX   Tel: 01225 446561

BELFAST
McCully, Mrs S
28 Eglantine Avenue
Belfast BT9 6DX
Mobile: 07985 947673   Tel: 028-9068 2031

BILLINGHAM
Gibson, Mrs S
Northwood
61 Tunstall Avenue
Billingham TS23 3QB
Mobile: 07813 407674   Tel: 01642 561071

BIRMINGHAM
Baker, Mr N K
41 King Edward Road
Mosley
Birmingham B13 8EL   Tel: 0121-449 8220

Mountain, Marlene P
268 Monument Road
Edgbaston
Birmingham B16 8XF   Tel: 0121-454 5900

Wilson, Mrs
17 Yew Tree Road
Edgbaston
Birmingham B15 2LX   Tel: 0121-440 5182

BLACKPOOL
Brereton Holiday Flats
186 Promenade
Blackpool FY1 1RJ
e-mail: bookings@selfcateringblackpool.co.uk
Fax: 01253 753038   Tel: 01253 623095

Lees, Jean
Ascot Flats, 6 Hull Road
Central Blackpool FY1 4QB   Tel: 01253 621059

Somerset Apartments
22 Barton Avenue, Blackpool FY1 6AP   Tel: 01253 346743

Waller, Veronica & Bob
The Brooklyn Hotel
7 Wilton Parade, Blackpool FY1 2HE   Tel: 01253 627003

[CONTACTS 2008]

BLACKPOOL

Somerset Apartments

VERY HIGH STANDARD - en suite studios & apartments
• Central Heating • Cooker • Fridge • Microwave & TV - **all new**
Beds • Linen provided • 'Highly recommended' by members of the profession
• 10 minutes walk to the Theatre
Irene Chadderton, 22 Barton Avenue, Blackpool FY1 6AP • Tel/Fax: 01253 346743

BOLTON
Duckworth, Paul
19 Burnham Avenue, Bolton BL1 6DB
Mobile: 07762 545129   Tel: 01204 495732

White, Mrs M
20 Heywood Gardens
Great Lever, Bolton BL3 6RB   Tel: 01204 531589

BOURNEMOUTH
Sitton, Martin
Flat 2, 9 St Winifreds Road
Meyrick Park
Bournemouth BH2 6NX   Tel: 01202 293318

BRADFORD
Smith, Theresa
8 Moorhead Terrace
Shipley, Bradford BD18 4LA   Tel: 01274 778568

BRIGHTON
Benedict, Peter
19 Madeira Place, Brighton BN2 1TN
Mobile: 07752 810122   Tel: 020-7703 4104

Cleveland, Carol
13 Belgrave Street, Brighton BN2 9NS
Mobile: 07973 363939   Tel: 01273 602607

Dyson, Kate
39 Arundel Street, Kemptown BN2 5TH
Mobile: 07812 949575   Tel: 01273 607490

Stanfield-Miller, Ms
Flat 1, 154 Freshfield Road
Brighton BN2 9YD
Website: www.geocities.com/rowanstanfield/brightondigs
e-mail: rowanstanfield@yahoo.com
Mobile: 07747 725331   Tel: 01273 696080

BURY ST EDMUNDS
Bird, Mrs S
30 Crown Street, Bury St Edmunds
Suffolk IP33 1QU   Tel: 01284 754492

Harrington-Spie, Sue
39 Well Street
Bury St Edmunds, Suffolk IP33 1EQ   Tel: 01284 768986

BUXTON
Kitchen, Mrs M
Flat 1, 17 Silverlands
Buxton, Derbyshire SK17 6QH   Tel: 01298 79381

CANTERBURY
Dolan, Mrs A
12 Leycroft Close
Canterbury, Kent CT2 7LD   Tel: 01227 453153

Ellen, Nikki
Crockshard Farmhouse
Wingham, Canterbury CT3 1NY
Website: www.crockshard.com
e-mail: crockshard_bnb@yahoo.com   Tel: 01227 720464

Stockbridge, Doris
Tudor House, 6 Best Lane
Canterbury
Kent CT1 2JB   Tel/Fax: 01227 765650

CARDIFF
Blade, Mrs Anne
25 Romilly Road
Canton, Cardiff CF5 1FH   Tel: 029-2022 5860

Lewis, Nigel
66 Donald Street
Roath, Cardiff CF24 4TR
e-mail: nigel.lewis66@btinternet.com
Mobile: 07813 069822   Tel: 029-2049 4008

Nelmes, Michael
12 Darran Street, Cathays, Cardiff
South Glamorgan CF24 4JF   Tel: 029-2034 2166

Taylor, T & Chichester, P
32 Kincraig Street
Roath, Cardiff
South Glamorgan CF24 3HW   Tel: 029-2048 6785

CHESTERFIELD
Cook, Linda & Chris
27 Tennyson Avenue
Chesterfield, Derbyshire
Mobile: 07929 850561   Tel: 01246 20263

Foston, Mr & Mrs
Anis Louise Guest House
34 Clarence Road
Chesterfield S40 1LN
Website: www.anislouiseguesthouse.com
e-mail: anislouise@gmail.com   Tel: 01246 235412

Popplewell, Mr & Mrs
23 Tennyson Avenue
Chesterfield
Derbyshire S40 4SN   Tel: 01246 201738

CHICHESTER
Potter, Iain & Lyn
Hunston Mill Cottages
Selsey Road
Chichester PO20 1AU   Tel: 01243 783375

COVENTRY
Snelson, Paddy & Bob
Banner Hill Farmhouse
Rouncil Lane
Kenilworth CV8 1NN   Tel: 01926 852850

DARLINGTON
Bird, Mrs
Gilling Old Mill
Gilling West, Richmond
N Yorks DL10 5JD   Tel: 01748 822771

Graham, Anne
Holme House
Piercebridge
Darlington DL2 3SY
Website: www.holme-house.co.uk
e-mail: graham.holmehouse@gmail.com   Tel: 01325 374280

The Proprietor
George Hotel
Piercebridge
Darlington DL2 3SW   Tel: 01325 374576

DUNDEE
Gill, Mrs J
Ash Villa
16 Arbroath Road
Dundee DD4 7RZ
Tel: 01382 450831

EASTBOURNE
Allen, Peter
Flat 1, 16 Enys Road
Eastbourne BN21 2DN
Mobile: 07712 439289
Tel: 01323 730235

Guess, Maggie
Hardy Drive
Langney Point
Eastbourne, East Sussex BN23 6ED
e-mail: guesswhom@btinternet.com
Mobile: 07710 273288
Tel: 01323 736689

EDINBURGH
Allen Miller, Edna
5 Bellevue Road
Edinburgh EH7 4DL
Tel: 0131-556 4131

Stobbart, Joyce
4 Bellevue Road
Edinburgh EH7 4DE
Mobile: 07740 503951
Day Tel: 0131-222 9889

Tyrrell, Helen
Lonsdale Terrace
Edinburgh EH3 9HN
e-mail: helen.tyrrell@vhscotland.org.uk
Tel: 0131-229 7219   Tel: 0131-652 5992 (Office)

GLASGOW
Laird, David W
Beaton Road
Maxwell Park
Glasgow G41 4LA
Mobile: 07752 954176
Tel: 0141-423 1340

Leslie-Carter, Simon
52 Charlotte Street
Glasgow G1 5DW
Website: www.52charlottestreet.co.uk
e-mail: slc@52charlottestreet.co.uk
Fax: 01436 810520
Tel: 0845 2305252

Robinson, Lesley
8 Marywood Square
Glasgow G41 2BJ
Mobile: 07957 188922
Tel: 0141-423 6920

GRAVESEND
Greenwood, Mrs S
Sutherland Close
Chalk, Gravesend
Kent DA12 4XJ
e-mail: chalkbandb1@activemail.co.uk Tel: 01474 350819

HULL
The Arches Guesthouse
38 Saner Street
Hull HU3 2TR
Tel: 01482 211558

INVERNESS
Blair, Mrs
McDonald House Hotel
Ardross Terrace
Inverness IV3 5NQ
Tel: 01463 232878

Kerr-Smith, Jennifer
Ardkeen Tower
Culduthel Road
Inverness IV2 4AD
Tel: 01463 233131

IPSWICH
Ball, Bunty
56 Henley Road
Ipswich IP1 3SA
Tel: 01473 256653

Bennett, Liz
Gayfers, Playford
Ipswich IP6 9DR
Tel: 01473 623343

Hyde-Johnson, Anne
64 Benton Street
Hadleigh, Ipswich
Suffolk IP7 5AT
Tel: 01473 823110

ISLE OF WIGHT
Ogston, Sue
Windward House
69 Mill Hill Road, Cowes
Isle of Wight PO31 7EQ
Tel: 01983 280940

KESWICK
Bell, Miss A
Flat 4, Skiddaw View
Penrith Road
Keswick CA12 5HF
Mobile: 07740 949250

KIRKCALDY
Nicol, Mrs
44 Glebe Park, Kirkcaldy
Fife KY1 1BL
Tel: 01592 264531

LEEDS
Baker, Mrs M
2 Ridge Mount
(off Cliff Road)
Leeds LS6 2HD
Tel: 0113-275 8735

LINCOLN
Carnell, Andrew
Tennyson Court Cottages
3 Tennyson Street
Lincoln LN1 1LZ
Website: www.tennyson-court.co.uk
Tel: 01522 569892
Tel: 0800 9805408

Sharpe, Mavis S
Bight House, 17 East Bight
Lincoln LN2 1QH
Tel: 01522 534477

Ye Olde Crowne Inn (Theatre Pub)
Clasketgate
Lincoln LN2 1JS
Tel: 01522 542896

LIVERPOOL
De Leng, Ms S
7 Beach Lawn
Waterloo
Liverpool L22 8QA
Tel: 0151-476 1563

Double, Ross
5 Percy Street
Liverpool L8 7LT
Tel: 0151-708 8821

Maloney, Anne
16 Sandown Lane, Wavertree
Liverpool L15 8HY
Tel: 0151-734 4839

LLANDUDNO
Bell, Alan
Quinton Hotel, 36 Church Walks
Llandudno LL30 2HN
Tel: 01492 876879

Blanchard, Mr & Mrs D
Oasis Hotel
4 Neville Crescent
Central Promenade
Llandudno LL30 1AT
e-mail: ann@oasis-hotel.co.uk
Tel: 01492 877822

LONDON

Allen, Mrs I
Flat 2
9 Dorset Square
London NW1 6QB — Tel: 020-7723 3979

Broughton, Mrs P A
31 Ringstead Road
Catford
London SE6 2BU — Tel: 020-8461 0146

Cardinal, Maggie
17A Gaisford Street
London NW5 2EB — Tel: 020-7681 7376

Maya, Ms Y
23 Lena Crescent
London N9 0FB — Mobile: 07958 461468

Mesure, Nicholas
16 St Alfege Passage
Greenwich
London SE10 9JS — Tel: 020-8853 4337

Montagu, Beverley
13 Hanley Road
London N4 3DU — Tel: 020-7263 3883

Rothner, Dora
23 The Ridgeway
Finchley
London N3 2PG — Tel: 020-8346 0246

Rothner, Stephanie
44 Grove Road
North Finchley
London N12 9DY
Mobile: 07956 406446 — Tel: 020-8446 1604

Shaw, Lindy
11 Baronsmede
London W5 4LS — Tel: 020-8567 0877

Warren, Mrs Sally
28 Prebend Gardens
Chiswick
London W4 1TW — Tel: 020-8994 0560

MALVERN

Emuss, Mrs
Priory Holme
18 Avenue Road
Malvern WR14 3AR — Tel: 01684 568455

Martin, Mr N
37 Quest Hills Road
Malvern WR14 1RL
e-mail: nick@questhills.co.uk
Mobile: 07979 851529 — Tel: 01684 562442

McLeod, Mr & Mrs
Sidney House
40 Worcester Road
Malvern WR14 4AA
Website: www.sidneyhouse.co.uk
e-mail: info@sidneyhouse.co.uk — Tel: 01684 574994

MANCHESTER

Dyson, Mrs Edwina
33 Danesmoor Road
West Didsbury
Manchester M20 3JT — Tel: 0161-434 5410

Heaton, Miriam
58 Tamworth Avenue
Whitefield
Manchester M45 6UA — Tel: 0161-773 4490

Jones, P M
375 Bury New Road
Whitefield
Manchester M45 7SU — Tel: 0161-766 9243

Prichard, Fiona & John
45 Bamford Road, Didsbury
Manchester M20 2QP — Tel: 0161-434 4877

Twist, Susan
45 Osborne Road
Levenshulme
Manchester M19 2DU — Tel: 0161-225 159

MILFORD HAVEN

Henricksen, Bruce & Diana
Belhaven House Hotel Ltd
29 Hamilton Terrace
Milford Haven SA73 3JJ
Website: www.west-wales-hotels.com
e-mail: bruce@westwaleshotels.com
Fax: 01646 690787 — Tel: 01646 695983

NEWCASTLE UPON TYNE

Stansfield, Mrs P
Rosebery Hotel
2 Rosebery Crescent
Jesmond
Newcastle upon Tyne NE2 1ET
Website: www.roseberyhotel.co.uk — Tel: 0191-281 3363

NEWPORT

Price, Mrs Dinah
Great House
Isca Road
Old Village, Caerleon
Gwent NP18 1QG
Website: www.visitgreathouse.co.uk
e-mail: dinah.price@amserve.net — Tel: 01633 420216

NORWICH

Busch, Julia
8 Chester Street
Norwich NR2 2AY
e-mail: juliacbusch@aol.com
Mobile: 07920 133250 — Tel: 01603 612833

Youd, Cherry
Whitegates
181 Norwich Road
Wroxham
NR12 8RZ — Tel: 01603 781037

NOTTINGHAM

Davis, Barbara
3 Tattershall Drive
The Park
Nottingham NG7 1BX — Tel: 0115-947 4179

Offord, Mrs
5 Tattershall Drive
The Park
Nottingham NG7 1BX — Tel: 0115-947 6924

Santos, Mrs S
Eastwood Farm
Hagg Lane
Epperstone
Nottingham NG14 6AX — Tel: 0115-966 3018

Walker, Christine
18A Cavendish Crescent North
The Park
Nottingham NG7 1BA — Tel: 0115-947 2485

OXFORD
Petty, Susan
74 Corn Street
Witney
Oxford OX28 6BS   Tel: 01993 703035

PLYMOUTH
Carson, Mr & Mrs
5 Beech Cottages
Parsonage Road
Newton Ferrers
Nr Plymouth PL8 1AX
e-mail: beechcottages@aol.com   Tel: 01752 872124

Humphreys, John & Sandra
Lyttleton Guest House (Self-Catering)
4 Crescent Avenue
Plymouth PL1 3AN   **Tel: 01752 220176**

Mead, Teresa
Ashgrove House
218 Citadel Road
The Hoe
Plymouth PL1 3BB   Tel: 01752 664046

Spencer, Hugh & Eloise
10 Grand Parade
Plymouth PL1 3DF
Mobile: 07966 412839   Tel: 01752 664066

POOLE
Moore, Sarah
Harbour View
11 Harbour View Road
Poole BH14 0PD
Mobile: 07731 187175   Tel: 01202 734763

Saunders, Mrs
Harbour Shallows
45 Whitecliff Road
Poole BH14 8DU   Tel: 01202 741637

READING
Estate Office
Mapledurham House and Watermill
Mapledurham Estate
Reading RG4 7TR   Tel: 0118-972 3350

SALISBURY
Brumfitt, Ms S
26 Victoria Road
Salisbury
Wilts SP1 3NG   Tel: 01722 334877

SHEFFIELD
Craig, J & Rosen, B
59 Nether Edge Road
Sheffield S7 1RW   Tel: 0114-258 1337

Slack, Penny
Rivelin Glen Quarry
Rivelin Valley Road
Sheffield S6 5SE
Website: www.quarryhouse.org.uk
e-mail: pennyslack@aol.com   Tel: 0114-234 0382

SOUTHSEA & PORTSMOUTH
Tyrell, Wendy
Douglas Cottage
27 Somerset Road
Southsea PO5 2NL   Tel: 023-9282 1453

STOKE-ON-TRENT
Griffiths, Dorothy
40 Princes Road
Hartshill
Stoke-on-Trent
Mobile: 07789 362960   Tel: 01782 416198

Hindmoor, Mrs
Verdon Guest House
44 Charles Street
Hanley
Stoke-on-Trent ST1 3JY   Tel: 01782 264244

Meredith, Mr K
2 Bank End Farm Cottage
Hammond Avenue
Brown Edge
Stoke-on-Trent, Staffs ST6 8QU   **Tel: 01782 502160**

STRATFORD-UPON-AVON
Caterham House
58-59 Rother Street
Stratford-upon-Avon CV37 6LT   Tel: 01789 267309

WESTCLIFF
Hussey, Joy
42A Ceylon Road
Westcliff-on-Sea SS0 7HP   Mobile: 07946 413496

WOLVERHAMPTON
Nixon, Sonia
39 Stubbs Road
Pennfields
Wolverhampton WV3 7DJ   Tel: 01902 339744

Prior, Julia
Treetops
The Hem, Shifnal
Shropshire TF11 9PS   Tel: 01952 460566

Riggs, Peter A
'Bethesda'
56 Chapel Lane, Codsall
Nr Wolverhampton WV8 2EJ
Mobile: 07930 967809   Tel: 01902 844068

WORTHING
Stewart, Mollie
School House
11 Ambrose Place
Worthing BN11 1PZ   Tel: 01903 206823

Symonds, Mrs Val
23 Shakespeare Road
Worthing BN11 4AR   Tel: 01903 201557

YORK
Blacklock, Tom
155 Lowther Street
York YO3 7LZ   Tel: 01904 620487

Blower, Iris & Dennis
Dalescroft Guest House
10 Southlands Road
York YO23 1NP
Website: www.dalescroft-york.co.uk
e-mail: info@dalescroft-york.co.uk   Tel: 01904 626801

Harrand, Greg
Hedley House Hotel & Apts
3 Bootham Terrace
York YO3 7DH   Tel: 01904 637404

Health & Wellbeing

Please note that while The Spotlight takes every care in screening the companies featured in this section, it cannot be held responsible for services or treatments received.

AHLOWALIA Dr B.S.
(Dentist & Botox)
3 Victoria Place, Biddleswade, Bedfordshire SG18 9RN
Website: www.thechrysalis.co.uk
e-mail: rajahlowalia@aol.com   Tel: 01767 31527

ALEXANDER ALLIANCE
(Alexander Technique, Voice & Audition Coaching)
3 Hazelwood Drive, St Albans, Herts
Website: www.alextech.co.uk
e-mail: bev.keech@ntlworld.com   Tel: 01727 84363

ALEXANDER CENTRE The Bloomsbury
(Alexander Technique)
Bristol House, 80A Southampton Row, London WC1B 4BB
Website: www.alexcentre.com
e-mail: enquiries@alexcentre.com   Tel: 020-7404 534

ALEXANDER TECHNIQUE
(Robert Macdonald)
13 Ascot Lodge, Greville Place, London NW6 5JD
Website: www.voice.org.uk   Mobile: 07956 85230.

ALEXANDER TECHNIQUE
(Jackie Coote MSTAT)
27 Britannia Road, London SW6 2HJ
Website: www.alexandertec.co.uk
e-mail: jackiecoote@alexandertec.co.uk   Tel: 020-7731 106

ALL ABOUT TEETH Ltd
The Club Room, Miserden, Gloucestershire GL6 7JA
e-mail: nicolas@ceramiccentre.com   Tel: 01285 82122

ALTERED IMAGE LIFE COACHING
Primrose Cottage, 6 Lee Place, Ilfracombe EX34 9BQ
Website: www.alteredimage2.co.uk
e-mail: lifecoach@merseymail.com
Fax: 08709 133624   Mobile: 07050 6441C

ARTS CLINIC The
(Psychological Counselling, Personal & Professional
Development)
14 Devonshire Place, London W1G 6HX
e-mail: mail@artsclinic.co.uk
Fax: 020-7224 6256   Tel: 020-7935 124.

ASPEY ASSOCIATES
(Management & Team Training, Executive Coaching,
Human Resources)
90 Long Acre, Covent Garden, London WC2E 9RZ
Website: www.aspey.com
e-mail: hr@aspey.com   Tel: 0845 170130C

BODYWISE
(Yoga and Complementary Therapies)
119 Roman Road, London E2 0QN
Website: www.bodywisehealth.org
e-mail: info@bodywisehealth.org   Tel: 020-8981 693

BOWES Sara
(Holistic Massage & Reflexology)
23 John Aird Court, London W2 1UY
e-mail: sara@sarabowes.com
Mobile: 07830 375389   Tel: 020-7262 354:

BRITISH DOULAS
(Baby Care Services)
49 Harrington Gardens, London SW7 4JU
Website: www.britishdoulas.co.uk
e-mail: info@britishdoulas.co.uk
Fax: 020-7244 9035   Tel: 020-7244 605

BURGESS Chris
(Counselling for Performing Artists)
81 Arne House, Tyers Street
London SE11 5EZ   Tel: 020-7582 822S

BURT Andrew
(Counselling)
74 Mill Hill Road, London W3 8JJ
e-mail: burt.counsel@tiscali.co.uk   Tel: 020-8992 599

[CONTACTS 2008]

p250

CLAYMORE PERSONAL TRAINING
Echline View, Edinburgh EH30 9XL
Website: www.claymorepersonaltraining.co.uk
e-mail: subtlesword@yahoo.co.uk   Mobile: 07756 822396

COCKBURN Daisy
(Alexander Technique Teacher (MSTAT)
Bloomsbury Alexander Centre, Bristol House
10A Southampton Row, London WC1B 4BB
e-mail: daisycockburn@btinternet.com   Mobile: 07734 725445

CONSTRUCTIVE TEACHING CENTRE Ltd
(Alexander Technique Teacher Training)
18 Lansdowne Rd, London W11 3LL   www.alexandertek.com
e-mail: info@alexandertek.com   Tel: 020-7727 7222

CORTEEN Paola MSTAT
(Alexander Technique)
20A Eversley Park Road, London N21 1JU
e-mail: pmcorteen@yahoo.co.uk   Tel: 020-8882 7898

COURTENAY Julian
(NLP Hypnotherapy)
12 Langdon Park Road, London N6 5QG
e-mail: julian@mentalfitness.uk.com   Tel: 020-8348 9033

CUSSONS Nicola Dip ITEC
(Holistic Massage Therapist, Qualified & Insured)
The Factory Fitness & Dance Centre
407 Hornsey Road, London N19 4DX
e-mail: info@tangolondon.com   Tel: 020-7272 1122

DAVIES Siobhan STUDIOS
Treatment room: Physiotherapy, Deep Tissue Massage)
55 St George's Road, London SE1 6ER
Website: www.siobhandavies.com
e-mail: info@siobhandavies.com
Fax: 020-7091 9669   Tel: 020-7091 9650

DAWN Elizabeth
(Hair, Beauty & Tanning)
3 Upper Orwell Street, Ipswich, Suffolk IP4 1HN
Mobile: 07708 854282   Tel: 01473 213141

DREAM
(Massage, Reflexology & Yoga for Events in the Workplace
and Home)
17B Gaisford Street, London NW5 2EG
Website: www.dreamtherapies.co.uk
e-mail: heidi@dreamtherapies.co.uk   Mobile: 07973 731026

EDGE OF THE WORLD HYPNOTHERAPY AND NLP
Central London, Essex/Suffolk   Website: www.edgehypno.com
e-mail: grahamhowes@dsl.pipex.com   Mobile: 07960 755626

EDWARDS Simon MCA Hyp
(Hypnotherapy for Professionals in Film, TV & Theatre)
5 Station Road, Quainton, Nr Aylesbury, Bucks HP22 4BW
e-mail: hypnotherapisttothestars@o2.co.uk
Mobile: 07889 333680   Tel: 01296 651259

FAITH Gordon BA DHC MCHC (UK)
(Hypnotherapy, Obstacles to Performing, Positive
Affirmation, Focusing)
1 Wavel Mews, Priory Road, West Hampstead
London NW6 3AB   Tel: 020-7328 0446

FIT 4 THE PART
(Jon Trevor, Personal Training)
One Malthus Path, London SE28 8AJ
Website: www.jontrevor.com   e-mail: info@jontrevor.com
Fax: 0845 4664477   Tel: 0845 0066348

FITNESS COACH The
(Jamie Baird)
Agua at The Sanderson, 50 Berners Street, London W1T 3NG
e-mail: jamie@thefitnesscoach.com
Mobile: 07970 782476   Tel: 020-7300 1414

Edge of the World Hypnotherapy and NLP

Over 30 years "in the Business" on all sides. Combining Hypnotherapy and Neuro Linguistic Programming to effect change.

Treatments include: Audition confidence, Giving up Cigarettes, Fear and Phobias,
Dealing with Trauma and Stress, Past Life Regression and Weight Loss.

Call or email for a Central London or Essex / Suffolk appointment at reasonable rates for **anyone** "in the Business".

Call Graham Howes (ASHPH, GHR and GSCH) on: 07960 755626   www.edgehypno.com   email: grahamhowes@dsl.pipex.com

---

FOCUSING EXPERIMENTAL SESSIONS
Central London & Brighton
Website: www.gregmadison.net/focusbrighton
e-mail: info@gregmadison.net   Mobile: 07941 300871

HAMMOND John B. Ed (Hons) ICHFST
(Fitness Consultancy, Sports & Relaxation Massage)
4 Glencree
Billericay, Essex CM11 1EB
Mobile: 07703 185198   Tel/Fax: 01277 632830

HARLEY STREET VOICE CENTRE The
The Harley Street ENT Clinic
109 Harley Street, London W1G 6AN
Website: www.harleystreetent.com
e-mail: info@harleystreetent.com
Fax: 020-7935 7701   Tel: 020-7224 2350

www.inspirationalwellbeing.com

Energy Healer

Corporate and Individual
Tailor-made Treatments
by
Karen Hague

01992 524340

www.inspirationalwellbeing.com
inspirationalwellbeing@f2s.com

HYPNOSIS WORKS
Tulip House, 70 Borough High Street, London SE1 1XE
Website: www.hypnosisdoeswork.net
e-mail: sssp@hypnosisdoeswork.net   Tel: 020-7237 581?

HYPNOTHERAPY & PSYCHOTHERAPY
(Including Performance Improvement
Karen Mann DCH DHP)
9 Spencer Hse, Vale of Health, Hampstead, London NW3 1AS
Website: www.karenmann.co.uk   Tel: 020-7794 584?

INSPIRATIONAL WELLBEING
(Energy Healer)
22 Wellington Road, North Weald Bassett
Epping, Essex CM16 6JU
Website: www.inspirationalwellbeing.com
e-mail: inspirationalwellbeing@f2s.com
Mobile: 07941 479178   Tel: 01992 52434?

LIFE COACHING
(Including Career, Relationship, Self-Confidence Coaching)
Dr Elspeth Reid
102 Clarence Road, Wimbledon SW19 8QD
Website: www.elspethreid.com
e-mail: coach@elspethreid.com   Tel: 020-8879 767?

LUCAS Hazel
(Qualified Holistic Masseur)
119 Brightwell Avenue, Westcliff-on-Sea, Essex SS0 9EQ
e-mail: hazeystar@blueyonder.co.uk   Mobile: 07870 862939

MAGIC KEY PARTNERSHIP The
(Lyn Burgess - Life Coach)
151A Moffat Road, Thornton Heath, Surrey CR7 8PZ
Website: www.magickey.co.uk
e-mail: lyn@magickey.co.uk   Tel: 0845 129740

MATRIX ENERGY FIELD THERAPY
Deal Castle House, 31 Victoria Road, Deal, Kent CT14 7AS
e-mail: donnie@lovingorganization.org
Mobile: 07762 821828   Tel: 020-8946 853?

McCALLION Anna
(Alexander Technique)
Flat 2, 11 Sinclair Gardens, London W14 0AU
e-mail: hildagarde007@yahoo.com   Tel: 020-7602 5599

MINDSCI CLINIC
(Clinical Hypnotism)
34 Willow Bank, Ham, Richmond, Surrey TW10 7QX
Website: www.mindsci-clinic.com
e-mail: bt@mindsci-clinic.com   Tel/Fax: 020-8948 243?

NORTON Michael R
(Implant/Reconstructive Dentistry)
98 Harley Street, London W1G 7HZ
Website: www.nortonimplants.com
e-mail: linda@nortonimplants.com
Fax: 020-7486 9119   Tel: 020-7486 922?

smile @richardcasson.com

cosmetic fillings, orthodontics, bleaching, veneers
crowns and bridges, implants, hygienist

Dr. Richard Casson, Dental Care
For further information phone 020 7580 9696
Flat 6, Milford House, 7 Queen Anne Street, London W1G 9HN
Website: www.richardcasson.com

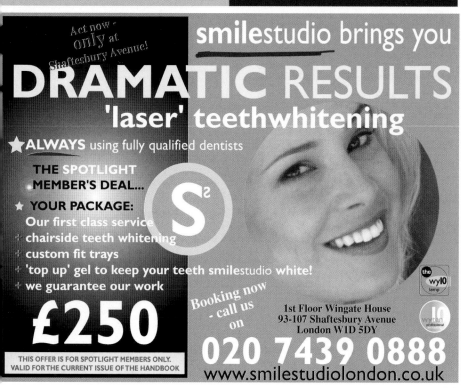

ThePsychologyGroup Ltd.

The British Psychological Society
Chartered Psychologist

- Psychotherapy & Counselling
- Life Coaching
- Occupational Assessments
- Expert Opinion
- Career Transition
- Stress Audits

Phone: 0870 609 2445   Fax: 0845 280 5243

Email: info@psychologygroup.co.uk

www.psychologygroup.co.uk

NUTRITIONAL THERAPY FOR PERFORMERS
(Vanessa May BSc)
18 Oaklands Road, Ealing, London W7 2DR
e-mail: vanessamay9@yahoo.co.uk   Mobile: 07962 978763

OGUNLARU Rasheed
(Life & Business Coach)
The Coaching Studio, 223A Mayall Road, London SE24 OPS
Website: www.rasaru.com
e-mail: rasaru_coaching@yahoo.com   Tel: 020-7207 1082

PEAK PERFORMANCE TRAINING
(Tina Reibl, Hypnotherapy, NLP, Success Strategies)
42 The Broadway, Maidenhead, Berkshire SL6 1LU
e-mail: tina.reibl@tesco.net   Tel: 01628 633509

POLAND DENTAL STUDIOS
(Film/Stage Dentistry)
1 Devonshire Place, London W1G 6HH
Fax: 020-7486 3952   Tel: 020-7935 6919

PRYCE Jacqui-Lee OCR ABA BAWLA GKFO
(Personal Training & Group Sessions, Boxing, Kick/Muay Thai Boxing)
e-mail: getfitquick@hotmail.com   Mobile: 07930 304809

RUOK4SPEX.COM
PO Box 1027 PE12 0SQ
Website: www.ruok4spex.com e-mail: info@ruok4spex.com

SELFSIGHT
(Counselling & EMDR)
111 Rainville Road, London W6 9HJ
Website: www.selfsight.com   e-mail: rf@selfsight.com
Mobile: 07961 152740   Tel: 020-7381 0202

SEYRI Kayvan BSc (Hons), NSCA-CPT*D, PES
(Personal Training & Nutrition Advice)
Cannons, Sidmouth Rd, Brondesbury Park, London NW2 1EU
Website: www.ultimatefitpro.com
e-mail: info@ultimatefitpro.com   Mobile: 07881 554636

SHENAS Dr DENTAL STUDIO
51 Cadogan Gardens, Sloane Square, London SW3 2TH
Website: www.shenasdental.co.uk
e-mail: info@shenasdental.co.uk   Tel: 020-7589 2319

SHER SYSTEM The
(Helping Skin with Acne & Rosacea)
30 New Bond Street, London W1S 2RN
Website: www.sher.co.uk   e-mail: skincare@sher.co.uk
Fax: 020-7629 7021   Tel: 020-7499 4022

SHIATSU HEALTH CENTRE
Moving Arts Base, 134 Liverpool Road, London N1 1LA
Website: www.shiatsuhealth.com
e-mail: japaneseyoga@btinternet.com   Mobile: 07905 504418

SMILE SOLUTIONS
(Dental Practice)
24 Englands Lane, London NW3 4TG
Website: www.smile-solutions.info
e-mail: enquiries@smile-solutions.info
Fax: 020-7449 1769   Tel: 020-7449 1760

SMILESTUDIO
First Floor, Wingate House
93-107 Shaftesbury Avenue, London W1D 8BT
Website: www.smile-studio.co.uk   Tel: 020-7439 0888

STAT (The Society of Teachers of the Alexander Technique)
1st Floor Linton House
39-51 Highgate Road, London NW5 1RS
Website: www.stat.org.uk   e-mail: office@stat.org.uk
Fax: 020-7482 5435   Tel: 0845 2307828

THEATRICAL DENTISTRY
(Richard D Casson)
6 Milford House, 7 Queen Anne Street, London W1G 9HN
Website: www.richardcasson.com
e-mail: smile@richardcasson.com   Tel/Fax: 020-7580 9696

TURNER Jeff
(Psychotherapy, Counselling & Performance Coaching)
Life Management Systems
14 Randell's Road, London N1 0DH
Website: www.lifemanagement.co.uk
e-mail: info@lifemanagement.co.uk   Tel: 020-7837 987

VITAL TOUCH The
(On-Site Massage Company)
11 Evering Road, London N16 7PX
Website: www.thevitaltouch.com
e-mail: suzi@thevitaltouch.com   Mobile: 07976 26369

WELLBEING
(Leigh Jones) (Personal Training, Yoga, Tai Chi)
22 Galloway Close, Broxbourne, Herts EN10 6BU
e-mail: williamleighjones@hotmail.com   Mobile: 07957 33392

WOODFORD HOUSE DENTAL PRACTICE
162 High Road, Woodford Green, Essex IG8 9EF
Website: www.improveyoursmile.co.uk
e-mail: mmalik-whdp@yahoo.co.uk
Fax: 020-8252 0835   Tel: 020-8504 2704

OPERA COMPANIES

ARTSWORLD PRESENTATIONS Ltd
Vicarage House
58-60 Kensington Church Street
London W8 4DB
Website: www.arts-world.co.uk
e-mail: p@triciamurraybett.com
Fax: 020-7368 3338   Tel: 020-7368 3337

CARL ROSA OPERA
359 Hackney Road
London E2 8PR
Website: www.carlrosaopera.co.uk
e-mail: info@carlrosaopera.co.uk
Fax: 020-7613 0859   Tel: 020-7613 0777

ENGLISH NATIONAL OPERA
London Coliseum
St Martin's Lane
London WC2N 4ES
Website: www.eno.org
Fax: 020-7845 9277   Tel: 020-7836 0111

ENGLISH TOURING OPERA
(James Conway)
1st Floor
52-54 Rosebery Avenue
London EC1R 4RP
Website: www.englishtouringopera.org.uk
e-mail: admin@englishtouringopera.org.uk
Fax: 020-7713 8686   Tel: 020-7833 2555

GLYNDEBOURNE FESTIVAL OPERA
Glyndebourne, Lewes
East Sussex BN8 5UU   Tel: 01273 812321

GRANGE PARK OPERA
The Coach House
12 St Thomas Street
Winchester SO23 9HF
Website: www.grangeparkopera.co.uk
e-mail: info@grangeparkopera.co.uk
Fax: 01962 868968   Tel: 01962 868600

GUBBAY Raymond Ltd
Dickens House
15 Tooks Court
London EC4A 1QH
Website: www.raymondgubbay.co.uk
e-mail: info@raymondgubbay.co.uk
Fax: 020-7025 3751   Tel: 020-7025 3750

KENT Ellen PRODUCTIONS
The Admiral's Offices
The Historic Dockyard
Chatham, Kent ME4 4TZ
Website: www.ellenkent.com
e-mail: info@ellenkentinternational.co.uk
Fax: 01634 819149   Tel: 01634 819141

KENTISH OPERA
Watermede
Wickhurst Road
Sevenoaks, Weald
Kent TN14 6LX
Website: www.kentishopera.fsnet.co.uk
e-mail: sallylangford@watermede.fslife.co.uk
                                      Tel: 01732 463284

[CONTACTS2008]

MUSIC THEATRE LONDON
Chertsey Chambers
12 Mercer Street
London WC2H 9QD
e-mail: musictheatre.london@virgin.net   Mobile: 07831 243942

OPERA DELLA LUNA
7 Cotmore House
Fringford
Bicester
Oxfordshire OX27 8RQ
Website: www.operadellaluna.org
e-mail: operadellaluna@aol.com
Fax: 01869 323533   Tel: 01869 325131

OPERA NORTH
Grand Theatre
46 New Briggate
Leeds LS1 6NU
Website: www.operanorth.co.uk
Fax: 0113-244 0418   Tel: 0113-243 9999

OPUS 1 OPERA
(AKA Opus 1 Music Ltd)
The Media Centre
7 Northumberland Street
Huddersfield HD1 5NA
Website: www.opus1opera.co.uk
e-mail: info@opus1opera.co.uk
Fax: 0870 9905141   Tel: 0870 9905140

PEGASUS OPERA COMPANY Ltd
The Brix, St Matthew's
Brixton Hill, London SW2 1JF
Website: www.pegopera.org   Tel/Fax: 020-7501 9501

PIMLICO OPERA
The Coach House
12 St Thomas Street
Winchester SO23 9HF
Website: www.grangeparkopera.co.uk
e-mail: pimlico@grangeparkopera.co.uk
Fax: 01962 868968   Tel: 01962 868600

ROYAL OPERA The
Royal Opera House
Covent Garden
London WC2E 9DD
Website: www.roh.org.uk   Tel: 020-7240 1200

SCOTTISH OPERA
39 Elmbank Crescent, Glasgow G2 4PT
Website: www.scottishopera.org.uk   Tel: 0141-248 4567

WELSH NATIONAL OPERA
Wales Millennium Centre
Bute Place
Cardiff CF10 5AL
Website: www.wno.org.uk
e-mail: marketing@wno.org.uk
Fax: 029-2063 5099   Tel: 029-2063 5000

SPOTLIGHT PUBLICATIONS
SPOTLIGHT INTERACTIVE
SPOTLIGHT SERVICES

www.spotlight.com
The industry's leading casting resource

7 Leicester Place London WC2H 7RJ   t 020 7437 7631   e info@spotlight.com   www.spotlight.com

CTORS' ADVISORY SERVICE
9 Talbot Road, Twickenham
iddlesex TW2 6SJ   Tel: 020-8287 2839

CTORS' BENEVOLENT FUND
Adam Street, London WC2N 6AD
ebsite: www.actorsbenevolentfund.co.uk
-mail: office@abf.org.uk
ax: 020-7836 8978   Tel: 020-7836 6378

CTORS CENTRE (LONDON) The
Tower Street, London WC2H 9NP
ebsite: www.actorscentre.co.uk
-mail: generalmgr@actorscentre.co.uk
ax: 020-7240 3896   Tel: 020-7240 3940

CTORS CENTRE (NORTHERN)
See NORTHERN ACTORS CENTRE)

CTORS CENTRE (MIDLANDS) The
tudio 214, The Jubilee Centre
0 Pershore Street, Birmingham B5 6ND
ebsite: www.theactorscentremidlands.co.uk
-mail: info@theactorscentremidlands.co.uk
                                          Tel: 0121-622 6777

CTORS' CHARITABLE TRUST
frica House, 64-78 Kingsway, London WC2B 6BD
-mail: robert@tactactors.org
ax: 020-7242 0234   Tel: 020-7242 0111

CTORS' CHURCH UNION
: Paul's Church, Bedford Street, London WC2E 9ED
mail: actors-church.union@tiscali.co.uk   Tel: 020-7240 0344

DVERTISING ASSOCIATION
h Floor North, Artillery House
-19 Artillery Row, London SW1P 1RT
ebsite: www.adassoc.org.uk   e-mail: aa@adassoc.org.uk
ax: 020-7222 1504   Tel: 020-7340 1100

AFTRA
(American Federation of Television & Radio Artists)
260 Madison Avenue
New York NY 10016
Website: www.aftra.com
Fax: (212) 545-1238   Tel: (212) 532-0800

5757 Wilshire Boulevard
9th Floor, Los Angeles CA 90036
Website: www.aftra.com
Fax: (323) 634-8246   Tel: (323) 634-8100

AGENTS' ASSOCIATION (Great Britain)
54 Keyes House
Dolphin Square, London SW1V 3NA
Website: www.agents-uk.com
e-mail: association@agents-uk.com
Fax: 020-7821 0261   Tel: 020-7834 0515

ARTS & BUSINESS
Nutmeg House
60 Gainsford Street
Butlers Wharf, London SE1 2NY
Website: www.aandb.org.uk
e-mail: head.office@aandb.org.uk
Fax: 020-7407 7527   Tel: 020-7378 8143

ARTS & ENTERTAINMENT TECHNICAL TRAINING
INITIATIVE (AETTI)
261 Baker Street, Derby DE24 8SG
Website: www.aetti.org.uk
e-mail: aetti@sumack.freeserve.co.uk   Tel: 01332 751740

ARTS CENTRE GROUP The
Menier Chocolate Factory
51 Southwark Street, London SE1 1RU
Website: www.artscentregroup.org.uk
e-mail: info@artscentregroup.org.uk   Tel: 0845 4581881

ARTS COUNCIL ENGLAND
2 Pear Tree Court, London EC1R 0DS
Website: www.artscouncil.org.uk
e-mail: enquiries@artscouncil.org.uk
Fax: 020-7608 4100   Tel: 0845 300 6200

ARTS COUNCIL NORTHERN IRELAND
MacNeice House, 77 Malone Road, Belfast BT9 6AQ
Website: www.artscouncil-ni.org
Fax: 028-9066 1715   Tel: 028-9038 5200

ARTS COUNCIL OF WALES The
9 Museum Place, Cardiff CF10 3NX
Website: www.artswales.org.uk
e-mail: info@artswales.org.uk
Fax: 029-2022 1447   Tel: 029-2037 6500

ARTSLINE
(Disability Access Information Service)
54 Chalton Street, London NW1 1HS
Website: www.artslineonline.org.uk
e-mail: admin@artsline.org.uk
Fax: 020-7383 2653   Tel: 020-7388 2227

ASSITEJ UK
(UK Centre of the International Association of Theatre for
Children and Young People)
c/o Kevin Lewis, Secretary, Theatre Iolo
The Old School Building, Cefn Road
Mynachdy, Cardiff CF14 3HS
Website: www.assitejuk.org
e-mail: admin@theatriolo.com   Tel: 029-2061 3782

ASSOCIATION OF BRITISH THEATRE TECHNICIANS
4th Floor, 55 Farringdon Road, London EC1M 3JB
Website: www.abtt.org.uk
e-mail: office@abtt.org.uk
Fax: 020-7242 9303   Tel: 020-7242 9200

ASSOCIATION OF LIGHTING DESIGNERS
PO Box 680, Oxford OX1 9DG
Website: www.ald.org.uk
e-mail: office@ald.org.uk   Mobile: 07817 060189

ASSOCIATION OF MODEL AGENTS
11-29 Fashion Street, London E1 6PX
e-mail: amainfo@btinternet.com
Info. Line: 09068 517644   Tel: 020-7422 0699

BECTU
(See BROADCASTING ENTERTAINMENT CINEMATOGRAPH &
THEATRE UNION)

BRITISH ACADEMY OF COMPOSERS & SONGWRITERS The
2nd Floor, British Music House
26 Berners Street, London W1T 3LR
Website: www.britishacademy.com
e-mail: info@britishacademy.com
Fax: 020-7636 2212   Tel: 020-7636 2929

BRITISH ACADEMY OF FILM & TELEVISION ARTS/LOS ANGELES The
8533 Melrose Avenue, West Hollywood, CA 90069
e-mail: info@baftala.org
Fax: (310) 854-6002   Tel: (310) 652-4121

BRITISH ACADEMY OF FILM & TELEVISION ARTS The
195 Piccadilly, London W1J 9LN
Website: www.bafta.org
e-mail: membership@bafta.org
Fax: 020-7292 5868   Tel: 020-7734 0022

BRITISH ACADEMY OF STAGE & SCREEN COMBAT
Suite 280, 14 Tottenham Court Road, London W1T 1JY
Website: www.bassc.org
e-mail: info@bassc.org   Mobile: 07981 806265

BRITISH ASSOCIATION FOR PERFORMING ARTS MEDICINE (BAPAM)
4th Floor, Totara Park House
34-36 Gray's Inn Road, London WC1X 8HR
Website: www.bapam.org.uk
e-mail: clinic@bapam.org.uk   Tel: 020-7404 588

BRITISH ASSOCIATION OF DRAMATHERAPISTS The
Waverley, Battledown Approach
Cheltenham, Glos GL52 6RE
Website: www.badth.org.uk
e-mail: badth1@aol.com   Tel: 01242 23551

BRITISH BOARD OF FILM CLASSIFICATION
3 Soho Square, London W1D 3HD
Website: www.bbfc.co.uk
Fax: 020-7287 0141   Tel: 020-7440 157

BRITISH COUNCIL The
(Performing Arts Department)
10 Spring Gardens, London SW1A 2BN
Website: www.britishcouncil.org/arts
e-mail: theatredance@britishcouncil.org   Tel: 020-7389 301

BRITISH EQUITY COLLECTING SOCIETY
66 Great Russell Street, London WC1B 3BN
Website: www.equitycollecting.org.uk
e-mail: info@equitycollecting.org.uk
Fax: 020-7831 1171   Tel: 020-7242 808

BRITISH FILM INSTITUTE
21 Stephen Street, London W1T 1LN
Website: www.bfi.org.uk
e-mail: library@bfi.org.uk
Fax: 020-7436 2338   Tel: 020-7255 144

BRITISH LIBRARY SOUND ARCHIVE
96 Euston Road, London NW1 2DB
Website: www.bl.uk/soundarchive
e-mail: sound-archive@bl.uk
Fax: 020-7412 7441   Tel: 020-7412 767

BRITISH MUSIC HALL SOCIETY
(Secretary: Daphne Masterton)
Meander, 361 Watford Road, Chiswell Green
St Albans, Herts AL2 3DB   Tel: 01727 76887

BROADCASTING ENTERTAINMENT CINEMATOGRAPH & THEATRE UNION (BECTU) (Formerly BETA & ACTT)
373-377 Clapham Road, London SW9 9BT
e-mail: smacdonald@bectu.org.uk
Fax: 020-7346 0901   Tel: 020-7346 090

CASTING DIRECTORS' GUILD
Website: www.thecdg.co.uk
e-mail: info@thecdg.co.uk

CATHOLIC STAGE GUILD
(Write SAE)
Ms Molly Steele (Hon Secretary)
1 Maiden Lane, London WC2E 7NB
e-mail: mary40steele@btinternet.com   Tel: 020-7240 122

CELEBRITY SERVICE Ltd
4th Floor, Kingsland House
122-124 Regent Street W1B 5SA
e-mail: celebritylondon@aol.com
Fax: 020-7494 3500   Tel: 020-7439 984

CHILDREN'S FILM & TELEVISION FOUNDATION Ltd
e-mail: annahome@cftf.org.uk   Mobile: 07887 57347

CHRISTIANS IN ENTERTAINMENT
(Charity)
PO Box 223, Bexhill-on-Sea TN40 9DP
Website: www.cieweb.org.uk
e-mail: chris@cieweb.org.uk   Tel: 01737 55037

WE CAN HELP ACTORS' CHILDREN

Are you:

- a professional actor?
- the parent of a child under 21?
- having trouble with finances?

Please get in touch for a confidential chat.

The Actors' Charitable Trust
020 7242 0111
robert@tactactors.org

TACT can help in many ways: with regular monthly payments, one-off grants, and long-term support and advice.
We help with clothing, child-care, music lessons, school trips, special equipment and adaptations, and in many other ways.

Our website has a link to a list of all the theatrical and entertainment charities which might be able to help you if you do not have children: www.tactactors.org

TACT, Africa House, 64 Kingsway, London WC2B 6BD.
Registered charity number 206809.

CIDA (CREATIVE INDUSTRIES DEVELOPMENT AGENCY)
(Professional Development & Business Support for Artists
& Creative Businesses)
Media Centre, Northumberland Street
Huddersfield, West Yorkshire HD1 1RL
Website: www.cida.org   e-mail: info@cida.org
Fax: 01484 483150   Tel: 01484 483140

CINEMA & TELEVISION BENEVOLENT FUND (CTBF)
22 Golden Square, London W1F 9AD
Website: www.ctbf.co.uk   e-mail: charity@ctbf.co.uk
Fax: 020-7437 7186   Tel: 020-7437 6567

CINEMA EXHIBITORS' ASSOCIATION
22 Golden Square, London W1F 9JW
e-mail: cea@cinemauk.ftech.co.uk
Fax: 020-7734 6147   Tel: 020-7734 9551

CLUB FOR ACTS & ACTORS
(Incorporating Concert Artistes Association)
20 Bedford Street, London WC2E 9HP
Website: www.thecaa.org   e-mail: office@thecaa.org
Office: 020-7836 3172   Members: 020-7836 2884

COMBINED THEATRICAL CHARITIES The
West Suite, 2nd Floor, 11 Garrick Street, London WC2E 9AR
e-mail: ctc@trtf.com
Fax: 020-7379 8273   Tel: 020-7379 6978

COMPANY OF CRANKS
1st Floor, 62 Northfield House
Frensham Street, London SE15 6TN
Website: www.mimeworks.com
e-mail: mimetic16@yahoo.com   Mobile: 07963 617981

CONCERT ARTISTES ASSOCIATION
(See CLUB FOR ACTS & ACTORS)

CONFERENCE OF DRAMA SCHOOLS
(Saul Hyman, Executive Secretary)
PO Box 34252, London NW5 1XJ
Website: www.drama.ac.uk   e-mail: info@cds.drama.ac.uk

**COUNCIL FOR DANCE EDUCATION & TRAINING (CDET)
The**
Old Brewer's Yard
17-19 Neal Street, London WC2H 9UY
Website: www.cdet.org.uk   e-mail: info@cdet.org.uk
Fax: 020-7240 2547   Tel: 020-7240 5703

CPMA
(Co-operative Personal Management Association)
The Secretary, c/o 1 Mellor Road, Leicester LE3 6HN
Website: www.cpma.co.uk
e-mail: cpmauk@yahoo.co.uk   Mobile: 07981 902525

CRITICS' CIRCLE The
c/o 69 Marylebone Lane, London W1U 2PH
Website: www.criticscircle.org.uk   Tel: 020-7224 1410

DANCE UK
(Including the Healthier Dancer Programme & 'The UK
Choreographers' Directory')
2nd Floor, Finsbury Town Hall
Rosebery Avenue, London EC1R 4QT
Website: www.danceuk.org
e-mail: info@danceuk.org
Fax: 020-7833 2363   Tel: 020-7713 0730

DENVILLE HALL
(Nursing Home)
62 Ducks Hill Road, Northwood, Middlesex HA6 2SB
Website: www.denvillehall.org
e-mail: denvillehall@yahoo.com
Fax: 01923 841855
Residents: 01923 820805   Office: 01923 825843

DIRECTORS' & PRODUCERS' RIGHTS SOCIETY
20-22 Bedford Row, London WC1R 4EB
Website: www.dprs.org
e-mail: info@dprs.org
Fax: 020-7269 0676   Tel: 020-7269 0677

DIRECTORS GUILD OF GREAT BRITAIN
Top Floor, Julian House, 4 Windmill Street, London W1T 2HZ
Website: www.dggb.org
e-mail: info@dggb.org
Fax: 020-7580 9132   Tel: 020-7580 913

D'OYLY CARTE OPERA COMPANY
295 Kennington Road, London SE11 4QE
Website: www.doylycarte.org.uk
e-mail: ian@doylycarte.org.uk
Fax: 020-7820 0240   Tel: 020-7793 710C

DRAMA ASSOCIATION OF WALES
(Specialist Drama Lending Library)
The Old Library, Singleton Road, Splott, Cardiff CF24 2ET
e-mail: aled.daw@virgin.net
Fax: 029-2045 2277   Tel: 029-2045 220C

DRAMATURGS' NETWORK
(Network of Professional Dramaturgs)
10 Glengarry Road, East Dulwich, London SE22 8PZ
Website: www.dramaturgy.co.uk
e-mail: info@dramaturgy.co.uk   Mobile: 07939 270566

ENGLISH FOLK DANCE & SONG SOCIETY
Cecil Sharp House, 2 Regent's Park Road, London NW1 7AY
Website: www.efdss.org
e-mail: info@efdss.org
Fax: 020-7284 0534   Tel: 020-7485 220

EQUITY inc Variety Artistes' Federation
Guild House
Upper St Martin's Lane, London WC2H 9EG
Website: www.equity.org.uk
e-mail: info@equity.org.uk
Fax: 020-7379 7001   Tel: 020-7379 600

(North West)
Conavon Court, 12 Blackfriars Street, Salford M3 5BQ
e-mail: info@manchester-equity.org.uk
Fax: 0161-839 3133   Tel: 0161-832 318?

(Scotland & Northern Ireland)
114 Union Street, Glasgow G1 3QQ
e-mail: igilchrist@glasgow.equity.org.uk
Fax: 0141-248 2473   Tel: 0141-248 247?

(Wales & South West)
Transport House, 1 Cathedral Road, Cardiff CF11 9SD
e-mail: info@cardiff-equity.org.uk
Fax: 029-2023 0754   Tel: 029-2039 797

ETF (Equity Trust Fund)
Suite 222, Africa House
64 Kingsway, London WC2B 6BD
Fax: 020-7831 4953   Tel: 020-7404 604

FAA
(See FILM ARTISTS ASSOCIATION)

FILM ARTISTS ASSOCIATION
(Amalgamated with BECTU)
373-377 Clapham Road, London SW9
Fax: 020-7346 0925   Tel: 020-7346 090

FILM LONDON
Suite 6.10, The Tea Building
56 Shoreditch High Street, London E1 6JJ
Website: www.filmlondon.org.uk
e-mail: info@filmlondon.org.uk
Fax: 020-7613 7677   Tel: 020-7613 767

The Actors Centre is the UK's premier resource for actors, providing them with further development of the highest quality and the opportunity to improve every aspect of their craft.

We enable the pursuit of excellence by promoting high artistic standards across the profession and initiating innovative work.

A friendly meeting place at the heart of the profession where actors can share information and exchange ideas.

the actors centre

Patron: Julie Walters
Artistic Director: Matthew Lloyd

Workshops and Classes

Audition Technique

TV and Film

Dialect

Musical Theatre

Sightreading

Singing

Radio

Voice

Shakespeare

Directing

Writing

Alexander Technique

Stage Combat

Physical Theatre

Dance

Career Advice

Casting Sessions

Financial Advice

Tristan Bates Theatre

Studio theatre space with a vibrant and varied programme of new and developing work. To discuss hire contact:
act@actorscentre.co.uk

Green Room Bar and Cafe

Relaxed and friendly atmosphere, drinks and snacks, internet access. Available for special events, contact:
greenroom@actorscentre.co.uk

Studio Hire

Range of studios for hire for casting sessions, auditions and meetings. To book, contact:
roomhire@actorscentre.co.uk

Want to join?

For further information about joining the Actors Centre please contact:
members@actorscentre.co.uk

The Actors Centre, 1a Tower Street, London, WC2H 9NP
Tel 020 7240 3940 Fax 020 7240 3896 www.actorscentre.co.uk

GLASGOW FILM OFFICE
(Production Finance for Feature Films)
City Chambers, Glasgow G2 1DU
Fax: 0141-287 0311   Tel: 0141-287 0424

GRAND ORDER OF WATER RATS
328 Gray's Inn Road, London WC1X 8BZ
Website: www.gowr.net
e-mail: info@gowr.net
Fax: 020-7278 1765   Tel: 020-7278 3248

GROUP LINE
(Group Bookings for London Theatre)
22-24 Torrington Place, London WC1E 7HJ
Website: www.groupline.com
e-mail: tix@groupline.com
Fax: 020-7436 6287   Tel: 020-7580 6793

HAMMER FILMS PRESERVATION SOCIETY
(Fan Club)
14 Kingsdale Road, Plumstead
London SE18 2DG   Tel: 020-8854 7383

INDEPENDENT THEATRE COUNCIL (ITC)
12 The Leathermarket, Weston Street, London SE1 3ER
Website: www.itc-arts.org
e-mail: admin@itc-arts.org
Fax: 020-7403 1745   Tel: 020-7403 1727

INSIGHT ARTS
7-15 Greatorex Street, London E1 5NF
e-mail: info@insightarts.org
Fax: 020-7247 8077   Tel: 020-7247 0778

INTERNATIONAL FEDERATION OF ACTORS (FIA)
Guild House, Upper St Martin's Lane
London WC2H 9EG
Website: www.fia-actors.com
e-mail: office@fia-actors.com
Fax: 020-7379 8260   Tel: 020-7379 0900

IRISH EQUITY GROUP (SIPTU)
(Group Organiser: Des Courtney)
9th Floor, Liberty Hall, Dublin 1, Ireland
Website: www.irishequity.ie
e-mail: equity@siptu.ie
Fax: 00 353 1 8743691   Tel: 00 353 1 8586403

IRVING SOCIETY The
(Michael Kilgarriff, Hon. Secretary)
10 Kings Avenue, London W5 2SH
e-mail: secretary@theirvingsociety.org.uk   Tel: 020-8566 8301

ITC
(See INDEPENDENT THEATRE COUNCIL)

ITV Plc
200 Gray's Inn Road, London WC1X 8HF
Website: www.itv.com
Fax: 020-7843 8158   Tel: 020-7843 8000

LONDON FILM COMPANY Ltd
Suite B, 5 South Bank Terrace, Surbiton, Surrey KT6 6DG
Website: www.doncapo.com
e-mail: info@doncapo.com
Mobile: 07884 056405   Tel/Fax: 020-8390 8535

LONDON SCHOOL OF CAPOEIRA The
Units 1 & 2 Leeds Place, Tollington Park, London N4 3RF
Website: www.londonschoolofcapoeira.co.uk
e-mail: info@londonschoolofcapoeira.co.uk
          Tel: 020-7281 2020

LONDON SHAKESPEARE WORKOUT
PO Box 31855, London SE17 3XP
Website: www.londonshakespeare.org.uk
e-mail: londonswo@hotmail.com   Tel/Fax: 020-7793 9755

MANDER & MITCHENSON THEATRE COLLECTION
Jerwood Library of the Performing Arts
King Charles Building, Old Royal Naval College
Greenwich, London SE10 9JF
e-mail: rmangan@tcm.ac.uk
Fax: 020-8305 9426   Tel: 020-8305 4426

MUSICIANS' UNION
60-62 Clapham Road, London SW9 0JJ
Website: www.musiciansunion.org.uk
Fax: 020-7582 9805   Tel: 020-7582 5566

NATIONAL ASSOCIATION OF SUPPORTING ARTISTES AGENTS
(NASAA)
Website: www.nasaa.org.uk
e-mail: info@nasaa.org.uk

NATIONAL ASSOCIATION OF YOUTH THEATRES (NAYT)
Arts Centre, Vane Terrace, Darlington
County Durham DL3 7AX
Website: www.nayt.org.uk
e-mail: nayt@btconnect.com
Fax: 01325 363313   Tel: 01325 363330

NATIONAL CAMPAIGN FOR THE ARTS
1 Kingly Street, London W1B 5PA
Website: www.artscampaign.org.uk
e-mail: nca@artscampaign.org.uk
Fax: 020-7287 4777   Tel: 020-7287 3777

NATIONAL COUNCIL FOR DRAMA TRAINING
1-7 Woburn Walk, Bloomsbury, London WC1H 0JJ
Website: www.ncdt.co.uk
e-mail: info@ncdt.co.uk
Fax: 020-7387 3860   Tel: 020-7387 3650

NATIONAL ENTERTAINMENT AGENTS COUNCIL
PO Box 112, Seaford, East Sussex BN25 2DQ
Website: www.neac.org.uk
e-mail: chrisbray@neac.org.uk
Fax: 0870 7557613   Tel: 0870 7557612

NATIONAL FILM THEATRE
BFI South Bank, Belvedere Road
South Bank, London SE1 8XT
Website: www.bfi.org.uk   Tel: 020-7928 3535

NATIONAL RESOURCE CENTRE FOR DANCE
University of Surrey, Guildford, Surrey GU2 7XH
Website: www.surrey.ac.uk/nrcd
e-mail: nrcd@surrey.ac.uk   Tel: 01483 689316

NEW PRODUCERS ALLIANCE
Unit 7.03, The Tea Building
56 Shoreditch High Street, London E1 6JJ
Website: www.npa.org.uk
e-mail: queries@npa.org.uk
Fax: 020-7729 7852   Tel: 020-7613 0440

NODA (National Operatic & Dramatic Association)
Noda House, 58-60 Lincoln Road, Peterborough PE1 2RZ
Website: www.noda.org.uk
e-mail: everyone@noda.org.uk
Fax: 0870 7702490   Tel: 0870 7702480

NORTH AMERICAN ACTORS ASSOCIATION
(Phone or e-mail only)
Website: www.naaa.org.uk
e-mail: americanactors@aol.com   Mobile: 07873 371891

NORTHERN ACTORS CENTRE
21-23 Oldham Street, Manchester M1 1JG
Website: www.northernactorscentre.co.uk
e-mail: info@northernactorscentre.co.uk
          Tel/Fax: 0161-819 2513

THEATRICAL MANAGEMENT ASSOCIATION

TMA

One of the most highly regarded and influential trade associations for organisations and individuals involved professionally in the production and presentation of theatre and the performing arts in the UK. Members include repertory and producing theatres, arts centres and presenting venues, opera and dance companies, commercial producers, associated individuals and businesses.

TMA, 32 Rose Street   London WC2E 9ET Tel: 020 7557 6700   Fax: 020 7557 6799
Email: enquiries@solttma.co.uk   Website: www.tmauk.org

NORTH WEST PLAYWRIGHTS
18 Express Networks
1 George Leigh Street, Manchester M4 5DL
Website: www.newplaysnw.co.uk
e-mail: newplaysnw@hotmail.com   Tel/Fax: 0161-237 1978

OFCOM
Ofcom Media Office, Riverside House
2A Southwark Bridge Road, London SE1 9HA
Website: www.ofcom.org.uk
e-mail: mediaoffice@ofcom.org.uk   Tel: 020-7981 3033

PACT
(Trade Association for Independent Television, Feature Film & New Media Production Companies)
2nd Floor, Procter House
1 Procter Street, London WC1V 6DW
Website: www.pact.co.uk   e-mail: enquiries@pact.co.uk
Fax: 020-7067 4377   Tel: 020-7067 4367

PERFORMING RIGHT SOCIETY Ltd
29-33 Berners Street, London W1T 3AB
Website: www.mcps-prs-alliance.co.uk
Fax: 020-7306 4455   Tel: 020-7580 5544

PERSONAL MANAGERS' ASSOCIATION Ltd
Rivercroft, 1 Summer Road
East Molesey, Surrey KT8 9LX
Website: www.thepma.com
e-mail: info@thepma.com   Tel/Fax: 020-8398 9796

ROYAL TELEVISION SOCIETY
Kildare House, 3 Dorset Rise, London EC4Y 8EN
Website: www.rts.org.uk   e-mail: info@rts.org.uk
Fax: 020-7822 2811   Tel: 020-7822 2810

ROYAL THEATRICAL FUND
11 Garrick Street, London WC2E 9AR
e-mail: admin@trtf.com
Fax: 020-7379 8273   Tel: 020-7836 3322

S A G
(Screen Actors Guild)
7th Floor, 5757 Wilshire Boulevard
Los Angeles, CA 90036-3600   Tel: (323) 954-1600

360 Madison Avenue, 12th Floor, New York NY 10017
Website: www.sag.org   Tel: (212) 944-1030

SAMPAD SOUTH ASIAN ARTS
(Promotes the appreciation & practice of South Asian Arts)
c/o Mac, Cannon Hill Park
Birmingham B12 9QH
Website: www.sampad.org.uk
e-mail: info@sampad.org.uk
Fax: 0121-440 8667   Tel: 0121-446 4312

SAVE LONDON'S THEATRES CAMPAIGN
Guild House
Upper St Martin's Lane
London WC2H 9EG
Website: www.savelondonstheatres.org.uk
e-mail: contactus@savelondonstheatres.org.uk
Fax: 020-7379 7001   Tel: 020-3077 1021

SCOTTISH ARTS COUNCIL
12 Manor Place, Edinburgh EH3 7DD
Website: www.scottisharts.org.uk
e-mail: help.desk@scottisharts.org.uk
Fax: 0131-225 9833   Tel: 0845 603600

SCOTTISH SCREEN PRODUCTION & DEVELOPMENT
249 West George Street, Glasgow G2 4QE
Website: www.scottishscreen.com
e-mail: info@scottishscreen.com
Fax: 0141-302 1711   Tel: 0141-302 1700

SCRIPT
(West Midlands Playwrights, Scriptwriters - Training & Support)
Unit 107 The Greenhouse
The Custard Factory
Gibb Street, Birmingham B9 4AA
Website: www.scriptonline.net   Tel: 0121-224 7415

SHOW-PAIRS - GUY Gillian ASSOCIATES
84A Tachbrook Street
London SW1V 2NB
Website: www.show-pairs.co.uk
e-mail: gillian@gillianguyassoc.com
Fax: 020-7976 5885   Tel: 020-7976 5888

SOCIETY FOR THEATRE RESEARCH The
PO Box 53971, London SW15 6UL
Website: www.str.org.uk
e-mail: e.cottis@btinternet.com

SOCIETY OF AUTHORS
84 Drayton Gardens, London SW10 9SB
Website: www.societyofauthors.org
e-mail: info@societyofauthors.org Tel: 020-7373 6642

SOCIETY OF BRITISH THEATRE DESIGNERS
4th Floor
55 Farringdon Road, London EC1M 3JB
Website: www.theatredesign.org.uk
e-mail: sbtd@ntu.ac.uk
Fax: 020-7242 9303 Tel: 020-7242 9200

SOCIETY OF LONDON THEATRE (SOLT)
32 Rose Street, London WC2E 9ET
e-mail: enquiries@solttma.co.uk
Fax: 020-7557 6799 Tel: 020-7557 6700

SOCIETY OF TEACHERS OF SPEECH & DRAMA The
Registered Office:
73 Berry Hill Road, Mansfield
Nottinghamshire NG18 4RU
Website: www.stsd.org.uk
e-mail: ann.k.jones@btinternet.com Tel: 01623 627636

SOCIETY OF THEATRE CONSULTANTS
4th Floor, 55 Farringdon Road
London EC1M 3JB
e-mail: office@abtt.org.uk
Fax: 020-7242 9303 Tel: 020-7242 9200

STAGE CRICKET CLUB
39-41 Hanover Steps
St George's Fields, Albion Street, London W2 2YG
Website: www.stagecc.co.uk
e-mail: brianjfilm@aol.com
Fax: 020-7262 5736 Tel: 020-7402 7543

STAGE GOLFING SOCIETY
Sudbrook Park, Sudbrook Lane
Richmond, Surrey TW10 7AS Tel: 020-8940 8861

STAGE MANAGEMENT ASSOCIATION
55 Farringdon Road, London EC1M 3JB
Website: www.stagemanagementassociation.co.uk
e-mail: admin@stagemanagementassociation.co.uk
Fax: 020-7242 9303 Tel: 020-7242 9250

STAGE ONE
(Formerly The Theatre Investment Fund Ltd)
32 Rose Street, London WC2E 9ET
Website: www.stageone.uk.com
e-mail: enquiries@stageone.uk.com
Fax: 020-7557 6799 Tel: 020-7557 6737

THEATRECARES
(Putting HIV & AIDS Centre Stage)
1st Floor, 1-5 Curtain Road, London EC2A 3JX
Website: www.theatrecares.org.uk
e-mail: office@theatrecares.org.uk Tel: 020-7539 3880

THEATRE MUSEUM The
1E Tavistock Street, London WC2E 7PR
Website: www.vam.ac.uk/theatre
e-mail: tmenquiries@vam.ac.uk
Fax: 020-7943 4777 Tel: 020-7943 4700

THEATRES TRUST The
22 Charing Cross Road, London WC2H 0QL
Website: www.theatrestrust.org.uk
e-mail: info@theatrestrust.org.uk
Fax: 020-7836 3302 Tel: 020-7836 8591

THEATRE WRITING PARTNERSHIP
Nottingham Playhouse
Wellington Circus, Nottingham NG1 5AF
e-mail: sarah@theatrewritingpartnership.org.uk
Fax: 0115-947 5759 Tel: 0115-947 4361

THEATRICAL GUILD The
PO Box 22712
London N22 5WQ
Website: www.ttg.org.uk
e-mail: admin@ttg.org.uk Tel: 020-8889 7570

THEATRICAL MANAGEMENT ASSOCIATION
(See TMA)

TMA
(Theatrical Management Association)
32 Rose Street, London WC2E 9ET
Website: www.tmauk.org
e-mail: enquiries@solttma.co.uk
Fax: 020-7557 6799 Tel: 020-7557 6700

UK CHOREOGRAPHERS' DIRECTORY The
(See DANCE UK)

UK FILM COUNCIL
10 Little Portland Street, London W1W 7JG
Website: www.ukfilmcouncil.org.uk
e-mail: info@ukfilmcouncil.org.uk
Fax: 020-7861 7862 Tel: 020-7861 7861

UK THEATRE CLUBS
54 Swallow Drive, London NW10 8TG
e-mail: uktheatreclubs@aol.com Tel/Fax: 020-8459 3972

UNITED KINGDOM COPYRIGHT BUREAU
110 Trafalgar Road
Portslade, East Sussex BN41 1GS
Website: www.copyrightbureau.co.uk
e-mail: info@copyrightbureau.co.uk
Fax: 01273 705451 Tel: 01273 277333

VARIETY & LIGHT ENTERTAINMENT COUNCIL
54 Keyes House
Dolphin Square, London SW1V 3NA
Fax: 020-7821 0261 Tel: 020-7798 5622

VARIETY CLUB CHILDREN'S CHARITY
Variety Club House
93 Bayham Street
London NW1 0AG
Website: www.varietyclub.org.uk
e-mail: info@varietyclub.org.uk
Fax: 020-7428 8111 Tel: 020-7428 8100

WOLFF Peter THEATRE TRUST The
Flat 22, 7 Princess Gate, London SW7 1QL
e-mail: pmwolff@msn.com Mobile: 07767 242552

WOMEN IN FILM AND TELEVISION
6 Langley Street, London WC2H 9JA
e-mail: info@wftv.org.uk
Fax: 020-7379 1625 Tel: 020-7240 4875

WRITERNET
Cabin V, Clarendon Buildings
25 Horsell Road, London N5 1XL
Website: www.writernet.org.uk
e-mail: info@writernet.org.uk
Fax: 020-7609 7557 Tel: 020-7609 7474

WRITERS' GUILD OF GREAT BRITAIN The
15-17 Britannia Street, London WC1X 9JN
Website: www.writersguild.org.uk
e-mail: admin@writersguild.org.uk
Fax: 020-7833 4777 Tel: 020-7833 0777

YOUTH MUSIC THEATRE: UK
1st Floor, Swiss Centre
10 Wardour Street
London W1D 6QF
Website: www.youth-music-theatre.org.uk
e-mail: mail@youth-music-theatre.org.uk Tel: 0870 240 5057

PHOTOGRAPHERS

ACTOR'S ONE-STOP SHOP
Website: www.actorsonestopshop.com
Tel: 020-8888 7006

ALLEN Stuart
Website: www.stuartallenphotos.com
Mobile: 07776 258829

AM LONDON
Website: www.am-london.com
Mobile: 07972 826065
Tel: 020-7193 1868

ANNAND Simon
Website: www.simonannand.com
Mobile: 07884 446776
Tel: 020-7241 6725

ARTSHOT.CO.UK
Website: www.artshot.co.uk
e-mail: angela@artshot.co.uk
Mobile: 07931 537363
Tel: 020-8521 7654

BACON Ric
Website: www.ricbacon.co.uk
Mobile: 07970 970799

BAILIE David PHOTOGRAPHY
Website: www.davidbailie.co.uk
e-mail: davidbailie@davidbailie.co.uk
Tel: 020-7603 6529

BAKER Chris
Website: www.chrisbakerphotographer.com
e-mail: chrisbaker@photos2000.demon.co.uk
Tel: 020-8441 3851

BAKER Sophie
Tel: 020-8340 3850

BARBER J.
Mobile: 07785 261513

BARRASS Paul
Website: www.paulbarrass.co.uk
Mobile: 07973 265931
Tel: 020-8533 1492

BARTLETT Pete
Website: www.petebartlett.com
e-mail: info@petebartlett.com
Mobile: 07971 653994

Photographers

Each photographer listed in this section has taken
an advertisement in this edition.
See Index to Advertisers pages 381-382
to view each advertisement.

Press Cutting Agencies
Promotional Services
(CVs, Showreels, Websites etc)
Properties & Trades
Publications
Publicity & Press Representatives

[CONTACTS 2008]

BEAN Jonathan
Website: www.beanphoto.co.uk
e-mail: mail@beanphoto.co.uk
Mobile: 07763 814587

BENNETT Graham
Website: www.grahambennett.biz
Tel: 020-8374 1697

BISHOP Brandon
Website: www.brandonbishopphotography.com
Mobile: 07931 383830
Tel: 020-7275 7468

BROWN Kelvin
Website: www.kelvinbrown.co.uk
Mobile: 07771 946640

BURNETT Sheila
Website: www.sheilaburnett-photography.com
Tel: 020-7289 3058

CABLE Paul
Website: www.paulcable.com
e-mail: info@paulcable.com
Mobile: 07958 932764

CAMILO Gustavo
Website: www.gcamilophotography.com
e-mail: info@gcamilophotography.com
Mobile: 07947 888247

CAMPLING Jon
Website: www.joncamplingheadshots.com
e-mail: photo@joncampling.com
Mobile: 07941 421101
Tel: 020-8679 8671

CLARK John
Website: www.johnclarkphotography.com
e-mail: info@johnclarkphotography.com
Mobile: 07702 627237
Tel: 020-8854 4069

DANCE SCENE PHOTOGRAPHIC
e-mail: dancepics4u.co.uk
Tel: 01737 552874

DEBAL
e-mail: debal@abeautifulimage.com
Tel: 020-8568 2122

DE LENG Stephanie
Website: www.stephaniedeleng.co.uk
e-mail: lookandsee@mac.com
Mobile: 07740 927765
Tel: 0151-476 1563

DE SOUZA Ava
Website: www.avadesouza.co.uk
Tel: 020-8392 9093

DEUCHAR Angus
Website: www.actorsphotos.co.uk
Mobile: 07973 600728
Tel: 020-8286 3303

DUNKIN Mary
Website: www.marydunkinphotography.co.uk
Tel: 020-8969 8043

DYE Debbie
Website: www.debbbiedye.com
Mobile: 07944 155454

GILCHRIST Paul
e-mail: pzgilchrist@hotmail.com
Tel: 07875 129747

GREGAN Nick
Website: www.nickgregan.com
e-mail: info@nickgregan.com
Mobile: 07774 421878
Tel: 020-8533 3003

GRÉGOIRE Stéphan
Website: www.studio-sg.com
Mobile: 07869 141510

GROGAN Claire
Website: www.clairegrogan.co.uk
Mobile: 07932 635381
Tel: 020-7272 1845

HALL Peter
Website: www.peterhall-photo.co.uk
e-mail: peter@peterhall.fsnet.co.uk
Mobile: 07803 345495   Tel: 020-8981 2822

HARWOOD-STAMPER Dan
Website: www.danharwoodstamper.co.uk
Mobile: 07779 165777

How do I find a photographer?

Having a good quality, up-to-date promotional headshot is crucial for every performer. Make sure you choose your photographer very carefully: do some research and try to look at different examples. Photographers' adverts run throughout this book, featuring many sample shots, although to get a real feel for their work you should also try to see their portfolio or website since this will give a more accurate impression of the quality of their photography.

If you live in or around London, please feel free to visit the Spotlight offices and look through current editions of our directories to find a style you like. We also have nearly sixty photographers' portfolios available for you to browse, many of them from photographers listed over the next few pages. Our offices are open Monday - Friday, 10.00am - 5.30pm at 7 Leicester Place, London WC2H 7RJ (nearest tube is Leicester Square).

The photo shoot

When it comes to your photo shoot, bear in mind that a casting director, agent or production company will want to see a photo of the 'real' you. Keep your appearance as neutral as possible so that they can imagine you in many different roles, rather than type-casting yourself from the outset and limiting your opportunities.

Your eyes are your most important feature, so make sure they are visible: face the camera straight-on and try not to smile too much because it makes them harder to see. Wear something simple and avoid jewellery, hats, scarves, glasses or props, since these will all add character. Do not wear clothes that detract from your face such as polo necks, big collars, busy patterns or logos. Always keep your hands out of the shot.

Also consider the background: some photographers like to do outdoor shots. A contrast between background and hair colour works well, whereas dark backgrounds work less well with dark hair, and the same goes for light hair on light backgrounds.

Choosing your photograph

When you get your contact sheet back from the photographer, make sure you choose a photo that looks like you - not how you would like to look. If you are unsure, ask friends or your agent for an honest opinion. Remember, you will be asked to attend meetings and auditions on the basis of your photograph, so if you turn up looking completely different you will be wasting everyone's time.

Due to copyright legislation, you must always credit the photographer when using the photo.

Submitting photos for Spotlight

The annual deadlines for submitting new photos for the Spotlight books are as follows:

- Actors: 15th October • Actresses: 15th April • Child Artists: 15th November
- Dancers: 15th June   • Graduates 2-3 year course: 15th October
- Postgraduates: 24th November • Presenters: 10th July

Photographers can get very busy, so try to start organising your photos a couple of months in advance.

Every Spotlight artist can also add extra photographs onto their web page, in addition to their 'principal photograph'. These are called 'portfolio photos', and they give you the opportunity to show yourself in a range of different shots and / or roles.

For more information please visit www.spotlight.com/artists/multimedia/portfolio.html

HASTINGS Magnus
Website: www.magnushastings.co.uk/headshots
Mobile: 07905 304705

HUGHES Jamie
Website: www.jamiehughesphotography.com
e-mail: jamie@jamiehughesphotography.com
Fax: 020-8355 8773
Mobile: 07850 122977

HUNTER Remy
Website: www.remyhunter.co.uk
Mobile: 07766 760724
Tel: 020-7431 8055

JAMES David
Website: www.davidjamesphotos.com
Mobile: 07808 597362

JAMES Nick
Website: www.nickjamesphotography.co.uk
Mobile: 07961 122030

JAMIE Matt
Website: www.mattjamie.co.uk/portraits

JEFFERSON Paris
Mobile: 07876 586601

JK PHOTOGRAPHY
Website: www.jk-photography.net
Mobile: 07816 825578

JONES Denis
Website: www.djpix.co.uk
Mobile: 07836 241158

JUDGE Tom
Website: www.tomjudge.co.uk
e-mail: mail@tomjudge.co.uk
Mobile: 07789 773489
Tel: 020-8671 9111

KEY.IMGS
Website: www.keyimageslondon.com
Mobile: 07872 008832

KOVAL STUDIO
Website: www.pitorkowalik.co.uk
e-mail: info@piotrkowalik.co.uk
mobile: 07946 323631

LACANDLER Stefan
Website: www.lacandler.com
e-mail: stefan@lacandler.com
Mobile: 07949 757457
Tel: 020-8509 7420

LADENBURG Jack
Website: www.jackladenburg.co.uk
e-mail: info@jackladenburg.co.uk
Mobile: 07932 053743

LATIMER Carole
Website: www.carolelatimer.com
e-mail: carole.latimer@freenet.co.uk
Tel: 020-7727 9371

LAWRENCE David
Website: www.davidlawrencephoto.co.uk
e-mail: david@davidlawrencephoto.co.uk
Tel: 020-8858 2820

LAWTON Steve
Website: www.stevelawton.com
Mobile: 07973 307487

L.B. PHOTOGRAPHY
Mobile: 07885 966192
Tel: 01737 224578

LE MAY Pete
Website: www.petelemay.co.uk
e-mail: photo@petelemay.co.uk
Mobile: 07703 649246

LENKA PHOTOGRAPHY
Website: www.galaxy-casting.com/photographer
e-mail: lenki13@yahoo.co.uk
Mobile: 07921 182055

LONEY Francis
e-mail: francisloney@talktalk.net
Mobile: 07753 634443
Tel: 020-7254 1199

M.A.D. PHOTOGRAPHY
Website: www.mad-photography.co.uk
e-mail: mad.photo@onetel.net
Mobile: 07949 581909
Tel: 020-8363 4182

MANN James
e-mail: james@actors-photography.com
Mobile: 07742 814160

MERCHANT-GREENBERG Natasha
Website: www.ngphotography.co.uk
Mobile: 07932 618111
Tel: 020-8653 5399

MOLLIÈRE Pascal
Website: www.pascalphoto.co.uk
e-mail: info@pascalphoto.co.uk
Mobile: 07713 242948

MOUNT Gemma
Website: www.gemmamountphotography.com
Mobile: 07976 824923

MULHOLLAND Ruth
Website: www.ruthmulholland.co.uk
Mobile: 07939 516987

NAMDAR Fatimah
e-mail: fn@fatimahnamdar.com
Mobile: 07973 287535
Tel: 020-8341 1332

NEWMAN-WILLIAMS Claire
Website: www.clairenewmanwilliams.com
e-mail: claire@clairenewmanwilliams.com
Mobile: 07963 967444

PADDON Jennifer
Website: www.jenniferpaddon.co.uk
Mobile: 07977 262827

PARKER Collette
Website: www.colletteparker.co.uk
e-mail: collette.parker@blueyonder.co.uk
Mobile: 07944 420625

PASSPORT PHOTO SERVICE
Website: www.passportphoto.co.uk
Tel: 020-7629 8540

POLLARD Michael
Website: www.michaelpollard.co.uk
e-mail: info@michaelpollard.co.uk
Tel: 0161-456 7470

PRICE David
Website: www.davidpricephotography.co.uk
e-mail: info@davidpricephotography.co.uk
Mobile: 07950 542494

PROFILE PHOTOGRAPHY
Website: www.profile-london.com
e-mail: info@profile-london.com
Mobile: 07971 431798
Tel: 020-7289 1088

RAFIQUE Harry
Website: www.hr-photographer.co.uk
Mobile: 07986 679498
Tel: 020-7266 5398

RICHMOND Eric
Website: www.ericrichmond.net
e-mail: eric@ericrichmond.net
Mobile: 07866 766240
Tel: 020-8880 6909

S. Mike
Website: www.mikephotos.co.uk
e-mail: mike@mbmphoto.fsnet.co.uk
Mobile: 07850 160311
Tel: 0121-323 4459

SAVAGE Rob
Website: www.robsavage.co.uk
Mobile: 07901 927597

SAYER Howard
Website: www.howardsayer.com
e-mail: howard@howardsayer.com
Mobile: 07860 559891

SCOTT Karen
Website: www.karenscottphotography.com
Mobile: 07958 975950

SHAKESPEARE LANE Catherine
Website: www.csl-art.co.uk
Tel: 020-7226 7694

SIBLEY David
Website: www.davidsibleyphotography.co.uk
e-mail: stockingfactory@hotmail.com
Mobile: 07740 587155

SKM STUDIO PHOTOGRAPHY
Website: www.skmstudio.com
e-mail: info@skmstudio.com
Mobile: 07974 159594
Tel: 01442 245555

SIMPKIN Peter
Website: www.petersimpkin.co.uk
e-mail: petersimpkin@aol.com
Mobile: 07973 224084
Tel: 020-8883 2727

SPARKLING PHOTOS
Website: www.sparklingphotos.com
e-mail: info@sparklingphotos.com
Mobile: 07948 806802

STILL Rosie
Website: www.rosiestillphotography.com
Tel: 020-8857 6920

SUGDEN Craig
Website: www.craigsugden.com
Mobile: 07967 380568
Tel: 020-8372 4435

SUMMERS Caroline
Website: www.homepage.mac.com/carolinesummers
Mobile: 07931 391234
Tel: 020-7223 7669

TARA PHOTOS
Website: taraphotos.net
Tel: 020-7435 7336

THOMAS Faye
Website: www.fayethomas.com
e-mail: fxt@blueyonder.co.uk
Mobile: 07813 449229

TM PHOTOGRAPHY
Website: www.tmphotography.co.uk
Mobile: 07931 755252
Tel: 020-7288 6846

TSANTILIS Dan
Website: www.dantsantilis.co.uk
Mobile: 07967 632216

ULLATHORNE Steve
Website: www.steveullathorne.com
Mobile: 07961 380969

USBORNE Martin
Website: www.martinusborne.com
Mobile: 07747 607930

VARLEY Luke
Website: www.lukevarley.com
Mobile: 07711 183631
Tel: 020-8674 9919

WHYTE Chalky
Website: www.chalkywhyte.co.uk
e-mail: chalkywhyte@supanet.com
Mobile: 07880 735912
Tel: 020-8960 9654

WILL C
Website: www.london-photographer.com
e-mail: billy_snapper@hotmail.com
Mobile: 07712 669953
Tel: 020-8438 0303

WINDHAM Marco
Mobile: 07768 330027
Tel: 020-7737 5954

WORKMAN Robert
Website: www.robertworkman.demon.co.uk
Tel: 020-7385 5442

PRESS CUTTING AGENCIES

DURRANTS
(Media Monitoring Agency)
Discovery House
28-42 Banner Street
London EC1Y 8QE
Website: www.durrants.co.uk
e-mail: sales@durrants.co.uk
Fax: 020-7674 0222   Tel: 020-7674 0200

INFORMATION BUREAU The
51 The Business Centre
103 Lavender Hill
London SW11 5QL
Website: www.informationbureau.co.uk
e-mail: info@informationbureau.co.uk
Fax: 020-7738 2513   Tel: 020-7924 4414

INTERNATIONAL PRESS-CUTTING BUREAU
224-236 Walworth Road
London SE17 1JE
e-mail: laura@ipcb.co.uk
Fax: 020-7701 4489   Tel: 020-7708 2113

McCALLUM MEDIA MONITOR
Tower House
10 Possil Road
Glasgow G4 9SY
Website: www.press-cuttings.com
Fax: 0141-333 1811   Tel: 0141-333 1822

TNS MEDIA INTELLIGENCE
66 Wilson Street
London EC2A 2JX
Website: www.tnsmi.co.uk
Fax: 020-7963 7609   Tel: 0870 2020100

What are Promotional services?

This section contains listings for a variety of companies who provide practical services which help performers to promote themselves effectively and professionally.

These include companies who can help artists to design and print their CVs; record a demo showreel; build their own websites; record voice-clips; duplicate CDs; or print photographic repros and Z-cards.

Why do I need to promote myself?

Performers need to invest in marketing and promotion as much as any other self-employed business-person: for example a plumber or a freelance make-up artist!

Even if you have trained at a leading drama school, have a well-known agent, or have just finished work on a popular TV series, you should never sit back and wait for your phone to ring or for the next job opportunity just to knock on your door. In such a competitive industry, successful performers are usually the ones who market themselves pro-actively and treat their careers as a 'business'.

Having up-to-date and well-produced promotional material makes a performer look professional and serious about their career: and hence an appealing person for a director or agent to work with.

The tools of the trade

Every performer should have a well-presented CV which is kept to a maximum of one page. Updates should be made regularly, including adding new credits, otherwise it may look as if you haven't been working and this can put some casting directors off.

Your CV should feature, or be accompanied by, a recent headshot which is an accurate current likeness. See the 'Photographers' section of Contacts for more information about promotional photography. You may need to print copies of your headshot through a repro company, some of whom are listed over the next few pages.

Up-to-date showreels and voice-reels are also invaluable promotional tools. These help casting directors and agents to build up a more detailed impression of your skills and your versatility, prior to meeting you. An actor's voice is in many ways as important as their physical appearance, so having a voice-reel should be as common as having a headshot photo.

Showreels and voice-reels should be professionally recorded and edited, with good sound and / or visual quality. Always use a variety of clips to demonstrate versatility, or a range of accents, pitch and tone. They can be extracts from previous work you've done, or recorded from scratch in a professional studio.

If you are a member of Spotlight, you should also add showreels and voice-reels to your online CV, for casting professionals to access via the Spotlight website.

Some performers also have their own websites where they feature more detail about themselves and their careers. Ideally the website should be professionally designed and updated regularly so as not to look amateur or out-of-date. Having a website can save money in the long-term since you may not need to send out as many copies of your CV, photos and showreels / voice-reels: you can just showcase them online.

How should I use these listings?

If you are looking for a company to help you with any of these promotional items, browse through this section carefully and get quotes from a number of places to compare. If you are a Spotlight member, some companies offer a discount on their services. Always ask to see samples of a company's work, and ask friends in the industry for their own recommendations.

A1 VOX Ltd
(Spoken Word Audio, ISDN Links, Demo CDs & Audio Clips)
20 Old Compton Street, London W1D 4TW
Website: www.a1vox.com
e-mail: info@a1vox.com
Tel: 020-7434 4404

ACTORS CV
(Print & Website Solutions)
17 Peabody Court, Martini Drive, Middlesex EN3 6GU
Website: www.actorscv.com
Tel: 01992 851082

ACTORS ILLUMINATED.COM
(Websites for Performing Artists)
90 Brondesbury Road
London NW6 6RX
Website: www.actorsilluminated.com
e-mail: mail@actorsilluminated.com Mobile: 07769 626074

ACTORS INTERACTIVE
(Web Design)
10 Frobisher Street
London SE10 9XB
Website: www.actorsinteractive.com
e-mail: office@actorsinteractive.com
Tel: 020-8465 5457

ACTOR'S ONE-STOP SHOP The
(Showreels for Performing Artists)
First Floor
Above The Gate Pub
Station Road, London N22 7SS
Website: www.actorsonestopshop.com
e-mail: info@actorsonestopshop.com Tel: 020-8888 7006

ACTUALLYACTORS.COM
(Websites)
3 Milestone Road
London SE19 2LL
Website: www.actuallyactors.com
e-mail: mail@actuallyactors.co.uk
Tel: 020-8325 1946

AN ACTOR PREPARES
70 Axminster Road
London N7 6BS
Website: www.an-actor-prepares.com
e-mail: s_b_management@hotmail.com Mobile: 07870 625701

BEWILDERING PICTURES
(Showreel Service) (Graeme Kennedy)
Flat 2, 8 Mildmay Park, London N1 4PD
Website: www.bewildering.co.uk
e-mail: gk@bewildering.co.uk
Mobile: 07974 916258
Tel: 020-7254 4116

CHASE Stephan PRODUCTIONS Ltd
(Director for Voice Overs and Showreels)
The Studio
22 York Avenue
London SW14 7LG
Website: www.stephanchase.com
e-mail: stephan@stephanchase.com
Tel: 020-8878 9112

CLICKS
Media Studios, Grove Road
Rochester
Kent ME2 4BX
e-mail: info@clicksstudios.co.uk
Fax: 01634 726000
Tel: 01634 723838

COURTWOOD PHOTOGRAPHIC Ltd
(Photographic Reproduction)
Profile Prints
Freepost TO55
Penzance, Cornwall TR18 2BF
Website: www.courtwood.co.uk
e-mail: people@courtwood.co.uk
Fax: 01736 350203
Tel: 01736 365222

CROWE Ben
(Voice Clip Recording)
23 John Aird Court
London W2 1UY
e-mail: bencrowe@hotmail.co.uk
Mobile: 07952 784911
Tel/Fax: 020-7262 3543

CRYING OUT LOUD
(Voice-Over Specialists/Voice-Over Demo CDs)
Website: www.cryingoutloud.co.uk
e-mail: simon@cryingoutloud.co.uk
Mobile: 07796 266265
Tel: 020-8980 0124

CRYSTAL MEDIA
28 Castle Street
Edinburgh EH2 3HT
Website: www.crystal-media.co.uk
e-mail: hello@crystal-media.co.uk
Fax: 0131-240 0989
Tel: 0131-240 0988

CUT GLASS PRODUCTIONS
(Voice-over Showreels/Voice-Over Production)
7 Crouch Hall Road
Crouch End
London N8 8HT
Website: www.cutglassproductions.com
e-mail: info@cutglassproductions.com Tel/Fax: 020-8374 470

DAEDALUS WEB DESIGN
Website: www.daedaluswebdesign.com
e-mail: info@daedaluswebdesign.com
Mobile: 07923 479419

DARK SIDE
(Photographic Repro Service)
4 Helmet Row
London EC1V 3QJ
Website: www.darksidephoto.co.uk
e-mail: info@darksidephoto.co.uk
Fax: 020-7250 1771   Tel: 020-7250 1200

DBUG MULTIMEDIA
(Showreels)
39A Ridgemount Gardens
London WC1E 7AT
Website: www.dbug.info
e-mail: info@dbug.info   Tel: 020-8393 8062

DENBRY REPROS Ltd
(Photographic Reproduction)
57 High Street
Hemel Hempstead
Herts HP1 3AF
e-mail: info@denbryrepros.com
Fax: 01442 242431   Tel: 01442 242411

DESIGN CREATIVES & OCTOPUS REACH
(Artistic Promotions & Graphic/Web Design & Hosting,
Anthony Rosato)
Suite B, 5 South Bank Terrace
Surbiton
Surrey KT6 6DG
Website: www.octopusreach.com
e-mail: octopusreach1@aol.com
Mobile: 07884 056405   Tel/Fax: 020-8390 8535

EXECUTIVE AUDIO VISUAL
(Showreels for Actors & Presenters)
80 York Street
London W1H 1QW   Tel/Fax: 020-7723 4488

FLYING DUCKS GROUP Ltd The
(Conference, Multimedia & Video Production)
Oakridge, Weston Road, Staffordshire ST16 3RS
Website: www.flyingducks.biz
e-mail: enquiries@flyingducks.biz
Fax: 01785 252448   Tel: 01785 610966

FREEDALE PRESS
(Printing)
36 Hedley Street, Maidstone, Kent ME14 5AD
e-mail: michael@freedale.co.uk
Fax: 01622 200131   Tel: 01622 200123

GENESIS UK.COM Ltd
18 Pendre Enterprise Park, Tywyn, Gwynedd LL36 9LW
Website: www.genesis-uk.com
e-mail: info@genesis-uk.com
Fax: 01654 712461   Tel: 01654 710137

HOTREELS
(Voice & Showreels)
Website: www.hotreels.co.uk
e-mail: info@hotreels.co.uk
Mobile: 07947 108132   Tel: 020-7952 4362

HOUSE OF WEB
(Voice and Showreels)
Website: www.hotreels.co.uk
e-mail: info@hotreels.co.uk
Mobile: 07947 108132   Tel: 020-7952 4362

HOUSE OF WEB
(Web Design)
16 Duncombe House, Windlesham Grove, London SW19 6AJ
Website: www.houseofweb.co.uk
e-mail: marte@houseofweb.co.uk   Mobile: 07962 471118

IMAGE PHOTOGRAPHIC
(Photographic Reproduction)
54 Shepherds Bush Road, London W6 7PH
Website: www.imagephotographic.com
e-mail: sales@imagephotographic.com
Fax: 020-7602 6219   Tel: 020-7602 1190

web design
- custom designed websites
  for agents/actors/models etc
- client managed databases
- low cost

www.tmphotography.co.uk **020 7288 6846**

tm photography & design ltd
suite 228, business design centre
islington, london, N1 0QH

INIMITABLE
(Flash Website Design)
PO Box 147, Dewsbury WF12 0WZ
Website: www.inimitable.us
e-mail: info@inimitable.us

MEDIAWEBS
(Graphic & Web Design)
20 Parker Road
Millbank Place, Colchester CO4 5BE
Website: www.mediawebs.co.uk
e-mail: jon@mediawebs.co.uk   Mobile: 07887 480241

MINAMON FILM
(Specialist in Showreels)
117 Downton Avenue, London SW2 3TX
e-mail: min@minamonfilm.co.uk
Fax: 020-8674 1779   Tel: 020-8674 3957

MOTIVATION SOUND STUDIOS
35A Broadhurst Gardens, London NW6 3QT
Website: www.motivationsound.co.uk
e-mail: info@motivationsound.co.uk
Fax: 020-7624 4879   Tel: 020-7328 8305

MYCLIPS
Flat 1
2 Blackdown Close
East Finchley
London N2 8JF
Website: www.myclipsdvd.com
e-mail: info@myclipsdvd.com   Tel: 020-8371 9526

PERFORMERS ONLINE Ltd
(Design, Web & Print)
18B High Street
London N8 7PB
Website: www.performersonline.co.uk
e-mail: info@performersonline.co.uk   Tel: 020-8347 0221

PROFILE PRINTS
(Photographic Reproduction)
Unit 2, Plot 1A
Rospeath Industrial Estate
Crowlas TR20 8DU
Website: www.courtwood.co.uk
e-mail: sales@courtwood.co.uk
Fax: 01736 350203   Tel: 01736 365222

Z-cards

- Send your photographs
- Supply text
- Proof sent
- Delivery anywhere in UK

Did you know we can
supply a range of Z-cards to
include your Spotlight
PIN NUMBER?

Contact: Michael Freeman ■ Mobile: 07734 193049 ■ e-mail: michael@freedale.co.uk
Freedale Press ■ 36 Hedley Street, Maidstone, Kent ME14 5AD ■ Tel: 01622 200123 ■ Fax: 01622 200131

REPLAY Ltd
(Showreels & Performance Recording)
Museum House
25 Museum Street, London WC1A 1JT
Website: www.replayfilms.co.uk
e-mail: sales@replayfilms.co.uk   Tel: 020-7637 0473

ROUND ISLAND SHOWREELS
(Ben Warren)
Website: www.roundisland.net
e-mail: mail@roundisland.net   Mobile: 07701 093183

SCARLET INTERNET
Suite 4
5 Market Square, Bishop's Stortford, Herts CM23 3UT
Website: www.scarletinternet.com
e-mail: info@scarletinternet.com
Fax: 0870 2241418   Tel: 0870 7771820

SHAW Bernard
(Specialist in Recording & Directing Voice Tapes)
Horton Manor
Canterbury CT4 7LG
Website: www.bernardshaw.co.uk
e-mail: bernard@bernardshaw.co.uk   Tel/Fax: 01227 730843

SHOWREELS 1
c/o Noughtie Casting Studios
45-46 Poland Street
London W1F 7NA
Website: www.ukscreen.com/company/showreels1
e-mail: showreels1@aol.com
Fax: 020-7437 2830   Mobile: 07932 021232

SHOWREEL The
(Voice-Over Showreels, Digital Editing etc)
Knightsbridge House
229 Acton Lane
Chiswick, London W4 5DD
Website: www.theshowreel.com
e-mail: info@theshowreel.com
Fax: 020-8995 2144   Tel: 020-7043 8660

SHOWREELZ
59 Church Street
St Albans
Herts AL3 5NG
Website: www.showreelz.com
e-mail: brad@showreelz.com
Mobile: 07885 253477   Tel: 01727 752960

SILVER-TONGUED PRODUCTIONS
(Specializing in the recording and production of
Voice Reels)
178 Ramillies Road
Sidcup DA15 9JH
Website: www.silver-tongued.co.uk
e-mail: contactus@silver-tongued.co.uk   Tel: 020-8309 0659

SMALL SCREEN SHOWREELS
The Production Office
17 Knole Road
Dartford
Kent DA1 3JN
Website: www.smallscreenshowreels.co.uk
e-mail: info@smallscreenshowreels.co.uk   Tel: 020-8816 8896

SMALL SCREEN VIDEO
(Showreels)
The Production Office
Small Screen Video
17 Knole Road
Dartford, Kent DA1 3JN
Website: www.smallscreenshowreels.co.uk
e-mail: showreels@smallscreenvideo.com   Tel: 020-8816 8896

STAGES CAPTURE THE MOMENT
(Showreels)
31 Evensyde
Croxley Green
Watford, Herts WD18 8WN
Website: www.stagescapturethemoment.com/showreels
e-mail: info@stagescapturethemoment.com
    Tel: 020-7193 8519

SUPPORT ACT SERVICES
(Ian McCracken) (CD Duplication & Web Design)
243A Lynmouth Avenue
Morden
Surrey SM4 4RX
Website: www.supportact.co.uk
e-mail: info@supportact.co.uk　　　Tel: 0845 0940796

TAKE FIVE CASTING STUDIO
(Showreels)
37 Beak Street
London W1F 9RZ
Website: www.takefivestudio.com
e-mail: info@takefivestudio.com
Fax: 020-7287 3035　　　Tel: 020-7287 2120

TM DESIGN SERVICES
(Web Design, Model Cards, Actors CVs)
Website: www.tmphotography.co.uk
e-mail: info@tmphotography.co.uk　　　Tel: 020-7288 6846

TOP TV ACADEMY
(Showreels)
309 Kentish Town Road
London NW5 2TJ
Website: www.toptvacademy.co.uk
e-mail: admin@toptvacademy.co.uk
Fax: 020-7485 7536　　　Tel: 020-7267 3530

TOUCHWOOD AUDIO PRODUCTIONS
6 Hyde Park Terrace
Leeds
West Yorkshire LS6 1BJ
Website: www.touchwoodaudio.com
e-mail: bruce@touchwoodaudio.com　　　Tel: 0113-278 7180

TTA PRODUCTIONS
34A Pollard Road
Morden, Surrey SM4 6EG
Website: www.tv-training.co.uk
e-mail: contact@tv-training.co.uk　　　Tel: 020-8665 2275

VISUALEYES IMAGING SERVICES
(Photographic Reproduction)
11 West Street
London WC2H 9NE
Website: www.visimaging.co.uk
e-mail: sales@visimaging.co.uk
Fax: 020-7240 0079　　　Tel: 020-7836 3004

VOICE MASTER
(Specialized Training for Voice-overs & TV Presenters)
88 Erskine Hill
London NW11 6HR
Website: www.voicemaster.co.uk
e-mail: stevehudson@voicemaster.co.uk　Tel: 020-8455 2211

VOICE OVER DEMOS
61 Cropley Street
London N1 7JB
Website: www.voiceoverdemos.co.uk
e-mail: daniel@voiceoverdemos.co.uk　　Tel: 020-7684 1645

VOICE TAPE SERVICES INTERNATIONAL Ltd
(Professional Voice-Over Direction & CDs)
80 Netherlands Road
New Barnet
Herts EN5 1BS
Website: www.vtsint.co.uk
e-mail: info@vtsint.co.uk
Fax: 020-8441 4828　　　Tel: 020-8440 4848

7000 BIG TOP
(Big Top, Seating, Circus)
The Arts Exchange, Congleton, Cheshire CW12 1JG
Website: www.arts-exchange.com
e-mail: phillipgandey@netcentral.co.uk
Fax: 01260 270777   Tel: 01260 276627

10 OUT OF 10 PRODUCTIONS Ltd
(Lighting, Sound, AV Hire, Sales & Installation)
Orchard Business Centre
Langley Bridge Road, London SE26 5AQ
Website: www.10outof10.co.uk
e-mail: sales@10outof10.co.uk
Fax: 020-8778 9217   Tel: 0845 1235664

3D CREATIONS
(Production Design, Scenery Contractors, Prop Makers &
Scenic Artists)
A Bells Road, Gorleston-on-Sea
Great Yarmouth, Norfolk NR31 6BB
Website: www.3dcreations.co.uk
e-mail: 3dcreations@rjt.co.uk
Fax: 01493 443124   Tel: 01493 652055

ACROBAT PRODUCTIONS
(Artistes & Advisors)
2 Oaklands Court, Hempstead Road, Watford WD17 4LF
Website: www.acrobatproductions.com
e-mail: info@acrobatproductions.com   Tel: 01923 224938

ACTIONAID RECYCLING MOBILE PHONE PROPS
4 Kingsland Trading Estate
St Phillips Road, Bristol BS2 0JZ
Website: www.actionaidrecycling.org.uk/props
e-mail: props@aarecycling.org.uk
Fax: 0117-3042396   Tel: 0845 3100200

ADAMS ENGRAVING
Unit G1A, The Mayford Centre
Mayford Green, Woking GU22 0PP
Website: www.adamsengraving.co.uk
e-mail: adamsengraving@pncl.co.uk
Fax: 01483 751787   Tel: 01483 725792

AIRBOURNE SYSTEMS INTERNATIONAL
(All Skydiving Requirements Arranged. Parachute Hire -
Period & Modern)
8 Burns Crescent, Chelmsford
Essex CM2 0TS   Tel: 01245 268772

ALCHEMICAL LABORATORIES ETC
(Medieval Science & Technology Recreated for
Museums & Films)
2 Stapleford Lane, Coddington
Newark, Nottinghamshire NG24 2QZ
Website: www.jackgreene.co.uk   Tel: 01636 707836

ALL SCENE ALL PROPS
(Props, Masks, Painting & Scenery Makers)
Units 2 & 3, Spelmonden Farm, Goudhurst, Kent TN17 1HE
Website: www.allscene.net   e-mail: info@allscene.net
Fax: 01580 211131   Tel: 01580 211121

ANELLO & DAVIDE
(Handmade Shoes)
15 St Albans Grove, London W8 5BP
Website: www.handmadeshoes.co.uk   Tel: 020-7938 2255

ANGLO PACIFIC INTERNATIONAL Plc
(Freight Forwarders & Removal Services)
5-9 Willenfield Road, Park Row
London NW10 7BQ
Website: www.anglopacific.co.uk
Fax: 020-8965 4954   Tel: 020-8965 1234

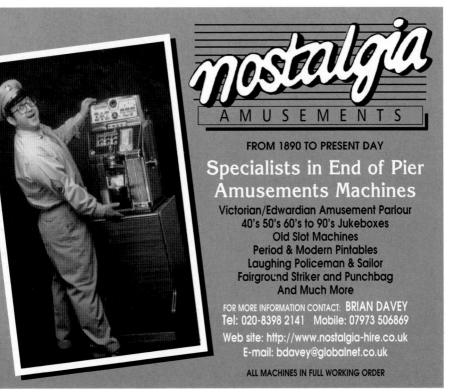

ANIMAL ARK
(Animals & Natural History Props)
The Studio, 29 Somerset Road
Brentford, Middlesex TW8 8BT
Website: www.animal-ark.co.uk
e-mail: info@animal-ark.co.uk
Fax: 020-8560 5762   Tel: 020-8560 3029

ANNUAL CLOWNS DIRECTORY The
(Salvo The Clown)
13 Second Avenue, Kingsleigh Park
Thundersley, Essex SS7 3QD
Website: www.annualclownsdirectory.com
e-mail: salvo@annualclownsdirectory.com Tel: 01268 745791

AQUARIUS
(Film & TV Stills Library)
PO Box 5, Hastings TN34 1HR
Website: www.aquariuscollection.com
e-mail: aquarius.lib@clara.net
Fax: 01424 717704   Tel: 01424 721196

AQUATECH
(Camera Boats)
Cobbies Rock, Epney, Gloucestershire GL2 7LN
Website: www.aquatech-uk.com
e-mail: office@aquatech-uk.com
Fax: 01452 741958   Tel: 01452 740559

ARCHERY CENTRE The
PO Box 39, Battle
East Sussex TN33 0ZT   Tel: 01424 777183

ARMS & ARCHERY
(Armour, Weaponry, Chainmail, X-bows, Longbows, Tents)
The Coach House, London Road, Ware, Herts SG12 9QU
e-mail: armsandarchery@btconnect.com Tel: 01920 460335

ART*
(Art Consultant, Supplier of Paintings & Sculpture)
89 Spencer Road, Mitcham CR4 1SJ
Website: www.artstar.clara.net
e-mail: h_artstar@hotmail.com
Fax: 07970 455956   Mobile: 07967 294985

ART DIRECTORS & TRIP PHOTO LIBRARY
(Digital Scans, Colour Slides - All Subjects)
57 Burdon Lane, Cheam, Surrey SM2 7BY
Website: www.artdirectors.co.uk
e-mail: images@artdirectors.co.uk
Fax: 020-8395 7230   Tel: 020-8642 3593

A. S. DESIGNS
(Theatrical Designer, Sets, Costumes, Heads, Masks,
Puppets etc)
Website: www.astheatricaldesign.co.uk
e-mail: maryannscadding@btinternet.com
Fax: 01279 435642   Tel: 01279 722416

ASH Riky
(Equity Registered Stunt Performer/Co-ordinator)
8 Balmoral Drive, Grantham NG31 8SY
Website: www.fallingforyou.tv
Mobile: 07850 471227   Tel: 0115-849 3470

AWESOME
(Designers & Manufacturers of Bespoke Upholstery)
The Stables, Grange Farm
Green End, Great Stukeley
Huntingdon, Cambridgeshire PE28 4AE
Website: www.awesome.eu.com
e-mail: glenn@awesome.eu.com
Fax: 01480 464879   Tel: 01480 457007

BAPTY 2000 Ltd
(Weapons, Dressing, Props etc)
Witley Works, Witley Gardens
Norwood Green, Middlesex UB2 4ES
e-mail: hire@bapty.demon.co.uk
Fax: 020-8571 5700   Tel: 020-8574 770■

BARNES CATERERS Ltd
9 Ripley Drive, Normanton, Wakefield
West Yorkshire WF6 1QT   Tel/Fax: 01924 89233■

BARTON Joe
(Puppeteer, Model & Prop Maker)
7 Brands Hill Avenue, High Wycombe
Buckinghamshire   Tel: 01494 43905■

BEAT ABOUT THE BUSH Ltd
(Musical Instrument Hire)
Unit 23, Enterprise Way, Triangle Business Centre
Salter Street (Off Hythe Road), London NW10 6UG
Website: www.beataboutthebush.com
e-mail: info@beataboutthebush.com
Fax: 020-8969 2281   Tel: 020-8960 208■

BEAVEROCK PRODUCTIONS Ltd
(Location & Transport services)
404A Glasgow Road, Clydebank
West Dunbartonshire G81 1PW
Website: www.beaverockproductions.com
e-mail: info@beaverockproductions.com
                                     Tel/Fax: 0141-952 043■

BIANCHI AVIATION FILM SERVICES
(Historic & Other Aircraft)
Wycombe Air Park, Booker Marlow
Buckinghamshire SL7 3DP
Website: www.bianchiaviation.com
e-mail: info@bianchiaviation.com
Fax: 01494 461236   Tel: 01494 44981■

BIDDLES Ltd
(Quality Book Binders & Printers)
24 Rollesby Road, Hardwick Industrial Estate
King's Lynn, Norfolk PE30 4LS
Website: www.biddles.co.uk
e-mail: enquiries@biddles.co.uk
Fax: 01553 764633   Tel: 01553 76472■

BIG BREAK CARDS
(Theatrical greetings cards featuring Hamlet the Pig, made
by actors for actors)
PO Box 45, Chipping Camden GL55 6WH
Website: www.bigbreakcards.co.uk
e-mail: info@bigbreakcards.co.uk   Tel: 01386 43895

BLUEBELL RAILWAY Plc
(Steam Locomotives, Pullman Coaches, Period Stations,
Much Film Experience)
Sheffield Park Station, East Sussex TN22 3QL
Website: www.bluebell-railway.co.uk
Fax: 01825 720804   Tel: 01825 72080■

BLUE MILL Ltd
(Dyers & Finishers)
84 Halstead Street, Leicester LE5 3RD
Website: www.bluemill.co.uk   e-mail: tom@bluemill.co.u■
Fax: 0116-253 7633   Tel: 0116-248 813■

BOLD BLUE DESIGN Ltd
(Design, Web & Print)
18B High Street, London N8 7PB
Website: www.boldblue.co.uk
e-mail: info@boldblue.co.uk
Mobile: 07985 245971   Tel: 020-8347 022■

OLDGATE COMMERCIAL SERVICES Ltd
he Crossbow Centre
0 Liverpool Road
lough, Berkshire SL1 4QZ
ax: 01753 610587   Tel: 01753 610525

OSCO LIGHTING
Design/Technical Consultancy)
7 Woodbourne Avenue, London SW16 1UX
-mail: boscolx@lineone.net   Tel: 020-8769 3470

OUNCY CASTLES BY P. A. LEISURE
Specialists in Amusements & Fairground Equipment)
elph House, Park Bridge Road
owneley Park, Burnley, Lancs BB10 4SD
Vebsite: www.paleisure.com
-mail: paleisure@btconnect.com
ax: 01282 420467   Tel: 01282 453939

RISTOL (UK) Ltd
Scenic Paint & StageFloor Duo Suppliers, VFX Solutions)
nit 3, Sutherland Court
olpits Lane, Watford WD18 9SP
Vebsite: www.bristolpaint.com
ax: 01923 779666   Tel: 01923 779333

RITISH-FOOD-GROCERIES
3ritish Food Export Service for British People Working
verseas)
6 Burrage Place, Plumstead, London SE18 7BE
Vebsite: www.british-food-groceries.co.uk
-mail: sales@directfoods.uk.com   Tel/Fax: 01322 448272

RODIE & MIDDLETON Ltd
Theatrical Suppliers, Paints, Powders, Glitter etc)
8 Drury Lane, London WC2B 5SP
Vebsite: www.brodies.net
-mail: info@brodies.net
ax: 020-7497 0554   Tel: 020-7836 3289

ULL Richard OCEANAIRE DIVING SERVICES Ltd
4 Townsend, Lower Almondsbury
outh Gloucestershire BS32 4EN
-mail: richard.bull6@btopenworld.com
lobile: 07766 674356   Tel/Fax: 01454 613357

AMDEN ATTIC
Period Prop Hire & Making)
ocation House
Dove Lane, Bristol BS2 9HP
Vebsite: www.camdenattic.co.uk
-mail: gene.lowson@virgin.net
ax: 0117-955 2480   Tel: 0117-941 1969

ANDLE MAKERS SUPPLIES
he Wax & Dyecraft Centre
8 Blythe Road, London W14 0HA
Vebsite: www.candlemakers.co.uk
-mail: candles@candlemakers.co.uk
ax: 020-7602 2796   Tel: 020-7602 4031

HALFONT CLEANERS & DYERS Ltd
Dry Cleaners, Launderers & Dyers, Stage Curtains &
ostumes)
22 Baker Street, London NW1 5RT   Tel: 020-7935 7316

HEVALIER EVENT DESIGN
Corporate Hospitality Caterers)
tudio 4-5, Garnett Close
Vatford, Herts WD24 7GN
Vebsite: www.chevalier.co.uk
-mail: enquiries@chevalier.co.uk
ax: 01923 211704   Tel: 01923 211703

CHRISANNE Ltd
(Specialist Fabrics & Accessories for Theatre & Dance)
Chrisanne House
14 Locks Lane, Mitcham, Surrey CR4 2JX
Website: www.chrisanne.co.uk
e-mail: sales@chrisanne.co.uk
Fax: 020-8640 2106   Tel: 020-8640 5921

CIRCUS MANIACS
(Circus Equipment, Rigging & Training)
Office 8A, The Kingswood Foundation
Britannia Road, Kingswood, Bristol BS15 8DB
Website: www.circusmaniacs.com
e-mail: info@circusmaniacs.com
Mobile: 07977 247287   Tel/Fax: 0117-947 7042

CIRCUS PROMOTIONS
(Entertainers)
36 St Lukes Road, Tunbridge Wells
Kent TN4 9JH   Tel: 01892 537964

CLEANING & FLAME RETARDING SERVICE The
Grove Farm, Grove Farm Road
Tolleshunt Major, Maldon, Essex CM4 8LR
Website: www.flameretarding.co.uk
e-mail: email@flameretarding.co.uk
Fax: 07092 036931   Tel: 01621 818477

COBO MEDIA Ltd
(Performing Arts, Entertainment & Leisure Marketing)
43A Garthorne Road, London SE23 1EP
Website: www.theatrenet.com
e-mail: admin@cobomedia.com
Fax: 020-8291 4969   Tel: 020-8291 7079

COMPTON Mike & Rosi
(Costumes, Props & Models)
11 Woodstock Road, Croydon, Surrey CR0 1JS
e-mail: mikeandrosicompton@btopenworld.com
Fax: 020-8681 3126   Tel: 020-8680 4364

CONCEPT ENGINEERING Ltd
(Smoke, Fog, Snow etc)
7 Woodlands Business Park
Woodlands Park Avenue, Maidenhead
Berkshire SL6 3UA
Website: www.concept-smoke.co.uk
Fax: 01628 826261   Tel: 01628 825555

COOK Sheila TEXTILES
(Textiles, Costumes & Accessories for Hire/Sale)
105-107 Portobello Road, London W11 2QB
Website: www.sheilacook.co.uk
e-mail: sheilacook@sheilacook.co.uk   Tel: 020-7792 8001

CREATIVE WORKS UK Ltd
(Floral Design)
Unit 1, The Stable Block
Brewer Street
Bletchingley, Surrey RH1 4QP
Website: www.ckworks.net
e-mail: info@ckworks.net   Tel: 01883 742999

CRESTA BLINDS Ltd
(Supplier of Vertical Blinds)
Crown Works, Tetnall Street, Dudley DY2 8SA
Website: www.crestablindsltd.co.uk
e-mail: info@crestablindsltd.co.uk
Fax: 01384 457675   Tel: 01384 255523

CROCKSHARD FARMHOUSE
(Bed & Breakfast, Contact: Nicola Ellen)
Wingham, Canterbury, Kent CT3 1NY
Website: www.crockshard.com
e-mail: crockshard_bnb@yahoo.com   Tel: 01227 720464

CROFTS Andrew
(Book Writing Services)
Westlands Grange, West Grinstead
Horsham, West Sussex RH13 8LZ
Website: www.andrewcrofts.com   Tel/Fax: 01403 864518

CUE ACTION POOL PROMOTIONS
(Advice for UK & US Pool, Snooker, Trick Shots)
PO Box 3941
Colchester, Essex CO2 8HN
Website: www.stevedaking.com
e-mail: sales@cueaction.com
Fax: 01206 729480   Tel: 07000 868689

DAVEY Brian
(See NOSTALGIA AMUSEMENTS)

DESIGN ASYLUM
(Design, Web & Print)
Unit 2, 6 Chase Road, Park Royal, London NW1 6HZ
Website: www.designasylum.co.uk
e-mail: info@designasylum.co.uk   Tel: 020-8838 355

DESIGN PROJECTS
Perrysfield Farm, Broadham Green
Old Oxted, Surrey RH8 9PG
Website: www.designprojects.co.uk
Fax: 01883 723707   Tel: 01883 73026

DEVEREUX DEVELOPMENTS Ltd
(Removals, Haulage, Trucking)
Daimler Drive
Cowpen Industrial Estate
Billingham, Cleveland TS23 4JD
Fax: 01642 566664   Tel: 01642 56085

DORANS PROPMAKERS/SET BUILDERS
53 Derby Road, Ashbourne, Derbyshire DE6 1BH
Website: www.doransprops.com
e-mail: props@dorans.demon.co.uk   Tel/Fax: 01335 30006

DRIVING CENTRE The
(Expert Driving Instructors on All Vehicles)
6 Marlott Road, Poole, Dorset BH15 3DX
Mobile: 07860 290437   Tel: 01202 6660

DURRENT Peter
(Audition & Rehearsal Pianist, Cocktail Pianist, Composer,
Vocalist)
Blacksmiths Cottage
Bures Road, Little Cornard
Sudbury, Suffolk CO10 0NR   Tel: 01787 37348

EAT TO THE BEAT
(Production & Location Caterers)
Studio 4-5, Garnett Close, Watford, Herts WD24 7GN
Website: www.eattothebeat.com
e-mail: enquiries@eattothebeat.com
Fax: 01923 211704   Tel: 01923 21170

ECCENTRIC TRADING COMPANY Ltd
(Antique Furniture & Props) incorporating COMPUHIRE
(Computer Hire)
Unit 2, Frogmore Estate, Acton Lane, London NW10 7NQ
Website: www.compuhire.com
e-mail: info@compuhire.com   Tel: 020-8453 112

ELECTRO SIGNS Ltd
97 Vallentin Road, London E17 3JJ
Fax: 020-8520 8127   Tel: 020-8521 806

ELMS LESTERS PAINTING ROOMS
(Scenic Painting)
1-3-5 Flitcroft Street, London WC2H 8DH
e-mail: office@elmslesters.co.uk
Fax: 020-7379 0789   Tel: 020-7836 674

ESCORT GUNLEATHER
(Custom Leathercraft)
602 High Road, Benfleet, Essex SS7 5RW
Website: www.escortgunleather.com
e-mail: info@escortgunleather.com
Fax: 01268 566775   Tel: 0870 751595

EVANS Peter STUDIOS Ltd
(Scenic Embellishment, Vacuum Forming)
12-14 Tavistock Street, Dunstable, Bedfordshire LU6 1NE
e-mail: sales@peterevansstudios.co.uk
Fax: 01582 481329   Tel: 01582 72573

-LOANS
oom 42, Millfield Business Centre
M House, Ashwells Road
entwood, Essex CM15 9ST
ebsite: www.floans.co.uk
mail: pb@floans.co.uk
ax: 01277 375808   Tel: 0845 0656267

ACADE
Musical Production Services)
3A Garthorne Road, London SE23 1EP
mail: facade@cobomedia.com   Tel: 020-8291 7079

AIRGROUNDS TRADITIONAL
alstead, Fovant
alisbury, Wiltshire SP3 5NL
ebsite: www.pozzy.co.uk
mail: sv@pozzy.co.uk
obile: 07710 287251   Tel: 01722 714786

ILM MEDICAL SERVICES
nits 5 & 7, Commercial Way
ark Royal, London NW10 7XF
ebsite: www.filmmedical.co.uk
mail: filmmed@aol.com
ax: 020-8961 7427   Tel: 020-8961 3222

IND ME ANOTHER
heatrical Prop Hire & Services. Gardenalia, Kitchenalia,
airy & Farming Bygones. Some 1960's)
ppointment Only) Mill Barns
o 10 Tenzing Grove
uton, Bedfordshire LU1 5JJ
ebsite: www.findmeanother.co.uk
mail: info@findmeanother.co.uk
obile: 07885 777751   Tel/Fax: 01582 415834

IREBRAND
Iambeaux Hire & Sales)
eac Na Ban, Tayvallich
y Lochgilphead, Argyll PA31 8PF
mail: firebrand.props@btinternet.com
    Tel/Fax: 01546 870310

LAMENCO PRODUCTIONS
ntertainers)
evilla 4 Cormorant Rise
ower Wick
orcester WR2 4BA   Tel: 01905 424083

LINT HIRE & SUPPLY Ltd
ueen's Row, London SE17 2PX
ebsite: www.flints.co.uk
mail: sales@flints.co.uk
ax: 020-7708 4189   Tel: 020-7703 9786

LYING BY FOY
lying Effects for Theatre, TV, Corporate Events etc)
nit 4, Borehamwood Enterprise Centre
heobald Street, Borehamwood
erts WD6 4RQ
ebsite: www.flyingbyfoy.co.uk
mail: mail@flyingbyfoy.co.uk
ax: 020-8236 0235   Tel: 020-8236 0234

FOXTROT PRODUCTIONS Ltd
(Armoury Services, Firearms, Weapons & Costume Hire)
Unit 46 Canalot Production Studios
222 Kensal Road, London W10 5BN   Tel: 020-8964 3555

FREEDALE PRESS
(Printing)
36 Hedley Street
Maidstone, Kent ME14 5AD
e-mail: michael@freedale.co.uk
Fax: 01622 200131   Tel: 01622 200123

FROST John NEWSPAPERS
(Historical Newspaper Service)
22B Rosemary Avenue, Enfield, Middlesex EN2 0SS
Website: www.johnfrostnewspapers.com
e-mail: andrew@johnfrostnewspapers.com
    Tel: 020-8366 1392

GARRATT Jonathan FRSA
(Suppliers of Traditional & Unusual Garden Pots &
Installations. Glazed Tableware)
Hare Lane Farmhouse
Cranborne, Dorset BH21 5QT
Website: www.jonathangarratt.com
e-mail: jonathan.garratt@talk21.com   Tel: 01725 517700

GAV NICOLA THEATRICAL FOOTWEAR
West Wick, Marshes
Burnham-on-Crouch, Essex CM0 8NE
e-mail: sale@gavnicola.freeserve.co.uk
Mobile: 07961 974278   Tel/Fax: 01621 785623

GET STUFFED
(Taxidermy)
105 Essex Road, London N1 2SL
Website: www.thegetstuffed.co.uk
e-mail: taxidermy@thegetstuffed.co.uk
Fax: 020-7359 8253   Tel: 020-7226 1364

GHOSTWRITER/AUTHOR
(John Parker)
21 Hindsleys Place, London SE23 2NF
e-mail: parkerwrite@aol.com   Tel: 020-8244 5816

GLOBAL CEILINGS & TILES
(Designers, Suppliers, Installers)
1B Argyle Road, Argyle Corner, Ealing, London W13 0LL
Website: www.globalceiling.co.uk
Mobile: 07976 159402   Tel: 020-8810 5914

GORGEOUS GOURMETS Ltd
(Caterers & Equipment Hire)
Gresham Way, Wimbledon SW19 8ED
Website: www.gorgeousgourmets.co.uk
e-mail: antoniaf@gorgeousgourmets.co.uk
Fax: 020-8946 1639   Tel: 020-8944 7771

GOULD Gillian ANTIQUES
(Scientific & Marine Antiques & Collectables)
18A Belsize Park Gardens, Belsize Park, London NW3 4LH
Website: www.gilliangouldantiques.co.uk
e-mail: gillgould@dealwith.com
Mobile: 07831 150060   Tel: 020-7419 0500

GRADAV HIRE & SALES Ltd
(Lighting & Sound Hire/Sales)
Units C6 & C9 Hastingwood Trading Estate
Harbet Road, Edmonton, London N18 3HU
e-mail: office@gradav.co.uk
Fax: 020-8803 5060   Tel: 020-8803 7400

GRAY Robin COMMENTARIES
(Saddles, Bridles, Racing Colours & Hunting Attire)
Comptons, Isington, Alton, Hampshire GU34 4PL
e-mail: gray@isington.fsnet.co.uk
Mobile: 07831 828424   Tel/Fax: 01420 23347

GREENPROPS
(Prop Suppliers, Artificial Trees, Plants, Flowers, Fruit,
Grass etc)
West Bovey Farm, Waterrow, Somerset TA4 2BA
Website: www.greenprops.com
e-mail: trevor@greenprops.com   Tel: 01398 361531

HAMPTON COURT HOUSE
(1757 Country House & Grounds)
East Molesey KT8 9BS
Website: www.hamptoncourthouse.com
Fax: 020-8977 5357   Tel: 020-8943 0889

HANDS UP PUPPETS
c/o Peter Charlesworth & Associates
68 Old Brompton Road, London SW7 3LD
Website: www.handsuppuppets.com
e-mail: handsuppuppets@btinternet.com
                    Tel: 020-7581 2478

HARLEQUIN (BRITISH HARLEQUIN Plc)
(Floors for Stage, Opera, Dance, Concert, Shows & Events)
Festival House, Chapman Way
Tunbridge Wells, Kent TN2 3EF
Website: www.harlequinfloors.com
e-mail: sales@harlequinfloors.co.uk
Fax: 01892 514222   Tel: 01892 514888

HAWES Joanne
(Children's Administrator for Theatre, Film & TV)
21 Westfield Road, Maidenhead, Berkshire SL6 5AU
e-mail: jo.hawes@virgin.net
Fax: 01628 672884   Tel: 01628 773048

HERON & DRIVER
(Scenic Furniture & Prop Makers)
Unit 7, Dockley Road Industrial Estate
Rotherhithe, London SE16 3SF
Website: www.herondriver.co.uk
e-mail: mail@herondriver.co.uk
Fax: 020-7394 8680   Tel: 020-7394 8688

HEWER Richard
(Props Maker)
7 Sion Lane, Bristol BS8 4BE   Tel/Fax: 0117-973 876

HI-FLI (Flying Effects)
2 Boland Drive
Manchester M14 6DS
e-mail: mikefrost@hi-fli.co.uk   Tel/Fax: 0161-224 608

HISTORICAL INTERPRETER & ROLE PLAYING
(Donald Clarke)
80 Warden Avenue
Rayners Lane
Harrow, Middlesex HA2 9LW
Website: www.historicalinterpretations.co.uk
e-mail: info@historicalinterpretations.co.uk
Mobile: 07811 606285   Tel: 020-8866 299

HISTORY IN THE MAKING Ltd
(Weapon & Costume Hire)
4A Aysgarth Road
Waterlooville, Hampshire PO7 7UG
Website: www.history-making.com   Tel: 023-9225 317

HORNE Nick
(Former Coach House Barn Conversion set in 4 Acres of
land & Landscaped Gardens overlooking Rolling
Countryside)
Holbrook View, Birchwood Farm
Portway, Coxbench, Derby DE21 5BE
e-mail: joy_horne@hotmail.com
Fax: 01332 881408   Tel: 01332 781C

HOTCHPOTCHPROPS
Website: www.hotchpotchprops.com
e-mail: jo@hotchpotchprops.com   Mobile: 07734 68525

HOWARD Rex DRAPES Ltd
Acton Park Industrial Estate
Eastman Road, The Vale, London W3 7QS
e-mail: rexdrapes@yahoo.com
Fax: 020-8740 5994   Tel: 020-8740 58

IMPACT DISTRIBUTION & MARKETING
(Leaflet & Poster Distribution & Display)
Tuscany Wharf
4B Orsman Road, London N1 5QJ
Website: www.impact.uk.com
e-mail: admin@impact.uk.com
Fax: 020-7729 5994   Tel: 020-7729 597

IMPACT PERCUSSION
(Percussion Instruments for Sale)
Unit 7 Goose Green Trading Estate
47 East Dulwich Road, London SE22 9BN
e-mail: sales@impactpercussion.com
Fax: 020-8299 6704   Tel: 020-8299 67C

JAPAN PROMOTIONS
(Organise Japanese Events)
200 Russell Court, 3 Woburn Place, London WC1H 0ND
Website: www.japan-promotions.co.uk
e-mail: info@japan-promotions.co.uk   Tel/Fax: 020-7278 409

JULIETTE DESIGNS
(Diamante Jewellery Manufacturer, Necklaces, Crowns etc
90 Yerbury Road, London N19 4RS
Website: www.stagejewellery.com
Fax: 020-7281 7326   Tel: 020-7263 787

KENSINGTON EYE CENTRE Ltd
(Special Eye Effects)
37 Kensington Church Street
London W8 4LL   Tel/Fax: 020-7937 828

KEW BRIDGE STEAM MUSEUM
(Steam Museum)
Green Dragon Lane, Brentford, Middlesex TW8 0EN
Website: www.kbsm.org
e-mail: jo@kbsm.org
Fax: 020-8569 9978   Tel: 020-8568 4757

KIRBY'S AFX Ltd
3 Greenford Avenue, Hanwell, London W7 3QP
Website: www.kirbysflying.co.uk
e-mail: mail@afxuk.com
Mobile: 07958 285608   Tel/Fax: 020-8723 8552

KNEBWORTH HOUSE, GARDENS & PARK
(Knebworth)
Herts SG3 6PY   Tel: 01438 812661

LAREDO Alex
(Expert with Ropes, Bullwhips, Shooting, Riding)
29 Lincoln Road, Dorking, Surrey RH4 1TE
Mobile: 07906 271766   Tel: 01306 889423

LAREDO WILD WEST TOWN
(Wild West Entertainment)
Bower Walk, Staplehurst, Tonbridge, Kent TN12 0LU
Website: www.laredo.org.uk
e-mail: enquiries@laredo.org.uk
Mobile: 07947 652771   Tel: 01580 891790

LEES-NEWSOME Ltd
(Manufacturers of Flame Retardant Fabrics)
Ashley Street, Westwood, Oldham, Lancashire OL9 6LS
e-mail: info@leesnewsome.co.uk
Fax: 0161-627 3362   Tel: 0161-652 1321

LEIGHTON HALL
(Historic House)
Carnforth, Lancashire LA5 9ST
Website: www.leightonhall.co.uk
e-mail: info@leightonhall.co.uk
Fax: 01524 720357   Tel: 01524 734474

LEVRANT Stephen - HERITAGE ARCHITECTURE Ltd
(Architects & Historic Building Consultants)
363 West End Lane, West Hampstead, London NW6 1LP
e-mail: info@heritagearchitecture.co.uk
Fax: 020-7794 9712   Tel: 020-7435 7502

LONDON BUSINESS EQUIPMENT
(Authorised Canon Dealer)
527-529 High Road, Leytonstone, London E11 4PB
Website: www.londonbusinessequipment.com
e-mail: sales@londonbusinessequipment.com
Fax: 020-8556 4865   Tel: 020-8558 0024

LONO DRINKS COMPANY The
The Hawthorns, Driffield, Cirencester
Gloucestershire GL7 5PY
Website: www.lono.co.uk
e-mail: info@lono.co.uk
Fax: 01285 850455   Tel: 01285 850682

LOS KAOS
(Street Theatre, Circus, Puppetry & Animatronics)
Crown Lodge, Tintern, Chepstow, Wales NP16 6TF
Website: www.loskaos.co.uk   Tel/Fax: 01291 680074

LYON EQUIPMENT
(Petzl & Beal Rope Access Equipment (PPE) for Industrial &
Theatrical Work)
Rise Hill Mill, Dent, Sedbergh, Cumbria LA10 5QL
Website: www.lyon.co.uk
e-mail: info@lyon.co.uk
Fax: 01539 625454   Tel: 01539 625493

M A C
(Sound Hire)
1-2 Attenburys Park, Park Road
Altrincham, Cheshire WA14 5QE
Website: www.macsound.co.uk
e-mail: hire@macsound.co.uk
Fax: 0161-962 9423   Tel: 0161-969 8311

MACKIE Sally LOCATIONS
(Location Finding & Management)
Cownham Farm, Broadwell, Moreton-in-Marsh
Gloucestershire GL56 0TT
Website: www.sallymackie-locations.com
e-mail: sally@mackie.biz   Tel: 01451 830294

MADDERMARKET THEATRE
(Contact Rhett Davies, Resident Stage Manager)
St John's Alley, Norwich NR2 1DR
Website: www.maddermarket.co.uk
e-mail: mmtheatre@btconnect.com
Fax: 01603 661357   Tel: 01603 626560

MAGICAL MART
(Magic, Ventriloquists' Dolls, Punch & Judy, Hire & Advising.
Callers by Appointment)
42 Christchurch Road, Sidcup, Kent DA15 7HQ
Website: www.johnstylesentertainer.co.uk
       Tel/Fax: 020-8300 3579

MARCUS HALL PROPS
80 Malyons Road, Ladywell, London SE13 7XG
Website: www.marcushallprops.com
e-mail: info@marcushallprops.com
Mobile: 07802 873127   Tel: 020-8690 2901

MARKSON PIANOS
8 Chester Court, Albany Street, London NW1 4BU
Website: www.marksonpianos.com
e-mail: info@marksonpianos.com
Fax: 020-7224 0957   Tel: 020-7935 8682

MIDNIGHT ELECTRONICS
(Sound Hire)
Off Quay Building, Foundry Lane
Newcastle upon Tyne NE6 1LH
Website: www.midnightelectronics.co.uk
e-mail: info@midnightelectronics.co.uk
Fax: 0191-224 0100   Tel: 0191-224 0088

MILITARY, MODELS & MINATURES
(Model Figures)
38A Horsell Road, London N5 1XP
e-mail: figsculpt@aol.com
Fax: 020-7700 4624   Tel: 020-7700 7036

MODEL BOX
(Computer Aided Design & Design Services)
2 Saddlers Way
Okehampton, Devon EX20 1TL
Website: www.modelbox.co.uk
e-mail: info@modelbox.co.uk
Tel: 01837 54026

MODERNEON LONDON Ltd
(Lighting)
Cromwell House
27 Brabourne Rise, Park Langley
Beckenham, Kent BR3 6SQ
Website: www.moderneon.org
e-mail: moderneon@tiscali.co.uk
Fax: 020-8658 2770
Tel: 020-8650 9690

MOORFIELDS PHOTOGRAPHIC Ltd
2 Old Hall Street, Liverpool L3 9RQ
Website: www.moorfieldsphoto.com
e-mail: info@moorfieldsphoto.com
Tel: 0151-236 1611

MORTON G & L
(Horses/Farming)
Hashome Carr, Holme-on-Spalding Moor
Yorkshire YO43 4BD
Tel: 01430 860393

NEWMAN HIRE COMPANY
16 The Vale, Acton, London W3 7SB
e-mail: info@newmanhire.co.uk
Tel: 020-8743 0741

NORTHERN LIGHT
Assembly Street
Leith, Edinburgh EH6 7RG
Website: www.northernlight.co.uk
e-mail: enquiries@northernlight.co.uk
Fax: 0131-622 9101
Tel: 0131-622 9100

NOSTALGIA AMUSEMENTS
(Brian Davey)
22 Greenwood Close
Thames Ditton, Surrey KT7 0BG
Mobile: 07973 506869
Tel: 020-8398 2141

NOTTINGHAM JOUSTING ASSOCIATION SCHOOL OF NATIONAL EQUITATION Ltd
(Jousting & Medieval Tournaments, Horses & Riders for Films & TV)
Bunny Hill Top, Costock
Loughborough, Leicestershire LE12 6XE
Website: www.bunnyhill.co.uk
e-mail: info@bunnyhill.co.uk
Fax: 01509 856067
Tel: 01509 852366

OCEAN LEISURE
(Scuba Diving, Watersports Retail)
11-14 Northumberland Avenue, London WC2N 5AQ
Website: www.oceanleisure.co.uk
e-mail: info@oceanleisure.co.uk
Fax: 020-7930 3032
Tel: 020-7930 5050

OFFSTAGE
(Theatre & Film Bookshop)
34 Tavistock Street, London WC2E 7PB
Website: www.offstagebooks.com
e-mail: offstagebookshop@aol.com
Tel: 020-7240 3883

PAPERFLOW Plc
(Stationery & Office Equipment)
Units 5 & 6
Meridian Trading Estate
20 Bugsbys Way, Charlton, London SE7 7SJ
e-mail: info@paperflowgroup.com
Fax: 020-8331 2007
Tel: 020-8331 2000

PATCHETTS EQUESTRIAN CENTRE
(Location)
Hillfield Lane, Aldenham, Watford, Herts WD25 8PE
Website: www.patchetts.co.uk
Fax: 01923 859289
Tel: 01923 85225

PATERSON Helen
(Typing Services)
40 Whitelands House, London SW3 4QY
e-mail: pater@waitrose.com
Tel: 020-7730 642

PAULA'S HABITAT
(House for Hire, Film & TV Locations)
37 Downfield Close, Maida Vale, London W9 2JH
e-mail: paulashabitat@aol.com
Mobile: 07930 887469
Tel: 020-7266 991

PERIOD PETROL PUMP COLLECTION
c/o Diss Ironworks
7 St Nicholas Street, Diss, Norfolk IP22 4LB
Website: www.periodpetrolpump.co.uk
Tel: 01379 64397

PHOSPHENE
(Lighting & Sound. Design, Sales, Hire)
Milton Road South, Stowmarket, Suffolk IP14 1EZ
Website: www.phosphene.co.uk
e-mail: cliff@phosphene.freeserve.co.uk
Tel: 01449 77001

PIANO PEOPLE The
(Piano Transport)
Website: www.pianopeople.co.uk
e-mail: info@pianopeople.co.uk
Fax: 01646 661439
Tel: 0845 607671

PICKFORDS Ltd
Heritage House, 345 Southbury Road, Enfield EN1 1UP
Website: www.pickfords.com
Fax: 020-8362 4219
Tel: 020-8219 800

PICTURES PROPS CO Ltd
(TV, Film & Stage Hire)
12-16 Brunel Road, London W3 7XR
Fax: 020-8740 5846
Tel: 020-8749 243

PINK POINTES DANCEWEAR
1A Suttons Lane, Hornchurch, Essex RM12 6RD
e-mail: pink.pointes@btconnect.com
Tel/Fax: 01708 43858

PLAYBOARD PUPPETS
2 Ockendon Mews, London N1 3JL
Tel/Fax: 020-7226 59

POLAND Anna: SCULPTOR AND MODELMAKER
(Sculpture, Models, Puppets, Masks etc)
Salterns, Old Bursledon
Southampton, Hampshire SO31 8DH
e-mail: polandanna@hotmail.com
Tel: 023-8040 516

POLLEX PROPS / FIREBRAND
(Prop Makers)
Leac Na Ban, Tayvallich
Lochgilphead, Argyll PA31 8PF
e-mail: firebrand.props@btinternet.com
Tel/Fax: 01546 87031

PRAETORIAN ASSOCIATES/PROCUREMENT SERVICES - SA
(Personal Safety & Anti-Stalking Consultancy & services for Film/TV industry within South Africa)
Suite 501, 2 Old Brompton Road, London SW7 3DG
Website: www.praetorianasc.com
e-mail: martin.beale@praetorianasc.com
Tel/Fax: 020-7096 182

PROBLOOD
11 Mount Pleasant, Framlingham
Suffolk IP13 9HQ
Tel/Fax: 01728 72386

SPUR
creative workshop

making props, sculptures and models for the UK and abroad

W: www.spurcreative.co.uk   E: info@spurcreative.co.uk   T: 020 8405 3436   M: 07970 805871

PROFESSOR PATTEN'S PUNCH & JUDY
(Hire & Performances/Advice on Traditional Show)
4 The Crest, Goffs Oak, Hertfordshire EN7 5NP
Website: www.dennispatten.co.uk   Tel: 01707 873262

PROP FARM Ltd
(Pat Ward)
Grange Farm, Elmton, Nr Creswell
North Derbyshire S80 4LX
e-mail: pat/les@propfarm.co.uk
Fax: 01909 721465   Tel: 01909 723100

PROPS GALORE
(Period Textiles/Jewellery)
5 Brunel Road, London W3 7XR
e-mail: propsgalore@farley.co.uk
Fax: 020-8354 1866   Tel: 020-8746 1222

PROPS STUDIOS Ltd
Unit 3, Old Kiln Works
Ditchling Common Industrial Estate
Hassocks, East Sussex BN6 8SG
Website: www.propsstudios.co.uk
e-mail: info@propsstudios.co.uk
Fax: 0870 7700961   Tel: 0870 7700960

PUNCH & JUDY PUPPETS & BOOTHS
(Hire & Advisory Service, Callers by Appointment)
32 Christchurch Road, Sidcup, Kent DA15 7HQ
Website: www.johnstylesentertainer.co.uk
    Tel/Fax: 020-8300 3579

Q2 Ltd
(Production Solutions)
Lyric Theatre, Shaftesbury Avenue, London W1D 7ES
Website: www.q2qgroup.com
e-mail: solutions@q2qgroupcom
Fax: 0870 9506727   Tel: 0870 9505727

RAINBOW PRODUCTIONS Ltd
(Creation & Appearances of Costume Characters/Stage
Shows)
Rainbow House
46 Windsor Avenue, London SW19 2RR
Website: www.rainbowproductions.co.uk
e-mail: info@rainbowproductions.co.uk
Fax: 020-8545 0777   Tel: 020-8545 0700

RENT-A-CLOWN
(Mattie Faint)
17 Sekeforde Street, Clerkenwell
London EC1R 0HA
    Tel/Fax: 020-7608 0312

REPLAY Ltd
(Showreels & TV Facilities Hire)
Museum House, 25 Museum Street
London WC1A 1JT
Website: www.replayfilms.co.uk
e-mail: sales@replayfilms.co.uk
    Tel: 020-7637 0473

ROBERTS Chris INTERIORS
(Film Set & Property Maintenance & Tiling)
17 Colebrook Lane
Loughton IG10 2HP
    Mobile: 07956 512074

ROOTSTEIN Adel Ltd
(Mannequin Manufacturer)
9 Beaumont Avenue, London W14 9LP
Fax: 020-7381 3263   Tel: 020-7381 1447

ROYAL HORTICULTURAL HALLS & CONFERENCE CENTRE
(Film Location: Art Deco & Edwardian Buildings)
80 Vincent Square
London SW1P 2PE
Website: www.horticultural-halls.co.uk
e-mail: horthalls@rhs.org.uk
Fax: 020-7834 2072   Tel: 020-7828 4125

RUDKIN DESIGN
(Design Consultants, Brochures, Advertising
Corporate etc)
10 Cottesbrooke Park
Heartlands Business Park
Daventry
Northamptonshire NN11 8YL
Website: www.rudkindesign.com
e-mail: studio@rudkindesign.com
Fax: 01327 872728   Tel: 01327 301770

RUMBLE Jane
(Props to Order, No Hire)
121 Elmstead Avenue, Wembley
Middlesex HA9 8NT   Tel: 020-8904 6462

SABAH
(Stylist, Costumes, Wardrobe, Sets, Props)
2841 N. Ocean Blvd, Apt 501
Fort Lauderdale, Florida 33308 USA
e-mail: sabah561@aol.com
Mobile: (954) 383-2179   Tel/Fax: (954) 566-6219

SAPEX SCRIPTS
Millennium Studios
5 Elstree Way
Borehamwood, Herts WD6 1SF
Website: www.sapex.co.uk
e-mail: scripts@sapex.co.uk
Fax: 020-8236 1591   Tel: 020-8236 1600

SCENE TWO HIRE
(Prop Hire Specialist 50's - 70's)
1-4 Bethune Road
London NW10 6NJ
Website: www.superhire.com
Fax: 020-8965 8107   Tel: 020-8965 9909

SCHULTZ & WIREMU FABRIC EFFECTS Ltd
(Dyeing/Printing/Distressing)
Unit B202 Faircharm Studios
8-12 Creekside
London SE8 3DX
Website: www.schultz-wiremufabricfx.co.uk
e-mail: swfabricfx@hotmail.co.uk   Tel/Fax: 020-8469 0151

SCRIPTRIGHT
(S.C. Hill - Script/Manuscript Typing Services/Script
Reading Services)
6 Valetta Road, London W3 7TN
e-mail: samc.hill@virgin.net   Tel: 020-8740 7303

SCRIPTS BY ARGYLE
(Play, Film & Book. Word Processing, Copying & Binding)
St John's Buildings
43 Clerkenwell Road, London EC1M 5RS
Website: www.scriptsbyargyle.co.uk
e-mail: info@scriptsbyargyle.co.uk
Fax: 0871 4336130   Tel: 020-7608 2095

SFD
Ground Floor, Sunningdale
The Belfry, Colonial Way
Watford, Herts WD24 4WH
Fax: 01923 232326   Tel: 01923 232425

SHAOLIN WAY
(Martial Arts Supplies, Lion Dance & Kung Fu Instruction)
10 Little Newport Street
London WC2H 7JJ
Website: www.shaolinway.com
e-mail: shaolinway@btconnect.com
Fax: 020-7287 6548   Tel: 020-7734 6391

21 Baron Street, Angel, London N1 9EX   Tel: 020-7833 8388

SHIRLEY LEAF & PETAL COMPANY Ltd
(Flower Makers Museum)
58A High Street, Old Town, Hastings
East Sussex TN34 3EN   Tel/Fax: 01424 427793

SIDE EFFECTS
(Props, Models & FX)
92 Fentiman Road, London SW8 1LA
e-mail: sfx@lineone.net
Fax: 020-7207 0062   Tel: 020-7587 1116

SMITH Tom
(Blacksmith)
Unit 2, Lopen Works, Lopen Road
Edmonton, London N18 1PU   Tel/Fax: 020-8884 2626

SNOW BUSINESS
(Snow/Winter Effects on Any Scale)
The Snow Mill, Bridge Road
Ebley, Stroud, Gloucestershire GL5 4TR
Website: www.snowfx.com
e-mail: snow@snowbusiness.com   Tel/Fax: 01453 840077

SOFT PROPS
(Costume & Modelmakers)
92 Fentiman Road
London SW8 1LA
e-mail: jackie@softprops.co.uk
Fax: 020-7207 0062   Tel: 020-7587 1116

SPUR CREATIVE WORKSHOP
169B Davidson Road
Croydon CR0 6DP
Website: www.spurcreative.co.uk
e-mail: info@spurcreative.co.uk   Tel: 020-8405 343[

STEELDECK RENTALS/SALES
(Theatre & Staging Equipment) (Modular Staging)
Unit 58, T Marchant Trading Estate
42-72 Verney Road, London SE16 3DH
e-mail: rentals@steeldeck.co.uk
Fax: 020-7232 1780   Tel: 020-7833 203[

STEVENSON Scott
(Prop Maker)
60 Ripley Road
Sawmills, Belper, Derbyshire DE56 2JQ
Website: www.bodymechprops.co.uk
e-mail: scott@bodymechprops.co.uk   Mobile: 07739 37857[

SUPERSCRIPTS
51 Buckingham Gardens, West Moseley, Surrey KT8 1TJ
Mobile: 07793 160138   Tel: 020-8979 804[

SUPERSCRIPTS
(Audio Typing, Rushes, Post-Prod Scripts)
56 New Road
Hanworth, Middlesex TW13 6TQ
e-mail: jackie@superscripts.fsnet.co.uk
Mobile: 07971 671011   Tel: 020-8898 793[

TALK TO THE HAND PUPPETS
(Custom Puppets for Television & Theatre)
24 Burstead Close
Brighton BN1 7HT
Website: www.talktothehandproductions.com
e-mail: talktothehandproductions@hotmail.com
Mobile: 07813 682293   Mobile: 07855 42145[

TAYLOR Charlotte
(Stylist/Props Buyer)
18 Eleanor Grove, Barnes, London SW13 0JN
e-mail: charlottetaylor1@blueyoner.co.uk
Mobile: 07836 708904   Tel/Fax: 020-8876 908[

THEATRESEARCH
(Theatre Consultants)
Dacre Hall, Dacre
North Yorkshire HG3 4ET
Website: www.theatresearch.co.uk
e-mail: info@theatresearch.co.uk
Fax: 01423 781957   Tel: 01423 78049[

THEATRICAL SHOEMAKERS Ltd
(Footwear)
Unit 7A, Thames Road Industrial Estate
Thames Road, Silvertown, London E16 2EZ
Website: www.shoemaking.co.uk
e-mail: ts@shoemaking.co.uk
Fax: 020-7476 5220   Tel: 020-7474 050[

THEME TRADERS Ltd
(Props)
The Stadium
Oaklands Road, London NW2 6DL
Website: www.themetraders.com
e-mail: mailroom@themetraders.com
Fax: 020-8450 7322   Tel: 020-8452 851[

TOP SHOW
(Props & Scenery, Conference Specialists)
North Lane, Huntington
Yorks YO32 9SU   Tel/Fax: 01904 75002[

POLLEX PROPS ✳ FIREBRAND

* Master Property Makers & Designers   * Burners & Torches   * Sale & Hire

Alexander & Polly Hamilton   Leac Na Ban, Tayvallich, Lochgilphead, Argyll PA31 8PF
t: 01546 870 310   firebrand.props@btinternet.com   www.pollex-props.co.uk

TRANSCRIPTS
(Audio + LTC/Post-prod)
42, 6 Cornwall Gardens, London SW7 4AL
e-mail: lucy@transcripts.demon.co.uk
Mobile: 07973 200197   Tel: 020-7584 9758

TRAPEZE & AERIAL COACH/CHOREOGRAPHER
(Jacqueline Welbourne)
c/o Circus Maniacs Agency
Office 8A, The Kingswood Foundation
Britannia Road, Kingswood, Bristol BS15 8DB
Website: www.circusmaniacs.com
e-mail: jackie@circusmaniacs.com
Mobile: 07977 247287   Tel/Fax: 0117-947 7042

TRYFONOS Mary MASKS
(Mask, Headdress & Puppet Specialist)
59 Shaftesbury Road, London N19 4QW
e-mail: marytryfonos@aol.com
Mobile: 07764 587433   Tel: 020-7561 9880

TURN ON LIGHTING
(Antique Lighting c1840-1950)
11 Camden Passage
London N1 8EA   Tel/Fax: 020-7359 7616

UPSTAGE
(Live Communications Agency)
Studio A
7 Maidstone Buildings Mews
72-76 Borough High Street
London SE1 1GD
Website: www.upstagelivecom.co.uk
e-mail: post@upstagelivecom.co.uk
Fax: 020-7403 6511   Tel: 020-7403 6510

VENTRILOQUIST DOLLS HOME
(Hire & Helpful Hints, Callers by Appointment)
12 Christchurch Road
Sidcup, Kent DA15 7HQ
Website: www.johnstylesentertainer.co.uk
      Tel/Fax: 020-8300 3579

VENTRILOQUIST DUMMY HIRE
(Dennis Patten - Hire & Advice)
4 The Crest
Goffs Oak, Herts EN7 5NP
Website: www.dennispatten.co.uk   Tel: 01707 873262

VINMAG ARCHIVE Ltd
84-90 Digby Road, London E9 6HX
Website: www.vinmagarchive.com
e-mail: piclib@vinmag.com
Fax: 020-8533 7283   Tel: 020-8533 7588

VOCALEYES
(Providers of Audio Description for Theatrical
Performance)
1st Floor
54 Commercial Street, London E1 6LT
Website: www.vocaleyes.co.uk
e-mail: enquiries@vocaleyes.co.uk
Fax: 020-7247 5622   Tel: 020-7375 1043

WALK YOUR DOG
(Dog Walking Service for South East London)
35 Harold Avenue, Belverdere, Kent DA17 5NN
Website: www.walkyourdog.co.uk
e-mail: info@walkyourdog.co.uk
Mobile: 07867 502333   Tel/Fax: 01322 448272

WEBBER Peter HIRE/RITZ STUDIOS
(Music Equipment Hire, Rehearsal Studios)
110-112 Disraeli Road, London SW15 2DX
e-mail: ben@ritzstudios.com
Fax: 020-8877 1036   Tel: 020-8870 1335

WESTED LEATHERS COMPANY
(Suede & Leather Suppliers/Manufacturers)
Little Wested House, Wested Lane, Swanley, Kent BR8 8EF
e-mail: wested@wested.com
Fax: 01322 667039   Tel: 01322 660654

WESTWARD Lynn BLINDS
(Window Blind Specialist)
458 Chiswick High Road, London W4 5TT
Website: www.lynnwestward.com
Fax: 020-8742 8444   Tel: 020-8742 8333

WILLIAMS Frank
(Bottles, Jars, Footwarmers, Flagons, Spitoons, Poisons,
Beers & Inks 1870-1940)
33 Enstone Road
Ickenham, Uxbridge, Middlesex
e-mail: wllmsfrn4@aol.com   Tel: 01895 672495

WILTSHIRE A. F. LLP
(Agricultural Vehicle Engineers, Repairs, etc)
The Agricultural Centre, Alfold Road
Dunsfold, Surrey GU8 4NP
e-mail: team@afwiltshire.co.uk
Fax: 01483 200491   Tel: 01483 200516

WORBEY Darryl STUDIOS
(Specialist Puppet Design)
Ground Floor, 33 York Grove, London SE15 2NY
e-mail: info@darrylworbeystudios.com
Fax: 020-7635 6397   Tel: 020-7639 8090

A & C BLACK (Publicity Dept)
38 Soho Square, London W1D 3HB
e-mail: publicity@acblack.com
Fax: 020-7758 0222   Tel: 020-7758 0200

ACADEMY PLAYERS DIRECTORY
(See PLAYERS DIRECTORY)

A C I D PUBLICATIONS
Room 7, Minus One House
Lyttelton Road, London E10 5NQ
e-mail: acidnews@aol.com   Tel/Fax: 07050 205206

ACTING: A DRAMA STUDIO SOURCE BOOK
(Peter Owen Publishers)
73 Kenway Road, London SW5 0RE
Website: www.peterowen.com
e-mail: admin@peterowen.com   Tel: 020-7373 5628

ACTIONS: THE ACTORS' THESAURUS
(By Marina Caldarone & Maggie Lloyd-Williams)
Nick Hern Books
The Glasshouse, 49A Goldhawk Road, London W12 8QP
Website: www.nickhernbooks.co.uk
e-mail: info@nickhernbooks.demon.co.uk
Fax: 020-8735 0250   Tel: 020-8749 4953

ACTORS' YEARBOOK 2007
(A & C Black Publishers), 38 Soho Square, London W1D 3HB
Website: www.acblack.com
e-mail: performing@acblack.com
Fax: 020-7758 0222   Tel: 020-7758 0200

AMATEUR STAGE MAGAZINE & COMMUNITY ARTS DIRECTORY
(Platform Publications Ltd)
Hampden House, 2 Weymouth Street, London W1W 5BT
e-mail: magazine@charlesvance.co.uk
Fax: 020-7636 2323   Tel: 020-7636 4343

ANNUAIRE DU CINEMA BELLEFAYE
(French Actors' Directory, Production, Technicians & All Technical Industries & Suppliers)
30 rue Saint Marc, 75002 Paris
Website: www.bellefaye.com
e-mail: contact@bellefaye.com
Fax: 00 331 42 33 39 00   Tel: 00 331 42 33 52 52

ARTISTES & AGENTS
(Richmond House Publishing Co Ltd)
70-76 Bell Street, Marylebone, London NW1 6SP
Website: www.rhpco.co.uk
e-mail: sales@rhpco.co.uk
Fax: 020-7224 9688   Tel: 020-7224 9666

AUDITIONS-THE ULTIMATE GUIDE
Website: www.auditionstheultimateguide.com

AURORA METRO PRESS (1989)
(Drama, Fiction, Reference & International Literature in English Translation)
2 Oriel Court, The Green, Twickenham TW2 5AG
Website: www.aurorametro.com
e-mail: info@aurorametro.com
Fax: 020-8898 0735   Tel: 020-8898 4488

BIG BREAK CARDS Ltd
(Theatrical greetings cards featuring Hamlet the pig, made by actors for actors)
PO Box 45, Chipping Campden GL55 6WH
Website: www.bigbreakcards.co.uk
e-mail: info@bigbreakcards.co.uk   Tel: 01386 438952

BIRTH OF THEATRE The - STAGE BY STAGE
(Drama/Theatre Studies/History/Reference)
(Peter Owen Publishers), 73 Kenway Road, London SW5 0RE
e-mail: admin@peterowen.com
Fax: 020-7373 6760   Tel: 020-7373 5628

BRITISH PERFORMING ARTS YEARBOOK
(Rhinegold Publishing)
241 Shaftesbury Avenue, London WC2H 8TF
Website: www.rhinegold.co.uk
e-mail: bpay@rhinegold.co.uk   Tel: 020-7333 1720

BRITISH THEATRE DIRECTORY
(Richmond House Publishing Co Ltd)
70-76 Bell Street, Marylebone, London NW1 6SP
Website: www.rhpco.co.uk
e-mail: sales@rhpco.co.uk
Fax: 020-7224 9688   Tel: 020-7224 9666

BROADCAST
33-39 Bowling Green Lane, London EC1R 0DA
Website: www.broadcastnow.co.uk
Fax: 020-7505 8020   Tel: 020-7505 8014

CASTCALL & CASTFAX
(Casting Information Services)
106 Wilsden Avenue, Luton LU1 5HR
Website: www.castcall.co.uk   e-mail: admin@castcall.co.uk
Fax: 01582 480736   Tel: 01582 45621.

CASTWEB
7 St Luke's Avenue, London SW4 7LG
Website: www.castweb.co.uk
e-mail: info@castweb.co.uk
Fax: 020-7720 3097   Tel: 020-7720 9002

CELEBRITY BULLETIN The
4th Floor, Kingsland House
122-124 Regent Street, London W1B 5SA
e-mail: celebritylondon@aol.com
Fax: 020-7494 3500   Tel: 020-7439 9840

CELEBRITY SERVICE Ltd
4th Floor, Kingsland House
122-124 Regent Street, London W1B 5SA
e-mail: celebritylondon@aol.com
Fax: 020-7494 3500   Tel: 020-7439 9840

CHAPPELL OF BOND STREET
(Sheet Music, Musical Instruments, Pianos, Synthesizers, Keyboards)
152-160 Wardour Street, London W1F 8YA
Website: www.chappellofbondstreet.co.uk
Fax: 020-7432 4410   Tel: 020-7432 4400

CONFERENCE & INCENTIVE TRAVEL MAGAZINE
174 Hammersmith Road, London W6 7JP
Website: www.citmagazine.com
e-mail: cit@haynet.com
Fax: 020-8267 4192   Tel: 020-8267 430

CREATIVE HANDBOOK
(Reed Business Information)
Windsor Court, East Grinstead House
East Grinstead, West Sussex RH19 1XA
Website: www.chb.com
e-mail: chb.mktg@reedinfo.co.uk
Fax: 01342 336113   Tel: 01342 335779

DANCE EXPRESSION
(A. E. Morgan Publications Ltd)
8A High Street, Epsom, Surrey KT19 8AD
Website: www.danceexpression.co.uk   Tel: 01372 7414.

DANCERS SPOTLIGHT
7 Leicester Place, London WC2H 7RJ
Website: www.spotlight.com
e-mail: info@spotlight.com
Fax: 020-7437 5881   Tel: 020-7437 763

DIRECTING DRAMA
(Peter Owen Publishers)
73 Kenway Road, London SW5 0RE
Website: www.peterowen.com
e-mail: admin@peterowen.com   Tel: 020-7373 562

UITY MAGAZINE
ld House, Upper St Martin's Lane, London WC2H 9EG
bsite: www.equity.org.uk
nail: mmcgrath@equity.org.uk
x: 020-7379 6074   Tel: 020-7670 0211

MLOG
bscriptions)
Box 100, Broadstairs, Kent CT10 1UJ
: 01843 860885   Tel: 01843 866538

RESIGHT-NEWS
e Profile Group (UK) Ltd)
agon Court, 27-29 Macklin Street, London WC2B 5LX
bsite: www.profilegroup.co.uk
x: 020-7190 7858   Tel: 020-7190 7777

RN Nick BOOKS
ays, Theatrebooks, Screenplays & Performing Rights)
e Glasshouse, 49A Goldhawk Road, London W12 8QP
bsite: www.nickhernbooks.co.uk
nail: info@nickhernbooks.demon.co.uk
x: 020-8735 0250   Tel: 020-8749 4953

LLYWOOD REPORTER The
1 Floor, Endeavour House
Shaftesbury Avenue, London WC2H 8TJ
bsite: www.hollywoodreporter.com
nail: london_one@eu.hollywoodreporter.com
x: 020-7420 6014   Tel: 020-7420 6000

Y'S UK & EUROPEAN PRODUCTION MANUALS
ewood Studios, Pinewood Road
r Heath, Bucks SL0 0NH
bsite: www.kays.co.uk   e-mail: info@kays.co.uk
x: 020-8960 6700   Tel: 020-8960 6900

MP'S FILM, TV & VIDEO
ed Business Information)
st Grinstead House
st Grinstead, West Sussex RH19 1XA
bsite: www.kftv.com   e-mail: kemps@reedinfo.co.uk
x: 01342 336113   Tel: 01342 335779

OWLEDGE The
rlequin House, 7 High Street
ddington, Middlesex TW11 8EL
bsite: www.theknowledgeonline.com
nail: knowledge@hollis-publishing.com
x: 020-8943 5141   Tel: 020-8973 3444

MELIGHT The
melight Publications, Contacts & Casting Directory)
stal Address: PO Box 760
ndpark Ridge, 2156, Gauteng, South Africa
bsite: www.limelight.co.za
nail: info@limelight.co.za   Tel/Fax: 00 27 11 793 7231

KING OF THE PROFESSIONAL ACTOR The
ter Owen Publishers)
Kenway Road, London SW5 0RE
bsite: www.peterowen.com
nail: admin@peterowen.com   Tel: 020-7373 5628

THUEN DRAMA
& C Black
Soho Square, London W1D 3HB
nail: methuendrama@acblack.com
x: 020-7758 0222   Tel: 020-7758 0200

VIE MEMORIES MAGAZINE
evoted to Films & Stars of the 40s, 50s & 60s)
Russett Close, Scunthorpe, N. Lincs DN15 8YJ
bsite: www.moviememoriesmagazine.com

SIC WEEK DIRECTORY/MUSIC WEEK
Mi
Floor, Ludgate House
5 Blackfriars Road, London SE1 9UR
bsite: www.musicweek.com
nail: mwdirectory@cmpi.biz

MUSICAL STAGES
(Musical Theatre Magazine)
Box 8365, London W14 0GL
Website: www.musicalstages.co.uk
e-mail: editor@musicalstages.co.uk Tel/Fax: 020-7603 2221

OFFICIAL LONDON SEATING PLAN GUIDE The
(Richmond House Publishing Co Ltd)
70-76 Bell Street, Marylebone, London NW1 6SP
Website: www.rhpco.co.uk   e-mail: sales@rhpco.co.uk
Fax: 020-7224 9668   Tel: 020-7224 9666

PA ENTERTAINMENT
292 Vauxhall Bridge Road, Victoria, London SW1V 1AE
Website: www.pa-entertainment.co.uk
e-mail: arts@pa-entertainment.co.uk
Fax: 020-7963 7805   Tel: 020-7963 7707

PACT
(Pact Directory of Independent Producers/Art of the
Deal/Rights Clearance)
The Eye, 2nd Floor, 1 Procter Street, London WC1V 6DW
Website: www.pact.co.uk
e-mail: enquiries@pact.co.uk
Fax: 020-7067 4377   Tel: 020-7067 4367

PANTOMIME BOOK The
(Peter Owen Publishers)
73 Kenway Road, London SW5 0RE
Website: www.peterowen.com
e-mail: admin@peterowen.com   Tel: 020-7373 5628

PCR
(See PRODUCTION & CASTING REPORT)

PLAYERS DIRECTORY
2210 W. Olive Avenue, Suite 320, Burbank, California 91506
Website: www.playersdirectory.com
e-mail: info@playersdirectory.com   Tel: (310) 247-3058

PLAYS INTERNATIONAL
33A Lurline Gardens
London SW11 4DD   Tel: 020-7720 1950

PRESENTERS CLUB The
Presenter Promotions
123 Corporation Road, Gillingham, Kent ME7 1RG
Website: www.presenterpromotions.com
e-mail: info@presenterpromotions.com
                          Tel/Fax: 01634 851077

PRESENTERS SPOTLIGHT
7 Leicester Place, London WC2H 7RJ
Website: www.spotlight.com
e-mail: info@spotlight.com
Fax: 020-7437 5881   Tel: 020-7437 7631

PRESENTING FOR TV & VIDEO
(Joanne Zorian-Lynn, published by A & C Black)
A & C Black Customer Services
c/o Robert Smith Literacy Agency
12 Bridge Wharf, 156 Caledonian Road, London N1 9UU
e-mail: mdl@macmillan.co.uk   Tel: 01256 302692

PRODUCTION & CASTING REPORT
(Editorial)
PO Box 11, London N1 7JZ
Website: www.pcrnewsletter.com
e-mail: info@pcrnewsletter.com
Fax: 020-7566 8284   Tel: 020-7566 8282

PRODUCTION & CASTING REPORT
(Subscriptions)
PO Box 100, Broadstairs, Kent CT10 1UJ
Website: www.pcrnewsletter.com
Tel: 01843 860885   Tel: 01843 866538

RADIO TIMES
80 Wood Lane, London W12 0TT
e-mail: radio.times@bbc.co.uk
Fax: 020-8433 3160   Tel: 020-8433 3400

RICHMOND HOUSE PUBLISHING COMPANY Ltd
70-76 Bell Street, Marylebone, London NW1 6SP
Website: www.rhpco.co.uk
e-mail: sales@rhpco.co.uk
Fax: 020-7224 9688   Tel: 020-7224 9666

ROGUES & VAGABONDS
(On-line Theatre Magazine)
13 Elm Road, London SW14 7JL
Website: www.roguesandvagabonds.co.uk
e-mail: contact@roguesandvagabonds.co.uk
                          Tel: 020-8876 1175

SBS Ltd
Suite 204, 254 Belsize Road, London NW6 4BT
e-mail: office@sbscasting.co.uk
Fax: 020-7372 1992   Tel: 020-7372 6337

SCREEN INTERNATIONAL
33-39 Bowling Green Lane, London EC1R 0DA
Website: www.screendaily.com
e-mail: mai.le@emap.com
Fax: 020-7505 8117   Tel: 020-7505 8080

SHOWCALL
47 Bermondsey Street, London SE1 3XT
Website: www.showcall.co.uk
e-mail: marcus@thestage.co.uk
Fax: 020-7378 0480   Tel: 020-7403 1818

SHOWCAST
PO Box 2001, Leumeah, NSW 2560 Australia
Website: www.showcast.com.au
e-mail: brian@showcast.com.au
Fax: 02 4647 4167   Tel: 02 4647 4166

SHOWDIGS.CO.UK
Website: www.showdigs.co.uk
e-mail: info@showdigs.co.uk   Mobile: 07984 422353

SIGHT & SOUND
(British Film Institute)
21 Stephen Street
London W1T 1LN
Website: www.bfi.org.uk/sightandsound
e-mail: s&s@bfi.org.uk
Fax: 020-7436 2327   Tel: 020-7957 89●

SO YOU WANT TO BE AN ACTOR?
(By Timothy West & Prunella Scales)
Nick Hern Books, The Glasshouse
49A Goldhawk Road, London W12 8QP
Website: www.nickhernbooks.co.uk
e-mail: info@nickhernbooks.demon.co.uk
Fax: 020-8735 0250   Tel: 020-8749 49●

SO YOU WANT TO BE A THEATRE DIRECTOR?
(By Stephen Unwin)
Nick Hern Books, The Glasshouse
49A Goldhawk Road, London W12 8QP
Website: www.nickhernbooks.co.uk
e-mail: info@nickhernbooks.demon.co.uk
Fax: 020-8735 0250   Tel: 020-8749 49

SPEECH FOR THE SPEAKER
(Peter Owen Publishers)
73 Kenway Road, London SW5 0RE
Website: www.peterowen.com
e-mail: admin@peterowen.com   Tel: 020-7373 56●

SPOTLIGHT The
7 Leicester Place, London WC2H 7RJ
Website: www.spotlight.com
e-mail: info@spotlight.com
Fax: 020-7437 5881   Tel: 020-7437 7●

STAGE NEWSPAPER Ltd The
47 Bermondsey Street
London SE1 3XT
Website: www.thestage.co.uk
e-mail: editorial@thestage.co.uk
Fax: 020-7357 9287   Tel: 020-7403 18●

TELEVISUAL
50 Poland Street, London W1F 7AX
Website: www.televisual.com
Fax: 020-7970 6733   Tel: 020-7970 65●

THEATRE RECORD
131 Sherringham Avenue, London N17 9RU
Website: www.theatrerecord.com
e-mail: editor@theatrerecord.com   Tel/Fax: 01243 5394●

THEATRE REPORT
(Subscriptions)
PO Box 100, Broadstairs, Kent CT10 1UJ
Website: www.pcrnewsletter.com
Tel: 01843 860885   Tel: 01843 8665●

TIME OUT GROUP Ltd
Universal House
251 Tottenham Court Road, London W1T 7AB
Website: www.timeout.com
Fax: 020-7813 6001   Tel: 020-7813 30●

TV TIMES
IPC Media
Blue Fin Building
110 Southwark Street, London SE1 0SU
Fax: 020-3148 8115   Tel: 020-3148 56●

VARIETY NEWSPAPER
7th Floor, 84 Theobalds Road, London WC1X 8RR
Website: www.variety.com
Fax: 020-7611 4581   Tel: 020-7611 45●

WHITE BOOK The
Bank House, 23 Warwick Road, Coventry CV1 2EW
Website: www.whitebook.co.uk
Fax: 024-7657 1172   Tel: 024-7657 ●

SPOTLIGHT PUBLICATIONS
SPOTLIGHT INTERACTIVE
SPOTLIGHT SERVICES

THE SPOTLIGHT
CASTING DIRECTORIES

Industry standard since 1927
Today featuring over 30,000 artists

The famous Spotlight books are the only comprehensive casting directories in the UK: the first place to look for performers of any age, type and expertise. All featured artists have one thing in common: professional training and/or experience. High standards of quality control make Spotlight the most trusted, repsected and accurate directory in the industry.

Our Publications include:

Actors I Actresses I Presenters I Graduates
Children and Young Performers I Contacts
Stunt Artists I Dancers

To order any of these directories, please phone 020 7440 5026
email: sales@spotlight.com or visit www.spotlight.com/shop

ARTHUR Leone PR
The Ground Floor
3 Charlotte Mews, London W1T 4DZ
Website: www.arthurleone.com
e-mail: name@arthurleone.com
Fax: 020-7637 2984   Tel: 020-7637 2994

ASH BLONDE MEDIA
Suite B, 5 South Bank Terrace
Surbiton, Surrey KT6 6DG
Mobile: 07715 709944   Tel/Fax: 020-8390 8535

AVALON PUBLIC RELATIONS
(Marketing/Arts)
4A Exmoor Street, London W10 6BD
e-mail: edt@avalonuk.com
Fax: 020-7598 7223   Tel: 020-7598 7222

BARLOW Tony ASSOCIATES
(Press & Marketing for Music, Dance & Theatre)
13 Burns Court, Park Hill Road
Wallington SM6 0SF
e-mail: artspublicity@hotmail.com
Mobile: 07711 929170   Tel: 020-8773 1919

BOLTON Erica & QUINN Jane Ltd
10 Pottery Lane, London W11 4LZ
e-mail: name@boltonquinn.com
Fax: 020-7221 8100   Tel: 020-7221 5000

BORKOWSKI Mark PR & IMPROPERGANDA Ltd
65 Clerkenwell Road, London EC1R 5BL
Website: www.borkowski.co.uk
e-mail: larry@borkowski.co.uk
Fax: 020-7404 5000   Tel: 020-7404 3000

CAHOOTS PRODUCTION & PR
(Denise Silvey)
9-15 Neal Street, London WC2H 9PW
Website: www.cahootstheatre.co.uk
e-mail: denise@cahootstheatre.co.uk   Tel: 020-7240 7000

CENTRESTAGE PUBLIC RELATIONS
Yeates Cottage
27 Wellington Terrace
Woking, Surrey GU21 2AP
Website: www.centrestage.com
e-mail: centrestagepr@dsl.pipex.com   Tel: 01483 487808

CHESTON Judith PUBLICITY
30 Telegraph Street, Shipston-on-Stour
Warwickshire CV36 4DA
e-mail: jcheston@tiscali.co.uk
Fax: 01608 663772   Tel: 01608 661198

CUE CONSULTANTS
18 Barrington Court, London N10 1QG
e-mail: cueconsultants@gmail.com   Mobile: 07974 704909

DAVEY Christine ASSOCIATES
29 Victoria Road, Eton Wick
Windsor, Berkshire SL4 6LY
Fax: 01753 851123   Tel: 01753 852619

DDA PUBLIC RELATIONS Ltd
192-198 Vauxhall Bridge Road, London SW1V 1DX
Website: www.ddapr.com
e-mail: info@ddapr.com
Fax: 020-7932 4950   Tel: 020-7932 9800

ELSON Howard PROMOTIONS
(Marketing & Management)
16 Penn Avenue, Chesham, Buckinghamshire HP5 2HS
e-mail: helson1029@aol.com
Fax: 01494 784760   Tel: 01494 785873

GADABOUTS Ltd
(Theatre Marketing & Promotions)
54 Friary Road
London N12 9PB
Website: www.gadaboutstravel.com
e-mail: info@gadabouts.co.uk
Fax: 0870 7059140   Tel: 020-8445 54

GAYNOR Avril ASSOCIATES
32 Brunswick Square
Hove, East Sussex BN3 1ED
e-mail: gaynorama@aol.com   Tel/Fax: 01273 8219

GOODMAN Deborah PUBLICITY
25 Glenmere Avenue, London NW7 2LT
Website: www.dgpr.co.uk
e-mail: publicity@dgpr.co.uk
Fax: 020-8959 7875   Tel: 020-8959 99

HYMAN Sue ASSOCIATES Ltd
St Martin's House
59 Martin's Lane, London WC2N 4JS
Website: www.suehyman.com
e-mail: sue.hyman@btinternet.com
Fax: 020-7379 4944   Tel: 020-7379 84

IMPACT AGENCY The
3 Bloomsbury Place, London WC1A 2QL
e-mail: mail@impactagency.co.uk
Fax: 020-7580 7200   Tel: 020-7580 17

KEAN LANYON Ltd
(Sharon Kean)
Rose Cottage, The Aberdeen Centre
22 Highbury Grove, London N5 2EA
Website: www.keanlanyon.com
e-mail: sharon@keanlanyon.com
Fax: 020-7359 0199   Tel: 020-7354 35

KELLER Don ARTS MARKETING
65 Glenwood Road, Harringay, London N15 3JS
e-mail: info@dakam.org.uk
Fax: 020-8809 6825   Tel: 020-8800 48

KWPR
(Kevin Wilson Public Relations)
187 Drury Lane, London WC2B 5QD
Website: www.kwpr.co.uk
e-mail: kevinwilsonpr@gmail.com
Mobile: 07884 368697   Tel: 020-7430 20

LAKE-SMITH GRIFFIN ASSOCIATES
Walter House
418 Strand, London WC2R 0PT
e-mail: info@lakesmithgriffin.co.uk
Fax: 020-7836 1040   Tel: 020-7836 10

LEEP MARKETING & PR
(Marketing, Press and Publicity)
5 Nassau House
122 Shaftesbury Avenue, London W1D 5ER
e-mail: philip@leep.biz
Fax: 020-7439 8833   Tel: 020-7439 97

MAYER Anne PR
82 Mortimer Road, London N1 4LH
e-mail: annemayer@btopenworld.com
Fax: 020-7254 8227   Tel: 020-7254 73

McAULEY ARTS MARKETING
118 Broxholm Road
London SE27 0BT
Website: www.mcauleyartsmarketing.co.uk
e-mail: sam@mcauleyartsmarketing.co.uk Tel: 020-8676 47

MITCHELL Jackie
(JM Communications)
1 Sims Cottages, The Green, Claygate, Surrey KT10 0JH
Website: www.jackiem.com
e-mail: pr@jackiem.com
Fax: 01372 471073   Tel: 01372 465041

MOBIUS
3A Great Newport Street, London WC2H 7JB
Website: www.mobiusindustries.com
e-mail: info@mobiusindustries.com   Tel: 020-7836 3864

MORGAN Jane ASSOCIATES (JMA)
(Marketing & Media)
3 Heathville Road, London N19 3AJ
e-mail: jma@janemorganassociates.com
Fax: 020-7263 9877   Tel: 020-7263 9867

NELSON BOSTOCK COMMUNICATIONS
Compass House
22 Redan Place, London W2 4SA
Website: www.nelsonbostock.com
e-mail: ali.mills@nelsonbostock.com
Fax: 020-7727 2025   Tel: 020-7229 4400

NEWLEY Patrick ASSOCIATES
45 Kingscourt Road, London SW16 1JA
e-mail: patricknewley@yahoo.com   Tel/Fax: 020-8677 0477

PARKER James ASSOCIATES
7 Richmond Park Road, London SW14 8JY
e-mail: jimparkerjpa@hotmail.com   Tel/Fax: 020-8876 1918

POWELL Martin COMMUNICATIONS
1 Lyons Court
Long Ashton Business Park
Hanley Lane, Bristol BS41 9LB
e-mail: info@martin-powell.com
Fax: 01275 393933   Tel: 01275 394400

PR PEOPLE The
1 St James Drive
Sale, Cheshire M33 7QX
Website: www.pr-people.uk.com
e-mail: graham@pr-people.uk.com   Tel: 0161-976 2729

PREMIER PR
91 Berwick Street, London W1F 0NE
Website: www.premierpr.com
Fax: 020-7734 2024   Tel: 020-7292 8330

PUBLIC EYE COMMUNICATIONS Ltd
Suite 313, Plaza
535 Kings Road, London SW10 0SZ
e-mail: ciara@publiceye.co.uk
Fax: 020-7351 1010   Tel: 020-7351 1555

RICHMOND TOWERS COMMUNICATIONS Ltd
26 Fitzroy Square, London W1T 6BT
Fax: 020-7388 7761   Tel: 020-7388 7421

RKM PUBLIC RELATIONS Ltd
(London. Los Angeles)
9B Grosvenor Gardens, London SW1W 0BD
Website: www.rkmpr.com
e-mail: info@rkmpr.com
Fax: 020-7821 1369   Tel: 020-7856 2233

S & X MEDIA
(Contact: Roulla Xenides)
11B The Big Peg
Vyse Street, Birmingham B18 6NF
Website: www.sx-media.com
e-mail: roulla@sx-media.com
Fax: 0121-694 6494   Tel: 0121-604 6366

SAVIDENT Paul
(Marketing & Press Management)
The Office, 27 St Dunstan's Road
London W7 2EY
Website: www.savident.com
e-mail: info@savident.com
Fax: 0870 0516418   Tel: 020-8567 2089

SHIPPEN Martin MARKETING & MEDIA
88 Purves Road, London NW10 5TB
e-mail: m.shippen@virgin.net
Mobile: 07956 879165   Tel/Fax: 020-8968 1943

SMEE'S ADVERTISING Ltd
3-5 Duke Street, London W1U 3BA
Fax: 020-7935 8588   Tel: 020-7486 6644

SNELL Helen Ltd
4th Floor
80-81 St Martin's Lane
London WC2N 4AA
e-mail: info@helensnell.com
Fax: 020-7240 2947   Tel: 020-7240 5537

STOTT Barbara
20 Sunbury Lane, London SW11 3NP
e-mail: b-stott@tiscali.co.uk   Tel: 020-7350 1159

TARGET LIVE Ltd
(Marketing & Press Support)
Fitzroy House
11 Chenies Street, London WC1E 7EY
e-mail: admin@target-live.co.uk
Fax: 020-7907 1751   Tel: 020-7907 1777

TAYLOR HERRING PUBLIC RELATIONS
11 Westway Centre
69 St Marks Road, London W10 6JG
Website: www.taylorherring.com
e-mail: james.herring@taylorherring.com
Fax: 020-8206 5155   Tel: 020-8206 5151

THOMPSON Peter ASSOCIATES
Flat One, 12 Bourchier Street
London W1V 5HN
Fax: 020-7439 1202   Tel: 020-7439 1210

THORNBORROW Bridget
110 Newark Street, London E1 2ES
e-mail: b.thornborrow@btinternet.com
Fax: 020-7377 6452   Tel: 020-7247 4437

TRE-VETT Eddie
Brink House, Avon Castle, Ringwood
Hampshire BH24 2BL   Tel: 01425 475544

WILLIAMS Tei PRESS & ARTS MARKETING
Post Office Cottage
Clifton, Oxon OX15 0PP
e-mail: artsmarketing@btconnect.com
Mobile: 07957 664116   Tel: 01869 337940

WILSON Stella PUBLICITY & PERSONAL MANAGEMENT
293 Faversham Road
Seasalter, Whitstable, Kent CT5 4BN
e-mail: stella@stellawilson.com   Mobile: 07860 174301

WINGHAM Maureen PRESS & PUBLIC RELATIONS
PO Box 125
Stowmarket
Suffolk IP14 1PB
e-mail: maureen.wingham@mwmedia.uk.com
     Tel: 01449 771200

WRIGHT Peter
(See CUE CONSULTANTS)

R

Radio
BBC Radio
BBC Local Radio Stations
Independent Local Radio

Recording Studios
Rehearsal Studios
Rehearsal Rooms & Casting Suites
Role Play Companies/Theatre Skills
in Business
Routes to Film & Television Studios

It is essential that anyone undertaking a journey to
the studios listed in the Routes section, double
checks these routes. Owing to constant changes of
rail/bus companies/operators routes may change.

[CONTACTS 2008]

BBC RADIO, Broadcasting House
London W1A 1AA
Tel: 020-7580 4468 (Main Switchboard)

• DRAMA

BBC Radio Drama
Bush House
The Aldwych, London WC2B 4PH
Tel: 020-7580 4468 (Main Switchboard)

Production
Head	Alison Hinde
Production Executive	Rebecca Wilmshurst
Administrator Radio Drama Company	Cynthia Fagan

Executive Producers
World Service	Marion Nancarrow
London	David Hunter
	Jeremy Mortimer
	Toby Swift
Manchester	Sue Roberts
Birmingham	Vanessa Whitburn

Producers - London
Marc Beeby	Peter Kavanagh
Steven Canny	Duncan Minshull
Cherry Cookson	Tracey Neale
Jessica Dromgoole	Jonquil Panting
Claire Grove	Liz Webb
Gemma Jenkins	Anne Edyvean (World Service)

Producers - Manchester
Gary Brown	Nadia Molinari
Pauline Harris	Polly Thomas

Producers Birmingham
Naylah Ahmed (Silver Street)
Julie Beckett (Archers)
Kate Chapman
Kate Oates (Archers)
James Peries (Silver Street)
Deborah Sathe (Silver Street)
Peter Wild

Development Producers
Justine Porter (Manchester)	Abigail Le Fleming
Kate Chapman (Birmingham)	Conor Lennon
Sam Hoyle	Justine Potter
	Toby Swift

Writersroom
Director	Kate Rowland

BROADCAST

Radio Drama - BBC Scotland
Head	Patrick Rayner
Editor, Radio Drama	Bruce Young
Management Assistant	Sue Mee

Producers
Gaynor Macfarlane	David Jackson Young
Lu Kemp	

Radio Drama - BBC Wales
Kate McAll

Radio Drama - BBC Northern Ireland
All enquiries to Anne Simpson

LIGHT ENTERTAINMENT/RADIO PRODUCTION

ead, Light Entertainment Radio	Paul Schlesinger
xecutive Producer	Sally Avens

roducers

olin Anderson	Victoria Lloyd
aire Bartlett	Katie Marsden
dam Bromley	Ed Morrish
awn Ellis	Simon Nicholls
Iusha Ghelani	Carol Smith
aire Jones	Katie Tyrrell

roduction Executive	Sophie Butler
usiness Planner	Mel Almond
eputy Head of Radio Entertainment	Will Saunders

NEWS AND CURRENT AFFAIRS

BC News (Television & Radio)
elevision Centre
ood Lane, London W12 7RJ
el: 020-8743 8000 (Main Switchboard)

rector News	Helen Boaden
eputy Director of News	Adrian Van Klaveren
ead of Newsgathering	Fran Unsworth
ead of Political Programmes	
Research & Analysis	Sue Inglish
ead of Radio News	Steve Mitchell
ead of TV News	Peter Horrocks
rector of Sport	Roger Mosey
ontroller of Children's	Richard Deverell
rector of English Networks	Gwyneth Williams
ead of News, Resources & Technology	Peter Coles
ead of Communications	Janie Ironside Wood

RADIO SPORT

ead of Sport	Gordon Turnbull

CONTROLLERS

rector of Audio & Music	Jenny Abramsky

ADIO 1

ontroller	Andy Parfitt

ADIO 2

ontroller	Lesley Douglas

ADIO 3

ontroller	Roger Wright

ADIO 4

ontroller	Mark Damazer

ADIO 5 LIVE

ontroller	Bob Shennan

BBC NEW WRITING

BC Writersroom
rafton House
79-381 Euston Road
ondon NW1 3AU   Tel: 020-7765 2703
mail: writersroom@bbc.co.uk
ebsite: www.bbc.co.uk/writersroom

eative Director	Kate Rowland
evelopment Manager	Paul Ashton

**BBC BEDFORDSHIRE, HERTFORDSHIRE &
BUCKINGHAMSHIRE THREE COUNTIES RADIO**
1 Hastings Street
Luton LU1 5XL
Website: www.bbc.co.uk/threecounties
e-mail: 3cr@bbc.co.uk
Fax: 01582 401467   Tel: 01582 637400
Managing Editor: Angus Mmoorat

BBC RADIO BRISTOL
PO Box 194
Bristol BS99 7QT
Website: www.bbc.co.uk/bristol
e-mail: radio.bristol@bbc.co.uk
Fax: 0117-923 8323   Tel: 0117-974 1111
Managing Editor: Tim Pemberton
News Editor: Charlotte Callen

BBC RADIO CAMBRIDGESHIRE
Broadcasting House
104 Hills Road
Cambridge CB2 1LD
Fax: 01223 460832   Tel: 01223 259696
Managing Editor: Jason Horton
Assistant Editor: Paul Jurgens

BBC RADIO CLEVELAND
PO Box 95 FM
Broadcasting House
Newport Road
Middlesbrough TS1 5DG
Website: www.bbc.co.uk/tees
Fax: 01642 211356   Tel: 01642 225211
Managing Editor: Matthew Barraclough

BBC RADIO CORNWALL
Phoenix Wharf
Truro
Cornwall TR1 1UA
Website: www.bbc.co.uk/cornwall
Fax: 01872 240679   Tel: 01872 275421
Managing Editor: Pauline Causey

BBC COVENTRY & WARWICKSHIRE
Priory Place
Coventry CV1 5SQ
Website: www.bbc.co.uk/coventry
e-mail: coventry.warwickshire@bbc.co.uk
Fax: 024-7655 2000   Tel: 024-7655 1000
Senior Broadcast Journalist: Tim Atkinson

BBC RADIO CUMBRIA
Annetwell Street
Carlisle
Cumbria CA3 8BB
Website: www.bbc.co.uk/radiocumbria
Fax: 01228 511195   Tel: 01228 592444
Managing Editor: Nigel Dyson

BBC RADIO DERBY
PO Box 104.5
Derby DE1 3HL
Website: www.bbc.co.uk/derby   Tel: 01332 361111
Managing Editor: Simon Cornes

BBC RADIO DEVON
PO Box 1034
Plymouth PL3 5YQ
Website: www.bbc.co.uk/devon
Fax: 01752 234564   Tel: 01752 260323
Managing Editor: Robert Wallace

BBC ESSEX
PO Box 765
Chelmsford, Essex CM2 9XB
Website: www.bbc.co.uk/essex
e-mail: essex@bbc.co.uk   Tel: 01245 6160C
Managing Editor: Gerald Main

BBC RADIO GLOUCESTERSHIRE
London Road
Gloucester GL1 1SW
Website: www.bbc.co.uk/gloucestershire   Tel: 01452 30858
Managing Editor: Mark Hurrell

BBC GUERNSEY
Broadcasting House
Bulwer Avenue
St Sampsons
Channel Islands GY2 4LA
Website: www.bbc.co.uk/guernsey
e-mail: radio.guernsey@bbc.co.uk
Fax: 01481 200361   Tel: 01481 2006C
Managing Editor: David Martin
Senior Broadcast Journalist: Simon Alexander

BBC HEREFORD & WORCESTER
Hylton Road
Worcester WR2 5WW
Website: www.bbc.co.uk/herefordandworcester
Managing Editor: James Coghill   Tel: 01905 74848

BBC RADIO HUMBERSIDE
Queens Court
Queens Gardens
Hull HU1 3RH
Website: www.bbc.co.uk/humber
e-mail: radio.humberside@bbc.co.uk
Fax: 01482 226409   Tel: 01482 3232.
Editor: Simon Pattern

BBC RADIO JERSEY
18 & 21 Parade Road
St Helier
Jersey JE2 3PL
Website: www.bbc.co.uk/jersey
Fax: 01534 732569   Tel: 01534 8700C
Editor: Denzil Dudley
Assistant Editor: Matthew Price

BBC RADIO KENT
The Great Hall
Mount Pleasant Road
Tunbridge Wells
Kent TN1 1QQ
Website: www.bbc.co.uk/kent
e-mail: radio.kent@bbc.co.uk   Tel: 01892 6700C
Managing Editor: Paul Leaper

BBC RADIO LANCASHIRE
20-26 Darwen Street
Blackburn
Lancashire BB2 2EA
Website: www.bbc.co.uk/lancashire   Tel: 01254 2624
Editor: John Clayton

BBC RADIO LEEDS
BBC Broadcasting Centre
2 St Peter's Square
Leeds LS9 8AH
Website: www.bbc.co.uk/leeds
Fax: 0113-224 7316   Tel: 0113-244 2⫶
Managing Editor: Phil Roberts

BBC RADIO LEICESTER
9 St Nicholas Place, Leicester LE1 5LB
Website: www.bbc.co.uk/leicester
e-mail: leicester@bbc.co.uk
Fax: 0116-251 1463   Tel: 0116-251 6688
Managing Editor: Kate Squire

BBC RADIO LINCOLNSHIRE
Newport, Lincoln LN1 3XY
Website: www.bbc.co.uk/lincolnshire
Fax: 01522 511058   Tel: 01522 511411
Managing Editor: Charlie Partridge

BBC LONDON 94.9 FM
35C Marylebone High Street
London W1U 4AA
Website: www.bbc.co.uk/london   Tel: 020-7224 2424
Managing Editor: David Robey
Editor: Nikki O'Donnell

BBC RADIO MANCHESTER
PO Box 951
Oxford Road, Manchester M60 1SD
Website: www.bbc.co.uk/manchester   Tel: 0161-200 2000
Managing Editor: John Ryan

BBC RADIO MERSEYSIDE
PO Box 95.8
Liverpool L69 1ZJ
Website: www.bbc.co.uk/liverpool
e-mail: radio.merseyside@bbc.co.uk   Tel: 0151-708 5500
Managing Editor: Mick Ord

BBC RADIO NEWCASTLE
Broadcasting Centre, Barrack Road
Newcastle upon Tyne NE99 1RN
Website: www.bbc.co.uk/tyne
Fax: 0191-232 5082   Tel: 0191-232 4141
Editor: Andrew Robson

BBC RADIO NORFOLK
The Forum
Millennium Plain, Norwich NR2 1BH
Website: www.bbc.co.uk/norfolk
e-mail: radionorfolk@bbc.co.uk
Fax: 01603 284488   Tel: 01603 617411
Managing Editor: David Clayton

BBC NORTHAMPTON
Broadcasting House
Abington Street
Northampton NN1 2BH
Website: www.bbc.co.uk/northamptonshire
e-mail: northampton@bbc.co.uk
Fax: 01604 230709   Tel: 01604 239100
Manager: Laura Moss

BBC RADIO NOTTINGHAM
London Road
Nottingham NG2 4UU
Website: www.bbc.co.uk/nottingham
Fax: 0115-902 1984   Tel: 0115-955 0500
Editor: Sophie Stewart
Editor News Gathering: Emma Agnew

BBC RADIO SHEFFIELD
54 Shoreham Street
Sheffield S1 4RS
Website: www.bbc.co.uk/southyorkshire
e-mail: radio.sheffield@bbc.co.uk
Fax: 0114-267 5454   Tel: 0114-273 1177
Managing Editor: Gary Keown
Senior Broadcast Journalist News: Mike Woodcock

BBC RADIO SHROPSHIRE
2-4 Boscobel Drive
Shrewsbury
Shropshire SY1 3TT
Website: www.bbc.co.uk/shropshire
e-mail: radio.shropshire@bbc.co.uk
Fax: 01743 271702   Tel: 01743 248484
Editor: Tim Beech
Senior Broadcast Journalist News: Sharon Simcock

BBC RADIO SOLENT
Broadcasting House
Havelock Road
Southampton SO14 7PW
Website: www.bbc.co.uk/hampshire
e-mail: radio.solent@bbc.co.uk
Fax: 023-8033 9648   Tel: 023-8063 1311
Managing Editor: Mia Costello

BBC RADIO STOKE
Cheapside
Hanley
Stoke-on-Trent
Staffordshire ST1 1JJ
Website: www.bbc.co.uk/stoke
e-mail: radio.stoke@bbc.co.uk
Fax: 01782 289115   Tel: 01782 208080
Managing Editor: Sue Owen

BBC RADIO SUFFOLK
Broadcasting House
St Matthews Street
Ipswich IP1 3EP
Website: www.bbc.co.uk/suffolk
e-mail: radiosuffolk@bbc.co.uk   Tel: 01473 250000
Editor: Peter Cook

BBC SOUTHERN COUNTIES RADIO
Broadcasting Centre
Guildford
Surrey GU2 7AP
Website: www.bbc.co.uk/southerncounties
e-mail: southern.counties.radio@bbc.co.uk
Fax: 01483 304952   Tel: 01483 306306
Managing Editor: Nicci Holliday
Assistant Editor: Nick Franklin

BBC RADIO SWINDON & BBC RADIO WILTSHIRE
Broadcasting House
56-58 Prospect Place
Swindon SN1 3RW
Website: www.bbc.co.uk/wiltshire
e-mail: radio.wiltshire@bbc.co.uk
Fax: 01793 513650   Tel: 01793 513626
Manager: Tony Worgan

BBC WEST MIDLANDS
The Mailbox
Birmingham B1 1RF
Website: www.bbc.co.uk/westmidlands
e-mail: bbcwm@bbc.co.uk   Tel: 0845 3009956
Editor Local Services: Keith Beech

BBC RADIO YORK
20 Bootham Row
York YO30 7BR
Website: www.bbc.co.uk/northyorkshire
e-mail: radio.york@bbc.co.uk
Fax: 01904 610937   Tel: 01904 641351
Managing Editor: Sarah Drummond

ABERDEEN
Northsound Radio
Abbotswell Road, West Tullos
Aberdeen AB12 3AG
Website: www.northsound.co.uk
e-mail: northsound@srh.co.uk   Tel: 01224 337000

AYR
West Sound FM
Radio House
54A Holmston Road, Ayr KA7 3BE
Website: www.westsound.co.uk
e-mail: westfm@srh.co.uk   Tel: 01292 283662

BELFAST
City Beat 96.7 FM & 102.5 FM
PO Box 967, Belfast BT9 5DF
Website: www.citybeat.co.uk
e-mail: news@citybeat967.co.uk
Fax: 028-9089 0100   Tel: 028-9023 4967

BELFAST
Cool FM
PO Box 974, Belfast BT1 1RT
Website: www.coolfm.co.uk
e-mail: music@coolfm.co.uk
Fax: 028-9181 4974   Tel: 028-9181 7181

BELFAST
Downtown Radio
Newtownards
Co Down BT23 4ES
e-mail: programmes@downtown.co.uk   Tel: 028-9181 5555

BERKSHIRE & NORTH HAMPSHIRE
2-Ten FM
PO Box 2020, Reading
Berkshire RG31 7FG
Website: www.2tenfm.co.uk   Tel: 0118-945 4400

BIRMINGHAM
96.4 BRMB & Capital Gold
Nine Brindley Place
4 Oozells Square
Birmingham B1 2DJ
Website: www.brmb.co.uk   Tel: 0121-226 9964

BORDERS The
Radio Borders Ltd
Tweedside Park, Galashiels TD1 3TD
Website: www.radioborders.com
e-mail: info@radioborders.com
Fax: 0845 3457080   Tel: 01896 759444

BRADFORD
Sunrise Radio
55 Leeds Road
Bradford BD1 5AF
Website: www.sunriseradio.fm
Fax: 01274 728534   Tel: 01274 735043

**BRADFORD, HUDDERSFIELD, HALIFAX,
KEIGHLEY, DEWSBURY**
Pulse Classic Gold
Forster Square
Bradford BD1 5NE
e-mail: general@pulse.co.uk   Tel: 01274 203040

BRIGHTON, EASTBOURNE & HASTINGS
Southern FM
Radio House
PO Box 2000
Brighton BN41 2SS
Website: www.southernfm.com
Fax: 01273 316909   Tel: 01273 430111

BRISTOL
GWR FM & Classic Gold 1260
1 Passage Street
PO Box 2000
Bristol BS99 7SN
Website: www.gwrfm.co.uk
Fax: 0117-984 3202   Tel: 0117-984 3200

CAMBRIDGE & NEWMARKET
Q103 FM
Q103, The Vision Park
Chivers Way, Histon
Cambridge CB4 9WW
Website: www.q103.co.uk   Tel: 01223 235255

CARDIFF & NEWPORT
Red Dragon FM & Capital Gold
Atlantic Wharf
Cardiff Bay
Cardiff CF10 4DJ
Website: www.reddragonfm.com   Tel: 029-2066 2066

CHESTER, NORTH WALES & WIRRAL
Marcher Group & Classic Gold
The Studios
Mold Road
Wrexham LL11 4AF
Website: www.marchersound.co.uk
e-mail: news@marcherradio.com   Tel: 01978 752202
Programme Controller: Lisa Marley

COVENTRY
Mercia FM
Hertford Place
Coventry CV1 3TT
Website: www.merciafm.co.uk
Fax: 024-7686 8209   Tel: 024-7686 8200

COVENTRY
Touch FM
Watch Close
Spon Street, Coventry CV1 3LN
Website: www.intouch.com
Fax: 024-7622 8270   Tel: 024-7652 5656

DUMFRIES
South West Sound FM
Unit 40, The Loreburn Centre
High Street, Dumfries DG1 2BD
Website: www.southwestsound.co.uk
Fax: 01387 265629   Tel: 01387 250999

DUNDEE & PERTH
Tay FM & Radio Tay AM
PO Box 123
6 North Isla Street
Dundee DD3 7JQ
Website: www.radiotay.co.uk
e-mail: tayfm@radiotay.co.uk   Tel: 01382 200800

EDINBURGH
Radio Forth Ltd
Forth House
Forth Street
Edinburgh EH1 3LE
Website: www.forthonline.co.uk
e-mail: info@radioforth.co.uk   Tel: 0131-556 9255

EXETER & TORBAY
Gemini FM
Hawthorn House
Exeter Business Park, Exeter EX1 3QS
Website: www.geminifm.co.uk
Fax: 01392 354249   Tel: 01392 444444

FALKIRK
Central FM
201-203 High Street, Falkirk FK1 1DU
Website: www.centralfm.co.uk
Fax: 01324 611168 · Tel: 01324 611164

GLASGOW
Radio Clyde 1 & Clyde 2
3 South Avenue
Clydebank Business Park, Glasgow G81 2RX
Website: www.clyde1.com / www.clyde2.com
Fax: 0141-565 2265 · Tel: 0141-565 2200

GLOUCESTER & CHELTENHAM
Severn Sound, FM & Classic Gold
Bridge Studios
Eastgate Centre, Gloucester GL1 1SS
Website: www.severnsound.co.uk
Fax: 01452 572409 · Tel: 01452 572400

GREAT YARMOUTH & NORWICH
Radio Broadland & Classic Gold Amber
St Georges Plain
47-49 Colegate, Norwich NR3 1DB
Website: www.radiobroadland.co.uk
Fax: 01603 671189 · Tel: 01603 630621

GUILDFORD
96.4 Eagle Radio
Eagle Radio Ltd, Dolphin House
3 North Street
Guildford, Surrey GU1 4AA
e-mail: onair@964eagle.co.uk · Tel: 01483 300964

HEREFORD & WORCESTER
Wyvern FM
1st Floor, Kirkham House
John Comyn Drive, Worcester WR3 7NS
Website: www.wyvernfm.co.uk · Tel: 01905 612212

INVERNESS
Moray Firth Radio
PO Box 271
Scorguie Place, Inverness IV3 8UJ
Website: www.mfr.co.uk
e-mail: mfr@mfr.co.uk
Fax: 01463 243224 · Tel: 01463 224433

IPSWICH
SGR-FM
Radio House, Alpha Business Park
Whitehouse Road, Ipswich IP1 5LT
Website: www.sgrfm.co.uk
Fax: 01473 467549 · Tel: 01473 461000

ISLE OF WIGHT
Isle of Wight Radio
Dodnor Park, Newport
Isle of Wight PO30 5XE
Website: www.iwradio.co.uk
e-mail: admin@iwradio.co.uk
Fax: 01983 821690 · Tel: 01983 822557

KENT
Invicta FM & Capital Gold
Radio House
John Wilson Business Park
Whitstable, Kent CT5 3QX
Website: www.invictafm.com · Tel: 01227 772004

LEEDS
96.3 Radio Aire & Magic 828
51 Burley Road, Leeds LS3 1LR
Website: www.radioaire.com
Fax: 0113-283 5501 · Tel: 0113-283 5500

LEICESTER, NOTTINGHAM & DERBY
96 Trent FM & Classic Gold GEM
29-31 Castle Gate
Nottingham NG1 7AP
Website: www.trentfm.co.uk
Fax: 0115-873 1569 · Tel: 0115-873 1500

LEICESTER, NOTTINGHAM & DERBY
Leicester Sound
6 Dominus Way, Meridian Business Park
Leicester LE19 1RD
Website: www.leicestersound.co.uk
Fax: 0116-256 1309 · Tel: 0116-256 1300

Nottingham 96 Trent FM & Classic Gold GEM
35-36 Irongate
Derby DE1 3GA
Website: www.musicradio.com
Fax: 0115-873 1509 · Tel: 0115-873 1500

Ram FM
35-36 Irongate
Derby DE1 3GA
Website: www.ramfm.co.uk · Tel: 01332 324000

LIVERPOOL
Radio City
St Johns Beacon
1 Houghton Street, Liverpool L1 1RL
Website: www.radiocity.co.uk · Tel: 0151-472 6800

LONDON
(Independent Radio News) ITN Radio
200 Gray's Inn Road, London WC1X 8XZ
Website: www.irn.co.uk
e-mail: irn@itn.co.uk · Tel: 020-7430 4814

LONDON
102.2 Smooth Radio
26-27 Castlereagh Street, London W1H 5DL
Website: www.smoothradio.com
e-mail: info@smoothradio.com · Tel: 020-7706 4100

LONDON
Capital Gold - London
(GCap Media Plc)
30 Leicester Square, London WC2H 7LA
Website: www.capitalradiogroup.com
Fax: 020-7766 6100 · Tel: 020-7766 6810

LONDON
Choice FM
(GCap Media Plc)
30 Leicester Square, London WC2H 7LA
Website: www.choicefm.com
Fax: 020-7766 6100 · Tel: 020-7766 6810

LONDON
Classic FM
(GCap Media Plc)
30 Leicester Square, London WC2H 7LA
Website: www.classicfm.com
Fax: 020-7344 2700 · Tel: 020-7343 9000

LONDON
Heart 106.2 FM
The Chrysalis Building
Bramley Road, London W10 6SP
Website: www.heart1062.co.uk
Fax: 020-7470 1066 · Tel: 020-7468 1062

LONDON
London Greek Radio
437 High Road, Finchley
London N12 0AP
Website: www.lgr.co.uk · Tel: 020-8349 6950

LONDON
Magic 105.4 FM
Mappin House, 4 Winsley Street, London W1W 8HF
Website: www.magic.co.uk   Tel: 020-7182 8233

LONDON
Time 106.8 FM/Time 107.3 FM
2-6 Basildon Road
London SE2 0EW   Tel: 020-8311 3112

LONDON
Virgin Radio
1 Golden Square, London W1F 9DJ
Website: www.virginradio.co.uk
Fax: 020-7434 1197   Tel: 020-7434 1215

LUTON & BEDFORD
97.6 Chiltern FM & Classic Gold Digital 792/828
Broadcast Centre
Chiltern Road
Dunstable LU6 1HQ
Website: www.chilternfm.co.uk
Fax: 01582 676209   Tel: 01582 676200

MANCHESTER
Key 103 FM & Magic 1152
Piccadilly Radio Ltd, Castle Quay
Castle Field, Manchester M15 4PR
Website: www.key103.co.uk
Fax: 0161-288 5151   Tel: 0161-288 5000

MILTON KEYNES
Horizon Radio
14 Vincent Avenue
Milton Keynes Broadcast Centre
Crownhill, Milton Keynes MK8 0AB
Website: www.horizonmk.co.uk   Tel: 01908 269111

NORTHAMPTON
Northhants 96/Classic Gold 1557
19-21 St Edmunds Road
Northampton NN1 5DT
Website: www.northants96.co.uk   Tel: 01604 795600

NORTHAMPTONSHIRE
Connect FM 97.2 & 107.4 FM
2nd Floor, 5 Church Street
Peterborough PE1 1XB
Website: www.connectfm.com
Fax: 01733 898107   Tel: 0844 8001769

NOTTINGHAM & DERBY
96 Trent FM
Chapel Quarter
Maid Marion Way
Nottingham NG1 6JR
Website: www.trentfm.co.uk   Tel: 0115-873 1500

OXFORD & BANBURY
Fox FM
Brush House
Pony Road, Oxford OX4 2XR
Website: www.foxfm.co.uk   Tel: 01865 871000

PETERBOROUGH
102.7 Hereward FM & Classic Gold
PO Box 225
Queensgate Centre
Peterborough PE1 1XJ
Website: www.hereward.co.uk   Tel: 01733 460460

PLYMOUTH
Plymouth Sound & Classic Gold
Earl's Acre, Alma Road
Plymouth PL3 4HX
Website: www.musicradio.com   Tel: 01752 275600

PORTSMOUTH & SOUTHAMPTON
Power, Ocean & Capital Gold
(GCap Media Plc)
Radio House
Whittle Avenue
Segensworth West
Fareham, Hampshire PO15 5SH
Website: www.powerfm.com   Tel: 01489 589911

SOMERSET
Orchard FM
Haygrove House
Shoreditch Road
Taunton TA3 7BT
Website: www.orchardfm.co.uk   Tel: 01823 338448

SOUTH MANCHESTER
Imagine FM (104.9)
Regent House
Heaton Lane
Stockport
Cheshire SK4 1BX
Website: www.imaginefm.net
e-mail: info@imaginefm.net
Fax: 0161-609 1401   Tel: 0161-609 1400

STOKE-ON-TRENT & STAFFORD
Signal Radio
Stoke Road
Stoke-on-Trent
Staffordshire ST4 2SR
Website: www.signalone.co.uk
e-mail: info@signalradio.com   Tel: 01782 441300

SWANSEA
96.4 FM The Wave
Victoria Road
Gowerton
Swansea SA4 3AB
Website: www.thewave.co.uk   Tel: 01792 511964

TEESSIDE
TFM 96.6 & Magic 1170
Yale Crescent
Teesdale
Thornaby
Stockton on Tees TS17 6AA
Website: www.tfmradio.co.uk   Tel: 01642 888222

TYNE & WEAR & NORTHUMBERLAND, DURHAM
Metro Radio
55 Degrees, Pilgrim Street
Newcastle upon Tyne NE1 6BF
Website: www.metroradio.co.uk   Tel: 0191-230 6100

WOLVERHAMPTON & BLACK COUNTRY/SHREWSBURY & TELFORD
West Midlands Beacon Radio
267 Tettenhall Road
Wolverhampton WV6 0DE
Website: www.beaconradio.co.uk   Tel: 01902 461200

YORKSHIRE
Hallam FM & Magic AM
Radio House
900 Herries Road
Hillsborough, Sheffield S6 1RH
Website: www.hallamfm.co.uk   Tel: 0114-209 1000

YORKSHIRE & LINCOLNSHIRE
96.9 Viking FM & Magic 1161 AM
Commercial Road
Hull HU1 2SG
Website: www.vikingfm.co.uk   Tel: 01482 325141

ABBEY ROAD STUDIOS
Abbey Road
St. John's Wood
London NW8 9AY
Website: www.abbeyroad.com
e-mail: bookings@abbeyroad.com
Fax: 020-7266 7250   Tel: 020-7266 7000

AIR-EDEL RECORDING STUDIOS Ltd
18 Rodmarton Street
London W1U 8BJ
e-mail: trevorbest@air-edel.co.uk
Fax: 020-7224 0344   Tel: 020-7486 6466

ANGEL RECORDING STUDIOS Ltd
311 Upper Street
London N1 2TU
e-mail: angel@angelstudio.co.uk
Fax: 020-7226 9624   Tel: 020-7354 2525

ANT FARM STUDIOS VOICE-OVERS
Outhend Farm
Outhend Lane
Waltham Abbey EN9 3SE
Website: www.antfarmstudios.co.uk
e-mail: antfarmstudio@yahoo.co.uk   Tel: 01992 714664

ASCENT MEDIA Ltd
Film House
142 Wardour Street
London W1F 8DD
Website: www.ascentmedia.co.uk
Fax: 020-7878 7870   Tel: 020-7878 0000

BLACKHEATH HALLS
23 Lee Road
Blackheath
London SE3 9RQ
Website: www.blackheathhalls.com
e-mail: piershenderson@blackheathhalls.com
Fax: 020-8852 5154   Tel: 020-8318 9758

CHANNEL 2020 Ltd
The Clerkenwell Workshops (G15)
27-31 Clerkenwell Close
London EC1R 0AT
Website: www.channel2020.co.uk
e-mail: info@channel2020.co.uk   Tel: 0844 8402020

CHANNEL 2020 Ltd
2020 House
26-28 Talbot Lane
Leicester LE1 4LR
Website: www.channel2020.co.uk
e-mail: info@channel2020.co.uk
Fax: 0116-222 1113   Tel: 0844 8402020

CONCEPT
PO Box 192, Liverpool L69 1JA
Website: www.soundconcept.co.uk
e-mail: info@soundconcept.co.uk   Tel: 0151-522 9133

CTS/LANSDOWNE RECORDING STUDIOS Ltd
PO Box 47189
London W6 6DA
Website: www.cts-lansdowne.co.uk
e-mail: info@cts-lansdowne.co.uk
Fax: 056-0115 5009   Tel: 020-8846 9444

CUT GLASS PRODUCTIONS
(Voice-over Showreels/Voice-over Production)
7 Crouch Hall Road
Crouch End, London N8 8HT
Website: www.cutglassproductions.com
e-mail: info@cutglassproductions.com
                                  Tel/Fax: 020-8374 4701

DE LANE LEA SOUND
(Post-Production, Re-Recording Studios)
75 Dean Street
London W1D 3PU
Website: www.delanelea.com
e-mail: solutions@delanelea.com
Fax: 020-7432 3838   Tel: 020-7432 3800

ELMS STUDIOS
(Mac G5/Logic Pro 7/O2RV2/Composing/Scoring for
Film & TV)
Phil Lawrence
10 Empress Avenue, London E12 5ES
Website: www.elmsstudios.com
e-mail: info@elmsstudios.com   Tel: 020-8518 8629

ESSENTIAL MUSIC
20 Great Chapel Street
London W1F 8FW
e-mail: admin@essentialmusic.co.uk
Fax: 020-7287 3597   Tel: 020-7439 7113

FARM DIGITAL POST-PRODUCTION The
27 Upper Mount Street
Dublin 2
Ireland
Website: www.thefarm.ie
e-mail: info@thefarm.ie
Fax: 00 353 1 676 8816   Tel: 00 353 1 676 8812

HEAVY ENTERTAINMENT Ltd
111 Wardour Street
London W1F 0UH
Website: www.heavy-entertainment.com
e-mail: info@heavy-entertainment.com
Fax: 020-7494 1100   Tel: 020-7494 1000

JMS GROUP Ltd
(Multimedia Production)
3 Montagu Row
London W1U 6DY
Website: www.jms-group.com
e-mail: info@jms-group.com
Fax: 020-7224 4035   Tel: 020-7224 1031

Park Farm Studios
Norwich Road
Hethersett, Norfolk NR9 3DL
Fax: 01603 812255   Tel: 01603 811855

KONK STUDIOS
84-86 Tottenham Lane
London N8 7EE
e-mail: linda@konkstudios.com
Fax: 020-8348 3952   Tel: 020-8340 7873

MOTIVATION SOUND STUDIOS
35A Broadhurst Gardens, London NW6 3QT
Website: www.motivationsound.co.uk
e-mail: info@motivationsound.co.uk
Fax: 020-7624 4879   Tel: 020-7328 830

MUSIC IN MOTION Ltd
1 Reubens Court
Chaseley Drive
Chiswick, London W4 4BD
Website: www.neilmyers.com
e-mail: neil@neilmyers.com
Mobile: 07813 070961   Tel: 020-8400 370

OTHERWISE STUDIOS
61D Gleneldon Road
London SW16 2BH
Website: www.otherwisestudios.com
e-mail: info@otherwisestudios.com   Tel: 020-8769 779

Q SOUND
Queen's Studios
117-121 Salusbury Road
London NW6 6RG
Website: www.qsound.uk.com
e-mail: info@qsound.uk.com   Tel: 020-7625 535

RED FACILITIES
61 Timberbush
Leith, Edinburgh EH6 6QH
Website: www.redfacilities.com
e-mail: doit@redfacilities.com
Fax: 0131-555 0088   Tel: 0131-555 228

SARM WEST STUDIOS Ltd
8-10 Basing Street, London W11 1ET
Website: www.sarmstudios.com
e-mail: mel@spz.com
Fax: 020-7221 9247   Tel: 020-7229 1229

SHAW Bernard
(Specialist in Recording & Directing Voice Tapes)
Horton Manor
Canterbury CT4 7LG
Website: www.bernardshaw.co.uk
e-mail: bernard@bernardshaw.co.uk   Tel/Fax: 01227 730843

SILVER-TONGUED PRODUCTIONS
(Specializing in the recording and production of Voice Reels)
78 Ramillies Road
Sidcup DA15 9JH
Website: www.silver-tongued.co.uk
e-mail: contactus@silver-tongued.co.uk   Tel: 020-8309 0659

SONIC POND STUDIO
(Specialising in Voice Reels for Actors)
70 Mildmay Grove South
Islington, London N1 4PJ
Website: www.sonicpond.co.uk
e-mail: info@sonicpond.co.uk   Tel: 020-7690 8561

SOUND COMPANY Ltd The
73 Gosfield Street, London W1W 6HG
Website: www.sound.co.uk
e-mail: info@sound.co.uk
Fax: 020-7580 6454   Tel: 020-7580 5880

SOUND CONCEPTION
The Fire Station
82-84 York Road, Bristol BS3 4AL
Website: www.soundconception.com
e-mail: soundconception@btconnect.com
Fax: 0117-963 5059   Tel: 0117-966 2932

SOUND HOUSE POST PRODUCTION Ltd The
10th Floor, Astley House
Quay Street
Manchester M3 4AE
Website: www.thesoundhouse.tv
e-mail: mail@thesoundhouse.tv
Fax: 0161-832 7266   Tel: 0161-832 7299

SOUND MARKETING
Strattons House, Strattons Walk
Melksham, Wiltshire SN12 6JL
Website: www.soundm.com
e-mail: nicki@soundm.com
Fax: 01225 701601   Tel: 01225 701600

STUDIO AVP
32 Clifton Hill
London NW8 0JT
Fax: 020-7624 9112   Tel: 020-7624 9111

UNIVERSAL SOUND (JUST PLAY) Ltd
Old Farm Lane
London Road East
Amersham
Buckinghamshire HP7 9DH
Website: www.universalsound.co.uk
e-mail: foley@universalsound.co.uk
Fax: 01494 723500   Tel: 01494 723400

VSI - VOICE & SCRIPT INTERNATIONAL
(Foreign Language Specialists - Translation, Subtitling, Casting, Dubbing, Recording Studios, Editing)
132 Cleveland Street
London W1T 6AB
Website: www.vsi.tv
e-mail: info@vsi.tv
Fax: 020-7692 7711   Tel: 020-7692 7700

WARWICK HALL OF SOUND
Warwick Hall
Off Banastre Avenue
Heath, Cardiff CF14 3NR
www.myspace.com/cardiffswarwickhallrecordingstudio
e-mail: adamstangroom@btconnect.com
     Tel/Fax: 029-2069 4455

WFS Ltd
(Sound Transfer/Optical & Magnetic)
Warwick Sound
111A Wardour Street
London W1F 0UJ
Website: www.warwicksound.com
e-mail: studio@warwicksound.com
Fax: 020-7439 0372   Tel: 020-7437 5532

WORLDWIDE SOUND Ltd
21-25 St Anne's Court
Soho, London W1F 0BJ
Website: www.worldwidegroup.ltd.uk
e-mail: sound@worldwidegroup.ltd.uk
Fax: 020-7734 0619   Tel: 020-7494 8000

3 MILLS STUDIOS
Three Mill Lane, London E3 3DU
Website: www.3mills.com
e-mail: info@3mills.com
Fax: 020-8215 3499   Tel: 020-7363 3336

ACTORS CENTRE The (LONDON)
(Audition Space Only)
1A Tower Street, London WC2H 9NP
e-mail: roomhire@actorscentre.co.uk
Fax: 020-7240 3896   Tel: 020-7632 8011

ACTOR'S TEMPLE The
13 Warren Street, London W1T 5LG
Website: www.actorstemple.com
e-mail: info@actorstemple.com
Mobile: 07771 734670   Tel: 020-7383 3535

ADI The
218 Lambeth Road, London SE1 7JY
e-mail: playltd@btconnect.com   Tel: 020-7928 6160

ALFORD HOUSE
Aveline Street, London SE11 5DQ
e-mail: tim@alfordhouse.org.uk   Tel: 020-7735 1519

ALL TALENT UK
Central Chambers, 93 Hope Street, Glasgow G2 6LD
Website: www.alltalentuk.co.uk
e-mail: enquiries@alltalentuk.co.uk
Fax: 0141-221 8883   Tel: 0141-221 8887

ALRA (Academy of Live and Recorded Arts)
The Royal Victoria Patriotic Building
Fitzhugh Grove, Trinity Road, London SW18 3SX
Website: www.alra.co.uk
e-mail: enquiries@alra.co.uk
Fax: 020-8875 0789   Tel: 020-8870 6475

AMADEUS CENTRE The
50 Shirland Road, London W9 2JA
Website: www.amadeuscentre.co.uk
e-mail: info@amadeuscentre.co.uk
Fax: 020-7266 1225   Tel: 020-7286 1686

AMERICAN CHURCH IN LONDON The
Whitefield Memorial Church
79A Tottenham Court Road, London W1T 4TD
Website: www.latchcourt.com
e-mail: latchcourt@amchurch.fsnet.co.uk
Fax: 020-7580 5013   Tel: 020-7580 2791

ARTSADMIN
Toynbee Studios, 28 Commercial Street, London E1 6AB
Website: www.artsadmin.co.uk
e-mail: admin@artsadmin.co.uk
Fax: 020-7247 5103   Tel: 020-7247 5102

AVIV DANCE STUDIOS
Wren House, 1st Floor
19-23 Exchange Road, Watford WD18 6JD
Website: www.avivdance.com
e-mail: nikkiavron@btconnect.com   Tel/Fax: 01923 250000

BAC
Lavender Hill, London SW11 5TN
Website: www.bac.org.uk
e-mail: mailbox@bac.org.uk
Fax: 020-7978 5207   Tel: 020-7223 6557

BELSIZE MUSIC ROOMS
(Casting, Auditioning, Filming)
67 Belsize Lane, Hampstead, London NW3 5AX
Website: www.belsize-music-rooms.co.uk
e-mail: info@belsize-music-rooms.co.uk
Fax: 020-7916 0222   Tel: 020-7916 0111

BIG CITY STUDIOS
Montgomery House
159-161 Balls Pond Road
Islington, London N1 4BG
Website: www.pineappleagency.com
Fax: 020-7241 3006   Tel: 020-7241 6655

BLACK BOX MERSEYSIDE Ltd
The Black Box Venue
91 Hutchinson Walk
Off West Derby Road
Liverpool
Merseyside L6 1JW
Website: www.blackbox.uk.net
e-mail: info@blackbox.uk.net
Fax: 0151-706 0252   Tel: 0151-706 0251

BLOOMSBURY THEATRE The
15 Gordon Street, London WC1H 0AH
Website: www.thebloomsbury.com
e-mail: blooms.theatre@ucl.ac.uk   Tel: 020-7679 2777

BRIXTON COMMUNITY SPACE
(Formerly Brixton St Vincent's Community Centre)
Talma Road, London SW2 1AS   Website: www.bsvcc.org
e-mail: carofunnell@bsvcc.org   Tel: 020-7326 4417

BRIXTON ST VINCENT'S COMMUNITY CENTRE
(See BRIXTON COMMUNITY SPACE)

CAST IN SPACE
27 Little Russell Street, London WC1A 2HN
Website: www.castinspace.com
e-mail: castinspace@btconnect.com
Fax: 020-7404 9641   Tel: 020-7404 9637

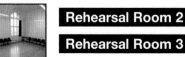

The Cameron Mackintosh **REHEARSAL STUDIO** *9x15 metres*

✳ Production Office also available ✳ Bar & Cafe open daily

⊖ Kilburn ⇌ Brondesbury Buses: 16, 31, 32, 98, 189, 206, 316, 328

The Tricycle, 269 Kilburn High Road, London NW6 7JR Telephone: 020 7372 6611 Fax: 020 7328 0795

CASTING AT SWEET
Sweet Entertainments Ltd
42 Theobalds Road, London WC1X 8NW
e-mail: casting@sweet-uk.net
Fax: 07092 863782   Tel: 020-7404 6411

CASTING STUDIOS INTERNATIONAL Ltd
Ramillies House
1-2 Ramillies Street, London W1F 7LN
Website: www.castingstudios.com
e-mail: info@castingstudios.com
Fax: 020-7437 2080   Tel: 020-7437 2070

CASTING SUITE The
8-10 Lower James Street
(Off Golden Square), London W1F 9EL
Website: www.thecastingsuite.co.uk
e-mail: info@thecastingsuite.co.uk
Fax: 020-7494 0803   Tel: 020-7534 5757

CECIL SHARP HOUSE
2 Regent's Park Road, London NW1 7AY
Website: www.efdss.org
e-mail: hire@efdss.org
Fax: 020-7284 0534   Tel: 020-7485 2206

CENTRAL LONDON GOLF CENTRE
Burntwood Lane, London SW17 0AT
Website: www.clgc.co.uk
Fax: 020-8874 7447   Tel: 020-8871 2468

CENTRAL STUDIOS
470 Bromley Road, Bromley, Kent BR1 4PN
Website: www.dandbperformingarts.co.uk
e-mail: bonnie@dandbmanagement.com
Fax: 020-8697 8100   Tel: 020-8698 8880

CHAIN REACTION THEATRE COMPANY
Three Mills Studios
Sugar House Yard, Sugar House Lane, London E15 2QS
Website: www.chainreactiontheatre.co.uk
e-mail: mail@chainreactiontheatre.co.uk
                              Tel/Fax: 020-8534 0007

CHATS PALACE ARTS CENTRE
42-44 Brooksby's Walk
Hackney, London E9 6DF
Website: www.chatspalace.com
e-mail: info@chatspalace.com   Tel: 020-8533 0227

CHELSEA THEATRE
(Contact: James Tilston)
World's End Place
King's Road, London SW10 0DR
Website: www.chelseatheatre.org.uk
e-mail: admin@chelseatheatre.org.uk
Fax: 020-7352 2024   Tel: 020-7349 7811

CIRCUS MANIACS SCHOOL OF CIRCUS ARTS
(Circus Skills Rehearsal & Casting Facilities)
Office 8A, The Kingswood Foundation
Britannia Road, Kingswood, Bristol BS15 8DB
Website: www.circusmaniacs.com
e-mail: rehearse@circusmaniacs.com
Mobile: 07977 247287   Tel/Fax: 0117-947 7042

CLAPHAM COMMUNITY PROJECT
St Anne's Hall, Venn Street, London SW4 0BN
Website: www.rehearseatccp.co.uk
e-mail: admin@claphamcommunityproject.org.uk
                              Tel/Fax: 020-7720 873

CLEAN BREAK
2 Patshull Road, London NW5 2LB
Website: www.cleanbreak.org.uk
e-mail: general@cleanbreak.org.uk
Fax: 020-7482 8611   Tel: 020-7482 860

CLUB FOR ACTS & ACTORS
(Incorporating Concert Artistes Association)
20 Bedford Street, London WC2E 9HP
Website: www.thecaa.org
e-mail: office@thecaa.org   Tel: 020-7836 317

COLOMBO CENTRE The
(Rehearsal & Auditon Space)
34-68 Colombo Street, London SE1 8DP
Website: www.colombo-cetre.org
e-mail: clubmanager@colombo-centre.org
                              Tel: 020-7261 1658

COPTIC STREET STUDIO Ltd
9 Coptic Street, London WC1A 1NH
Fax: 020-7636 1414   Tel: 020-7636 203

COVENT GARDEN CASTING SUITES & AUDITION ROOMS
14-16 Betterton Street, London WC2H 9BU
e-mail: castingsuite@aol.com
Fax: 020-7681 0612   Tel: 020-7240 143

CRAGRATS Ltd
The Mill, Dunford Road
Holmfirth, Huddersfield HD9 2AR
Website: www.cragrats.com
e-mail: benroot@cragrats.com
Fax: 01484 686212   Tel: 01484 68645

CUSTARD FACTORY The
Gibb Street, Digbeth, Birmingham B9 4AA
Website: www.custardfactory.co.uk
e-mail: post@custardfactory.co.uk
Fax: 0121-604 8888   Tel: 0121-224 777

DANCE ATTIC STUDIOS
368 North End Road
London SW6   Tel: 020-7610 205

HOLY INNOCENTS CHURCH *Rehearsal Spaces Available*

Lower Hall: 900 sq feet. Kitchen. Piano
Upper Hall: 1800 sq feet. Kitchen. Piano
Church: Sympathetic Acoustics for Music Rehearsals. Max 50 Players.
Hourly & Weekly rates on request.
Paddenswick Road London W6 Tel: 020~8748 2286 Fax: 020~8563 8735

DANCE COMPANY STUDIOS
76 High Street
Beckenham, Kent BR3 1ED
Website: www.dancecompanystudios.co.uk
e-mail: hire@dancecompanystudios.co.uk
Tel: 020-8402 2424

DANCEWORKS
16 Balderton Street
London W1K 6TN
Website: www.danceworks.net
Fax: 020-7629 2909 Tel: 020-7318 4100

DAVIES Siobhan STUDIOS
85 St George's Road, London SE1 6ER
Website: www.siobhandavies.com
e-mail: info@siobhandavies.com
Fax: 020-7091 9669 Tel: 020-7091 9650

DIORAMA ARTS
1 Euston Centre
London NW1 3JG
Website: www.diorama-arts.org.uk
e-mail: admin@diorama-arts.org.uk Tel: 020-7916 5467

DRILL HALL The
16 Chenies Street, London WC1E 7EX
Website: www.drillhall.co.uk
e-mail: box.office@drillhall.co.uk
Fax: 020-7307 5062 Tel: 020-7307 5060

EALING STUDIOS
Ealing Green
London W5 5EP
Website: www.ealingstudios.com
e-mail: bookings@ealingstudios.com
Fax: 020-8758 8658 Tel: 020-8567 6655

ELMS LESTERS PAINTING ROOMS
1-3-5 Flitcroft Street, London WC2H 8DH
e-mail: info@elmslester.co.uk
Fax: 020-7379 0789   Tel: 020-7836 6747

ENGLISH FOLK DANCE & SONG SOCIETY
Cecil Sharp House, 2 Regent's Park Road, London NW1 7AY
Website: www.efdss.org
e-mail: info@efdss.org
Fax: 020-7284 0534   Tel: 020-7485 2206

ENGLISH NATIONAL OPERA
Lilian Baylis House
165 Broadhurst Gardens, London NW6 3AX
Website: www.eno.org
e-mail: receptionlbh@eno.org
Fax: 020-7625 3398   Tel: 020-7624 7711

ENGLISH TOURING THEATRE
25 Short Street, Waterloo, London SE1 8LJ
Website: www.ett.org.uk
e-mail: admin@ett.org.uk
Fax: 020-7633 0188   Tel: 020-7450 1990

ESSEX HALL
Unitarian Headquarters
1-6 Essex Street, London WC2R 3HY
Fax: 020-7240 3089   Tel: 020-7240 2384

ET-NIK-A CASTING STUDIO
30 Great Portland Street, London W1W 8QU
Website: www.etnikastudios.com
e-mail: info@etnikastudios.com
Fax: 020-7299 3558   Tel: 020-7193 4230

ETCETERA THEATRE
265 Camden High Street, London NW1 7BU
Website: www.etceteratheatre.com
e-mail: etc@etceteratheatre.com
Fax: 020-7482 0378   Tel: 020-7482 4857

EUROKIDS & ADULTS AGENCY CASTING STUDIOS
The Warehouse Studios, Glaziers Lane, Culcheth
Warrington, Cheshire WA3 4AQ
Website: www.eka-agency.com
e-mail: castings@eka-agency.com
Fax: 01925 767563   Tel: 01925 761088

EXCHANGE The
Old Market Hill, Sturminster Newton DT10 1QU
Website: www.stur-exchange.com
e-mail: info@stur-exchange.com
Fax: 01258 475137

EXPRESSIONS STUDIOS
Linton House, 39-51 Highgate Road, London NW5 1RS
Website: www.expressionsstudios.com
e-mail: info@expressionsstudios.com
Fax: 020-7813 1582   Tel: 020-7813 1580

FACTORY DANCE CENTRE
407 Hornsey Road, London N19 4DX
e-mail: info@tangolondon.com   Tel: 020-7272 1122

FOX CASTING STUDIOS & REHEARSAL SPACE
Pinewood Studios, Pinewood Rd, Iver Heath, Bucks SL0 0NH
e-mail: info@actorsstudio.co.uk   Tel: 01753 656848

FSU LONDON STUDY CENTRE
98-104 Great Russell Street, London WC1B 3LA
Fax: 020-7813 3270   Tel: 020-7813 3223

HAMPSTEAD THEATRE
Eton Avenue, Swiss Cottage, London NW3 3EU
Website: www.hampsteadtheatre.com
e-mail: info@hampsteadtheatre.com
Fax: 020-7449 4201   Tel: 020-7449 4200

HATSTAND CIRCUS STUDIO
98 Milligan Street, Westferry, London W14 8AS
Website: www.hatstandcircus.co.uk
e-mail: helenahatstand@btconnect.com Tel: 020-7538 3368

HAYLOFT The
The Hayloft Rehearsal Room
The Stables Gallery & Arts Centre
Brent Arts Council, Gladstone Park, Dollis Hill Lane
London NW2 6HT   Tel: 020-8452 8655

HER MAJESTY'S THEATRE
(Michael Townsend)
Haymarket, London SW1Y 4QL
Website: www.rutheatres.com
e-mail: mike.townsend@rutheatres.com Tel: 020-7240 0880

HOLY INNOCENTS CHURCH
Paddenswick Road, London W6 0UB
e-mail: innocent@fish.co.uk
Fax: 020-8563 8735   Tel: 020-8748 2286

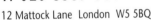

OPE STREET Ltd
A Hope Street
verpool L1 9BQ
ebsite: www.hope-street.org
mail: arts@hope-street.org
x: 0151-709 3242　　　　　Tel: 0151-708 8007

OXTON HALL THEATRE & YOUTH ARTS CENTRE
0 Hoxton Street, London N1 6SH
ebsite: www.hoxtonhall.co.uk
mail: admin@hoxtonhall.co.uk
x: 020-7729 3815　　　　　Tel: 020-7684 0060

T SPACE Ltd
it 2, 210 Cambridge Heath Road
ndon E2 9NQ
ebsite: www.imagemusictext.com
mail: mail@imagemusictext.com　Tel: 020-8980 5475

ISLINGTON ARTS FACTORY
2 Parkhurst Road, London N7 0SF
Website: www.islingtonartsfactory.org.uk
e-mail: iaf@islingtonartsfactory.fsnet.co.uk
Fax: 020-7700 7229　　　　Tel: 020-7607 0561

JACKSONS LANE
(Various Spaces incl Rehearsal Rooms & Theatre Hire)
269A Archway Road, London N6 5AA
Website: www.jacksonslane.org.uk
e-mail: mail@jacksonslane.org.uk
Tel: 020-8340 5226　　　　Tel: 020-8340 8902

JERWOOD SPACE
171 Union Street, London SE1 0LN
Website: www.jerwoodspace.co.uk
e-mail: space@jerwoodspace.co.uk
Fax: 020-7654 0172　　　　Tel: 020-7654 0171

BRIXTON COMMUNITY BASE
* FORMERLY BRIXTON ST VINCENT'S COMMUNITY CENTRE *

◄ REHEARSAL STUDIO 16 x 7.5 metres ►
SECOND SPACE AVAILABLE
Piano / keyboards / showers / facility for aerial work / WiFi
Full Disabled Access
TEL − 020 7326 4417
Brixton Tube − Victoria line   **www.bsvcc.org**   Talma Road SW2 1AS

LA MAISON VERTE
31 Avenue Henri Mas, 34320 Roujan, France
Website: www.lamaisonverte.co.uk
e-mail: anne.roberts@lamaisonverte.co.uk
Tel: 00 33 4 67 24 88 52

LEGAL CAFE The
81 Haverstock Hill, London NW3 4SL
Website: www.81haverstockhill.com
e-mail: thelegalcafe@81haverstockhill.com
Tel/Fax: 020-7586 7149

LIVE THEATRE
27 Broad Chare, Quayside, Newcastle upon Tyne NE1 3DQ
Website: www.live.org.uk
e-mail: info@live.org.uk
Tel: 0191-261 2694

LONDON BUBBLE THEATRE COMPANY Ltd
5 Elephant Lane, London SE16 4JD
Website: www.londonbubble.org.uk
e-mail: admin@londonbubble.org.uk
Fax: 020-7231 2366
Tel: 020-7237 4434

LONDON SCHOOL OF CAPOEIRA
Units 1 & 2 Leeds Place
Tollington Park, London N4 3RF
Website: www.londonschoolofcapoeira.co.uk
e-mail: info@londonschoolofcapoeira.co.uk
Tel: 020-7281 2020

LONDON STUDIO CENTRE
42-50 York Way, London N1 9AB
e-mail: info@london-studio-centre.co.uk
Fax: 020-7837 3248
Tel: 020-7837 7741

LONDON WELSH TRUST Ltd
157-163 Gray's Inn Road, London WC1X 8UE
Fax: 020-7837 6268
Tel: 020-7837 3722

LYRIC HAMMERSMITH
King Street, London W6 0QL
Website: www.lyric.co.uk
e-mail: enquiries@lyric.co.uk
Fax: 020-8741 5965
Tel: 0870 0500511

MACKINTOSH Cameron REHEARSAL STUDIO
The Tricycle, 269 Kilburn High Road, London NW6 7JR
Website: www.tricycle.co.uk
e-mail: admin@tricycle.co.uk
Fax: 020-7328 0795
Tel: 020-7372 6611

MADDERMARKET THEATRE
St John's Alley, Norwich, Norfolk NR2 1DR
Website: www.maddermarket.co.uk
e-mail: mmtheatre@btconnect.com
Fax: 01603 661357
Tel: 01603 62656

MARIA ASSUMPTA CENTRE
23 Kensington Square, London W8 5HN
Website: www.maria-assumpta.org.uk
e-mail: conf@maria-assumpta.org.uk
Tel: 020-7361 470

MENIER CHOCOLATE FACTORY
53 Southwark Street, London SE1 1RU
Website: www.menierchocolatefactory.com
e-mail: office@menierchocolatefactory.com
Fax: 020-7378 1713
Tel: 020-7378 17

MOBERLY SPORTS & EDUCATION CENTRE
Kilburn Lane, London W10 4AH
Fax: 020-7641 5878
Tel: 020-7641 480

MOUNTVIEW
Academy of Theatre Arts
Ralph Richardson Memorial Studios
Kingfisher Place
Clarendon Road, London N22 6XF
Website: www.mountview.ac.uk
e-mail: enquiries@mountview.ac.uk
Fax: 020-8829 0034
Tel: 020-8881 22

MUSIC ROOM AT COLE KITCHENN
212 Strand, London WC2R 1AP
e-mail: info@colekitchenn.com
Tel: 020-7427 568

NATIONAL YOUTH THEATRE OF GREAT BRITAIN
443-445 Holloway Road, London N7 6LW
Website: www.nyt.org.uk   e-mail: info@nyt.org.
Fax: 020-7281 8246
Tel: 020-7281 38

NETTLEFOLD The
West Norwood Library Centre
1 Norwood High Street, London SE27 9JX
e-mail: thenettlefold@lambeth.gov.uk   Tel: 020-7926 80

NEW PLAYERS THEATRE
The Arches, Off Villiers Street, London WC2N 6NG
Website: www.newplayerstheatre.com
e-mail: info@newplayerstheatre.com
Fax: 0845 6382102
Tel: 020-7930 66

▮LPAC PERFORMING ARTS
Production & Casting Office Facilities)
6 St James Lane, Muswell Hill, London N10 3DF
Website: www.nlpac.co.uk   e-mail: nlpac@aol.com
ax: 020-8444 4040   Tel: 020-8444 4544

▮OUGHTE CASTING STUDIOS
5-46 Poland Street, London W1F 7NA
-mail: info@noughte.co.uk
ax: 020-7437 2830   Tel: 020-7437 2823

▮CTOBER GALLERY
4 Old Gloucester Street, London WC1N 3AL
Website: www.octobergallery.co.uk
-mail: rentals@octobergallery.co.uk
ax: 020-7405 1851   Tel: 020-7831 1618

▮LD VIC THEATRE The
ne Cut, London SE1 8NB
Website: www.oldvictheatre.com
                                     Tel: 020-7928 2651

▮PEN DOOR COMMUNITY CENTRE
eaumont Road, Wimbledon SW19 6TF
Website: www.wandsworth.gov.uk
-mail: opendoor@wandsworth.gov.uk Tel/Fax: 020-8871 8174

▮UT OF JOINT
Thane Works, Thane Villas, London N7 7NU
Website: www.outofjoint.co.uk e-mail: ojo@outofjoint.co.uk
ax: 020-7609 0203   Tel: 020-7609 0207

VAL HOUSE
2-54 Kennington Oval, London SE11 5SW
Website: www.ovalhouse.com
-mail: info@ovalhouse.com   Tel: 020-7582 0080

AINES PLOUGH AUDITION SPACE
th Floor, 43 Aldwych, London WC2B 4DN
Website: www.painesplough.com
-mail: office@painesplough.com
ax: 020-7240 4534   Tel: 020-7240 4533

▮EOPLE SHOW
eople Show Studios, Pollard Row, London E2 6NB
ebsite: www.peopleshow.co.uk
-mail: people@peopleshow.co.uk
ax: 020-7739 0203   Tel: 020-7729 1841

▮HA
anzaro House, Ardwick Green North, Manchester M12 6FZ
Website: www.pha-agency.co.uk
-mail: info@pha-agency.co.uk
ax: 0161-273 4567   Tel: 0161-273 4444

▮NEAPPLE DANCE STUDIOS
Langley Street, London WC2H 9JA
ebsite: www.pineapple.uk.com
-mail: studios@pineapple.uk.com
ax: 020-7836 0803   Tel: 020-7836 4004

PLACE The
Robin Howard Dance Theatre
17 Duke's Road
London WC1H 9PY
Website: www.theplace.org.uk
e-mail: info@theplace.org.uk
Fax: 020-7121 1142   Tel: 020-7121 1000

PLAYGROUND STUDIO The
Unit 8, Latimer Road
London W10 6RQ
Website: www.the-playground.co.uk
e-mail: info@the-playground.co.uk   Tel/Fax: 020-8960 0110

POOR SCHOOL The
242 Pentonville Road, London N1 9JY
Website: www.thepoorschool.com
e-mail: acting@thepoorschool.com   Tel: 020-7837 6030

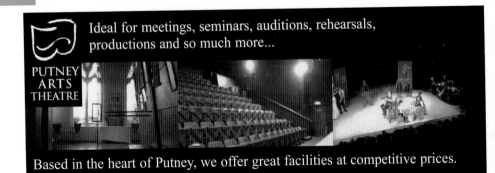
PRECINCT THEATRE The
Units 2/3 The Precinct
Packington Square, London N1 7UP
Website: www.breakalegman.com
e-mail: reima@breakalegman.com
Fax: 020-7359 3660
Tel: 020-7359 3594

PUPPET CENTRE TRUST
BAC Lavender Hill
London SW11 5TN
Website: www.puppetcentre.org.uk
e-mail: space@puppetcentre.org.uk
Tel: 020-7228 5335

QUESTORS THEATRE EALING The
12 Mattock Lane, London W5 5BQ
Website: www.questors.org.uk
e-mail: alice@questors.org.uk
Fax: 020-8567 2275
Tel: 020-8567 0011

QUICKSILVER THEATRE
The Glasshouse, 4 Enfield Road, London N1 5AZ
Website: www.quicksilvertheatre.org
e-mail: talktous@quicksilvertheatre.org
Fax: 020-7254 3119
Tel: 020-7241 2942

RAG FACTORY The
16-18 Heneage Street, London E1 5LJ
Website: www.ragfactory.org.uk
e-mail: hello@ragfactory.org.uk
Fax: 020-7092 9099
Tel: 020-7650 8749

RAMBERT DANCE COMPANY
94 Chiswick High Road, London W4 1SH
Website: www.rambert.org.uk   e-mail: rdc@rambert.org.uk
Fax: 020-8747 8323
Tel: 020-8630 0600

REALLY USEFUL THEATRES
(Michael Townsend)
22 Tower Street, London WC2H 9TW
Website: www.ruttheatres.com
e-mail: mike.townsend@ruttheatres.com
Fax: 020-7240 1292
Tel: 020-7240 0880

RED ONION DANCE STUDIO
26-28 Hatherley Mews, London E17 4QP
Website: www.redonion.uk.com
e-mail: info@redonion.uk.com
Fax: 020-8521 6646
Tel: 020-8520 4215

RIDGEWAY STUDIOS
Fairley House, Andrews Lane, Cheshunt, Herts EN7 6LB
Fax: 01992 633844
Tel: 01992 633775

RIVERSIDE STUDIOS
Crisp Road, Hammersmith, London W6 9RL
Website: www.riversidestudios.co.uk
e-mail: info@riversidestudios.co.uk
Fax: 020-8237 1001
Tel: 020-8237 1000

ROOFTOP STUDIO THEATRE
Rooftop Studio, Somerfield Arcade
Stone, Staffordshire ST15 8AU
Website: www.rooftopstudio.co.uk
Fax: 01785 818176
Tel: 01785 76123

ROOMS ABOVE The
(Opposite The Emmanuel School)
Westheath Yard, 174 Mill Lane
West Hampstead, London NW6 1TB
Website: www.theroomsabove.org.uk
e-mail: info@theroomsabove.org.uk
Fax: 020-8201 9464
Tel: 0845 686080

ROTHERHITHE STUDIOS
119 Rotherhithe Street, London SE16 4NF
Website: www.sandsfilms.co.uk
e-mail: ostockman@sandsfilms.co.uk
Fax: 020-7231 2119
Tel: 020-7231 220

The Playground Studio
2,500sq.ft beautiful rehearsal space
London W10

Sprung Floor
Mirrored Wall
Natural Day Light

www.the-playground.co.uk
info@the-playground.co.uk
T: 020 8960 0110

The Playground

ROYAL ACADEMY OF DANCE
36 Battersea Square, London SW11 3RA
Website: www.rad.org.uk
e-mail: info@rad.org.uk
Fax: 020-7924 3129 Tel: 020-7326 8000

ROYAL ACADEMY OF DRAMATIC ART
62-64 Gower Street, London WC1E 6ED
e-mail: bookings@rada.ac.uk Tel: 020-7908 4754

ROYAL SHAKESPEARE COMPANY
35 Clapham High Street, London SW4 7TW
e-mail: london@rsc.org.uk
Fax: 020-7845 0505 Tel: 020-7845 0500

SADLER'S WELLS
Rosebery Avenue, London EC1R 4TN
Website: www.sadlerswells.com
e-mail: events@sadlerswells.com
Fax: 020-7863 8061 Tel: 020-7863 8065

SEA CADET DRILL HALL
Fairways, Off Broom Road
Teddington TW11 9PL Tel: 01784 241020

SEBBON STREET COMMUNITY CENTRE
Sebbon Street, Islington
London N1 2DZ Tel: 020-7354 2015

SHARED EXPERIENCE THEATRE
The Soho Laundry, 9 Dufours Place, London W1F 7SJ
Website: www.sharedexperience.org.uk
e-mail: admin@sharedexperience.org.uk
Fax: 020-7287 8763 Tel: 020-7734 8570

SMA CENTRE
Vicarage Gate, Kensington, London W8 4HN
Website: www.smacentre.com
e-mail: manager@smacentre.com
Fax: 020-7368 6505 Tel: 020-7937 8885

SPOTLIGHT PUBLICATIONS
SPOTLIGHT INTERACTIVE
SPOTLIGHT SERVICES

THE SPOTLIGHT ROOMS
& STUDIOS

Spacious rooms and studios
in the heart of the West End

- Free receptionist service
- Large waiting room
- Wireless Internet
- Video conference facilities
- Post free audition clips online
- Competitive rates

www.spotlight.com/rooms
For bookings: 020 7440 5030 email: rooms@spotlight.com
7 Leicester Place London WC2H 7RJ

SOHO GYMS
Clapham Common Gym
95-97 Clapham High Street, London SW4 7TB
Website: www.sohogyms.com
Fax: 020-7720 6510   Tel: 020-7720 0321

Covent Garden Gym
12 Macklin Street, London WC2B 5NF
Fax: 020-7242 0899   Tel: 020-7242 1290

Earl's Court Gym
254 Earl's Court Road, London SW5 9AD
Fax: 020-7244 6893   Tel: 020-7370 1402

Camden Town Gym
193-199 Camden High Street, London NW1 7JY
Website: www.sohogyms.com
Fax: 020-7267 0500   Tel: 020-7482 4524

SOHO THEATRE
21 Dean Street, London W1D 3NE
Website: www.sohotheatre.com
e-mail: jenny@sohotheatre.com
Fax: 020-7287 5061   Tel: 020-7478 0115

SPACE @ CLARENCE MEWS
40 Clarence Mews, London E5 8HL
e-mail: frith.salem@virgin.net   Tel: 020-8986 5260

SPACE ARTS CENTRE The
269 Westferry Road, London E14 3RS
Website: www.space.org.uk
e-mail: info@space.org.uk   Tel: 020-7515 7799

SPACE CITY STUDIOS
77 Blythe Road, London W14 0HP
Website: www.spacecity.co.uk
e-mail: info@spacecity.co.uk
Fax: 020-7371 4001   Tel: 020-7610 5000

SPACE PRODUCTIONS
Media Centre, 67 Dulwich Road, London SE24 0NJ
e-mail: space_productions@yahoo.com
Mobile: 07957 249911   Tel/Fax: 020-7924 9766

S.P.A.C.E. The
(Studio for Performing Arts & Creative Enterprise)
1st Floor, 84 Miller Street, Glasgow G1 1DT
Website: www.west-endmgt.com
e-mail: info@west-endmgt.com
Fax: 0141-226 8983   Tel: 0141-222 2942

SPOTLIGHT The
2nd Floor, 7 Leicester Place, London WC2H 7RJ
Website: www.spotlight.com/rooms
e-mail: info@spotlight.com
Fax: 020-7437 5881   Tel: 020-7437 7631

ST GEORGE'S CHURCH BLOOMSBURY
Vestry Hall, 6 Little Russell Street
London WC1A 2HR
Website: www.stgeorgesbloomsbury.org.uk
e-mail: stgeorgebloomsbury@hotmail.com
                                     Tel/Fax: 020-7242 1979

ST JAMES'S CHURCH PICCADILLY
197 Piccadilly, London W1J 9LL
Website: www.st-james-piccadilly.org
e-mail: roomhire@st-james-piccadilly.org
Fax: 020-7734 7449   Tel: 020-7734 451

ST JOHN'S CHURCH
Waterloo Road
Southbank, London SE1 8TY
Fax: 020-7928 4470   Tel: 020-7633 981

ST MARY'S CHURCH HALL PADDINGTON
c/o Bill Kenwright Ltd
106 Harrow Road, London W2 1RR
e-mail: zoe.caldwell@kenwright.com
Fax: 020-7446 6222   Tel: 020-7446 620

ST MARY NEWINGTON CHURCH HALL
The Parish Office
57 Kennington Park Road
London SE11 4JQ   Tel: 020-7735 189

STUDIO 326
Royal Exchange, St Ann's Square
Manchester M2 7BR
Website: www.emmastafford.tv
e-mail: info@emmastafford.tv
Fax: 0161-833 4264   Tel: 0161-833 426

SUMMERS Mark STUDIOS
137 Freston Road
London W10 6TH
Website: www.marksummers.com
e-mail: info@marksummers.com
Fax: 020-7243 1987   Tel: 020-7299 841

TAKE FIVE CASTING STUDIO
(Casting Suite)
37 Beak Street, London W1F 9RZ
Website: www.takefivestudio.com
e-mail: info@takefivestudio.com
Fax: 020-7287 3035   Tel: 020-7287 212

THEATRE ROYAL DRURY LANE
(Michael Townsend)
Catherine Street
London WC2B 5JF
Website: www.rutheatres.com
e-mail: mike.townsend@rutheatres.com
                                     Tel: 020-7240 088

TREADWELL'S
4 Tavistock Street
London WC2E 7PB
Website: www.treadwells-london.com/rehearsal.asp
e-mail: info@treadwells-london.com   Tel: 020-7240 8906

TRESTLE ARTS BASE
(Home of Trestle Theatre Company)
Russet Drive, St Albans, Herts AL4 0JQ
Website: www.trestle.org.uk
e-mail: admin@trestle.org.uk
Fax: 01727 855558   Tel: 01727 850950

TRICYCLE The
269 Kilburn High Road, London NW6 7JR
Website: www.tricycle.co.uk
e-mail: admin@tricycle.co.uk
Fax: 020-7328 0795   Tel: 020-7372 6611

TS
206 The Greenhouse
Custard Factory, Gibb Street
Digbeth, Birmingham B9 4AA
Website: www.myspace.com/trustudies
e-mail: trustreetdance@fresnomail.com
Fax: 0121-224 8257   Tel: 0121-471 3893

TWICKENHAM SEA CADETS
Fairways, Off Broom Road
Teddington
Middlesex TW11 9PL   Tel: 01784 241020

UNION CHAPEL PROJECT
Compton Avenue, London N1 2XD
Website: www.unionchapel.org.uk
e-mail: spacehire@unionchapel.org.uk
Fax: 020-7354 8343   Tel: 020-7226 3750

URDANG ACADEMY The
Finsbury Town Hall
Rosebery Avenue, London EC1
Website: www.theurdangacademy.com
e-mail: info@theurdangacademy.com
Fax: 020-7278 6727   Tel: 020-7713 7710

WALKING FORWARD Ltd
Studio 1
35 Britannia Row, London N1 8QH
Website: www.walkingforward.co.uk
e-mail: info@walkingforward.co.uk
Fax: 020-7359 5091   Tel: 020-7359 5249

WATERMANS
40 High Street, Brentford TW8 0DS
Website: www.watermans.org.uk
e-mail: info@watermans.org.uk
Fax: 020-8232 1030   Tel: 020-8232 1020

Y TOURING THEATRE COMPANY
One KX, 120 Cromer Street
London WC1H 8BS
Website: www.ytouring.org.uk
e-mail: info@ytouring.org.uk   Tel: 020-7520 3090

YOUNG ACTORS THEATRE
70-72 Barnsbury Road, London N1 0ES
Website: www.yati.org.uk
e-mail: info@yati.org.uk
Fax: 020-7833 9467   Tel: 020-7278 2101

YOUNG Sylvia THEATRE SCHOOL
Rossmore Road
Marylebone, London NW1 6NJ
e-mail: info@sylviayoungtheatreschool.co.uk
Fax: 020-7723 1040   Tel: 020-7723 0037

ACTIVATION
Riverside House, Feltham Avenue
Hampton Court, Surrey KT8 9BJ
Website: www.activation.co.uk
e-mail: info@activation.co.uk
Fax: 020-8783 9345　　　　　　　Tel: 020-8783 9494

ACT UP
Unit 88, 99-109 Lavender Hill, London SW11 5QL
Website: www.act-up.co.uk
e-mail: info@act-up.co.uk
Fax: 020-7924 6606　　　　　　　Tel: 020-7924 7701

APROPOS PRODUCTIONS Ltd
2nd Floor
91A Rivington Street, London EC2A 3AY
Website: www.aproposltd.com
e-mail: info@aproposltd.com
Fax: 020-7739 3852　　　　　　　Tel: 020-7739 2857

BARKING PRODUCTIONS/INSTANT WIT
(Comedy Improvisation Show/Corporate Entertainment &
Drama Based Training)
PO Box 597, Bristol BS99 2BB
Website: www.barkingproductions.co.uk
e-mail: info@barkingproductions.co.uk
Fax: 0117-908 5384　　　　　　　Tel: 0117-939 3171

BROWNE Michael ASSOCIATES Ltd
The Cloisters, 168C Station Road
Lower Standon, Bedfordshire SG16 6JQ
Website: www.mba-roleplay.co.uk
e-mail: enquiries@mba-roleplay.co.uk
　　　　　　　　　　　Tel/Fax: 01462 812483

BUZZWORD FILMS
(Role Play, Film Training Dramas)
Website: www.buzzword-films.co.uk
e-mail: mike.ferrand@buzzword-films.co.uk
Mobile: 07974 355885　　　　　　Tel: 01395 44689

CRAGRATS Ltd
Cragrats Mill
Dunford Road
Holmfirth
Huddersfield HD9 2AR
Website: www.cragrats.com
e-mail: info@cragrats.com
Fax: 01484 686212　　　　　　　Tel: 01484 68645

DRAMA FOR TRAINING
Impact Universal
Hopebank House
Woodhead Road
Honley
Huddersfield HD9 6PF
Website: www.impactonlearning.com
e-mail: sharon.taylor@impactonlearning.com
Fax: 01484 660088　　　　　　　Tel: 01484 66888

INTERACT
Bowden House
14 Bowden Street
London SE11 4DS
Website: www.interact.eu.com
e-mail: info@interact.eu.com
Fax: 020-7793 7755　　　　　　　Tel: 020-7793 774

'Improvement through Performance'

Theatre and is a creative training and communications company delivering drama based training workshops to public and private sector clients and motivational performances to young people.

Our available contract lengths vary from just a few weeks to a few months.

For further information on the types of contract available and the benefits of working with **Theatre and**, please have a look at the Recruitment Section of our website

T: 01484 532967
E: clare@theatreand.com
W: www.theatreand.com

NV MANAGEMENT Ltd
Central Office
4 Carters Leaze
Great Wolford
Warwickshire CV36 5NS
Website: www.nvmanagement.co.uk
e-mail: hello@nvmanagement.co.uk

PERFORMANCE BUSINESS The
78 Oatlands Drive
Weybridge, Surrey KT13 9HT
Website: www.theperformance.biz
e-mail: michael@theperformance.biz   Tel: 01932 888885

ROLEPLAY UK
2 St Mary's Hill, Stamford PE9 2DW
Website: www.roleplayuk.com
Fax: 01780 764436   Tel: 01780 761960

STEPS DRAMA LEARNING DEVELOPMENT
Unit 4.1.1, The Leathermarket
Weston Street, London SE1 3ER
Website: www.stepsdrama.com   e-mail: mail@stepsdrama.com
Fax: 020-7403 0909   Tel: 020-7403 9000

THEATRE AND
Church Hall, St James Road
Marsh, Huddersfield HD1 4QA
Website: www.theatreand.com
e-mail: clare@theatreand.com
Fax: 01484 532962   Tel: 01484 532967

WEST END WORKSHOPS
(Audition Coaching/Arts Workshops)
Website: www.westendworkshops.co.uk
e-mail: info@westendworkshops.co.uk
Mobile: 07989 422808

www.interact.eu.com

interact – a training, development and communications company utilising the skills of professional actors, directors and writers for training and assessment throughout the private and public sectors. Roleplay is only a part of what we do.

To be considered for work with us send a hard copy (no emails or phone calls) of your Acting CV, casting photograph and covering letter or corporate CV detailing relevant experience in the corporate world. We cannot reply to individual applicants, however, all CVs are read and prioritised. Applications from ethnic minorities especially welcomed.

To: CV Interact Bowden House 14 Bowden St. London SE11 4DS

3 MILLS STUDIOS
UNDERGROUND - DISTRICT OR HAMMERSMITH & CITY LINE to BROMLEY-BY-BOW. Buses 52, 108, S5 or N25.

BBC TELEVISION
UNDERGROUND – CENTRAL LINE to WHITE CITY. Turn left from tube, cross zebra crossing. Studios outside station.

BBC South (Elstree) – BOREHAMWOOD
Trains from KINGS CROSS - Thames Link. Take stopping train to Elstree then walk (7/8 mins down Shenley High St.)
UNDERGROUND – NORTHERN LINE to EDGWARE or HIGH BARNET.
107 & 292 BUSES FROM EDGWARE VIA HIGH BARNET TO BOREHAMWOOD.

BRAY STUDIOS (BRAYSWICK)
BR Train from PADDINGTON to MAIDENHEAD. Then take taxi to studios
BR WATERLOO - WINDSOR RIVERSIDE. Take taxi. Coach from VICTORIA to WINDSOR. Take taxi.

THE LONDON STUDIOS
(LONDON TELEVISION CENTRE)
UNDERGROUND (Bakerloo, Jubilee and Northern Lines) to WATERLOO, take South Bank exit, follow signs to National Theatre then two buildings along.

PINEWOOD
UNDERGROUND – METROPOLITAN or PICCADILLY LINE to UXBRIDGE. BRITISH RAIL from PADDINGTON to SLOUGH. CHILTERN LINE from MARYLEBONE to GERRARDS CROSS and DENHAM. We offer a shuttle bus service from the stations in UXBRIDGE and SLOUGH at various times throughout the day. For pick up points and times see www.pinewoodgroup.com/bus. Taxis are also available from UXBRIDGE, GERRARDS CROSS, DENHAM and SLOUGH and take about 10 minutes.

RIVERSIDE STUDIOS
UNDERGROUND – HAMMERSMITH and CITY, DISTRICT or PICCADILLY LINE to HAMMERSMITH – then short walk to studios (behind the Carling Apollo Hammersmith). Numerous BUS ROUTES from the WEST END. 7 minutes from Hammersmith Broadway.

ROTHERHITHE STUDIOS
UNDERGROUND – DISTRICT LINE to WHITECHAPEL – then change to EAST LONDON LINE to ROTHERHITHE. JUBILEE LINE to CANADA WATER then EAST LONDON LINE to ROTHERHITHE (5 mins walk). BUS – 188 from EUSTON STATION via WATERLOO or 47 from LONDON BRIDGE or 381 from WATERLOO (best one to catch stops outside Studios).

SHEPPERTON STUDIOS
BRITISH RAIL – SOUTHERN REGION WATERLOO to SHEPPERTON then BUS Route 400 to studios. Taxi or 15 Minute Walk.

TEDDINGTON STUDIOS
(THAMES TELEVISION)
BRITISH RAIL – WATERLOO to TEDDINGTON. Cross over footbridge at station. Come out of Station Road entrance. Turn Left past Garden Centre to NatWest at right hand side. Turn Right walk 10 mins to set of lights, cross over into Ferry Road and follow road to Studios (next to Anglers Pub on river).
UNDERGROUND – DISTRICT LINE to RICHMOND – then take taxi or Bus R68 to TEDDINGTON to top of Ferry Road. Ask for Landmark Centre then go back to traffic lights, cross over and continue past the Tide End Public House to Anglers Pub etc.

TWICKENHAM
BRITISH RAIL – SOUTHERN REGION – WATERLOO to ST MARGARET'S. UNDERGROUND – DISTRICT LINE to RICHMOND then SOUTHERN REGION or BUS 37 to ST MARGARET'S.

D SET COMPANY
Sets, Scenery Design & Construction)
Temperance Street, Manchester M12 6HR
Website: www.3dsetco.com
-mail: twalsh@3dsetco.com
ax: 0161-273 6786   Tel: 0161-273 8831

LBEMARLE SCENIC STUDIOS
Suppliers of Scenery & Costumes Construction/Hire)
O Box 166, Heathfield, East Sussex TN21 8UD
Website: www.freespace.virgin.net/albemarle.productions
-mail: albemarle.productions@virgin.net
ax: 01435 867854   Tel: 0845 6447021

LL SCENE ALL PROPS
Scenery, Props, Painting Contractors)
nits 2 & 3, Spelmonden Farm, Goudhurst, Kent TN17 1HE
Website: www.allscene.net
-mail: info@allscene.net
ax: 01580 211131   Tel: 01580 211121

RISTOL (UK) Ltd
Scenic Paint)
nit 3, Southerland Court, Tolpits Lane, Watford WD18 9SP
Website: www.bristolpaint.com
-mail: tech.sales@bristolpaint.com
ax: 01923 779666   Tel: 01923 779333

CT LIGHTING UK Ltd
Lighting, Dimmers, Sound & Stage Machinery)
nit 3, Ellesmere Business Park, Haydn Road
herwood, Nottingham NG5 1DX
Website: www.cctlighting.com
-mail: office@cctlighting.co.uk
ax: 0115-985 7091   Tel: 0115-985 8919

OD STEAKS
Set Construction, Design, Model Making, Exhibitions,
ostume)
Cole Road, Bristol BS2 0UG
Website: www.codsteaks.com
-mail: mail@codsteaks.com   Tel: 0117-980 3910

REW CO
Stage & Technical Crew for London & Midlands)
5 Main Street, Long Compton, Warwickshire CV36 5JS
Website: www.crewco.net
-mail: contactus@crewco.net
ax: 0845 4589411   Tel: 0845 4589400

ECORATIVE ART PROJECTS
4 Kenley Road, Merton Park, London SW19 3DS
Website: www.dapstudio.co.uk
-mail: james@dapstudio.co.uk   Tel/Fax: 01892 730897

ISPLAY MAINTENANCE Ltd
nit 4 Redhouse Farm, Bridgehewick
ipon, North Yorkshire HG4 5AY
Website: www.dmnsolutions.co.uk
-mail: enquiries@dmnsolutions.co.uk   Tel: 0870 8508500

OBSON SOUND PRODUCTION Ltd
Sound Hire, Design & Installation)
6 Windsor Avenue, Merton, London SW19 2RR
-mail: enquiries@dobsonsound.co.uk
ax: 020-8543 3636   Tel: 020-8545 0202

OVETAIL SPECIALIST SCENERY
Scenery, Prop & Furniture Builders)
2-50 York Way, London N1 9AB
-mail: dovetail.ss@btopenworld.com   Tel/Fax: 020-7278 7379

UTURIST SOUND & LIGHT Ltd
layton Wood Road
ingroad West Park, Leeds LS16 6RA
ax: 0113-230 5233   Tel: 0113-230 5222

S

**Set Construction, Lighting,
Sound & Scenery**

[CONTACTS 2008]

HALL STAGE Ltd
Unit 4, Cosgrove Way, Luton, Beds LU1 1XL
Website: www.hallstage.com
e-mail: sales@hallstage.com
Fax: 0845 3454256   Tel: 0845 3454255

HARLEQUIN (British Harlequin Plc)
Festival House, Chapman Way
Tunbridge Wells, Kent TN2 3EF
Website: www.harlequinfloors.com
e-mail: sales@harlequinfloors.com
Fax: 01892 514222   Tel: 01892 514888

HENSHALL John
(Director of Lighting & Photography)
68 High Street, Stanford in the Vale, Oxfordshire SN7 8NL
e-mail: john@epi-centre.com   Tel: 01367 710191

HERON & DRIVER
(Scenic Furniture & Structural Prop Makers)
Unit 7, Dockley Road Industrial Estate
Rotherhithe, London SE16 3SF
Website: www.herondriver.co.uk
e-mail: mail@herondriver.co.uk
Fax: 020-7394 8680   Tel: 020-7394 8688

KNIGHT Robert
1-2 Wyvern Way, Henwood, Ashford, Kent TN24 8DW
Fax: 01233 634999   Tel: 01233 634777

LEE LIGHTING Ltd
Wycombe Road, Wembley, Middlesex HA0 1QD
e-mail: info@lee.co.uk
Fax: 020-8902 5500   Tel: 020-8900 2900

LIGHT WORKS Ltd
2A Greenwood Road, London E8 1AB
Fax: 020-7254 0306   Tel: 020-7249 3627

LIVERPOOL SCENIC WORKSHOP Ltd
Baltic Road, Bootle, Liverpool L20 1AW
Website: www.liverpoolscenicworkshop.com
e-mail: scenic@liverpoolscenicworkshop.com
Fax: 0151-933 6699   Tel: 0151-933 6677

MALTBURY STAGING
(Portable Staging Sales & Consultancy)
72A Beaconsfield Road, Brighton BN1 6DD
Website: www.maltbury.com   e-mail: info@maltbury.com
Fax: 01273 504748   Tel: 0845 1308881

MASSEY Bob ASSOCIATES
(Electrical & Mechanical Stage Consultants)
9 Worrall Avenue, Arnold, Nottinghamshire NG5 7GN
e-mail: bm.associates@virgin.net   Tel/Fax: 0115-967 3969

MODELBOX
(Computer Aided Design & Design Services)
2 Saddlers Way, Okehampton, Devon EX20 1TL
Website: www.modelbox.co.uk
e-mail: info@modelbox.co.uk   Tel/Fax: 01837 54026

MOUNSEY Matthew
(Scenic Artist)
16 White Cliff House, Vermont Road, London SW18 2LH
e-mail: matthewmounsey@hotmail.com Mobile: 07941 355450

NEED Paul J
(Lighting Designer)
5 Orchard Business Centre
Kangley Bridge Road, London SE26 5AQ
Website: www.10outof10.co.uk e-mail: paul@10outof10.co.uk
Fax: 020-8778 9217   Tel: 020-8291 6885

NORTHERN LIGHT
(Lighting, Sound, Communications & Stage Equipment)
Assembly Street, Leith, Edinburgh EH6 7RG
Website: www.northernlight.co.uk
e-mail: info@northernlight.co.uk
Fax: 0131-622 9101   Tel: 0131-622 9100

ORBITAL
(Sound Hire & Design)
57 Acre Lane, Brixton, London SW2 5TN
Website: www.orbital.sound.co.uk
e-mail: hire@orbitalsound.co.uk
Fax: 020-7501 6869   Tel: 020-7501 686

P.L. PARSONS (1995) Ltd
Unit 58, T Marchant Trading Estate
42-72 Verney Road, London SE16 3DH
Website: www.steeldeck.co.uk
e-mail: info@steeldeck.co.uk
Fax: 020-7232 1780   Tel: 020-7833 20

PMB THEATRE & EXHIBITION SERVICES Ltd
The Barn, Kingston Wood Manor
Arrington, Royston, Herts SG8 0AP
Website: www.pmbltd.co.uk
Fax: 01954 718032   Tel: 01954 71822

RE VAMP EVENTS & ENTERTAINMENT
(Cabaret, Decor, Event Management & Entertainment)
Ealing House
33 Hanger Lane, London W5 3HJ
e-mail: revampevents@aol.com   Tel: 020-8997 335

REVOLVING STAGE COMPANY Ltd The
Unit F5, Little Heath Industrial Estate
Old Church Road, Coventry
Warwickshire CV6 7ND
Website: www.therevolvingstagecompany.co.uk
e-mail: enquiries@therevolvingstagecompany.co.uk
Fax: 024-7668 9355   Tel: 024-7668 705

RWS ELECTRICAL & AUDIO CONTRACTORS Ltd
(All Aspects of Electrical Services including Installation,
Design & Consultancy)
1 Spinners Close, Biddenden, Kent TN27 8AY
Website: www.rwselectrical.com   Tel: 01580 2917€

S + H TECHNICAL SUPPORT Ltd
(Starcloths, Drapes)
Starcloth Way, Mullacott Industrial Estate
Ilfracombe, Devon EX34 8PL
Website: www.starcloth.co.uk
e-mail: shtsg@aol.com
Fax: 01271 865423   Tel: 01271 86683

S2 EVENTS
(Production - Lighting, Set Construction & Scenery)
3-5 Valentine Place, London SE1 8QH
Fax: 020-7928 6082   Tel: 020-7928 547

SCENA PROJECTS Ltd
(Set Construction)
240 Camberwell Road, London SE5 0DP
Website: www.scenapro.com
e-mail: info@scenapro.com
Fax: 020-7703 7012   Tel: 020-7703 444

SCOTT FLEARY PRODUCTIONS Ltd
Unit 2, Southside Industrial Estate
Havelock Terrace, London SW8 4AH
e-mail: matt@scottflearyltd.com
Fax: 020-7622 0322   Tel: 020-7978 178

SCOTT MYERS
(Sound Design & Original Music for Theatre)
36 Madras Road, Cambridge CB1 3PX
Website: www.sound.design.freeuk.com
e-mail: scott.myers100@gmail.com
Mobile: 07757 283702   Tel: 01223 41563

SETS IN THE CITY Ltd
Location House, 5 Dove Lane, Bristol BS2 9HP
Website: www.setsinthecity.co.uk
e-mail: info@setsinthecity.co.uk
Fax: 0117-955 2480   Tel: 0117-955 553

AGECRAFT Ltd
re & Sales of Lighting, Sound, Audio Visual & Staging for
nference & Live Events)
hfield Trading Estate
lisbury, Wiltshire SP2 7HL
bsite: www.stagecraft.co.uk
mail: hire@stagecraft.co.uk
x: 01722 414076   Tel: 01722 326055

AGE SYSTEMS
esigners & Suppliers of Modular Staging, Tiering &
ditorium Seating)
age House, Prince William Road
ughborough LE11 5GU
bsite: www.stagesystems.co.uk
mail: info@stagesystems.co.uk
x: 01509 233146   Tel: 01509 611021

AGEWORKS WORLDWIDE PRODUCTIONS
cenery, Props, Lighting & Sound)
5 Ocean Boulevard, Blackpool, FY4 1EZ
bsite: www.stageworkswwp.com
mail: info@stageworkswwp.com
x: 01253 342702   Tel: 01253 342427

EWART Helen
heatre Designer)
Quernmore Road, London N4 4QP
bsite: www.helenstewart.co.uk
mail: design@helenstewart.co.uk   Mobile: 07887 682186

ORM LIGHTING Ltd
it 6 Wintonlea Industrial Estate
nument Way West, Woking, Surrey GU21 5EN
mail: info@stormlighting.co.uk
x: 01483 757710   Tel: 01483 757211

RAND LIGHTING Ltd
ghting Equipment for Stage, Studio, Film & TV)
it 2 Royce Road, Fleming Way
awley, West Sussex RH10 9JY
bsite: www.strandlighting.com
x: 01293 554019   Tel: 01293 554010

FFOLK SCENERY
The Street, Brettenham, Ipswich, Suffolk IP7 7QP
bsite: www.suffolkscenery.info   e-mail: piehatch@aol.com
x: 01449 737620   Tel: 01449 736679

EME PARTY COMPANY The
et Design Backdrops & Props)
The Cour, Pledgdon Hall, Henham CM22 6BJ
bsite: www.maineventpartiesuk.co.uk
mail: steve@maineventpartiesuk.co.uk
x: 01279 850732   Tel: 01279 851999

TMS INT Ltd
(Set Construction & Painting)
306 St James Road, London SE5 5JX
e-mail: admin@tmsi.co.uk   Tel: 020-7277 5156

TOP SHOW
(Props, Scenery, Conference Specialists)
North Lane, Huntington
York YO32 9SU   Tel: 01904 750022

WEST John ASSOCIATES
(Painting & Design)
103 Abbotswood Close
Winyates Green
Redditch
Worcestershire B98 0QF
Website: www.johnwestartist.co.uk
e-mail: johnwest@blueyonder.co.uk
Mobile: 07753 637451   Tel/Fax: 01527 516771

WHITE LIGHT Ltd
(Stage & TV Lighting)
20 Merton Industrial Park
Jubilee Way
London SW19 3WL
Website: www.whitelight.ltd.uk
e-mail: info@whitelight.ltd.uk
Fax: 020-8254 4801   Tel: 020-8254 4800

WOOD Rod
(Scenic Artist, Backdrops, Scenery, Props, Design &
Fine Art Copies)
41 Montserrat Road
London SW15 2LD
Mobile: 07887 697646   Tel: 020-8788 1941

Television
Television (BBC London)
BBC Television & Sound (Regional)
Independent

Theatre Producers
Theatre
Alternative & Community
Children's, Young People's & TIE
English Speaking in Europe
London
Outer London, Fringe & Venues
Provincial/Touring
Puppet Theatre Companies
Repertory (Regional)

Where appropriate, Rep periods are indicated,
e.g. (4 Weekly) and matinee times e.g. Th 2.30 for
Thursday 2.30pm.
SD Stage Door
BO Box Office
TIE Theatre in Education (For further details of
TIE/YPT
        See Theatre - Children's, Young People's & TIE

BBC Television
Wood Lane, London W12 7RJ
Tel: 020-8743 8000

• TALENT RIGHTS GROUP
BBC Finance, Property & Business Affairs
MC1 A2 Media Centre
201 Wood Lane, London W12 7TQ

Head of Talent Rights Group   Simon Hayward-Ta

LITERARY COPYRIGHT
Rooms 395 & 396 Design Building
Television Centre, Wood Lane
London W12 7SB

Rights Manager   Neil Hu
Rights Executives   Sara
                                     Harriet Coo
                                     Sharon Cowl
                                     Sue Dicks
                                     Julie Gallagh
                                     Jane Har
                                     Rebecca Hog
                                     Hazel Ki
                                     David Knig
                                     Wai Lan La
                                     Julieann M
                                     Sally Millwo
                                     Hilary Sag
                                Andrew Livingst
                                     Carolyn Tu

FACTUAL & CLASSICAL MUSIC
Room 3205, White City Building
Wood Lane, London W12 7TR

CLASSICAL MUSIC
Rights Manager   Simon Brow
Rights Executives   Penelope Davi
                                     Hilary Dod
                                     John Hunt
                                     Shirley No
                                Sheilagh Morris
                                     Pamela Wi
                                     Selena Harv
                                     Naomi Anders

FACTUAL TV
Rights Manager   Annie Thom
Rights Executives   Lorraine Cla
                                     Chris Dab
                                     Selena Harv
                                     Jonathan Sla
                                     Naomi Anders

[CONTACTS2008]

TALENT RIGHTS GROUP Cont'd

MUSIC COPYRIGHT
Room 201, EBX Blk
Television Centre
Wood Lane
London W12 7SB

Rights Manager	Nicky Bignell
Rights Executives	Sally Dunsford
	Catherine Grimes
	Rosarie O'Sullivan
	Victoria Payne
	Natasha Pullin
	Debbie Rogerson

DRAMA, ENTERTAINMENT & CHILDRENS
Rooms 341-352
Design Building
Television Centre
Wood Lane, London W12 7RJ

Rights Manager	John Holland
Rights Executives	
Stephanie Beynon	Annie Pollard
Mike Bickerdike	Thalia Reynolds
Alex Davenport	Colette Robertson
Sally Dean	Lloyd Shepherd

ENGLISH REGIONS:

BIRMINGHAM
Level 10, The Mailbox
Birmimgham B1 1RF

Rights Manager (Job Share)	Andrea Coles
	Jill Ridley
Rights Executive	Chanel Camilleri

BRISTOL
Room 17.3 TPR
Bristol BH BS8 2LR

Rights Manager	Annie Thomas

MANCHESTER
Room 2030
Manchester NBH
Manchester M60 1SJ

Rights Manager	Shirley Chadwick

• DRAMA

Controller, Drama Production Studio	John Yorke
Director, Drama Production Studio	Nicolas Brown
Head of Series & Serials	Kate Harwood
Executive Producer, Eastenders	Diederick Santer
Creative Director	Manda Levin
Head of Production	Susy Liddell
Head of Development	Lisa Osborne

Executive Producers, Drama Production

Ruth Caleb	Sue Hogg
Belinda Campbell	Jessica Pope
Phillippa Giles	Hilary Salmon
Kate Harwood	Diederick Santer
	Will Trotter

Producers, Drama Production

Sarah Brown	George Ormond
Ben Evans	Paul Rutman
Mike Hobson	Sally Stokes
Kate Lewis	Annie Tricklebank
Peter Lloyd	Pier Wilkie
Jadie Montgomery	Colin Wratten

• COMMISSIONING

Controller, BBC Knowledge	Glenwyn Benson
Controller, Entertainment Commissioning	Elaine Bedell
Controller, Fiction	Jane Tranter
Commissioning Editor, Independent	Polly Hill
	Lucy Richer
Head of Drama Commisssioning, Development	Sarah Brandist
Controller, Drama Production Studios	John Yorke
Arts Commissioner	Adam Kemp
Current Affairs Commissioner, Radio	George Entwistle
Head of Documentaries	Richard Klein
Head of Knowledge Mutlimedia Commissioning	Emma Swain
Head of Drama Series & Serials	Kate Harwood
Head of Drama Commissioning	Ben Stephenson

• NEWS AND CURRENT AFFAIRS

BBC News (Television & Radio)
Television Centre, Wood Lane, London W12 7RJ
Tel: 020-8743 8000 (Main Switchboard)

Director News	Helen Boaden
Deputy Director of News	Adrian Van Klaveren
Head of Newsgathering	Fran Unsworth
Head of Political Programmes Research & Analysis	Sue Inglish
Head of Radio News	Steve Mitchell
Head of TV News	Peter Horrocks
Director of Sport	Roger Mosey
Controller of Children's	Richard Deverell
Head of TV Current Affairs	Peter Horrocks
Controller, Operations & Technology, News	Peter Coles
Head of MC & A (Marketing, Communications & Audiences), BBC Journalism	Janie Ironside-Wood
Commissioning Editor, CA and Head of TV Current Affairs	Karen O'Connor

• DOCUMENTARIES & SPECIALIST FEATURES

Head of Studio, Documentaries & Specialist Features	Sarah Hargreaves
Head of Cross-Genre Productions	Tessa Finch
Head of Features and Documentaries, BBC Bristol	Tom Archer

• ARTS

BBC Television (Arts)
201 Wood Lane
London W12 7TS   Tel: 020-8752 549[ ]

Acting Head of Arts	Basil Come[ ]
Editor, Arena	Anthony Wa[ ]
Editor, Arts Series	Kim Thoma[ ]
Executive Producer, Imagine	Janet Le[ ]
Editor, Reports & Events	David Okuefur[ ]
Executive Producer	Eddie Morga[ ]

• MUSIC

Head of Television Classical Music & Performance	Peter Maniu[ ]
Managing Editor, Classical Music, Television	Caroline Spee[ ]
Editor Music Programmes - Television, Classical Music & Performance	Oliver Macfarlar[ ]

• CHILDREN'S CONTACTS

Controller	Richard Devere[ ]
Creative Director, CBBC	Anne Gilchri[ ]
Creative Director, CBeebies	Michael Carringtc[ ]
Head of Entertainment (inc on-air talent management)	Joe Godw[ ]
Head of Drama	Jon Ea[ ]
Head of Children's Programmes, Scotland	Simon Parsor[ ]
Head of News, Factual & Learning	Reem Nou[ ]
Head of Interactive and On-Demand	Marc Goodchi[ ]

• SPORT

Director of Sport	Roger Mose[ ]
Head of Major Events	Dave Gordc[ ]
Head of Sport Production	Barbara Slat[ ]
Head of Football	Niall Sloar[ ]
H.R. & Development Partner	Pam Siko[ ]
Head of Radio	Gordon Turnbu[ ]
Head of TV Sport Editorial	Philip Barn[ ]

• SCIENCE

Series Editor, Horizon	Andrew Cohe[ ]
Director of Development, Science	Michael Mosle[ ]
Executive Producer	Anne Lakir[ ]

• NEW WRITING

BBC Writersroom
Grafton House
379-381 Euston Road
London NW1 3AU   Tel: 020-7765 270[ ]
e-mail: writersroom@bbc.co.uk
Website: www.bbc.co.uk/writersroom

Creative Director	Kate Rowla[ ]
Development Manager	Paul Ashtc[ ]

BBC BRISTOL

Broadcasting House
Whiteladies Road
Bristol BS8 2LR   Tel: 0117-973 2211

NETWORK TELEVISION AND RADIO FEATURES

Head of Programmes	Tom Archer
Executive Producers	
Rob Dar	Simon Shaw
Julian Mercer	Ben Southwell
Michael Poole	Jo Vale
	Tom Ware

TELEVISION

Producers

Lyn Barlow	Alistair Laurence
Robert Bayley	Peter Lawrence
Kathryn Broome	Kim Littlemore
Michelle Burgess	Colin Naptune
Roy Chapman	David Olusoga
Hannah Corneck	Inge Samuels
Anna Gravelle	Peter Smith
Reosina Harvey	Tuppence Stone
Louise Hibbins	Kate Thomas-Couth
Chris Hutchins	Paul Tucker
	Jonny Young

RADIO

Unit Manager, Radio	Kate Chaney
Editor	Clare McGinn

Producers

John Byrne	Jolyon Jenkins
Sara Davies	Chris Ledgard
Kim Dee	Mark Smalley
Christine Hall	Mary Ward Lowery
	Miles Warde

NATURAL HISTORY UNIT

Head of Natural History Unit	Neil Nightingale
Executive Editor, Natural World	Tim Martin
Series Producer	Alastair Fothergill

Television Producers

Paul Appleby	Sara Ford
Miles Barton	Liz Green
Karen Bass	Martin Hughes-Games
Vanessa Berlowitz	Mark Jacobs
Lucy Bowden	Hilary Jeffkins
Mark Brownlow	Mark Linfield
Paul Chapman	Patrick Morris
Mary Colwell	Stephen Moss
Huw Cordey	Tim Scoones
	Mary Summerhill

Managing Editor, NHU Radio	Julian Hector
Director of Development	Mike Gunton

• BBC WEST

Whiteladies Road
Bristol BS8 2LR   Tel: 0117-973 2211

Head of Regional & Local Programmes,
including BBC West, Radio Bristol &
Somerset Sound

Radio Gloucestershire & BBC Wiltshire Sound	Lucio Mesquita
Editor, Output	Stephanie Marshall
News Gathering	Neil Bennett

• BBC SOUTH WEST

Seymour Road
Mannamead
Plymouth PL3 5BD   Tel: 01752 229201

Head of BBC South West	John Lilley
Editor TV Current Affairs	Simon Willis
Output Editor	Simon Read

• BBC SOUTH

Havelock Road
Southampton SO14 7PU   Tel: 023-8022 6201

Head of Regional & Local Programmes	Mike Hapgood
Managing Editor, BBC Oxford	Steve Taschini
Managing Editor, Radio Solent	Mia Costello
Managing Editor, Radio Berkshire	Lizz Loxam

• BBC LONDON

35C Marylebone High Street
London W1M 4AA   Tel: 020-7224 2424

BBC London News:
TV: *The Politics Show*
Radio: *BBC London Radio 94.9FM*
Online: *BBC London online*

Head of BBC London	Michael MacFarlane
News/Output Editor	Antony Dore
Editor, Inside Out	Dippy Chaudhary
Managing Editor, BBC Radio London 94.9FM	David Robey
Political Editor	Tim Donovan
Editor, BBC London Online	Claire Timms

• BBC SOUTH EAST

The Great Hall Arcade
Mount Pleasant Road
Tunbridge Wells
Kent TN1 1QQ   Tel: 01892 670000

Head of Regional & Local Programmes BBC South East	vacant
Managing Editor BBC Radio Kent	Mark Hayman
Managing Editor BBC Southern Counties	Paul Leaper
Editor BBC South East Today	Quentin Smith
Editor Inside Out	Linda Bell
Editor Politics Show	Dan Fineman

• BBC NORTH WEST

New Broadcasting House
Oxford Road
Manchester M60 1SJ   Tel: 0161-200 2020
Website: www.bbc.co.uk/manchester

Entertainment & Features

Editor, Entertainment & Features   Helen Bullough

Religion & Ethics

Head of Religion & Ethics   Michael Wakelin

Network News & Current Affairs

Editor, Network News
& Current Affairs   Liz Molyneux

Regional & Local Programmes

Head of Regional & Local
   Programmes North West   Tamsin O'Brien
Head of Regional & Local Programmes
   North East & Cumbria   Wendy Pilmer

• BBC BIRMINGHAM

BBC Birmingham
The Mailbox
Birmingham B1 1RF
Fax: 0121-567 6875   Tel: 0121-567 6767

English Regions

Controller, English Regions. Head of Centre
   (Birmingham)   Andy Griffee
Head of New Services, English Regions   John Allen
Chief Operating Officer, English Regions   Ian Hughes
Senior Officer, Press & PR   Jenny Walford
Secretary, BBC Trust   Louise Hall
Head of Regional & Local
   Programmes West Midlands   David Holdsworth

Factual & Learning
BBC Birmingham

Head of Studios   Nick Patten
Managing Editor, BBC Vision,
   Birmingham & Manchester   Jane Booth

Network Radio

Executive Editor, Audio & Music Factual   Andrew Thorman
Head of Specialist, Radio 2
   Music & Compliance   David Barber

Drama

BBC Brimingham TV Drama Village
Archibald House
1059 Bristol Road, Selly Oak
Birmingham B29 6LT   Tel: 0121-567 7350

Executive Producer   Will Trotter

• SCOTLAND

40 Pacific Quay
Glasgow G51 1DA   Tel: 0141-422 600●
Website: www.bbc.co.uk/scotland

SCOTTISH DIRECTION GROUP

Controller Scotland   Ken MacQuarrie
Head of Programme and Services   Donalda Mackinnon &
                                         Maggie Cunningham
Head of Drama, Television   Anne Menzale
Head of Drama, Radio   Patrick Rayne
Head Factual Programmes   Andrea Mille
Head of Gaelic   Margaret Mary Murray
Head of Radio   Jeff Zycinski
Head of News and Current Affairs   Atholl Duncan
Commissioning Editor, Television   Ewan Angus
Head of Finance & Business Affairs   Irene Tweedie
Head of Production   Nancy Brai
Lead HR Partner, Scotland   Wendy Aslet
Head of Marketing, Communication
   and Audiences   Mairead Ferguso
Secretary and Head of Public Policy, Scotland   Ian Sma

Headquarters of BBC Scotland with centres in
Aberdeen, Dundee, Edinburgh, Dumfries, Inverness,
Orkney, Shetland and Stornaway. Regular and recent
programmes include Reporting Scotland, Sportscene and
Monarch of The Glen on television and Good Morning
Scotland and Fred Macaulay on radio.

Aberdeen
Broadcasting House, Beechgrove Terrace
Aberdeen AB15 5ZT   Tel: 01224 62523
Dundee
Nethergate Centre, 66 Nethergate
Dundee DD1 4ER   Tel: 01382 20248
Dumfries
Elmbank, Lover's Walk
Dumfries DG1 1NZ   Tel: 01387 268008
Edinburgh
The Tun, Holyrood Road
Edinburgh EH8 8JF   Tel: 0131-557 588●
Inverness
7 Culduthel Road, Inverness IV2 4AD   Tel: 01463 72072●
Editor   Norrie MacLennon
Orkney
Castle Street, Kirkwall
Orkney KW15 1DF   Tel: 01856 873939
Portree
Clydesdale Bank Buildings, Somerled Square, Portree
Isle of Skye IV51 9BT   Tel: 01478 61200
Selkirk
Unit 1, Ettrick Riverside
Dunsdale Road, Selkirk TD7 5EB   Tel: 01750 72456
Shetland
Pitt Lane, Lerwick
Shetland ZE1 0DW   Tel: 01595 69474
Stornoway
Radio nan Gaidheal, Rosebank, Church Street
Stornoway, Isle of Lewis HS1 2LS   Tel: 01851 70500●

• WALES

Broadcasting House
Llandaff
Cardiff CF5 2YQ   Tel: 029-2032 2000

Controller	Menna Richards
Head of Programmes (Welsh)	Keith Jones
Head of Programmes (English)	Clare Hudson
Head of Marketing, Communications & Audiences	Rhodri Talfan Davies
Head of News & Current Affairs	Mark O'Callaghan
Head of HR & Development	Jude Gray
Chief Operating Officer	Gareth Powell
Head of Broadcast Development	Julie Gardner
Head of Sport	Nigel Walker
Head of North Wales	Marian Wyn Jones
Head of Factual	Adrian Davies
Head of Education & Learning	Eleri Wyn-Williams
Editor Radio Wales	Sali Collins
Editor Radio Cymru	Sian Gwynedd
Head of Music	David Jackson
Editor New Media	Iain Tweedale

• NORTHERN IRELAND

Belfast
Ormeau Avenue
Belfast BT2 8HQ   Tel: 028-9033 8000

Controller	Peter Johnston
Head of Programmes	Ailsa Orr
Head of Public Policy & Corporate Affairs	Mark Adair
Head of Drama	Patrick Spence
Finance Partner	Crawford MacLean
Head of HR & Development	Lawrence Jackson
Head of Learning & Interactive	Kieran Hegarty
Head of Marketing, Communications & Audiences	Kathy Martin
Head of News & Current Affairs	Andrew Colman
Head of Production, Planning and Development	Stephen Beckett
Head of Entertainment, Events and Sport	Mike Edgar
Head of TV Factual	Paul McGuigan
Head of Radio Ulster	Susan Lovell

Londonderry

BBC Radio Foyle	Tel: 028-7137 8600
Editor Foyle	Paul McCauley

Anglia

ITV ANGLIA
Head Office
Anglia House, Norwich NR1 3JG
Fax: 01603 631032   Tel: 01603 615151
East of England: Weekday & Weekend

Regional News Centres

Cambridge
26 Newmarket Road, Cambridge CB5 8DT
Fax: 01223 467106   Tel: 01223 322619

Chelmsford
64-68 New London Road
Chelmsford CM1 0YU
Fax: 01245 267228   Tel: 01245 357676

Northampton
77B Abington Street
Northampton NN1 2BH
Fax: 01604 629856   Tel: 01604 624343

Peterborough
6 Bretton Green Village, Rightwell, Bretton PE3 8DY
Fax: 01733 269424   Tel: 01733 269440

Ipswich
Hubbard House, Civic Drive, Ipswich IP1 2QA
Fax: 01473 233279   Tel: 01473 226157

 Border

ITV BORDER
Head Office & Studios
The Television Centre
Carlisle CA1 3NT   Tel: 01228 525101
Cumbria, South West Scotland,
Scottish Border Region
North Northumberland and the Isle of Man;
Weekday and Weekend

Managing Director   Paddy Merrall

itv Channel Television

CHANNEL TELEVISION Ltd
Registered Office

The Television Centre, La Pouquelaye
St Helier, Jersey JE1 3ZD, Channel Islands
Fax: 01534 816817   Tel: 01534 816816
Website: www.channelonline.tv
Channel Islands: Weekday and Weekend

Managing Director   Michael Lucas
Director of Programmes   Karen Rankine
Commercial Director   Mike Elsey
Director of Transmission & Resources Kevin Banner
Director of Finance   Martin Maack
News Editor   Allan Watts

CHANNEL FOUR TELEVISION CORPORATION
London Office
124 Horseferry Road
London SW1P 2TX
Textphone: 020-7396 8691   Tel: 020-7396 444

Members of the Board
Chairman   Luke Johnson
Deputy Chairman   Lord David Puttnam
Chief Executive   Andy Duncan
Director of Television   Kevin Lyg
Group Finance Director   Anne Bulfor
Sales Director   Andy Barne
New Business Director   Rod Henwoo

Non-Executive Directors
Sue Ashtiany   Martha Lane Fo
Karren Brady   Andy Molle
Tony Hall   Stephen Hi

Heads of Department
Head of Features   Sue Murph
Head of E4 and Factual Entertainment   vacan
Head of History, Science & Religion Hamish Mykur
Controller of Broadcasting   Rosemary Newe
Head of Scheduling and T4   Julie Oldroy
Head of More 4   Peter Da
Head of News & Current Affairs   Dorothy Byrn
Head of Entertainment   Andrew Newma
Head of Drama and FilmFour   Tessa Ros
Head of Documentaries   Angus Macquee
Head of Comedy and Film   Caroline Ledd
Head of Education &
    Managing Editor Commissioning   Janey Walke
Head of Information Systems   Ian Dob
Head of Channel Operations   Stephen Whit
Controller of Legal & Compliance   Jan Tomali
Managing Director, New Media   Andy Taylc
Head of Commercial Affairs   vacan
Director of Nations and Regions   Stuart Cosgrov
Director of Corporate Relations   Nick Too
Head of Corporate Development   Michael Hodgso
Director of Strategy and Research   Jonathan Thompso
Controller of Research & Insight   Claire Grimmon
Director of Human Resources   Diane Herbe
Head of Facilities Management   Julie Korten
Director of Acquisitions   Jeff For
Director of Marketing   Polly Cochran
Head of Media Planning   Greg Smit
Head of Press and Publicity   Matt Bake

CHANNEL FOUR TELEVISION CORPORATION Cont'd

Network Creative Director	Brett Foraker
Head of Marketing	Rufus Radcliffe
Head of Sponsorship	David Charlesworth
Head of Airtime Management	Merlin Inkley
Head of Agency Sales	Matt Shreeve
Head of Strategic Sales	Mike Parker
Head of Channel 4	Julian Bellamy

CHANNEL 5 BROADCASTING

22 Long Acre
London WC2E 9LY
Fax: 020-7550 5554   Tel: 020-7550 5555
Website: www.five.tv

Chief Executive	Jane Lighting
Director of Programmes	Lisa Opie
Director of Strategy	Charles Constable
Director of Sales	Mark White
Director of Finance	Grant Murray
Director of Legal & Business Affairs	Colin Campbell
Director of Broadcasting	Richard Brent
Senior Programme Controller	
News & Current Affairs	Chris Shaw
Controller of Entertainment & Features	Ben Frow
Controller of Factual Entertainment	Steve Gowans
Controller of Sport	Robert Charles
Controller Children's	Nick Wilson
Controller Daytime Arts & Religion	Kim Peat

GMTV

London Television Centre
Upper Ground
London SE1 9TT
Fax: 020-7827 7001   Tel: 020-7827 7000

Chairman	Clive Jones
Managing Director	Paul Corley
Director of Programmes	Peter McHugh
Finance Director	Rhian Walker
Director of Sales	Clive Crouch
Head of Press	Nikki Johnceline
Managing Editor	John Scammell
Editor	Martin Frizell
Chief Engineer	Geoff Wright

INDEPENDENT TELEVISION NEWS

200 Gray's Inn Rd
London WC1X 8XZ   Tel: 020-7833 3000

Chief Executive	Mark Wood
Editor-in-Chief, ITV News	David Mannion
Editor, ITV Networks News	Deborah Turness
Editor, Channel 4 News	Jim Gray

itv

ITV Productions & TLS

The London Television Centre
Upper Ground
London SE1 9LT

Executive Board:

Executive Chairman, ITV Plc	Michael Grade
Chief Operating Officer	
& Finance Director, ITV Plc	John Cresswell
Director of Television, ITV	Simon Shaps
Director of ITV Productions	John Whiston
Director, ITV Consumer	Jeff Henry
Director of Group Development	
& Strategy	Carolyn Fairburn
Deputy Group Finance Director	Mike Green
Group HR Director	Philippa Hird
Director of Strategy	Ben McOwen Wilson
Legal Director	Kyla Mullins
Director of Regulatory Affairs &	
Managing Director of ITV London	Christy Swords
Company Secretary & Director	
of Investor Relations	James Tibbets
Group Communications Director	Brigitte Trafford
Director, Corporate Affairs	Jim Godfrey
Director of Communications,	
Channels & Commercials	Ruth Settle

Three divisions:

1. ITV Broadcasting
2. Granada
3. ITV News Group

ITV Productions & TLS Cont'd
Licence Companies:
- Anglia Television Limited
- Border Television Limited
- Carlton Broadcasting Limited
- Central Independent Television Limited
- Granada Television Limited
- HTV Group Limited
- LWT (Holdings) Limited
- Meridian Broadcasting Limited
- Tyne Tees Television Limited
- Westcountry Television Limited
- Yorkshire Television Limited

 **Meridian**

MERIDIAN BROADCASTING Ltd
Meridian is part of ITV BROADCASTING Ltd
Forum One
Solent Business Park
Whiteley, Hants PO15 7PA
Fax: 0844 881207   Tel: 0844 8812000

MERIDIAN BOARD
Executive Chairman	Michael Grade
Financial Director, ITV News	Mike Fegan
Director of Regional Sales	David Croft
Managing Director, ITV Meridian	Mark Southgate
Controller of Regional Programmes	Mark Southgate

EXECUTIVES
Managing Director	
Controller of Regional Programmes	Mark Southgate
Head of Personnel	Elaine Austin
Finance Manager	Dan Spencer
Head of Regional Affairs	Alison Pope

 Wales

ITV - WALES
Television Centre, Culverhouse Cross
Cardiff CF5 6XJ   Tel: 029-2059 0590

Television Centre, Bath Road
Bristol BS4 3HG   Tel: 0117-972 2722

Wales/West of England: All week

Managing Director & Head of Programmes	Elis Owen
Managing Director, West	Mark Haskell
Director of Programmes, ITV 1 West	Jane McCloskey
ITV Wales Head of Drama Development	Peter Edwards

S4/C

S4C-THE WELSH FOURTH CHANNEL
Parc Tŷ Glas, Llanishen, Cardiff CF14 5DU
Fax: 029-2075 4444   Tel: 029-2074 744
e-mail: s4c@s4c.co.uk

The Welsh Fourth Channel Authority
Chair	John Walker Jones OB
Members:	Dr. Christopher Llewely
Eira Davies	Enid Rowland
Carys Howell	
Sir Roger Jones OBE	
Winston Roddick CB QC	
John Walter Jones OBE	

Senior Staff
Chief Executive	Iona Jone
Director of Commissioning	Rhian Gibso
Director of Communications	Huw Rossite
Director of Finance & Human Resources	Kathryn Morr
Director of Broadcast & Distribution	Arshad Rasr
Director of Business Affairs	Delyth Wynne Griffith
Director of Commercial & Corporate Policy	Nerys Hopkin

STV CENTRAL
Pacific Quay, Glasgow G51 1PQ
Tel: 0141-300 3000   Website: www.stv.

STV NORTH
Television Centre
Craigshaw Business Park
West Tullos, Aberdeen AB12 3QH
Tel: 01224 848848   Website: www.stv.
Managing Director	Bobby Hai
Deputy Managing Director	Derrick Thompso
Head of News & Current Affairs	Gordon MacMilla

SMG TV PRODUCTIONS
Glasgow Office
Pacific Quay, Glasgow G51 1PQ
Fax: 0141-300 3030   Tel: 0141-300 30C
Managing Director	Elizabeth Partyk
Head of Drama	Eric Coult
Head of Factual	Jim Mansc

London Office
1st Floor
3 Waterhouse Square, 138-142 Holborn
London EC1N 2NY   Tel: 020-7882 10

Tyne Tees

ITV TYNE TEES
ITV Tyne Tees
Television House, The Watermark, Gateshead NE11 9SZ
Fax: 0844 8815010   Tel: 0844 8815000

Teesside Studio
Colman's Nook
Belasis Hall Technology Park
Billingham
Cleveland TS23 4EG
Fax: 01642 566560   Tel: 01642 566999

North East and North Yorkshire:
Weekday and Weekend

Executive Chair ITV	Michael Grade
Managing Director, Controller of Programmes	Graeme Thompson
Acting Head of News	Andrew Friend
Managing Director, Signpost	Malcolm Wright

UTV Plc
Ormeau Road
Belfast BT7 1EB
Fax: 028-9024 6695   Tel: 028-9032 8122

Northern Ireland: Weekday and Weekend

Chairman	J B McGuckian BSc (Econ)
Group Chief Executive	J McCann BSc, FCA
Group Financial Director	Jim Downey
Head of Television	Michael Wilson
Head of Press & Public Relations	Orla McKibbin
Head of News & Current Affairs	Rob Morrison
Sales Director	Paul Hutchinson

Yorkshire

ITV - YORKSHIRE
The Television Centre
Leeds LS3 1JS
Fax: 0113-244 5107   Tel: 0113-243 8283

London Office
London Television Centre
Upperground, London SE1 9LT   Tel: 020-7620 1620

Hull Office
23 Brook Street
The Prospect Centre
Hull HU2 8PN   Tel: 01482 324488

Sheffield Office
Charter Square
Sheffield S1 3EJ   Tel: 0114-272 7772

Lincoln Office
88 Bailgate
Lincoln LN1 3AR   Tel: 01522 530738

Grimsby Office
Margaret Street
Immingham
North East Lincs DN40 1LE   Tel: 01469 515151

York Office
8 Coppergate
York YO1 1NR   Tel: 01904 610066

Executives

Managing Director	David M B Croft
Director of Business Affairs	Filip Cieslik
Head of News	Will Venters
Controller of Comedy Drama & Drama Features	David Reynolds
Controller of Drama, Leeds	Keith Richardson
Director of Finance	Ian Roe
Director of ITV Productions	John Whiston
Producer of Regional Features	Mark Witty

SKY Satellite Television
BRITISH SKY BROADCASTING LIMITED (BSkyB)
6 Centaurs Business Park
Grant Way, Isleworth
Middlesex TW7 5QD
Fax: 0870 240 3060   Tel: 0870 240 3000

Chief Executive	James Murdoch
Chief Financial Officer	Jeremy Darroch
Managing Director, Sky Networks	Sophie Turner-Laing
Director for People & Organisational Development	Beryl Cook
Group Commercial and Strategy Director	Mike Darcey
Group Director for Communications	Matthew Anderson
Managing Director, Customer Group	Brian Sullivan
Group Director for IT & Strategy	Jeff Hughes
General Counsel	James Conyers
Managing Director, Sky Media	Nick Milligan
Head of Regulatory Affairs	Vicky Sandy
Managing Director, Sky Sports	Vic Wakeling
Group Director of Engineering & Platform Technology	Alun Webber

30 BIRD PRODUCTIONS
24 Wroxton Road, London SE15 2BN
e-mail: thirtybirdproductions@ntlworld.com
Tel: 01223 722112

ACORN ENTERTAINMENTS Ltd
PO Box 64, Cirencester, Glos GL7 5YD
Website: www.acornents.co.uk
e-mail: info@acornents.co.uk
Fax: 01285 642291							Tel: 01285 644622

ACTING PRODUCTIONS
Unit 88, Battersea Business Centre
99-109 Lavender Hill, London SW11 5QL
Website: www.acting-productions.co.uk
e-mail: info@acting-productions.co.uk
Fax: 020-7924 6606						Tel: 020-7924 7701

ACTOR'S TEMPLE The
13 Warren Street, London W1T 5LG
Website: www.actorstemple.com
e-mail: info@actorstemple.com
Mobile: 07771 734670						Tel: 020-7383 3535

ACT PRODUCTIONS Ltd
20-22 Stukeley Street, London WC2B 5LR
Website: www.actproductions.co.uk
e-mail: info@act.tt
Fax: 020-7242 3548						Tel: 020-7438 9520

A.J. ASSOCIATES
Suite 4, Anglia House, North Station Road
Colchester, Essex CO1 1SB
Website: www.ajassociates.co.uk
e-mail: info@ajassociates.co.uk
Fax: 01206 548730						Tel: 01206 548700

AJTC THEATRE COMPANY
28 Rydes Hill Crescent, Guildford, Surrey GU2 9UH
Website: www.ajtctheatre.co.uk		Tel/Fax: 01483 232795

AKA PRODUCTIONS
First Floor, 115 Shaftesbury Avenue
Cambridge Circus, London WC2H 8AF
Website: www.akauk.com
e-mail: aka@akauk.com
Fax: 020-7836 8787						Tel: 020-7836 4747

ALGERNON Ltd
24B Cleveleys Road, London E5 9JN
Website: www.algernonproductions.com
e-mail: info@algernonproductions.com
Fax: 0870 1388516						Tel: 07092 805026

AMBASSADOR THEATRE GROUP
39-41 Charing Cross Road, London WC2H 0AR
e-mail: atglondon@theambassadors.com
Fax: 020-7534 6109						Tel: 020-7534 6100

ANTIC DISPOSITION
4A Oval Road, London NW1 7EB
Website: www.anticdisposition.co.uk
e-mail: info@anticdisposition.co.uk		Tel: 020-7284 0760

AOD - ACTORS OF DIONYSUS
14 Cuthbert Road, Brighton BN2 0EN
Website: www.actorsofdionysus.com
e-mail: info@actorsofdionysus.com		Tel/Fax: 01273 692604

ARDEN ENTERTAINMENT
Nederlander House
7 Great Russell Street, London WC1B 3NH
Website: www.arden-entertainment.co.uk
e-mail: info@arden-entertainment.co.uk
Fax: 020-7079 0276						Tel: 020-7079 0277

ARTS MANAGEMENT (Redroofs Associates)
(Write)
Novello Theatre, High Street
Sunninghill, Ascot SL5 9NE

ASHTON GROUP THEATRE The
The Old Fire Station,
Abbey Road, Barrow-in-Furness, Cumbria LA14 1XH
Website: www.ashtongroup.co.uk
e-mail: info@ashtongroup.co.uk		Tel/Fax: 01229 430636

ATC
Malvern House, 15-16 Nassau Street, London W1W 7AB
Website: www.atc-online.com
e-mail: atc@atc-online.com
Fax: 020-7580 7724						Tel: 020-7580 7723

ATTIC THEATRE COMPANY (LONDON) Ltd
New Wimbledon Theatre
The Broadway, London SW19 1QG
Website: www.attictheatrecompany.com
e-mail: info@attictheatrecompany.com		Tel: 020-8543 7838

BACKGROUND Ltd
44 Carnaby Street, London W1F 9PP
e-mail: insight@background.co.uk
Fax: 020-7479 4710						Tel: 020-7479 470C

BARKING PRODUCTIONS/INSTANT WIT
(Comedy Improvisation Show/Corporate Entertainment &
Drama Based Training)
PO Box 597, Bristol BS99 2BB
Website: www.barkingproductions.co.uk
e-mail: info@barkingproductions.co.uk
Fax: 0117-908 5384						Tel: 0117-939 317

BARNES Andy PRODUCTIONS
28B Compton Road, London N21 3NX
Website: www.andybarnesproductions.com
e-mail: andybarnes@ukonline.co.uk		Mobile: 07957 31366

BEE & BUSTLE ENTERPRISES
32 Exeter Road, London NW2 4SB
Website: www.beeandbustle.co.uk
e-mail: info@beeandbustle.co.uk
Fax: 020-8450 1057						Tel: 020-8450 037

BIRMINGHAM STAGE COMPANY The
Suite 228, The Linen Hall
162 Regent Street, London W1B 5TB
Website: www.birminghamstage.net
e-mail: info@birminghamstage.net
Fax: 020-7437 3395						Tel: 020-7437 339

BLUE BOX ENTERTAINMENT Ltd
Top Floor
80-81 St Martin's Lane, London WC2N 4AA
Website: www.blue-box.biz
e-mail: info@blue-box.biz
Fax: 020-7240 2947						Tel: 020-7240 752

BORDER CROSSINGS
13 Bankside, Enfield EN2 8BN
Website: www.bordercrossings.org.uk
e-mail: borcross@aol.com			Tel/Fax: 020-8366 523

BORDERLINE THEATRE COMPANY
North Harbour Street, Ayr KA8 8AA
e-mail: enquiries@borderlinetheatre.co.uk
Tel: 01292 28101

BRIT-POL THEATRE Ltd
10 Bristol Gardens, London W9 2JG
Website: www.britpoltheatre.com
e-mail: admin@britpoltheatre.com		Tel: 020-7266 032

BRITISH SHAKESPEARE COMPANY
Adelaide Grove, London W12 0JJ
Website: www.britishshakespearecompany.com
E-mail: info@britishshakespearecompany.com
Mobile: 07702 474430

BRITISH STAGE PRODUCTIONS
55 Waterloo Road, Blackpool FY4 4BW
E-mail: britstage@aol.com Tel/Fax: 01253 692289

BRITISH THEATRE SEASON IN MONACO
Théâtre Princesse Grace, Monaco

Grand Union Walk, Camden Town, London NW1 9LP
Website: www.montecarlotheatre.co.uk
E-mail: mail@montecarlotheatre.co.uk Tel: 020-8455 3278

BROADHOUSE PRODUCTIONS Ltd
Edge Rocks House
Ilbrook, Minehead, Somerset TA24 6RD
E-mail: admin@broadhouse.co.uk
Fax: 01984 641027 Tel: 01984 640773

BROOKE Nick Ltd
2nd Floor, 80-81 St Martin's Lane, London WC2N 4AA
E-mail: nick@nickbrooke.com
Fax: 020-7240 2947 Tel: 020-7240 3901

BUSH THEATRE
Shepherd's Bush Green, London W12 8QD
Website: www.bushtheatre.co.uk
E-mail: info@bushtheatre.co.uk
Fax: 020-7602 7614 Tel: 020-7602 3703

CAM SHAW Matthew for ST ELMO PRODUCTIONS
3rd Floor, 20-22 Stukeley Street, London WC2B 5LR
Fax: 020-7242 3548 Tel: 020-7438 9520

CAHOOTS THEATRE COMPANY
(Denise Silvey)
15 Neal Street, London WC2H 9PW
Website: www.cahootstheatre.co.uk
E-mail: denise@cahootstheatre.co.uk Tel: 020-7240 7000

CAP PRODUCTION SOLUTIONS Ltd
1 Merton Industrial Park
Jubilee Way, Wimbledon, London SW19 3WL
E-mail: leigh@leighporter.com
Fax: 07970 763480 Tel: 020-8544 8668

CAPRICORN STAGE (& SCREEN) DIRECTIONS
Spencer House, Vale of Health
Hampstead, London NW3 1AS Tel: 020-7794 5843

CELEBRATION
(Theatre Company for the Young)
Chiswick Staithe, London W4 3TP
E-mail: nevillewortman@beeb.net
Mobile: 07976 805976 Tel: 020-8994 8886

CENTRELINE PRODUCTIONS
3 Lea Bridge Road, London E10 7NE
Website: www.centrelinenet.com
E-mail: jenny@centrelinenet.com Mobile: 07710 522438

CHAIN REACTION THEATRE COMPANY
Free Mills Studios
Sugar House Yard, Sugar House Lane, London E15 2QS
Website: www.chainreactiontheatre.co.uk
E-mail: mail@chainreactiontheatre.co.uk
Tel/Fax: 020-8534 0007

CHANNEL THEATRE PRODUCTIONS
Central Studios, 36 Park Place, Margate, Kent CT9 1LE
Website: www.channel-theatre.co.uk
E-mail: info@channel-theatre.co.uk
Fax: 01843 280088 Tel: 01843 280077

Richard Jordan Productions Ltd

- **Producing**
- **General Management**
  UK and International Productions,
  and International Festivals
- **Consultancy**

Richard Jordan Productions Ltd
Mews Studios, 16 Vernon Yard
London W11 2DX

Tel: 020 7243 9001
Fax: 020 7313 9667
e-mail: richard.jordan@virgin.net

CHAPMAN Duggie ASSOCIATES
(Pantomime, Concerts, Musicals)
The Old Coach House
202 Common Edge Road, Blackpool FY4 5DG
Website: www.duggiechapman.co.uk
e-mail: duggie@chapmanassociates.fsnet.co.uk
Tel/Fax: 01253 691823

CHEEK BY JOWL
Stage Door, Barbican Centre
Silk Street, London EC2Y 8DS
Website: www.cheekbyjowl.com Tel: 020-7382 7281

CHEEKY MAGGOT PRODUCTIONS
Website: www.cheekymaggot.co.uk
e-mail: info@cheekymaggot.co.uk

CHICHESTER FESTIVAL THEATRE
Oaklands Park, Chichester
West Sussex PO19 6AP
Website: www.cft.org.uk
e-mail: admin@cft.org.uk
Fax: 01243 787288 Tel: 01243 784437

CHICKEN SHED THEATRE
Chase Side, Southgate, London N14 4PE
Website: www.chickenshed.org.uk
e-mail: info@chickenshed.org.uk
Minicom: 020-8350 0676 Tel: 020-8351 6161

CHURCHILL THEATRE BROMLEY Ltd
The Churchill, High Street, Bromley, Kent BR1 1HA
Website: www.churchilltheatre.co.uk
Fax: 020-8290 6968 Tel: 020-8464 7131

CLOSE FOR COMFORT THEATRE COMPANY
34 Boleyn Walk, Leatherhead, Surrey KT22 7HU
Website: www.hometown.aol.com/close4comf
e-mail: close4comf@aol.com
Mobile: 07710 258290 Tel: 01372 378613

CLUBWEST PRODUCTIONS
Arundel Town Hall
Arundel, West Sussex BN18 9AP
Website: www.clubwest.co.uk
e-mail: admin@clubwest.co.uk Tel/Fax: 01903 889821

CODRON Michael PLAYS Ltd
Aldwych Theatre Offices, London WC2B 4DF
Fax: 020-7240 8467 Tel: 020-7240 8291

COLE KITCHENN Ltd
212 Strand, London WC2R 1AP
Website: www.colekitchenn.com
e-mail: info@colekitchenn.com
Fax: 020-7353 9639 Tel: 020-7427 5680

COMPASS THEATRE COMPANY
St Jude's Parish Hall
175 Gibraltar Street, Sheffield S3 8UA
Website: www.compasstheatrecompany.com
e-mail: info@compasstheatrecompany.com
Fax: 0114-278 6931   Tel: 0114-275 5328

COMPLICITE
14 Anglers Lane, London NW5 3DG
Website: www.complicite.org
e-mail: email@complicite.org
Fax: 020-7485 7701   Tel: 020-7485 7700

CONCORDANCE
(Neil McPherson)
Finborough Theatre
118 Finborough Road, London SW10 9ED
Website: www.concordance.org.uk
e-mail: admin@concordance.org.uk
Fax: 020-7835 1853   Tel: 020-7244 7439

CONTEMPO THEATRE COMPANY
37 White House, Vicarage Crescent, London SW11 3LJ
Website: www.contempotheatrecompany.com
e-mail: contemp1@mac.com   Mobile: 07906 348741

CONTEMPORARY STAGE COMPANY
3 Etchingham Park Road, Finchley, London N3 2DU
Website: www.contemporarystage.co.uk
e-mail: contemp.stage@hotmail.co.uk
Fax: 020-8349 2458   Tel: 020-8349 4402

CONWAY Clive CELEBRITY PRODUCTIONS Ltd
32 Grove Street, Oxford OX2 7JT
e-mail: info@celebrityproductions.org
Fax: 01865 514409   Tel: 01865 514830

CREATIVE CONCERTS Ltd
PO Box 745, Guildford, Surrey GU3 1XJ
Website: www.creativeconcerts.co.uk   Tel: 01483 813294

CRISP THEATRE
8 Cornwallis Crescent
Clifton, Bristol BS8 4PL
Website: www.crisptheatre.co.uk
e-mail: crisptheatre@btconnect.com   Tel: 0117-973 7106

DALE TEATER KOMPANI
434B Hornsey Road, London N19 4EB
Website: www.daletk.co.uk
e-mail: info@daletk.co.uk   Tel: 020-7281 4322

DEAD EARNEST THEATRE
The Quadrant, 99 Parkway Avenue, Sheffield S9 4WG
Website: www.deadearnest.co.uk
e-mail: info@deadearnest.co.uk   Tel: 0114-227 0085

DEAN Lee
PO Box 10703, London WC2H 9ED
e-mail: admin@leedean.co.uk
Fax: 020-7836 6968   Tel: 020-7497 5111

DEBUT PRODUCTIONS
(Actor Showcases in London's West End & Manchester)
29 Station Road, Chertsey, Surrey KT16 8BE
Website: www.debutproductions.co.uk
e-mail: enquiries@debutproductions.co.uk
                                    Tel: 01932 423102

DELFONT MACKINTOSH THEATRES Ltd
(Theatre Owners)
The Novello Theatre, Aldwych, London WC2B 4LD
e-mail: info@delfontmackintosh.co.uk
Fax: 020-7240 3831   Tel: 020-7379 4431

DISNEY THEATRICAL PRODUCTIONS (UK)
Lyceum Theatre, 21 Wellington Street, London WC2E 7RQ
Fax: 020-7845 0999   Tel: 020-7845 090⬛

DONEGAN David Ltd
PO Box LB689, London W1A 9LB
e-mail: daviddonegan@hotmail.co.uk   Mobile: 07957 35890⬛

DOODAH THEATRE
10 Shrewsbury Road, Redhill, Surrey RH1 6BH
e-mail: doodahtc@aol.com   Tel: 01737 77804⬛

DRAMATIS PERSONAE Ltd
(Nathan Silver, Nicolas Kent)
19 Regency Street, London SW1P 4BY
e-mail: ns@nathansilver.com   Tel: 020-7834 930⬛

DUAL CONTROL THEATRE COMPANY
The Admiral's Offices
The Historic Dockyard, Chatham, Kent ME4 4TZ
Website: www.ellenkent.com
e-mail: info@ellenkentinternational.co.uk
Fax: 01634 819149   Tel: 01634 8191⬛

EASTERN ANGLES THEATRE COMPANY
(Touring)
Sir John Mills Theatre
Gatacre Road, Ipswich, Suffolk IP1 2LQ
Website: www.easternangles.co.uk
e-mail: admin@easternangles.co.uk
Fax: 01473 384999   Tel: 01473 2182⬛

ELLIOTT Paul Ltd
(Triumph Entertainment Ltd)
1st Floor, 18 Exeter Street, London WC2E 7DU
e-mail: pre@paulelliott.ltd.uk
Fax: 020-7379 4860   Tel: 020-7379 48⬛

ENGLISH CHAMBER THEATRE The
(No Drama School Applicants)
Flat 3, 6 St Simon's Avenue, London SW15 6DU
Website: www.englishchambertheatre.co.uk
e-mail: jane@janemcculloch.com
Mobile: 07951 912435   Tel: 020-8789 24⬛

ENGLISH NATIONAL OPERA
London Coliseum
St Martin's Lane, London WC2N 4ES
Website: www.eno.org
Fax: 020-7845 9277   Tel: 020-7836 0⬛

ENGLISH STAGE COMPANY Ltd
Royal Court, Sloane Square, London SW1W 8AS
Website: www.royalcourttheatre.com
e-mail: info@royalcourttheatre.com
Fax: 020-7565 5001   Tel: 020-7565 50⬛

ENGLISH THEATRE COMPANY Ltd The
(TMA Member)
Nybrogatan 35, 114 39 Stockholm, Sweden
Website: www.englishtheatre.se
e-mail: etc.ltd@telia.com
Fax: 00 46 8660 1159   Tel: 00 46 8662 41

ENGLISH TOURING THEATRE (ETT)
25 Short Street, London SE1 8LJ
Website: www.ett.org.uk
e-mail: admin@ett.org.uk
Fax: 020-7633 0188   Tel: 020-7450 19⬛

ENTERTAINMENT BUSINESS Ltd The
2nd Floor, 28 Charing Cross Road, London WC2H 0DB
Website: www.cardiffmusicals.com
Fax: 020-7836 3982   Tel: 020-7240 8⬛

EUROPEAN THEATRE COMPANY The
9 Oxford Avenue, London SW20 8LS
Website: www.europeantheatre.co.uk
e-mail: admin@europeantheatre.co.uk
Fax: 020-8544 1999   Tel: 020-8544 1994

FACADE
(Musicals)
3A Garthorne Road, London SE23 1EP
e-mail: facade@cobomedia.com   Tel: 020-8291 7079

FAIRBANK PRODUCTIONS
7 Harcourt Road, London E15 3DX
Website: www.fairbankproductions.co.uk
e-mail: fairbank@fpuk.freeserve.co.uk
Tel/Fax: 020-8555 3085

FEATHER PRODUCTIONS Ltd
The Studio, 137 Sheen Road, Richmond, Surrey TW9 1YJ
Website: www.featherproductions.com
e-mail: info@featherproductions.com
Fax: 020-8940 2335   Tel: 020-8439 9848

FELL Andrew Ltd
Ching Court, 49-51 Monmouth Street, London WC2H 9EY
e-mail: hq@andrewfell.co.uk
Fax: 020-7240 2499   Tel: 020-7240 2420

FIELDER Simon Ltd
The Theatre, 7 Church Street
Leatherhead, Surrey KT22 8DN
e-mail: enquiries@simonfielder.com
Fax: 01372 365135   Tel: 01372 365134

FIERY ANGEL Ltd
22-24 Torrington Place, London WC1E 7HJ
Website: www.fiery-angel.com
e-mail: mail@fiery-angel.com
Fax: 020-7436 6287   Tel: 020-7907 7012

FORBIDDEN THEATRE COMPANY
Rupert Street, London W1D 6DE
Website: www.forbidden.org.uk
mail: info@forbidden.org.uk   Tel: 0845 0093084

FORD Vanessa PRODUCTIONS Ltd
Upper House Farm
Upper House Lane, Shamley Green, Surrey GU5 0SX
Website: www.vfpltd.com
mail: vfpltd@btinternet.com   Tel: 01483 278203

FOX Robert Ltd
Beauchamp Place, London SW3 1NG
Website: www.robertfoxltd.com
e-mail: info@robertfoxltd.com
Fax: 020-7225 1638   Tel: 020-7584 6855

FREEDMAN Bill Ltd
Room 311, Bedford Chambers
The Piazza, Covent Garden, London WC2E 8HA
Fax: 020-7836 9903   Tel: 020-7836 9900

FRICKER Ian (THEATRE) Ltd
PO Box 65, Arundel, West Sussex BN18 9WZ
Website: www.ianfricker.com
mail: mail@ianfricker.com
Fax: 01903 885372   Tel: 01903 885391

FRIEDMAN Sonia PRODUCTIONS
Duke of York's Theatre
104 St Martin's Lane, London WC2N 4BG
Website: www.soniafriedman.com
mail: mail@soniafriedman.com
Fax: 020-7854 7059   Tel: 020-7854 7050

FUTURA MUSIC (PRODUCTIONS) Ltd
(Write only)
29 Emanuel House, Rochester Row
London SW1P 1BS

GALE PRODUCTIONS
24 Wimbledon Park Road, London SW18 1LT
e-mail: gale.prod@which.net
Fax: 020-8875 1582   Tel: 020-8870 1149

GALLEON THEATRE COMPANY Ltd
(Alice De Sousa)
Greenwich Playhouse
Greenwich BR Station Forecourt
189 Greenwich High Road, London SE10 8JA
Website: www.galleontheatre.co.uk
e-mail: boxoffice@galleontheatre.co.uk
Fax: 020-8310 7276   Tel: 020-8858 9256

GBM PRODUCTIONS Ltd
Bidlake Toft, Roadford Lake
Germansweek, Devon EX21 5BD
Website: www.musicaltheatrecreations.com
e-mail: gbm@bidlaketoft.com
Fax: 01837 871123   Tel: 01837 871522

GLASS David ENSEMBLE
59 Brewer Street, London W1F 9UN
Website: www.davidglassensemble.com
e-mail: info@davidglassensemble.com
Tel/Fax: 020-7734 6030

GODOT COMPANY
51 The Cut, London SE1 8LF
e-mail: godot@calderpublications.com
Fax: 020-7928 5930   Tel: 020-7633 0599

GOOD COMPANY
at St Michaels, Powis Road, Brighton BN1 3HJ
Fax: 01273 779955   Tel: 01273 771777

GOSS Gerald Ltd
19 Gloucester Street, London SW1V 2DB
e-mail: info@geraldgoss.co.uk
Fax: 020-7592 9301   Tel: 020-7592 9202

GOUCHER Mark Ltd
3rd Floor, 20-22 Stukeley Street, London WC2B 5LR
e-mail: jamie@markgoucher.com
Fax: 020-7438 9577   Tel: 020-7438 9570

GRAEAE THEATRE COMPANY
LVS Resource Centre
356 Holloway Road, London N7 6PA
Website: www.graeae.org
e-mail: info@graeae.org
Fax: 020-7609 7324   Tel: 020-7700 2455

GRAHAM David ENTERTAINMENT Ltd
72 New Bond Street, London W1S 1RR
Website: www.davidgrahamentertainment.com
e-mail: info@davidgraham.co.uk
Fax: 0870 3211700   Tel: 0870 3211600

GRANT Derek ORGANISATION Ltd
13 Beechwood Road, West Moors, Dorset BH22 0BN
Website: www.derekgrant.co.uk
e-mail: admin@derekgrant.co.uk   Tel/Fax: 01202 855777

HAMPSTEAD THEATRE PRODUCTIONS Ltd
Eton Avenue, Swiss Cottage, London NW3 3EU
Website: www.hampsteadtheatre.com
e-mail: info@hampsteadtheatre.com
Fax: 020-7449 4201   Tel: 020-7449 4200

HANDSTAND PRODUCTIONS
13 Hope Street, Liverpool L1 9BH
Website: www.handstand-uk.com
e-mail: info@handstand-uk.com
Fax: 0151-709 3515   Tel: 0151-708 7441

HARLEY PRODUCTIONS
68 New Cavendish Street, London W1G 8TE
e-mail: harleyprods@aol.com
Fax: 020-8202 8863   Tel: 020-7580 3247

HAYMARKET THEATRE COMPANY Ltd
c/o The Anvil Trust, Wote Street
Basingstoke, Hampshire RG21 7NW
Website: www.haymarket.org.uk
e-mail: info@haymarket.org.uk
Fax: 01256 357130   Tel: 0870 7701029

HEADLONG THEATRE Ltd
Chertsey Chambers, 12 Mercer Street, London WC2H 9QD
Website: www.headlongtheatre.co.uk
e-mail: info@headlongtheatre.co.uk
Fax: 020-7438 9941   Tel: 020-7438 9940

HENDERSON Glynis PRODUCTIONS Ltd
69 Charlotte Street, London W1T 4PJ
e-mail: info@ghmp.co.uk
Fax: 020-7436 1489   Tel: 020-7580 9644

HENGE PRODUCTIONS
(John Mackay)
85B Torriano Avenue, London NW5 2RX
e-mail: johnmackay2001@aol.com   Tel: 020-7284 3733

HESTER John PRODUCTIONS
(Intimate Mysteries Theatre Company)
105 Stoneleigh Park Road
Epsom, Surrey KT19 0RF
e-mail: hjohnhester@aol.com   Tel/Fax: 020-8393 5705

HISS & BOO COMPANY Ltd The
(Ian Liston)
Nyes Hill, Wineham Lane
Bolney, West Sussex RH17 5SD
Website: www.hissboo.co.uk
e-mail: email@hissboo.co.uk
Fax: 01444 882057   Tel: 01444 881707

HISTORIA THEATRE COMPANY
8 Cloudesley Square, London N1 0HT
Website: www.historiatheatre.com
e-mail: kateprice@lineone.net
Fax: 020-7278 4733   Tel: 020-7837 8008

HOIPOLLOI
Office F, Dale's Brewery
Gwydir Street, Cambridge CB1 2LJ
Website: www.hoipolloi.org.uk
e-mail: info@hoipolloi.org.uk   Tel: 01223 322748

HOLLOW CROWN PRODUCTIONS
2 Norfolk Road, London E17 5QS
Website: www.hollowcrown.co.uk
e-mail: enquiries@hollowcrown.co.uk
                                  Mobile: 07930 530948

HOLMAN Paul ASSOCIATES Ltd
Morritt House
58 Station Approach
South Ruislip, Middlesex HA4 6SA
Website: www.paulholmanassociates.co.uk
e-mail: enquiries@paulholmanassociates.co.uk
Fax: 020-8839 3124   Tel: 020-8845 9408

HOLT Thelma Ltd
Noel Coward Theatre
85 St Martin's Lane, London WC2N 4AU
Website: www.thelmaholt.co.uk
e-mail: thelma@dircon.co.uk
Fax: 020-7812 7550   Tel: 020-7812 745

HOUSE OF GULLIVER Ltd
(Write)
60 Beaconsfield Road
Tring, Herts HP23 4DW

HUGHES Steve
Oakwood, 4 Armitage Road
Armitage Bridge HD4 7PG
Website: www.hughes-productions.co.uk
e-mail: steve@hughes-productions.co.uk
                                  Mobile: 07816 84402

HULL TRUCK THEATRE
Spring Street, Hull HU2 8RW
Website: www.hulltruck.co.uk
e-mail: admin@hulltruck.co.uk
Fax: 01482 581182   Tel: 01482 2248C

IAN David PRODUCTIONS Ltd
Third Floor, 33 Henrietta Street, London WC2E 8NA
Fax: 020-7257 6381   Tel: 020-7257 638

ICARUS THEATRE COLLECTIVE
105 Bell Street, London NW1 6TL
Website: www.icarustheatre.co.uk
e-mail: info@icarustheatre.co.uk
Fax: 0871 7145787   Tel: 020-7870 37

IMAGE MUSICAL THEATRE
23 Sedgeford Road
Shepherd's Bush, London W12 0NA
Website: www.imagemusicaltheatre.co.uk
e-mail: brian@imagemusicaltheatre.co.uk
Fax: 020-8749 9294   Tel: 020-8743 93

IMAGINATION ENTERTAINMENTS
25 Store Street
South Crescent, London WC1E 7BL
Website: www.imagination.com
e-mail: entertainments@imagination.com
Fax: 020-7323 5801   Tel: 020-7323 33

INCISOR
Flat 4, 2 Somerhill Avenue, Hove BN3 1RJ
Website: www.theatre-company-incisor.com
e-mail: sarah.mann5@ntlworld.com
Fax: 020-8830 4992   Mobile: 07979 4984

INDIGO ENTERTAINMENTS
Tynymynydd, Bryneglwys
Corwen, Denbighshire LL21 9NP
e-mail: info@indigoentertainments.com   Tel: 01978 790

INGRAM Colin Ltd
Suite 526, Linen Hall
162-168 Regent Street, London W1B 5TE
Website: www.coliningramltd.com
e-mail: info@coliningramltd.com
Fax: 020-7038 3907   Tel: 020-7038 39

INSIDE INTELLIGENCE
(Theatre, Contemporary Opera & Music)
13 Athlone Close, London E5 8HD
Website: www.inside-intelligence.org.uk
e-mail: admin@inside-intelligence.org.uk
Fax: 020-8985 7211   Tel: 020-8986 8

INTERNATIONAL THEATRE & MUSIC Ltd
(Piers Chater Robinson)
Garden Studios, 11-15 Betterton Street
Covent Garden, London WC2H 9BP
Website: www.internationaltheatreandmusic.com
e-mail: info@internationaltheatreandmusic.com
Fax: 020-7379 0801   Tel: 020-7470 8786

ISLEWORTH ACTORS COMPANY
38 Eve Road, Isleworth
Middlesex TW7 7HS   Tel/Fax: 020-8891 1073

JAMES Bruce PRODUCTIONS Ltd
68 St Georges Park Avenue
Westcliff-on-Sea, Essex SS0 9UD
Website: www.brucejamesproductions.co.uk
e-mail: info@brucejamesproductions.co.uk
Mobile: 07850 369018   Tel/Fax: 01702 335970

JENKINS Andrew Ltd
63 Kidbrooke Park Road
London SE3 0EE
Website: www.andrewjenkinsltd.com
e-mail: enquiries@andrewjenkinsltd.com
Fax: 020-8856 7106   Tel: 020-8319 3657

JOHNSON David
85B Torriano Avenue, London NW5 2RX
e-mail: david@johnsontemple.co.uk   Tel: 020-7284 3733

JOHNSON Gareth Ltd
Plas Hafren, Eglwyswrw
Crymych, Pembrokeshire SA41 3UL
e-mail: gjltd@mac.com
Fax: 07779 007845   Mobile: 07770 225227

JORDAN Andy PRODUCTIONS Ltd
42 Durlston Road, London E5 8RR
e-mail: ANDYJAndyjordan@aol.com   Mobile: 07775 615205

JORDAN PRODUCTIONS Ltd
Dyke House
110 South Street
Eastbourne, East Sussex BN21 4LB
e-mail: mia@jordanproductionsltd.co.uk
Fax: 01323 417766   Tel: 01323 417745

JORDAN Richard PRODUCTIONS Ltd
Mews Studios, 16 Vernon Yard, London W11 2DX
e-mail: richard.jordan@virgin.net
Fax: 020-7313 9667   Tel: 020-7243 9001

KELLY Robert C Ltd
The Alhambra Suite
82 Mitchell Street, Glasgow G1 3NA
Website: www.robertckelly.co.uk
e-mail: robert@robertckelly.co.uk
Fax: 0141-229 1441   Tel: 0141-229 1444

KENWRIGHT Bill Ltd
BKL House, 106 Harrow Road
Off Howley Place, London W2 1RR
e-mail: info@kenwright.com
Fax: 020-7446 6222   Tel: 020-7446 6200

KING'S HEAD THEATRE PRODUCTIONS Ltd
115 Upper Street, London N1 1QN
Website: www.kingsheadtheatre.org
Fax: 020-7226 8507   Tel: 020-7226 8561

KIRK David PRODUCTIONS
11A Marwick Terrace
St Leonards-on-Sea, East Sussex TN38 0RE
e-mail: david@kirk01.wanadoo.co.uk   Tel: 01424 445081

LATCHMERE THEATRE
(Chris Fisher)
Unit 5A, Imex Business Centre
Ingate Place, London SW8 3NS
e-mail: latchmere@fishers.org.uk
Fax: 020-7978 2631   Tel: 020-7978 2620

LINNIT PRODUCTIONS Ltd
123A King's Road, London SW3 4PL
Fax: 020-7352 3450   Tel: 020-7352 7722

LIVE NATION
35-36 Grosvenor Street, London W1K 4QX
Website: www.livenation.com
Fax: 020-7529 4345   Tel: 020-7529 4300

LIVE THEATRE
7-8 Trinity Chare, Quayside, Newcastle upon Tyne NE1 3DF
Website: www.live.org.uk   Tel: 0191-261 2694

LONDON BUBBLE THEATRE COMPANY Ltd
5 Elephant Lane, London SE16 4JD
Website: www.londonbubble.org.uk
e-mail: admin@londonbubble.org.uk
Fax: 020-7231 2366   Tel: 020-7237 4434

LONDON CLASSIC THEATRE
The Production Office
63 Shirley Avenue, Sutton, Surrey SM1 3QT
Website: www.londonclassictheatre.co.uk
e-mail: admin@londonclassictheatre.co.uk
      Tel/Fax: 020-8395 2095

LONDON COMPANY INTERNATIONAL PLAYS Ltd The
(Licensing of own Plays, No Casting, No CVs)
6th Floor, Empire House, 175 Piccadilly, London W1J 9TB
e-mail: derek@glynnes.co.uk
Fax: 020-7486 2164   Tel: 020-7486 3166

LONDON PRODUCTIONS Ltd
PO Box 10703, London WC2H 9ED
e-mail: admin@leedean.co.uk
Fax: 020-7836 6968   Tel: 020-7497 5111

LONDON REPERTORY COMPANY
27 Old Gloucester Street, London WC1N 3XX
Website: www.londonrepertorycompany.com
e-mail: info@londonrepertorycompany.com
      Tel/Fax: 020-7258 1944

LOUDER THAN WORDS Ltd
75 Church Walk, London N16 8QR
e-mail: giles@louderthanwords.info
Fax: 0870 1333085   Mobile: 07851 729078

MACKINTOSH Cameron Ltd
1 Bedford Square, London WC1B 3RB
Fax: 020-7436 2683   Tel: 020-7637 8866

MACNAGHTEN PRODUCTIONS Ltd
Dundarave, Bushmills
Co. Antrim, Northern Ireland BT57 8ST
Fax: 028-2073 2575   Tel: 028-2073 1215

MALCOLM Christopher Ltd
11 Claremont Walk, Bath BA1 6HB
Website: www.christophermalcolm.co.uk
e-mail: cm@christophermalcolm.co.uk
Fax: 01225 458077   Tel: 01225 445459

MANS Johnny PRODUCTIONS Ltd
PO Box 196, Hoddesdon, Herts EN10 7WG
Website: www.johnnymansproductions.co.uk
e-mail: real@legend.co.uk
Fax: 01992 470516   Tel: 01992 470907

MASTERSON Guy PRODUCTIONS
Millfield Theatre, Silver Street, Edmonton N18 1PJ
Website: www.theatretoursinternational.com
e-mail: admin@theatretoursinternational.com
Tel/Fax: 020-8807 5770

MCM LIMELIGHT Ltd
The Gateway, 2A Rathmore Road, London SE7 7QW
e-mail: enquiries@limelightents.co.uk
Fax: 020-8305 2684   Tel: 020-8858 6141

MEADOW Jeremy Ltd
73 Great Titchfield Street, London W1W 6RD
e-mail: info@jeremymeadow.com
Fax: 0870 7627882   Tel: 020-7436 2244

MENZIES Lee Ltd
118-120 Wardour Street, London W1F 0TU
Website: www.leemenzies.co.uk
e-mail: leemenzies@leemenzies.co.uk
Fax: 020-7734 4224   Tel: 020-7734 9559

MIDDLE GROUND THEATRE CO Ltd
3 Gordon Terrace
Malvern Wells, Malvern, Worcestershire WR14 4ER
Website: www.middlegroundtheatre.co.uk
e-mail: middleground@middlegroundtheatre.co.uk
Fax: 01684 574472   Tel: 01684 577231

MIRTOS PRODUCTIONS
3, 307 Norwood Road, London SE24 9AQ
Website: www.mirtosproductions.co.uk
e-mail: info@mirtosproductions.co.uk
Mobile: 07973 302908

MITCHELL Matthew Ltd
New Barn Farm
London Road, Hassocks, West Sussex BN6 9ND
e-mail: matthew@matthewmitchell.org
Tel/Fax: 01273 842572

MJE PRODUCTIONS Ltd
(Carole Winter, Michael Edwards)
Amadeus House, Floral Street
Covent Garden, London WC2E 9DP
Website: www.mjeproductions.com
e-mail: info@mjeproductions.com
Fax: 020-7812 6495   Tel: 020-7812 7290

MONSTAR PRODUCTIONS
65A Huddleston Road, London N7 0AE
Website: www.monstarproductions.co.uk
e-mail: monstar@fsmail.net   Mobile: 07900 864694

MONSTER PRODUCTIONS
Buddle Arts Centre
258B Station Road, Wallsend, Tyne & Wear NE28 8RG
Website: www.monsterproductions.co.uk
e-mail: info@monsterproductions.co.uk
Fax: 0191-240 4016   Tel: 0191-240 4011

MUSIC THEATRE LONDON
Chertsey Chambers, 12 Mercer Street, London WC2H 9QD
Website: www.capriolfilms.co.uk
e-mail: musictheatre.london@virgin.net   Tel: 07831 243942

MUZIKANSKY
The Forum, Fonthill
The Common, Tunbridge Wells TN4 8YU
Website: www.mzky.co.uk
e-mail: admin@mzky.co.uk   Tel/Fax: 01892 542260

NATIONAL THEATRE
South Bank, London SE1 9PX
Website: www.nationaltheatre.org.uk
Fax: 020-7452 3344   Tel: 020-7452 3333

NEAL STREET PRODUCTIONS Ltd
1st Floor, 26-28 Neal Street
London WC2H 9QQ
e-mail: post@nealstreetproductions.com
Fax: 020-7240 7099   Tel: 020-7240 8890

NEW GODS AND HEROES
Glebe Barn, Peper Harow Lane
Shackleford, Surrey GU8 6AN
Website: www.loveanddeath.co.uk
e-mail: info@loveanddeath.co.uk   Mobile: 07813 615878

NEWPALM PRODUCTIONS
26 Cavendish Avenue, London N3 3QN
Fax: 020-8346 8257   Tel: 020-8349 0802

NEW SHAKESPEARE COMPANY Ltd The
Open Air Theatre
The Iron Works, Inner Circle
Regent's Park, London NW1 4NR
Website: www.openairtheatre.org
Fax: 020-7487 4562   Tel: 020-7935 5756

NEW VIC THEATRE OF LONDON Inc
Suite 42, 91 St Martin's Lane
London WC2H 0DL   Tel/Fax: 020-7240 2929

NICHOLAS Paul & IAN David ASSOCIATES Ltd
Third Floor, 33 Henrietta Street
London WC2E 8NA
Fax: 020-7257 6381   Tel: 020-7257 6380

NITRO
(Formerly Black Theatre Co-operative)
6 Brewery Road, London N7 9NH
Website: www.nitro.co.uk
e-mail: info@nitro.co.uk
Fax: 020-7609 1221   Tel: 020-7609 1331

NML PRODUCTIONS
(Neil Laidlaw)
14 Spectrum Tower
20 Hainault Street, Ilford IG1 4GZ
e-mail: info@nml.org.uk
Fax: 0870 4601483   Tel: 020-8911 9276

NORDIC NOMAD PRODUCTIONS
64 Tulse Hill, London SW2 2PT
Website: www.nordicnomad.com
e-mail: info@nordicnomad.com   Mobile: 07980 619165

NORTHERN BROADSIDES THEATRE COMPANY
Dean Clough, Halifax HX3 5AX
Website: www.northern-broadsides.co.uk
e-mail: sue@northern-broadsides.co.uk
Fax: 01422 383175   Tel: 01422 369704

NORTHERN STAGE (THEATRICAL PRODUCTIONS) Ltd
Barras Bridge
Newcastle upon Tyne NE1 7RH
Website: www.northernstage.co.uk
e-mail: info@northernstage.co.uk
Fax: 0191-261 8093   Tel: 0191-232 3366

NORTHUMBERLAND THEATRE COMPANY (NTC)
The Playhouse, Bondgate Without
Alnwick, Northumberland NE66 1PQ
Website: www.ntc-touringtheatre.co.uk
e-mail: admin@ntc-touringtheatre.co.uk
Fax: 01665 605837   Tel: 01665 602586

NOT THE NATIONAL THEATRE
(Write) (Small/Mid-Scale Touring - UK & Abroad)
116 Dalberg Road, London SW2 1AW

NOTIONAL THEATRE Ltd
PO Box 130, Hexham NE46 4WA
Website: www.notionaltheatre.com
e-mail: info@notionaltheatre.org   Mobile: 07766 661795

O'BRIEN Barry (1968) Ltd
26 Cavendish Avenue, London N3 3QN
Fax: 020-8346 8257   Tel: 020-8346 8011

OFF THE CUFF THEATRE COMPANY
2nd Floor
91A Rivington Street, London EC2A 3AY
Website: www.otctheatre.co.uk
e-mail: otctheatre@aol.com
Fax: 020-7739 3852   Tel: 020-7739 2857

OLD VIC PRODUCTIONS Plc
The Old Vic Theatre
The Cut, Waterloo, London SE1 8NB
e-mail: ros.povey@oldvictheatre.com
Fax: 020-7981 0946   Tel: 020-7928 2651

ONE NIGHT BOOKING COMPANY The
3 Grand Union Walk
Camden Town, London NW1 9LP
Website: www.onenightbooking.com
e-mail: mail@onenightbooking.com   Tel: 020-8455 3278

OPEN AIR THEATRE
(See NEW SHAKESPEARE COMPANY Ltd The)

OPERATING THEATRE COMPANY
22 Burghley Road, London NW5 1UE
Website: www.operating-theatre.co.uk
e-mail: info@operating-theatre.co.uk   Tel: 020-7419 2476

OUT OF JOINT
7 Thane Works
Thane Villas, London N7 7NU
Website: www.outofjoint.co.uk
e-mail: ojo@outofjoint.co.uk
Fax: 020-7609 0203   Tel: 020-7609 0207

OUT OF THE BOX PRODUCTIONS Ltd
48 New Cavendish Street, London W1G 8TG
Website: www.outoftheboxproductions.org
e-mail: info@outoftheboxproductions.org
Tel/Fax: 020-7935 1360

OVATION
Upstairs at The Gatehouse
The Gatehouse
Highgate Village, London N6 4BD
Website: www.ovationtheatres.com
e-mail: events@ovationproductions.com
Fax: 020-8340 3466   Tel: 020-8340 4256

P&S PRODUCTIONS
Top Flat, 51 Norroy Road
London SW15 1PQ
e-mail: timsawers@msn.com   Tel: 020-8788 8521

PAINES PLOUGH
Fourth Floor
43 Aldwych, London WC2B 4DN
Website: www.painesplough.com
e-mail: office@painesplough.com
Fax: 020-7240 4534   Tel: 020-7240 4533

PENDLE PRODUCTIONS
Bridge Farm
249 Hawes Side Lane, Blackpool FY4 4AA
Website: www.pendleproductions.co.uk
e-mail: admin@pendleproductions.co.uk
Fax: 01253 792930   Tel: 01253 839375

PENTABUS
(National Touring Company for New Writing)
Bromfield, Ludlow, Shropshire SY8 2JU
Website: www.pentabus.co.uk
e-mail: john@pentabus.co.uk
Fax: 01584 856254   Tel: 01584 856564

PEOPLE SHOW
People Show Studios, Pollard Row, London E2 6NB
Website: www.peopleshow.co.uk
e-mail: people@peopleshow.co.uk
Fax: 020-7739 0203   Tel: 020-7729 1841

PERFORMANCE BUSINESS The
78 Oatlands Drive, Weybridge, Surrey KT13 9HT
Website: www.theperformance.biz
e-mail: info@theperformance.biz   Tel: 01932 888885

PILOT THEATRE
(New Writing & Multimedia YPT)
York Theatre Royal, St Leonard's Place, York YO1 7HD
Website: www.pilot-theatre.com
e-mail: info@pilot-theatre.com
Fax: 01904 656378   Tel: 01904 635755

PLANTAGENET PRODUCTIONS
Westridge (Open Centre), (Drawing Room Recitals)
Star Lane, Highclere
Nr Newbury RG20 9PJ   Tel: 01635 253322

PLUTO PRODUCTIONS Ltd
New End Theatre, 27 New End
Hampstead, London NW3 1JD
Website: www.newendtheatre.co.uk
e-mail: briandaniels@newendtheatre.co.uk
Fax: 020-7794 4044   Tel: 020-7472 5800

POLKA THEATRE
240 The Broadway, Wimbledon SW19 1SB
Website: www.polkatheatre.com
e-mail: admin@polkatheatre.com
Fax: 020-8545 8365   Tel: 020-8545 8320

POPULAR PRODUCTIONS Ltd
18B High Street, London N8 7PB
Website: www.popularproductions.co.uk
e-mail: info@popularproductions.co.uk
Mobile: 07812 859767   Tel: 020-8347 0221

POSTER Kim
4th Floor, 80-81 St Martin's Lane, London WC2N 4AA
e-mail: admin@stanhopeprod.com
Fax: 020-7504 8656   Tel: 020-7240 3098

PREMIER SHOWS Ltd
PO Box 65, Arundel, West Sussex BN18 9WZ
Website: www.premiershows.co.uk
e-mail: mail@premiershows.co.uk
Fax: 01903 885372   Tel: 01903 885391

PROMENADE PRODUCTIONS Ltd
6 Russell Grove, London SW9 6HS
Website: www.promenadeproductions.com
e-mail: info@promenadeproductions.com
Tel: 020-7582 9354

PUGH David & ROGERS Dafydd
Wyndhams Theatre, Charing Cross Road, London WC2H 0DA
e-mail: dpl@davidpughltd.com
Fax: 020-7292 0399   Tel: 020-7292 0390

PURSUED BY A BEAR PRODUCTIONS
Farnham Maltings, Bridge Square, Farnham GU9 7QR
Website: www.pursuedbyabear.co.uk
e-mail: pursuedbyabear@yahoo.co.uk   Tel: 01252 723237

PW PRODUCTIONS Ltd
2nd Floor, 80-81 St Martin's Lane
London WC2N 4AA
Website: www.pwprods.co.uk
Fax: 020-7240 2947   Tel: 020-7395 7580

QDOS ENTERTAINMENT
Qdos House, Queen Margaret's Road
Scarborough, North Yorkshire YO11 2YH
Website: www.qdosentertainment.co.uk
e-mail: info@qdosentertainment.co.uk
Fax: 01723 361958   Tel: 01723 500038

QUANTUM THEATRE
The Old Button Factory
1-11 Bannockburn Road
Plumstead, London SE18 1ET
Website: www.quantumtheatre.co.uk
e-mail: office@quantumtheatre.co.uk   Tel: 020-8317 9000

RAGGED RAINBOW PRODUCTIONS Ltd
45 Nightingale Lane
Crouch End, London N8 7RA
e-mail: rainbowrp@onetel.com   Tel/Fax: 020-8341 6241

RAGS & FEATHERS THEATRE COMPANY
80 Summer Road
Thames Ditton, Surrey KT7 0QP
e-mail: jill@ragsandfeathers.freeserve.co.uk
Mobile: 07958 724374   Tel: 020-8224 2203

RAIN OR SHINE THEATRE COMPANY
25 Paddock Gardens
Longlevens, Gloucester GL2 0ED
Website: www.rainorshine.co.uk
e-mail: theatre@rainorshine.co.uk   Tel/Fax: 01452 521575

REAL CIRCUMSTANCE THEATRE COMPANY
100 Lexden Road
West Bergholt, Colchester CO6 3BW
Website: www.realcircumstance.com
e-mail: info@realcircumstance.com

REALLY USEFUL GROUP Ltd The
22 Tower Street, London WC2H 9TW
Fax: 020-7240 1204   Tel: 020-7240 0880

REC PRODUCTIONS Ltd
260 Kings Road, Kingston, Surrey KT2 5HX
Website: www.recproductions.com
e-mail: roger@recproductions.com
Fax: 020-7099 1156   Tel: 020-7099 1149

RED ROOM The
Cabin E, Clarendon Buildings
11 Ronalds Road, London N5 1XJ
Website: www.theredroom.org.uk
e-mail: info@theredroom.org.uk   Tel: 020-7697 8685

RED ROSE CHAIN
1 Fore Hamlet, Ipswich IP3 8AA
Website: www.redrosechain.co.uk
e-mail: info@redrosechain.co.uk   Tel: 01473 288886

RED SHIFT THEATRE COMPANY
Trowbray House
108 Weston Street, London SE1 3QB
Website: www.redshifttheatreco.co.uk
e-mail: mail@redshifttheatreco.co.uk
Fax: 020-7378 9789   Tel: 020-7378 9787

REDINGTON Michael Ltd
10 Maunsel Street, London SW1P 2QL
Fax: 020-7828 6947   Tel: 020-7834 5119

REFRACTION
4A St Bernard's Crescent
Edinburgh EH4 1NP
e-mail: claremprenton@hotmail.com Mobile: 07887 932588

REVEAL THEATRE COMPANY
40 Pirehill Lane
Walton, Stone, Staffs ST15 0JN
Website: www.revealtheatre.co.uk
e-mail: robert.marsden@hotmail.com
Tel/Fax: 0115-878 065

RHO DELTA Ltd
(Greg Ripley-Duggan)
26 Goodge Street, London W1T 2QG
e-mail: info@ripleyduggan.com   Tel: 020-7436 1392

RICHMOND PRODUCTIONS
47 Moor Mead Road
St Margarets, Twickenham TW1 1JS
e-mail: alister@richmondproductions.co.uk
Mobile: 07968 026768   Tel/Fax: 020-8891 228C

ROCKET THEATRE
245 Broadfield Road, Manchester M14 7JT
Website: www.rockettheatre.co.uk
e-mail: martin@rockettheatre.co.uk
Mobile: 07788 723570   Tel: 0161-226 8788

ROSE Michael Ltd
The Old Dairy, Throop Road
Holdenhurst
Bournemouth, Dorset BH8 0DL
e-mail: michael@michaelroseltd.com
Fax: 01202 522311   Tel: 01202 52271

ROSENTHAL Suzanna Ltd
PO Box 40001, London N6 4YA
e-mail: admin@suzannarosenthal.com
Tel/Fax: 020-8340 4421

ROYAL COURT THEATRE PRODUCTIONS Ltd
Sloane Square, London SW1W 8AS
Website: www.royalcourttheatre.com
e-mail: info@royalcourttheatre.com
Fax: 020-7565 5001   Tel: 020-7565 5050

ROYAL EXCHANGE THEATRE
St Ann's Square
Manchester M2 7DH
Website: www.royalexchange.co.uk   Tel: 0161-833 9333

ROYAL SHAKESPEARE COMPANY
1 Earlham Street, London WC2H 9LL
Website: www.rsc.org.uk
Fax: 020-7845 0505   Tel: 020-7845 0500

Waterside, Stratford-upon-Avon CV37 6BB
Fax: 01789 294810   Tel: 01789 296655

RUBINSTEIN Mark Ltd
25 Short Street, London SE1 8LJ
e-mail: info@mrluk.com
Fax: 0870 7059731   Tel: 020-7021 0787

SALBERG & STEPHENSON Ltd
18 Soho Square, London W1D 3QL
e-mail: soholondon@aol.com
Fax: 020-7025 8100   Tel: 020-7025 8701

SANDIS PRODUCTIONS
Office 423, 266 Banbury Road
Summertown, Oxford OX2 7DL
Website: www.sandisproductions.com
e-mail: info@sandisproductions.com
Mobile: 07775 520906   Tel/Fax: 01865 514327

ANDPIPER PRODUCTIONS Ltd
A Ossington Street, London W2 4LY
e-mail: harold@sanditen.fsworld.co.uk
x: 0871 7333998   Tel: 020-7229 6708

CAMP
therland Callow Arts Management and Production
Church Lane, Arlesley, Beds SG15 6UX
ebsite: www.scamptheatre.com
mail: admin@scamptheatre.com
obile: 07710 491111   Tel: 01462 734843

CARLET THEATRE
udio 4, The Bull
High Street, Barnet, Herts EN5 5SJ
ebsite: www.scarlettheatre.co.uk
mail: admin@scarlettheatre.co.uk   Tel: 020-8441 9779

EABRIGHT James
d Floor, 118-120 Wardour Street, London W1F 0TU
ebsite: www.seabright.info
mail: contacts@seabright.info
x: 08701 255706   Tel: 020-7439 1173

HAKESPEARE'S MEN
Dee Close, Upminster
sex RM14 1QD
ebsite: www.terencemustoo.com
mail: terence@terencemustoo.com   Tel: 01708 222938

HARED EXPERIENCE
ational/International Touring)
e Soho Laundry
Dufour's Place, London W1F 7SJ
ebsite: www.sharedexperience.org.uk
mail: admin@sharedexperience.org.uk
x: 020-7287 8763   Tel: 020-7434 9248

HOW OF STRENGTH
Chessel Street
edminster, Bristol BS3 3DN
ebsite: www.showofstrength.org.uk
ax: 0117-902 0196   Tel: 0117-902 0235

IMPLY THEATRE
hemin des Couleuvres 8B
95 Tannay, Switzerland 1295
ebsite: www.simplytheatre.com
mail: info@simplytheatre.com
ax: 00 41 22 8600519   Tel: 00 41 22 8600518

INDEN Marc PRODUCTIONS
Grand Union Walk
amden Town, London NW1 9LP
ebsite: www.sindenproductions.com
mail: mail@sindenproductions.com   Tel: 020-8455 3278

OHO THEATRE COMPANY
Dean Street, London W1D 3NE
ebsite: www.sohotheatre.com
ax: 020-7287 5061   Tel: 020-7287 5060

PHINX THEATRE COMPANY
5 Short Street, London SE1 8LJ
ebsite: www.sphinxtheatre.co.uk
mail: info@sphinxtheatre.co.uk
ax: 020-7401 9995   Tel: 020-7401 9993

PIEGEL Adam PRODUCTIONS
tage Entertainment Ltd
th Floor Swan House
2 Poland Street, London W1F 7NQ
mail: enquiries@adamspiegel.com
ax: 020-7025 6971   Tel: 020-7025 6970

SPLATS ENTERTAINMENT
5 Denmark Street, London WC2H 8LP
e-mail: admin@splatsentertainment.com
Fax: 020-7240 8409   Tel: 020-7240 8400

SPLITMOON THEATRE COMPANY
Flat 1, 17 Westgrove Lane, London SE10 8QP
Website: www.splitmoontheatre.org
e-mail: info@splitmoontheatre.org   Tel: 020-8694 3703

SQUAREDEAL PRODUCTIONS Ltd
(Jenny Topper)
24 De Beauvoir Square, London N1 4LE
e-mail: jenny@jennytopper.com
Fax: 020-7275 7553   Tel: 020-7249 5966

SQUIRES & JOHNS PRODUCTIONS Ltd
Sullon Lodge, Sullon Side Lane
Garstang PR3 1GH
Fax: 01253 407715   Tel: 0871 2003343

STACEY Barrie UK PRODUCTIONS Ltd
Flat 8, 132 Charing Cross Road, London WC2H 0LA
Website: www.barriestacey.com
e-mail: hopkinstacey@aol.com
Fax: 020-7836 2949   Tel: 020-7836 6220

STAGE ENTERTAINMENT Ltd
Swan House, 52 Poland Street
London W1F 7NH
Fax: 020-7025 6971   Tel: 020-7025 6970

STAGE FURTHER PRODUCTIONS Ltd
Westgate House, Stansted Road
Eastbourne, East Sussex BN22 8LG
e-mail: davidsfp@hotmail.com
Fax: 01323 736127   Tel: 01323 739478

STAND UP DRAMA
Unit 8, 8 Balmes Road, London N1 5TQ
Website: www.standupdrama.com
e-mail: info@standupdrama.com   Tel: 020-7923 2295

STANHOPE PRODUCTIONS Ltd
4th Floor, 80-81 St Martin's Lane
London WC2N 4AA
e-mail: admin@stanhopeprod.com
Fax: 020-7504 8656   Tel: 020-7240 3098

STRAIGHT LINE PRODUCTIONS
58 Castle Avenue, Epsom, Surrey KT17 2PH
e-mail: mary@straightlinemanagement.co.uk
Fax: 020-8393 8079   Tel: 020-8393 4220

SUPPORT ACT PRODUCTIONS
(Ian McCracken)
243A Lynmouth Avenue,
Morden, Surrey SM4 4RX
Website: www.supportact.co.uk
e-mail: info@supportact.co.uk   Tel: 0845 0940796

SUSPECT CULTURE
CCA, 350 Sauchiehall Street, Glasgow G2 3JD
Website: www.suspectculture.com
e-mail: info@suspectculture.com
Fax: 0141-332 8823   Tel: 0141-332 9775

TABS PRODUCTIONS
57 Chamberlain Place
Higham Street
Walthamstow, London E17 6AZ
Website: www.tabsproductions.co.uk
e-mail: adrianmljames@aol.com
Fax: 08714 332938   Tel: 020-8527 9255

TALAWA THEATRE COMPANY
3rd Floor, 23-25 Great Sutton Street
London EC1V 0DN
Website: www.talawa.com
e-mail: hq@talawa.com
Fax: 020-7251 5969   Tel: 020-7251 6644

TAMASHA THEATRE COMPANY Ltd
Unit 220, Great Guildford Business Square
30 Great Guildford Street, London SE1 0HS
Website: www.tamasha.org.uk
e-mail: info@tamasha.org.uk
Fax: 020-7021 0421   Tel: 020-7633 2270

TBA MUSIC
1 St Gabriels Road, London NW2 4DS
e-mail: peter@tbagroup.co.uk
Fax: 0871 9943658   Tel: 0845 1203722

TEG PRODUCTIONS Ltd
73 Great Titchfield Street, London W1W 6RD
e-mail: info@tegproductions.com
Fax: 0870 7627882   Tel: 020-7436 2244

TENTH PLANET PRODUCTIONS
75 Woodland Gardens, London N10 3UD
Website: www.10thplanetproductions.com
e-mail: admin@10thplanetproductions.com
Fax: 020-8883 1708   Tel: 020-8442 2659

Medius House, 2 Sheraton Street, London W1F 8BH
Fax: 020-7439 3584   Tel: 020-7297 9474

THAT'S ENTERTAINMENT PRODUCTIONS
8 Ellis Avenue
High Salvington, Worthing BN13 3DY
Website: www.thatsentertainmenment.co.uk
e-mail: info@thatsentertainmentproductions.co.uk
                                      Tel: 01903 263454

THEATRE ABSOLUTE
57-61 Corporation Street, Coventry CV1 1GQ
Website: www.theatreabsolute.co.uk
e-mail: info@theatreabsolute.co.uk   Tel: 024-7625 7380

THEATRE ALIVE!
c/o Menier Chocolate Factory
4 O'Meara Street, London SE1 1TE
Website: www.theatrealive.org.uk
e-mail: theatrealiveinfo@tiscali.co.uk
                                      Tel/Fax: 020-7403 4405

THEATRE BABEL
98 Saltmarket, Glasgow G1 5LD
Website: www.theatrebabel.co.uk
e-mail: admin@theatrebabel.co.uk
Fax: 0141-249 9900   Tel: 0141-553 1346

THEATRE NORTH
Woodlands, The Mains
Giggleswick
Settle, North Yorkshire BD24 0AX
Website: www.theatrenorth.co.uk
e-mail: info@theatrenorth.co.uk   Tel/Fax: 01729 822058

THEATRE OF COMEDY COMPANY Ltd
Shaftesbury Theatre
210 Shaftesbury Avenue, London WC2H 8DP
Fax: 020-7836 8181   Tel: 020-7379 3345

THEATRE ROYAL HAYMARKET PRODUCTIONS
Theatre Royal Haymarket
18 Suffolk Street, London SW1Y 4HT
e-mail: nigel.everett@trh.co.uk
Fax: 020-7389 9698   Tel: 020-7389 9669

THEATRE ROYAL STRATFORD EAST
Gerry Raffles Square, Stratford, London E15 1BN
Website: www.stratfordeast.com
e-mail: theatreroyal@stratfordeast.com
Fax: 020-8534 8381   Tel: 020-8534 737

THEATRE SANS FRONTIERES
The Queen's Hall Arts Centre
Beaumont Street, Hexham NE46 3LS
Website: www.tsf.org.uk
e-mail: admin@tsf.org.uk
Fax: 01434 607206   Tel: 01434 65248

THEATRE SET-UP
12 Fairlawn Close, Southgate, London N14 4JX
Website: www.ts-u.co.uk   Tel: 020-8886 957

THEATRE TOURS INTERNATIONAL
Millfield Theatre, Silver Street, Edmonton N18 1PJ
Website: www.theatretoursinternational.com
e-mail: mail@theatretoursinternational.com
                                      Tel: 020-8807 57

THEATRE WORKOUT Ltd
13A Stratheden Road, Blackheath, London SE3 7TH
Website: www.theatreworkout.co.uk
e-mail: enquiries@theatreworkout.co.uk Tel: 020-8144 229

THEATREWORKS
2 Hanley Road, Malvern Wells, Worcs WR14 4PQ
Website: www.theatreworks.info
e-mail: info@theatreworks.info   Tel: 01684 57834

TIATA FAHODZI
AH 112 Aberdeen Centre
22-24 Highbury Grove, London N5 2EA
Website: www.tiatafahodzi.com
e-mail: info@tiatafahodzi.com   Tel/Fax: 020-7226 380

TOLD BY AN IDIOT
Battersea Arts Centre
Lavender Hill, London SW11 5TF
Website: www.toldbyanidiot.org
e-mail: info@toldbyanidiot.org   Tel: 020-7978 420

TOPPER Jenny
(Squaredeal Productions Ltd)
24 De Beauvoir Square, London N1 4LE
e-mail: jenny@jennytopper.com
Fax: 020-7275 7553   Tel: 020-7249 596

TOURING TALES THEATRE COMPANY Ltd
Suite 228, The Linen Hall
162 Regent Street, London W1B 5TG
e-mail: info@birminghamstage.net
Website: www.birminghamstage.net
Fax: 020-7437 3395   Tel: 020-7437 339

TOWER THEATRE COMPANY
(Full-time non-professional)
St Bride Foundation, Bride Lane, London EC4Y 8EQ
Website: www.towertheatre.org.uk
e-mail: info@towertheatre.freeserve.co.uk
                                      Tel/Fax: 020-7353 570

TREAGUS Andrew ASSOCIATES Ltd
5th Floor, 35 Soho Square, London W1D 3QX
e-mail: admin@at-assoc.co.uk
Fax: 020-7851 0151   Tel: 020-7851 015

TREAGUS STONEMAN ASSOCIATES Ltd
5th Floor, 35 Soho Square, London W1D 3QX
Website: www.treagusstoneman.com
e-mail: info@treagusstoneman.com
Fax: 020-7851 0151   Tel: 020-7851 015

RESTLE THEATRE COMPANY
isual/Physical Theatre, Music, Choreography
ew Writing)
estle Arts Base, Russet Drive, Herts, St Albans AL4 0JQ
ebsite: www.trestle.org.uk
mail: admin@trestle.org.uk
ax: 01727 855558   Tel: 01727 850950

RICYCLE LONDON PRODUCTIONS
59 Kilburn High Road, London NW6 7JR
ebsite: www.tricycle.co.uk
mail: admin@tricycle.co.uk
ax: 020-7328 0795   Tel: 020-7372 6611

RIUMPH PROSCENIUM PRODUCTIONS Ltd
t Floor, 18 Exeter Street, London WC2E 7DU
ax: 020-7379 4860   Tel: 020-7379 4870

URTLE KEY ARTS
adbroke Hall, 79 Barlby Road, London W10 6AZ
mail: admin@turtlekeyarts.org.uk
        Tel: 020-8964 5060

WIST & CHEETHAM
9 Rosslyn Crescent, Edinburgh EH6 5AT
mail: ben.twist@blueyonder.co.uk   Tel/Fax: 0131-477 7425

WO'S COMPANY
44 Upland Road, London SE22 0DN
mail: graham@2scompanytheatre.co.uk
ax: 020-8299 3714   Tel: 020-8299 4593

K ARTS INTERNATIONAL
rst Floor, 6 Shaw Street, Worcester WR1 3QQ
ebsite: www.ukarts.com
mail: janryan@ukarts.com
ax: 01905 22868   Tel: 01905 26424

K PRODUCTIONS Ltd
me House, 78 Meadrow, Godalming, Surrey GU7 3HT
ebsite: www.ukproductions.co.uk
mail: mail@ukproductions.co.uk
ax: 01483 418486   Tel: 01483 423600

NRESTRICTED VIEW
oove Hen & Chickens Theatre Bar
9 St Paul's Road, London N1 2NA
ebsite: www.henandchickens.com
mail: james@henandchickens.com   Tel: 020-7704 2001

ANCE Charles
V Productions Ltd
ampden House, 2 Weymouth Street, London W1W 5BT
mail: cvtheatre@aol.com
ax: 020-7636 2323   Tel: 020-7636 4343

ANDER ELST Anthony PRODUCTIONS
he Studio, 14 College Road, Bromley, Kent BR1 3NS
ax: 020-8313 0443   Tel: 020-8466 5580

AYU NAIDU COMPANY
nit LFB2, Lafone House, The Leathermarket
-13 Leathermarket Street, London SE1 3HN
ebsite: www.vayunaiducompany.org.uk
mail: info@vayunaiducompany.org.uk
        Tel/Fax: 020-7378 0739

OLCANO THEATRE COMPANY Ltd
wansea Institute, Townhill Road, Swansea SA2 0UT
ebsite: www.volcanotheatre.co.uk
mail: volcano.tc@virgin.net
ax: 01792 281282   Tel: 01792 281280

VALKING FORWARD Ltd
tudio 1, 35 Britannia Row, London N1 8QH
ebsite: www.walkingforward.co.uk
mail: info@walkingforward.co.uk
ax: 020-7359 5091   Tel: 020-7359 5249

WALLACE Kevin Ltd
10 (H) St Martin's Place, London WC2N 4JL
e-mail: enquiries@kevinwallace.co.uk
Fax: 020-7836 9587   Tel: 020-7836 9586

WAREHOUSE THEATRE COMPANY
Dingwall Road, Croydon CR0 2NF
Website: www.warehousetheatre.co.uk
e-mail: info@warehousetheatre.co.uk
Fax: 020-8688 6699   Tel: 020-8681 1257

WAX Kenneth H Ltd
2nd Floor, 80-81 St Martin's Lane
London WC2N 4AA
e-mail: k.wax@virgin.net
Fax: 020-7240 2947   Tel: 020-7395 7584

WEAVER HUGHES ENSEMBLE
12B Carholme Road
London SE23 2HS
Website: www.weaverhughesensemble.co.uk
e-mail: ensemble@weaverhughesensemble.co.uk
        Tel/Fax: 020-8291 0514

WEST END PROPERTY PRODUCTIONS
Rapley House, 76 Station Road
Hayling Island, Hampshire PO11 0EL
Website: www.angelsandkings.co.uk
e-mail: terry@angelsandkings.co.uk
Fax: 023-9263 7264   Tel: 023-9263 7067

WHITALL Keith
25 Solway, Hailsham
East Sussex BN27 3HB   Tel: 01323 844882

WHITEHALL Michael
10 Lower Common South, London SW15 1BP
e-mail: mwhitehall@msn.com
Fax: 020-8788 2340   Tel: 020-8785 3737

WILDCARD THEATRE COMPANY
Suite A, Swan House
White Hart Street
High Wycombe, Bucks HP11 2HL
Website: www.wildcardtheatre.org.uk
e-mail: admin@wildcardtheatre.org.uk
Fax: 07092 024967   Tel: 0870 7606158

WILLS Newton MANAGEMENT
The Studio, 29 Springvale Avenue
Brentford, Middlesex TW8 9QH
e-mail: newtoncttg@aol.com
Fax: 00 33 468 218685   Mobile: 07989 398381

WOOD Kevin PRODUCTIONS
Langdon Abbey, West Langdon, Dover, Kent CT15 5HJ
e-mail: sylviasims@btconnect.com
Fax: 01304 853506   Tel: 01304 853539

WRESTLING SCHOOL The
(The Howard Baker Company)
42 Durlston Road, London E5 8RR
Website: www.thewrestlingschool.co.uk
        Tel/Fax: 020-8442 4229

YELLOW EARTH THEATRE
18 Rupert Street, London W1D 6DE
Website: www.yellowearth.org
e-mail: admin@yellowearth.org
Fax: 020-7287 3141   Tel: 020-7734 5988

YOUNG VIC THEATRE
66 The Cut, London SE1 8LZ
Website: www.youngvic.org
e-mail: info@youngvic.org
Fax: 020-7820 3355   Tel: 020-7922 2800

7:84 THEATRE COMPANY (SCOTLAND) Ltd
Film City Glasgow
No. 4 Summertown Road, Glasgow G51 2LY
Website: www.784theatre.com
e-mail: admin@784theatre.com   Tel: 0141-445 7245

ABERYSTWYTH ARTS CENTRE
Penglais Campus
Aberystwyth, Ceredigion SY23 3DE
Website: www.aber.ac.uk/artscentre
e-mail: ggo@aber.ac.uk
Fax: 01970 622883   Tel: 01970 621512

AGE EXCHANGE THEATRE TRUST
(Administrator: Suzanne Lockett)
The Reminiscence Centre
11 Blackheath Village, London SE3 9LA
Website: www.age-exchange.org.uk
e-mail: administrator@age-exchange.org.uk
Fax: 020-8318 0060   Tel: 020-8318 9105

ALTERNATIVE ARTS
Top Studio, Montefiore Centre
Hanbury Street, London E1 5HZ
Website: www.alternativearts.co.uk
e-mail: info@alternativearts.co.uk
Fax: 020-7375 0484   Tel: 020-7375 0441

ANGLES THEATRE The
Alexandra Road, Wisbech
Cambridgeshire PE13 1HQ
e-mail: astromanis@anglestheatre.co.uk
Fax: 01945 581967   Tel: 01945 585587

ASHTON GROUP THEATRE The
The Old Fire Station, Abbey Road
Barrow-in-Furness, Cumbria LA14 1XH
Website: www.ashtongroup.co.uk
e-mail: theashtongroup@btconnect.com
          Tel/Fax: 01229 430636

ATTIC THEATRE COMPANY (LONDON) Ltd
New Wimbledon Theatre
The Broadway, London SW19 1QG
Website: www.attictheatrecompany.com
e-mail: info@attictheatrecompany.com   Tel: 020-8543 7838

BANNER THEATRE
Oaklands New Church Centre
Winleigh Road, Handsworth Wood
Birmingham B20 2HN
e-mail: info@bannertheatre.co.uk   Tel: 0845 4581909

BECK THEATRE
Grange Road, Hayes
Middlesex UB3 2UE   Tel: 020-8561 7506

BENT BACK TULIPS THEATRE COMPANY
67A Graveney Road, London SW17 0EG
Website: www.bentbacktulips.com
e-mail: info@bentbacktulips.com   Mobile: 07971 159940

BLUEYED THEATRE PRODUCTIONS
76 Barcombe Avenue, London SW2 3AZ
Website: www.blueyedtheatreproductions.co.uk
e-mail: info@blueyedtheatreproductions.co.uk
          Mobile: 07957 215965

BLUNDERBUS THEATRE COMPANY Ltd
1st Floor, The Brook Theatre
Old Town Hall, Chatham, Kent ME4 4SE
Website: www.blunderbus.co.uk
e-mail: admin@blunderbus.co.uk
Fax: 01634 818138   Tel: 01623 835888

BORDERLINE THEATRE COMPANY
(Eddie Jackson)
North Harbour Street, Ayr KA8 8AA
Website: www.borderlinetheatre.co.uk
e-mail: enquiries@borderlinetheatre.co.uk
Fax: 01292 618685   Tel: 01292 2810

BRUVVERS THEATRE COMPANY
(Venue - The Round)
36 Lime Street, Ouseburn, Newcastle upon Tyne NE1 2PQ
Website: www.bruvvers.co.uk
e-mail: mikeofbruvvers@hotmail.com   Tel: 0191-261 923

CAPITAL ARTS YOUTH THEATRE
Wyllyotts Centre, Darkes Lane, Potters Bar, Herts EN6 2HN
e-mail: capitalarts@btconnect.com
Mobile: 07885 232414   Tel/Fax: 020-8449 234

CARIB THEATRE COMPANY
73 Lancelot Road, Wembley, Middlesex HA0 2AN
e-mail: antoncarib@yahoo.co.uk   Tel/Fax: 020-8903 459

CENTRE FOR PERFORMANCE RESEARCH
Penglais Campus, Aberystwyth SY23 3AJ
Website: www.thecpr.org.uk
e-mail: cprwww@aber.ac.uk
Fax: 01970 622132   Tel: 01970 62213

CHAIN REACTION THEATRE COMPANY
Three Mills Studios, Sugar House Yard
Sugar House Lane, London E15 2QS
Website: www.chainreactiontheatre.co.uk
e-mail: mail@chainreactiontheatre.co.uk
          Tel/Fax: 020-8534 00C

CHALKFOOT THEATRE ARTS
Central Studios, 36 Park Place, Margate, Kent CT9 1LE
Website: www.chalkfoot.org.uk
e-mail: info@chalkfoot.org.uk
Fax: 01843 280088   Tel: 01843 28007

CHATS PALACE ARTS CENTRE
42-44 Brooksby's Walk, Hackney, London E9 6DF
Website: www.chatspalace.com
e-mail: info@chatspalace.com   Tel: 020-8533 022

CHEEKY MAGGOT PRODUCTIONS
Website: www.cheekymaggot.co.uk
e-mail: info@cheekymaggot.co.uk

CHERUB COMPANY LONDON The
Office: 9 Park Hill, London W5 2JS
Website: www.cherub.org.uk
e-mail: casting@cherub.org.uk
Fax: 020-8248 0318   Tel/Fax: 020-8723 435

CHICKEN SHED THEATRE
Chase Side, Southgate, London N14 4PE
Website: www.chickenshed.org.uk
e-mail: info@chickenshed.org.uk
Minicom: 020-8350 0676   Tel: 020-8351 61

CLEAN BREAK
(Theatre Education, New Writing)
2 Patshull Road, London NW5 2LB
Website: www.cleanbreak.org.uk
e-mail: general@cleanbreak.org.uk
Fax: 020-7482 8611   Tel: 020-7482 860

CLOSE FOR COMFORT THEATRE COMPANY
34 Boleyn Walk
Leatherhead, Surrey KT22 7HU
Website: www.hometown.aol.com/close4comf
e-mail: close4comf@aol.com
Mobile: 07710 258290   Tel: 01372 3786

There are hundreds of theatres in the UK, varying dramatically in size and type. The theatre sections are organised under headings which best indicate a theatre's principal area of work. A summary of each of these is below.

Alternative and Community

Many of these companies tour to Arts Centres, small and middle-scale theatres, and non-theatrical venues which do not have a resident company, or they may be commissioned to develop site specific projects. The term 'alternative' is sometimes used to describe work that is more experimental in style and execution.

Children's, Young People's and TIE

The primary focus of these theatre companies is to reach younger audiences. They often tour to smaller theatres, schools and non-theatrical venues. Interactive teaching - through audience participation and workshops - is often a feature of their work.

English Speaking Theatre Companies in Europe

These work principally outside of the UK. Some are based in one venue whilst others are touring companies. Their work varies enormously and includes Young People's Theatre, large scale musicals, revivals of classics and dinner theatre. Actors are employed either for an individual production or a 'season' of several plays.

London Theatres

Larger theatres situated in the West End and Central London. A few are producing houses, but most are leased to Theatre Producers who take responsibility for putting together a company for a run of a single show. In such cases it is they and not the venue who cast productions (often with the help of Casting Directors). Alternatively, a production will open outside London and tour to Provincial Theatres. Then subsequently, if successful, transfer to a London venue.

Outer London, Fringe and Venues

Small and middle-scale theatres in Outer London and around the country. Some are producing houses, others are only available for hire. Many of the London venues have provided useful directions on how they may be reached by public transport.

Provincial / Touring

Theatre Producers and other companies sell their ready-made productions to the Provincial/Touring Theatres, a list of larger venues outside London. A run in each theatre varies between a night and several weeks, but a week per venue for tours of plays is usual. Even if a venue is not usually a producing house, most Provincial Theatres and Arts Centres put on a family show at Christmas.

Puppet Theatre Companies

Some Puppet Theatres are one-performer companies who literally create their own work from scratch. The content and style of productions varies enormously. For example, not all are aimed at children, and some are more interactive than others. Although we list a few theatres with Puppet Companies in permanent residence, this kind of work often involves touring. As with all small and middle scale touring, performers who are willing, and have the skills, to involve themselves with all aspects of company life are always more valuable.

Repertory (Regional) Theatres

Theatres situated outside London which employ a resident company of actors (i.e. the 'repertory company') on a play-by-play basis or for a season of several plays. In addition to the main auditorium (usually the largest acting space) these theatres may have a smaller studio theatre attached, which will be home to an additional company whose focus is education or the production of new plays (see Children's, Young People's and TIE). In recent years the length of repertory seasons has become shorter; this means that a number of productions are no longer in-house. It is common for gaps in the performance calendar to be filled by tours mounted by Theatre Producers, other Repertory (Regional) Theatres and non-venue based production companies.

COLLUSION THEATRE COMPANY
131 Renfrew Street, Glasgow G3 6QZ
Website: www.collusiontheatre.co.uk
e-mail: admin@collusiontheatre.co.uk
Fax: 0141-644 4163   Tel: 0141-332 7001

COMPLETE WORKS CREATIVE COMPANY Ltd The
The Old Truman Brewery, 91 Brick Lane, London E1 6QL
Website: www.tcw.org.uk
e-mail: info@tcw.org.uk
Fax: 0870 1431979   Tel: 0870 1431969

CORNELIUS & JONES ORIGINAL PRODUCTIONS
49 Carters Close, Sherington
Newport Pagnell, Buckinghamshire MK16 9NW
Website: www.corneliusjones.com
e-mail: admin@corneliusjones.com   Tel/Fax: 01908 612593

CRAGRATS THEATRE
The Mill, Dunford Road, Holmfirth, Huddersfield HD9 2AR
Website: www.cragrats.com
e-mail: benroot@cragrats.com
Fax: 01484 686212   Tel: 01484 686451

CUT-CLOTH THEATRE
41 Beresford Road, Highbury
London N5 2HR   Tel: 020-7503 4393

DRAMA ZONE
Arundel Town Hall, Arundel, West Sussex BN18 9AP
Website: www.dramazone.net
e-mail: admin@dramazone.net   Tel/Fax: 01903 889821

ELAN WALES
(European Live Arts Network)
17 Douglas Buildings, Royal Stuart Lane, Cardiff CF10 5EL
Website: www.elanwales.org
e-mail: david@elanwales.org   Tel/Fax: 029-2019 0077

ELECTRIC CABARET
107 High Street, Brackley, Northants NN13 7BN
Website: www.electriccabaret.co.uk
e-mail: richard@electriccabaret.co.uk
Mobile: 07714 089763   Tel: 01280 700956

EUROPEAN THEATRE COMPANY The
39 Oxford Avenue, London SW20 8LS
Website: www.europeantheatre.co.uk
e-mail: admin@europeantheatre.co.uk
Fax: 020-8544 1999   Tel: 020-8544 1994

FOREST FORGE THEATRE COMPANY
The Theatre Centre, Endeavour Park
Crow Arch Lane, Ringwood, Hampshire BH24 1SF
Website: www.forestforge.co.uk
e-mail: forestforge@btconnect.com
Fax: 01425 471158   Tel: 01425 470188

FOUND THEATRE
12 Blenheim Avenue, Whalley Range, Manchester M16 8JT
Website: www.foundtheatre.org.uk
e-mail: found_theatre@yahoo.co.uk   Tel: 0161-861 8219

FOURSIGHT THEATRE Ltd
Newhampton Arts Centre
Dunkley Street, Wolverhampton WV1 4AN
Website: www.foursighttheatre.co.uk
e-mail: admin@foursighttheatre.co.uk
Fax: 01902 428413   Tel: 01902 714257

FRANTIC THEATRE COMPANY
32 Woodlane, Falmouth TR11 4RF
Website: www.frantictheatre.com
e-mail: info@frantictheatre.com   Tel/Fax: 0870 1657350

GALLEON THEATRE COMPANY Ltd
Greenwich Playhouse, Greenwich BR Station Forecourt
189 Greenwich High Road, London SE10 8JA
Website: www.galleontheatre.co.uk
e-mail: alice@galleontheatre.co.uk
Fax: 020-8310 7276   Tel: 020-8858 92

GRANGE ARTS CENTRE
Rochdale Road, Oldham, Greater Manchester OL9 6EA
Website: www.grangeartsoldham.co.uk
e-mail: grangearts@oldham.ac.uk
Fax: 0161-785 4263   Tel: 0161-785 42

GREASEPAINT ANONYMOUS
4 Gallus Close, Winchmore Hill, London N21 1JR
e-mail: info@greasepaintanonymous.co.uk
Fax: 020-8882 9189   Tel: 020-8886 22

HALL FOR CORNWALL
(Community & Education) (Contact Anna Coombs)
Back Quay, Truro, Cornwall TR1 2LL
Website: www.hallforcornwall.co.uk
e-mail: annac@hallforcornwall.org.uk
Fax: 01872 260246   Tel: 01872 3219

HIJINX THEATRE
(Adults with Learning Disabilities, Community)
Wales Millennium Centre
Bute Place, Cardiff CF10 5AL
Website: www.hijinx.org.uk
e-mail: info@hijinx.org.uk
Fax: 029-2063 5621   Tel: 029-2030 03

HISTORIA THEATRE COMPANY
8 Cloudesley Square, London N1 0HT
Website: www.historiatheatre.com
e-mail: kateprice@lineone.net
Fax: 020-7278 4733   Tel: 020-7837 80

ICON THEATRE
15 Darcy House, London Fields East Side, London E8 3RY
Website: www.icontheatre.org.uk
e-mail: sally@icontheatre.org.uk   Tel/Fax: 020-7923 18

IMAGE MUSICAL THEATRE
23 Sedgeford Road, Shepherd's Bush, London W12 0NA
Website: www.imagemusicaltheatre.co.uk
e-mail: brian@imagemusicaltheatre.co.uk
Fax: 020-8749 9294   Tel: 020-8743 93

IMMEDIATE THEATRE
1.2 Hoxton Works
128 Hoxton Street, London N1 6SH
Website: www.immediate-theatre.com
e-mail: info@immediate-theatre.com
Fax: 020-7012 1682   Tel: 020-7012 16

INOCENTE ART & FILM Ltd
(Film, Multimedia, Music Videos & two Rock 'n' Roll
Musicals)
5 Denmans Lane, Haywards Heath
West Sussex RH16 2LA
e-mail: tarascas@btopenworld.com   Mobile: 07973 5181

ISOSCELES
7 Amity Grove, Raynes Park, London SW20 0LQ
Website: www.isosceles.freeserve.co.uk
e-mail: patanddave@isosceles.freeserve.co.uk
                                      Tel: 020-8946 39

JET THEATRE
11 Clovelly Road, London W5 5HF
Website: www.jettheatre.co.uk
e-mail: jettheatre@aol.com   Tel: 020-8579 10

OMEDIA
4-47 Gardner Street, Brighton BN1 1UN
ebsite: www.komedia.co.uk
mail: info@komedia.co.uk
x: 01273 647102   Tel: 01273 647101

ADDER TO THE MOON ENTERTAINMENT
it 105, Battersea Business Centre
-109 Lavender Hill
ndon SW11 5QL
mail: enquiries@laddertothemoon.co.uk
    Tel: 020-7228 9700

VE THEATRE
ew Writing)
8 Trinity Chare, Quayside
ewcastle upon Tyne NE1 3DF
ebsite: www.live.org.uk
mail: info@live.org.uk
x: 0191-232 2224   Tel: 0191-261 2694

NDON ACTORS THEATRE COMPANY
it 5A, Imex Business Centre
gate Place, London SW8 3NS
mail: latchmere@fishers.org.uk
x: 020-7978 2631   Tel: 020-7978 2620

NDON BUBBLE THEATRE COMPANY Ltd
Elephant Lane, London SE16 4JD
ebsite: www.londonbubble.org.uk
mail: admin@londonbubble.org.uk
x: 020-7231 2366   Tel: 020-7237 4434

W JUNIOR INTER-ACT
) Box 31855, London SE17 3XP
ebsite: www.londonshakespeare.org.uk
mail: londonswo@hotmail.com   Tel/Fax: 020-7793 9755

W PRISON PROJECT
) Box 31855, London SE17 3XP
ebsite: www.londonshakespeare.org.uk
mail: londonswo@hotmail.com   Tel/Fax: 020-7793 9755

W SENIOR RE-ACTION
) Box 31855, London SE17 3XP
ebsite: www.londonshakespeare.org.uk
mail: londonswo@hotmail.com   Tel/Fax: 020-7793 9755

JNG HA'S THEATRE COMPANY
ic Liddell Centre
Morningside Road, Edinburgh EH10 4DP
ebsite: www.lunghas.co.uk
mail: info@lunghas.co.uk
x: 0131-447 3290   Tel: 0131-447 8496

6 THEATRE COMPANY
udio Theatre, Hamer CP School
bert Royds Street, Rochdale OL16 2SU
ebsite: www.m6theatre.co.uk
mail: info@m6theatre.co.uk
x: 01706 712601   Tel: 01706 355898

ADDERMARKET THEATRE
esident Community Theatre Company & Small-Scale
oducing & Receiving House)
John's Alley, Norwich NR2 1DR
ebsite: www.maddermarket.co.uk
mail: mmtheatre@btconnect.com
x: 01603 661357   Tel: 01603 626560

ANCHESTER ACTORS COMPANY
) Box 54, Manchester M60 7AB
ebsite: www.manactco.org.uk
mail: dramatic@amserve.com   Tel: 0161-227 8702

MAN MELA THEATRE COMPANY
(Admin Contact: Caroline Goffin)
Brady Centre, 192-196 Hanbury Street, London E1 5HU
Website: www.manmela.org.uk
e-mail: dominic@manmela.org.uk
Mobile: 07973 349101   Mobile: 07966 215090

MAYA PRODUCTIONS Ltd
156 Richmond Road, London E8 3HN
Website: www.mayaproductions.co.uk
e-mail: mayachris@aol.com   Tel/Fax: 020-7923 0675

MIKRON THEATRE COMPANY Ltd
Marsden Mechanics, Peel Street
Marsden, Huddersfield HD7 6BW
Website: www.mikron.org.uk
e-mail: admin@mikron.org.uk   Tel: 01484 843701

MONTAGE THEATRE ARTS
(Artistic Director: Judy Gordon)
The Albany, Douglas Way, London SE8 4AG
Website: www.montagetheatre.com
e-mail: office@montagetheatre.com   Tel: 020-8692 7007

MOVING THEATRE
16 Laughton Lodge, Laughton
Nr Lewes, East Sussex BN8 6BY
Website: www.movingtheatre.com
e-mail: info@movingtheatre.com
Fax: 01323 815737   Tel: 01323 815726

NATURAL THEATRE COMPANY
(Street Theatre & Touring)
Widcombe Institute, Widcombe Hill, Bath BA2 6AA
Website: www.naturaltheatre.co.uk
e-mail: info@naturaltheatre.co.uk
Fax: 01225 442555   Tel: 01225 469131

NET CURTAINS THEATRE COMPANY
The Bath House, 96 Dean Street, London W1D 3TD
Website: www.netcurtains.org
e-mail: claire@netcurtains.org   Mobile: 07968 564687

NETTLEFOLD The
West Norwood Library Centre
1 Norwood High Street, London SE27 9JX
e-mail: thenettlefold@lambeth.gov.uk   Tel: 020-7926 8070

NEWFOUND THEATRE COMPANY
18 India House
73 Whitworth Street, Manchester M1 6LG
Website: www.newfoundtheatre.co.uk
e-mail: newfoundtheatre@fsmail.net

NEW PERSPECTIVES THEATRE COMPANY
(Regional/National New Writing Touring Theatre)
Park Lane Business Centre, Park Lane
Basford, Nottinghamshire NG6 0DW
Website: www.newperspectives.co.uk
e-mail: info@newperspectives.co.uk   Tel: 0115-927 2334

NORTHERN STAGE THEATRICAL PRODUCTIONS Ltd
Barras Bridge, Newcastle upon Tyne NE1 7RH
Website: www.northernstage.co.uk
e-mail: info@northernstage.co.uk
Fax: 0191-261 8093   Tel: 0191-232 3366

NORTHUMBERLAND THEATRE COMPANY (NTC)
(Touring Regionally & Nationally)
The Playhouse, Bondgate Without
Alnwick, Northumberland NE66 1PQ
Website: www.ntc-touringtheatre.co.uk
e-mail: admin@ntc-touringtheatre.co.uk
Fax: 01665 605837   Tel: 01665 602586

NPVARTS@MAGIC EYE THEATRE
Havil Street, London SE5 7SD
Website: www.npvarts.co.uk
e-mail: admin@npvarts.co.uk   Tel: 020-7708 5401

NUFFIELD THEATRE
(Touring & Projects)
University Road
Southampton SO17 1TR
Website: www.nuffieldtheatre.co.uk
e-mail: abi.linnartz@nuffieldtheatre.co.uk
Fax: 023-8031 5511   Tel: 023-8031 5500

OLD TYME PLAYERS THEATRE COMPANY
(Music Hall, Revues - Locally Based)
35 Barton Court Avenue
Barton on Sea, Hants BH25 7EP
Website: www.oldetymeplayers.co.uk
e-mail: oldetymeplayers@tiscali.co.uk   Tel: 01425 612830

ONATTI THEATRE COMPANY
9 Field Close, Warwick
Warwickshire CV34 4QD
Website: www.onatti.co.uk
e-mail: info@onatti.co.uk
Fax: 0870 1643629   Tel: 01926 495220

OPEN STAGE PRODUCTIONS
49 Springfield Road
Moseley, Birmingham B13 9NN
e-mail: info@openstage.co.uk   Tel/Fax: 0121-777 9086

OXFORDSHIRE TOURING THEATRE COMPANY
The Annexe, SS Mary & John School
Meadow Lane, Oxford OX4 1TJ
Website: www.ottc.org.uk
e-mail: info@ottc.oxfordshire.co.uk
Fax: 01865 247266   Tel: 01865 249444

PASCAL THEATRE COMPANY
35 Flaxman Court, Flaxman Terrace
Bloomsbury, London WC1H 9AR
Website: www.pascal-theatre.com
e-mail: pascaltheatreco@aol.com   Tel: 020-7383 0920

PAUL'S THEATRE COMPANY
Fairkytes Arts Centre
51 Billet Lane, Hornchurch, Essex RM11 1AX
Website: www.paulstheatreschool.co.uk
e-mail: info@paulstheatreschool.co.uk
Fax: 01708 475286   Tel: 01708 447123

PEOPLE'S THEATRE COMPANY The
12E High Street, Egham, Surrey TW20 9EA
Website: www.ptc.org.uk
e-mail: admin@ptc.org.uk   Tel: 01784 470439

PHANTOM CAPTAIN The
618B Finchley Road, London NW11 7RR
Website: www.phantomcaptain.netfirms.com
e-mail: lambhorn@tiscali.co.uk   Tel: 020-8455 4564

PLAYTIME THEATRE COMPANY
18 Bennells Avenue
Whitstable, Kent CT5 2HP
Website: www.playtime.dircon.co.uk
e-mail: playtime@dircon.co.uk
Fax: 01227 266648   Tel: 01227 266272

PRIME PRODUCTIONS
54 Hermiston Village
Currie EH14 4AQ
Website: www.primeproductions.co.uk
e-mail: primeproductions@talktalk.net Tel/Fax: 0131-449 4055

PROTEUS THEATRE COMPANY
(Multimedia and Cross-art Form Work)
Queen Mary's College, Cliddesden Road
Basingstoke, Hampshire RG21 3HF
Website: www.proteustheatre.com
e-mail: info@proteustheatre.com   Tel: 01256 354£

PURSUED BY A BEAR PODUCTIONS
Farnham Maltings, Bridge Square, Farnham GU9 7QR
Website: www.pursuedbyabear.co.uk
e-mail: pursuedbyabear@yahoo.co.uk   Tel: 01252 7232

Q20 THEATRE COMPANY
19 Wellington Crescent, Shipley
West Yorkshire BD18 3PH
e-mail: info@q20theatre.co.uk   Tel: 0845 12606

QUICKSILVER THEATRE
The Glasshouse, 4 Enfield Road, London N1 5AZ
Website: www.quicksilvertheatre.org
e-mail: talktous@quicksilvertheatre.org
Fax: 020-7254 3119   Tel: 020-7241 29

RIDING LIGHTS THEATRE COMPANY
Friargate Theatre, Lower Friargate, York YO1 9SL
Website: www.ridinglights.org   e-mail: info@rltc.c
Fax: 01904 651532   Tel: 01904 6553

SALTMINE THEATRE COMPANY
St James House, Trinity Road, Dudley
West Midlands DY1 1JB
Website: www.saltmine.org
e-mail: creative@saltmine.org   Tel: 01384 4548

SPANNER IN THE WORKS
155 Station Road, Sidcup, Kent DA15 7AA
Website: www.spannerintheworks.org.uk
e-mail: info@spannerintheworks.org.uk Tel: 020-8304 76

SPARE TYRE THEATRE COMPANY
(Community Drama & Music Projects)
Hampstead Town Hall, 213 Haverstock Hill, London NW3 4
Website: www.sparetyretheatrecompany.co.uk
e-mail: sttc@sparetyretheatrecompany.co.uk
                                     Tel/Fax: 020-7419 70

SPECTACLE THEATRE
Coleg Morgannwg, Rhondda
Llwynypia, Tonypandy CF40 2TQ
Website: www.spectacletheatre.co.uk
e-mail: info@spectacletheatre.co.uk
Fax: 01443 439640   Tel: 01443 4307

SPINNING WHEEL THEATRE
5 Haughmond, Woodside Grange Road
Finchley, London N12 8ST
Website: www.spinningwheeltheatre.com
e-mail: info@spinningwheeltheatre.com
                                     Mobile: 07990 5754

SPONTANEITY SHOP The
85-87 Bayham Street, London NW1 0AG
Website: www.the-spontaneity-shop.com
e-mail: info@the-spontaneity-shop.com
                                     Tel: 020-7788 40

STABLES GALLERY & ARTS CENTRE The
The Hayloft, Gladstone Park
Dollis Hill Lane, London NW2 6HT
e-mail: stablesgallery@msn.com   Tel: 020-8452 86

TAG THEATRE COMPANY
Citizens' Theatre, 119 Gorbals Street, Glasgow G5 9DS
Website: www.tag-theatre.co.uk
e-mail: info@tag-theatre.co.uk
Fax: 0141-429 7374   Tel: 0141-429 55

ARA ARTS GROUP
(Rachel Sanger)
56 Garratt Lane, London SW18 4ES
Website: www.tara-arts.com
Fax: 020-8870 9540　　　　　　　Tel: 020-8333 4457

THEATRE AND
Church Hall, St James Road
Marsh, Huddersfield HD1 4QA
Website: www.theatreand.com
e-mail: clare@theatreand.com
Fax: 01484 532962　　　　　　　Tel: 01484 532967

THEATRE EXPRESS MANAGEMENT
(Write)
Spindle Cottage, Allens Farm
Rigby Fen, Billinghay, Lincoln LN4 4DT
e-mail: theatre-express.com

THEATRE IN EDUCATION TOURS (TIE TOURS)
PO Box 433, Weston Super Mare
Somerset BS24 0WY
Website: www.actionwork.com
e-mail: admin@actionwork.com　　　　Tel: 01934 815163

THEATRE IS, ...
Ground Floor Office, Millars 3
Southmill Road, Bishops Stortford CM23 3DH
Website: www.theatreis.org
e-mail: info@theatreis.org
Fax: 01279 506694　　　　　　　Tel: 01279 461607

THEATRE OF LITERATURE The
(Dramatised Readings)
The Cut, London SE1 8LF
e-mail: info@calderpublications.com
Fax: 020-7928 5930　　　　　　　Tel: 020-7633 0599

THEATRE WORKSHOP
Hamilton Place, Edinburgh EH3 5AX
Website: www.theatre-workshop.com
Fax: 0131-220 0112　　　　　　　Tel: 0131-225 7942

THEATR POWYS
The Drama Centre, Tremont Road
Llandrindod Wells, Powys LD1 5EB
Website: www.theatrpowys.co.uk
e-mail: theatr.powys@powys.gov.uk
Fax: 01597 824381　　　　　　　Tel: 01597 824444

THIRD PARTY PRODUCTIONS Ltd
7 St Thomas' Road, Hastings
East Sussex TN34 3LD
Website: www.thirdparty.org
e-mail: gleave@thirdparty.org
Mobile: 07768 694211　　　　　Mobile: 07768 694212

TIME OF OUR LIVES MUSIC THEATRE Ltd
Monkhams Drive, Woodford Green, Essex IG8 0LG
Website: www.toolmusictheatre.co.uk
e-mail: dympna@toolmusictheatre.co.uk
　　　　　　　　　　　　Tel/Fax: 020-8491 6695

TOBACCO FACTORY
Raleigh Road, Southville, Bristol BS3 1TF
Website: www.tobaccofactory.com
e-mail: theatre@tobaccofactory.com
Fax: 0117-902 0162　　　　　　　Tel: 0117-902 0345

TRADING FACES
(Mask & Physical Theatre)
Bicton, Clun, Shropshire SY7 8NF
Website: www.tradingfaces.org.uk
e-mail: admin@tradingfaces.org.uk　　Tel: 01588 640150

TRICYCLE THEATRE
269 Kilburn High Road
London NW6 7JR
Website: www.tricycle.co.uk
e-mail: admin@tricycle.co.uk
Fax: 020-7328 0795　　　　　　　Tel: 020-7372 6611

WAREHOUSE THEATRE COMPANY
Dingwall Road
Croydon CR0 2NF
Website: www.warehousetheatre.co.uk
e-mail: info@warehousetheatre.co.uk
Fax: 020-8688 6699　　　　　　　Tel: 020-8681 1257

WIGAN PIER THEATRE COMPANY
The Wigan Pier Experience
Wallgate, Wigan WN3 4EU
Website: www.wiganpier.net
e-mail: s.aitken@wlct.org　　　　　Tel: 01942 709305

WINCHESTER HAT FAIR, FESTIVAL OF STREET THEATRE
5A Jewry Street
Winchester
Hampshire SO23 8RZ
Website: www.hatfair.co.uk
e-mail: info@hatfair.co.uk　　　　　Tel: 01962 849841

WOMEN & THEATRE BIRMINGHAM Ltd
220 Moseley Road, Highgate
Birmingham B12 0DG
e-mail: info@womenandtheatre.co.uk
Fax: 0121-446 4280　　　　　　　Tel: 0121-440 4203

Y TOURING THEATRE COMPANY
120 Cromer Street, London WC1H 8BS
Website: www.ytouring.org.uk
e-mail: d.jackson@ytouring.org.uk
Fax: 020-7520 3099　　　　　　　Tel: 020-7520 3092

YELLOW EARTH THEATRE
18 Rupert Street, London W1D 6DE
Website: www.yellowearth.org
e-mail: admin@yellowearth.org
Fax: 020-7287 3141　　　　　　　Tel: 020-7734 5988

YORICK INTERNATIONALIST THEATRE ENSEMBLE
(Yorick Theatre & Film)
4 Duval Court, 36 Bedfordbury
Covent Garden, London WC2N 4DQ
e-mail: yorickx@hotmail.com　　Tel/Fax: 020-7836 7637

YORKSHIRE WOMEN THEATRE COMPANY
(Touring Theatre in Health Education)
Host Media Centre
21 Savile Mount, Leeds LS7 3HZ
Website: www.yorkshirewomentheatre.com
e-mail: admin@yorkshirewomentheatre.com
Fax: 0113-200 7033　　　　　　　Tel: 0113-200 7200

YOUNG VIC THEATRE
66 The Cut, London SE1 8LZ
Website: www.youngvic.org
e-mail: info@youngvic.org
Fax: 020-7922 2801　　　　　　　Tel: 020-7922 2800

ZIP THEATRE
Newhampton Arts Centre
Dunkley Street
Wolverhampton WV1 4AN
Website: www.ziptheatre.co.uk
e-mail: cathy@ziptheatre.co.uk
Fax: 01902 572251　　　　　　　Tel: 01902 572250

ACTION TRANSPORT THEATRE COMPANY
(New Writing, Professional Production for, by and with Young People)
Whitby Hall, Stanney Lane
Ellesmere Port, Cheshire CH65 9AE
Website: www.actiontransporttheatre.co.uk
e-mail: info@actiontransporttheatre.co.uk
Tel: 0151-357 2120

ACTIONWORK
(Theatre & Film Productions with Young People)
PO Box 433, Weston-super-Mare, Somerset BS24 0WY
Website: www.actionwork.com
e-mail: admin@actionwork.com
Tel: 01934 815163

ARTY-FACT THEATRE COMPANY Ltd
18 Weston Lane, Crewe, Cheshire CW2 5AN
Website: www.arty-fact.co.uk
Fax: 07020 982098
Tel: 07020 962096

ASHCROFT YOUTH THEATRE
Ashcroft Academy of Dramatic Art, Malcolm Primary School, Malcolm Road, Penge, London SE20 8RH
Website: www.ashcroftacademy.com
e-mail: geraldi.gillma@btconnect.com
Mobile: 07799 791586
Tel: 01634 856900

BARKING DOG THEATRE COMPANY
14 Leaside Mansions, Fortis Green, London N10 3EB
Website: www.barkingdog.co.uk
e-mail: mike@barkingdog.co.uk
Tel: 020-8883 0034

BECK THEATRE
Grange Road, Hayes
Middlesex UB3 2UE
Tel: 020-8561 7506

BIG WOODEN HORSE THEATRE FOR YOUNG PEOPLE
30 Northfield Road, West Ealing, London W13 9SY
Website: www.bigwoodenhorse.com
e-mail: info@bigwoodenhorse.com
Tel: 020-8567 8431

BIRMINGHAM STAGE COMPANY The
Suite 228, The Linen Hall
162 Regent Street, London W1B 5TB
Website: www.birminghamstage.net
e-mail: info@birminghamstage.net
Fax: 020-7437 3395
Tel: 020-7437 3391

BITESIZE THEATRE COMPANY
8 Green Meadows, New Broughton, Wrexham LL11 6SG
Website: www.bitesizetheatre.co.uk
Fax: 01978 358315
Tel: 01978 358320

BLAH BLAH BLAH THEATRE COMPANY The
The West Park Centre, Spen Lane, Leeds LS16 5BE
Website: www.blahs.co.uk
e-mail: admin@blahs.co.uk
Tel: 0113-274 0030

BLUE MOON THEATRE COMPANY
20 Sandpiper Road, Blakespool Park
Bridgwater, Somerset TA6 5QU
Website: www.bluemoontheatre.co.uk
e-mail: info@bluemoontheatre.co.uk
Tel/Fax: 01278 458253

BLUNDERBUS THEATRE COMPANY Ltd
1st Floor, The Brook Theatre
Old Town Hall, Chatham, Kent ME4 4SE
Website: www.blunderbus.co.uk
e-mail: admin@blunderbus.co.uk
Fax: 01634 818138
Tel: 01623 835888

BOOSTER CUSHION THEATRE COMPANY
75 How Wood, Park Street, St Albans, Herts AL2 2RW
Website: www.booster-cushion.co.uk
e-mail: boostercushion@hotmail.com
Fax: 01727 872597
Tel: 01727 873874

BORDERLINE THEATRE COMPANY
(Producer: Eddie Jackson)
North Harbour Street, Ayr KA8 8AA
Website: www.borderlinetheatre.co.uk
e-mail: enquiries@borderlinetheatre.co.uk
Fax: 01292 618685
Tel: 01292 281010

BRIDGE HOUSE THEATRE
Warwick School, Myton Road, Warwick CV34 6PP
Website: www.bridgehousetheatre.co.uk
Fax: 01926 776476
Tel: 01926 776437

BRIEF CANDLE THEATRE
Peel House, Brimington Rd, Chesterfield, Debyshire S41 7UG
Website: www.briefcandle.co.uk
e-mail: office@briefcandle.co.uk
Tel: 01246 556161

CAUGHT IN THE ACT
Conygree House, Church Street
Kingham, Oxfordshire OX7 6YA
Website: www.caughtintheact.co.uk
e-mail: cita@caughtintheact.co.uk   Tel/Fax: 01608 659555

CHAIN REACTION THEATRE COMPANY
Three Mills Studios, Sugar House Yard
Sugar House Lane, London E15 2QS
Website: www.chainreactiontheatre.co.uk
e-mail: mail@chainreactiontheatre.co.uk
Tel/Fax: 020-8534 0007

CHALKFOOT THEATRE ARTS
(Artistic Director: Philip Dart)
Central Studios, 36 Park Place, Margate, Kent CT9 1LE
Website: www.chalkfoot.org.uk
e-mail: info@chalkfoot.org.uk
Tel: 01843 280077

CHICKENSHED
(Artistic Director: Mary Ward MBE)
Chase Side, Southgate, London N14 4PE
Website: www.chickenshed.org.uk
e-mail: info@chickenshed.org.uk
Minicom: 020-8350 0676
Tel: 020-8351 6161

CIRCUS MANIACS YOUTH CIRCUS
(International Award-Winning Youth Circus Company)
Office 8A, The Kingswood Foundation
Britannia Road, Kingswood, Bristol BS15 8DB
e-mail: info@circusmaniacs.com
Mobile: 07977 247287
Tel/Fax: 0117-947 7042

CLWYD THEATR CYMRU THEATRE FOR YOUNG PEOPLE
(Contact: Education Administator)
Mold, Flintshire CH7 1YA
Website: www.ctctyp.co.uk
e-mail: education@clwyd-theatr-cymru.co.uk
Fax: 01352 701558
Tel: 01352 701575

COMPLETE WORKS CREATIVE COMPANY Ltd The
(Artistic Director: Phil Evans)
The Old Truman Brewery, 91 Brick Lane, London E1 6QL
Website: www.tcw.org.uk
e-mail: info@tcw.org.uk
Fax: 0870 1431979
Tel: 0870 143196

CRAGRATS Ltd
The Mill, Dunford Road, Holmfirth, Huddersfield HD9 2AR
Website: www.cragrats.com
e-mail: info@cragrats.com
Fax: 01484 686212
Tel: 01484 68645

CTC THEATRE
Arts Centre, Vane Terrace, Darlington
County Durham DL3 7AX
Website: www.ctctheatre.org.uk
e-mail: ctc@ctctheatre.org.uk
Fax: 01325 369404
Tel: 01325 35200

AYLIGHT THEATRE
6 Middle Street, Stroud
Gloucestershire GL5 1EA   Tel: 01453 763808

DONNA MARIA COMPANY
Bell Meadow, Dulwich, London SE19 1HP
Website: www.donna-marias-world.co.uk
e-mail: info@donna-marias-world.co.uk   Tel: 020-8670 7814

DRAGON DRAMA
(Theatre Company, Tuition, Workshops, Parties)
47 Hanworth Road, Surrey TW12 3EJ
Website: www.dragondrama.co.uk
e-mail: info@dragondrama.co.uk   Tel/Fax: 020-8255 8356

EUROPA CLOWN THEATRE SHOW
5 St Lukes Road, Tunbridge Wells, Kent TN4 9JH
Website: www.clownseuropa.co.uk   Tel: 01892 537964

EUROPEAN THEATRE COMPANY The
9 Oxford Avenue, London SW20 8LS
Website: www.europeantheatre.co.uk
e-mail: admin@europeantheatre.co.uk
Tel: 020-8544 1999   Tel: 020-8544 1994

FUSE: NEW THEATRE FOR YOUNG PEOPLE
(General Manager: Michael Quirke, Artistic Producer: Kathy McArdle)
Hope Street, Liverpool L1 9BH
Website: www.fusetheatre.com
e-mail: info@fusetheatre.com   Tel/Fax: 0151-708 0877

FUTURES THEATRE COMPANY
St John's Crypt, 73 Waterloo Road, London SE1 8UD
Website: www.futurestheatrecompany.co.uk
e-mail: info@futurestheatrecompany.co.uk
Fax: 020-7928 6724   Tel: 020-7928 2832

GAZEBO TIE COMPANY Ltd
7 Bizspace House, Bizspace Business Park
Upper Villiers Street, Wolverhampton WV2 4XE
Website: www.gazebotie.org
e-mail: gazebotie@tiscali.co.uk
Fax: 01902 313229   Tel: 01902 313009

GREENWICH & LEWISHAM YOUNG PEOPLES' THEATRE (GLYPT)
Royal Laboratory Office, No 1 Street
Royal Arsenal West, Woolwich, London SE18 6ST
Website: www.glypt.co.uk
e-mail: postbox@glypt.co.uk
Fax: 020-8317 8595   Tel: 020-8854 1316

GROUP 64 YOUTH THEATRE
Putney Arts Theatre, Ravenna Road, London SW15 6AW
Website: www.putneyartstheatre.org.uk
Fax: 020-8788 6940   Tel: 020-8788 6935

GWENT TIE COMPANY
The Drama Centre Pen-y-pound
Abergavenny, Monmouthshire NP7 5UD
Website: www.gwenttheatre.com
e-mail: gwenttie@uwclub.net
Fax: 01873 853910   Tel: 01873 853167

HALF MOON YOUNG PEOPLE'S THEATRE
43 White Horse Road, London E1 0ND
Website: www.halfmoon.org.uk
e-mail: admin@halfmoon.org.uk
Fax: 020-7709 8914   Tel: 020-7265 8138

HOXTON HALL YOUTH ARTS CENTRE
130 Hoxton Street, London N1 6SH
Website: www.hoxtonhall.co.uk
e-mail: info@hoxtonhall.co.uk
Fax: 020-7729 3815   Tel: 020-7684 0060

IMAGE MUSICAL THEATRE
23 Sedgeford Road, Shepherd's Bush, London W12 0NA
Website: www.imagemusicaltheatre.co.uk
e-mail: brian@imagemusicaltheatre.co.uk
Fax: 020-8749 9294   Tel: 020-8743 9380

IMPACT ON LEARNING
Impact Universal, Hopebank House, Woodhead Road
Honley, Huddersfield HD9 6PF
Website: www.impactonlearning.com
e-mail: gideon.clear@impactonlearning.com
Fax: 01484 660088   Tel: 01484 668881

INDIGO MOON THEATRE
35 Waltham Court, Beverley, East Yorkshire HU17 9JF
Website: www.indigomoontheatre.com
e-mail: info@indigomoontheatre.com   Mobile: 07855 328552

INTERPLAY THEATRE
Armley Ridge Road, Leeds LS12 3LE
Website: www.interplayleeds.co.uk
e-mail: info@interplayleeds.co.uk   Tel: 0113-263 8556

KINETIC THEATRE COMPANY Ltd
Suite H, The Jubilee Centre
Lombard Road, Wimbledon, London SW19 3TZ
Website: www.kinetictheatre.co.uk
e-mail: paul@kinetictheatre.co.uk
Fax: 020-8286 2645   Tel: 020-8286 2613

KOMEDIA
44-47 Gardner Street, Brighton BN1 1UN
Website: www.komedia.co.uk/brighton
e-mail: info@komedia.co.uk
Fax: 01273 647102   Tel: 01273 647100

LANGUAGE ALIVE!/CATALYST THEATRE
The Play House, Longmore Street, Birmingham B12 9ED
Website: www.theplayhouse.org.uk
e-mail: info@theplayhouse.org.uk
Fax: 0121-464 5713   Tel: 0121-464 5712

LEIGHTON BUZZARD YOUTH THEATRE
6 Hillside Road, Leighton Buzzard LU7 3BU
e-mail: info@lbyt.org   Tel: 01525 377222

LITTLE ACTORS THEATRE COMPANY
16 Hawthorn Road, Parkgate, Cheshire CH64 6SX
e-mail: info@littleactorstheatre.com
Fax: 0870 9157551   Tel: 0151-336 4302

M6 THEATRE COMPANY
Studio Theatre, Hamer C. P. School
Albert Royds Street, Rochdale OL16 2SU
Website: www.m6theatre.co.uk
e-mail: info@m6theatre.co.uk
Fax: 01706 712601   Tel: 01706 355898

MAGIC CARPET THEATRE
18 Church Street, Sutton-on-Hull HU7 4TS
Website: www.magiccarpettheatre.com
e-mail: admin@magiccarpettheatre.com
Fax: 01482 787362   Tel: 01482 709939

MUZIKANSKY YOUTH & COMMUNITY
The Forum, Fonthill
The Common, Tunbridge Wells, Kent TN4 8YU
Website: www.mzky.co.uk
e-mail: admin@mzky.co.uk   Tel/Fax: 01892 542260

NATIONAL ASSOCIATION OF YOUTH THEATRES (NAYT)
Arts Centre, Vane Terrace
Darlington, County Durham DL3 7AX
Website: www.nayt.org.uk
e-mail: nayt@btconnect.com
Fax: 01325 363313   Tel: 01325 363330

NATIONAL STUDENT THEATRE COMPANY
c/o National Student Drama Festival
19-20 Rheidol Mews, London N1 8NU
Website: www.nsdf.org.uk
e-mail: admin@nsdf.org.uk   Tel: 020-7354 8070

NATIONAL YOUTH MUSIC THEATRE The
2-4 Great Eastern Street, London EC2A 3NW
Website: www.nymt.org.uk
e-mail: enquiries@nymt.org.uk
Fax: 0870 9033785   Tel: 020-7422 8290

NATIONAL YOUTH THEATRE OF GREAT BRITAIN
443-445 Holloway Road, London N7 6LW
Website: www.nyt.org.uk   e-mail: info@nyt.org.uk
Fax: 020-7281 8246   Tel: 020-7281 3863

NETTLEFOLD The
West Norwood Library Centre
1 Norwood High Street, London SE27 9JX
e-mail: thenettlefold@lambeth.gov.uk   Tel: 020-7926 8070

OILY CART
Smallwood School Annexe
Smallwood Road, London SW17 0TW
Website: www.oilycart.org.uk
e-mail: oilies@oilycart.org.uk
Fax: 020-8672 0792   Tel: 020-8672 6329

ONATTI THEATRE COMPANY
(Artistic Director: Andrew Bardwell)
9 Field Close, Warwick, Warwickshire CV34 4QD
Website: www.onatti.co.uk
e-mail: info@onatti.co.uk
Fax: 0870 1643629   Tel: 01926 495220

PANDEMONIUM TOURING PARTNERSHIP
228 Railway Street, Cardiff CF24 2NJ   Tel: 029-2047 2060

PANDORA'S BOX THEATRE COMPANY
(National Touring Young Children's Theatre)
43 Fallsbrook Road, London SW16 6DU
Website: www.pandora-box.co.uk
e-mail: info@pandora-box.co.uk   Tel/Fax: 020-8769 8710

PAUL'S THEATRE COMPANY
Fairkytes Arts Centre
51 Billet Lane, Hornchurch, Essex RM11 1AX
Website: www.paulstheatreschool.co.uk
e-mail: info@paulstheatreschool.co.uk
Fax: 01708 475286   Tel: 01708 447123

PIED PIPER COMPANY
(In association with The Yvonne Arnaud Theatre Guildford)
1 Lilian Place, Coxcombe Lane
Chiddingfold, Surrey GU8 4QA
Website: www.piedpipertheatre.co.uk
e-mail: twpiedpiper@aol.com   Tel/Fax: 01428 684022

PILOT THEATRE
York Theatre Royal, St Leonard's Place, York YO1 7HD
Website: www.pilot-theatre.com
e-mail: info@pilot-theatre.com
Fax: 01904 656378   Tel: 01904 635755

PLAYTIME THEATRE COMPANY
18 Bennells Avenue, Whitstable, Kent CT5 2HP
Website: www.playtime.dircon.co.uk
e-mail: playtime@dircon.co.uk
Fax: 01227 266648   Tel: 01227 266272

POLKA THEATRE
240 The Broadway, Wimbledon SW19 1SB
Website: www.polkatheatre.com
e-mail: admin@polkatheatre.com
Fax: 020-8545 8365   Tel: 020-8545 8320

Q20 THEATRE COMPANY
19 Wellington Crescent, Shipley, West Yorkshire BD18 3PH
e-mail: info@q20theatre.co.uk   Tel: 0845 12606

QUAKER YOUTH THEATRE
Ground Floor, 1 The Lodge
1046 Bristol Road, Birmingham B29 6LJ
Website: www.leaveners.org
e-mail: qyt@leaveners.org
Fax: 0121-414 0090   Tel: 0121-414 00

QUANTUM THEATRE FOR SCIENCE
(Artistic Directors: Michael Whitmore, Jessica Selous)
The Old Button Factory
1-11 Bannockburn Road, Plumstead, London SE18 1ET
Website: www.quantumtheatre.co.uk
e-mail: office@quantumtheatre.co.uk   Tel: 020-8317 90

QUICKSILVER THEATRE COMPANY
(National Touring - New Writing for the under 12's,
Participatory Outreach Projects)
4 Enfield Road, London N1 5AZ
Website: www.quicksilvertheatre.org
e-mail: talktous@quicksilvertheatre.org
Fax: 020-7254 3119   Tel: 020-7241 29

RAINBOW BIGBOTTOM & Co Ltd
The Studio, 1A Park View, Stanley, Ave
Chesham, Bucks HP5 2JF
Website: www.rainbowbigbottom.com
e-mail: laneatrainbows@aol.com
Mobile: 07778 106552   Tel: 01494 7919

RED LADDER THEATRE COMPANY Ltd
3 St Peter's Buildings, York Street, Leeds LS9 8AJ
Website: www.redladder.co.uk
e-mail: rod@redladder.co.uk
Fax: 0113-245 5351   Tel: 0113-245 5

REDROOFS THEATRE COMPANY
(Write)
The Novello Theatre, Sunninghill
Nr Ascot, Berkshire SL5 9NE
Website: www.novellotheatre.co.uk

ROUNDABOUT THEATRE IN EDUCATION
Nottingham Playhouse
Wellington Circus, Nottingham NG1 5AF
e-mail: roundabout@nottinghamplayhouse.co.uk
Fax: 0115-947 5759   Tel: 0115-947 43

ROYAL & DERNGATE THEATRES
19-21 Guildhall Road, Northampton NN1 1DP
e-mail: education@ntt.org   Tel: 01604 6275

ROYAL COURT YOUNG WRITERS PROGRAMME
(Playwriting Projects for Young People aged 13-25)
Royal Court Theatre, Sloane Square, London SW1W 8AS
Website: www.royalcourttheatre.com
e-mail: ywp@royalcourttheatre.com
Fax: 020-7565 5001   Tel: 020-7565 50

SCOTTISH YOUTH THEATRE
The Old Sheriff Court, 105 Brunswick Street, Glasgow G1 1
Website: www.scottishyouththeatre.org
e-mail: info@scottishyouththeatre.org
Fax: 0141-552 7615   Tel: 0141-552 39

SEAHORSE THEATRE & PARTY COMPANY
Ealing House, 33 Hanger Lane, London W5 3HJ
e-mail: revampevents@aol.com   Tel: 020-8997 33

SHAKESPEARE 4 KIDZ THEATRE COMPANY The
42 Station Road East, Oxted, Surrey RH8 0PG
Website: www.shakespeare4kidz.com
e-mail: theatre@shakespeare4kidz.com
Fax: 01883 730384   Tel: 01883 7234

▌AKESPEAREWORKS
Chilswell Road, Oxford OX1 4PJ
mail: info@shakespeareworks.co.uk   Tel/Fax: 01865 241281

▌ARED EXPERIENCE YOUTH THEATRE
e Soho Laundry
Dufours Place, London W1F 7SJ
mail: admin@sharedexperience.org.uk
x: 020-7287 8763   Tel: 020-7434 9248

▌EFFIELD THEATRES
ducation Administrator: Sue Burley, Education Director:
ren Simpson)
Norfolk Street, Sheffield S1 1DA
ebsite: www.sheffieldtheatres.co.uk/education
x: 0114-249 6003   Tel: 0114-249 5999

▌ECTACLE THEATRE
leg Morgannwg, Rhondda
wynypia, Tonypandy CF40 2TQ
ebsite: www.spectacletheatre.co.uk
mail: info@spectacletheatre.co.uk
x: 01443 439640   Tel: 01443 430700

▌OPWATCH THEATRE COMPANY
it 318 Solent Business Centre
llbrook Road West, Southampton SO15 0HW
ebsite: www.stopwatchtheatre.com
mail: info@stopwatchtheatre.com   Tel: 023-8078 3800

▌ORYTELLERS THEATRE COMPANY The
idge Farm, 249 Hawes Side Lane
ackpool FY4 4AA
ebsite: www.pendleproductions.co.uk
mail: admin@pendleproductions.co.uk
x: 01253 792930   Tel: 01253 839375

▌PPORT ACT PRODUCTIONS
n McCracken)
3A Lynmouth Avenue
orden, Surrey SM4 4RX
ebsite: www.supportact.co.uk
mail: info@supportact.co.uk   Tel: 0845 0940796

▌AM PLAYERS THEATRE COMPANY
ngfield Countryside Centre, Mount Pleasant Way
ulby, Newham, Middlesbrough TS8 0XF
x: 01642 577121   Tel: 01642 592648

▌EATRE ALIBI
dult & Young People)
orthcott Studio Theatre, Emmmanuel Road
eter EX4 1EJ
ebsite: www.theatrealibi.co.uk
mail: info@theatrealibi.co.uk   Tel/Fax: 01392 217315

▌EATRE AND
urch Hall, St James Road
arsh, Huddersfield HD1 4QA
ebsite: www.theatreand.com
mail: clare@theatreand.com
x: 01484 532962   Tel: 01484 532967

▌EATRE CENTRE
ational Touring & New Writing for Young Audiences)
oreditch Town Hall, 380 Old Street, London EC1V 9LT
ebsite: www.theatre-centre.co.uk
mail: admin@theatre-centre.co.uk
x: 020-7739 9741   Tel: 020-7729 3066

▌EATRE IS,...
ound Floor Office, Millars Three
uthmill Road, Bishops Stortford CM23 3DH
ebsite: www.theatreis.org
mail: info@theatreis.org
x: 01279 506694   Tel: 01279 461607

THEATRE NA N'OG
Unit 3
Millands Road Industrial Estate
Neath SA11 1NJ
Website: www.theatr-nanog.co.uk
e-mail: drama@theatr-nanog.co.uk
Fax: 01639 647941   Tel: 01639 641771

THEATRE WORKOUT Ltd
13A Stratheden Road
Blackheath, London SE3 7TH
Website: www.theatreworkout.co.uk
e-mail: enquiries@theatreworkout.co.uk   Tel: 020-8144 2290

THEATR IOLO Ltd
The Old School Building, Cefn Road
Mynachdy, Cardiff CF14 3HS
Website: www.theatriolo.com
e-mail: info@theatriolo.com
Fax: 029-2052 2225   Tel: 029-2061 3782

TICKLISH ALLSORTS SHOW
57 Victoria Road
Wilton, Salisbury, Wiltshire SP2 0DZ
Website: www.ticklishallsorts.co.uk
e-mail: garynunn@ntlworld.com   Tel/Fax: 01722 744949

TIE ACTION WORK
PO Box 433, Weston-Super-Mare
Somerset BS24 0WY
Website: www.actionwork.com
e-mail: admin@actionwork.com   Tel: 01934 815163

TOURING TALES THEATRE COMPANY Ltd
Suite 228 The Linen Hall
162 Regent Street, London W1B 5TB
Website: www.birminghamstage.net
e-mail: info@birminghamstage.net
Fax: 020-7437 3395   Tel: 020-7437 3391

TRICYCLE THEATRE
(Education Director: Gillian Christie)
269 Kilburn High Road, London NW6 7JR
Website: www.tricycle.co.uk
e-mail: education@tricycle.co.uk   Tel/Fax: 020-7372 6611

TWISTING YARN THEATRE
Alhambra Theatre
Morley Street, Bradford BD7 1AJ
Website: www.bradford-theatres.co.uk
e-mail: twisting-yarn@bradford.gov.uk
Fax: 01274 437571   Tel: 01274 437490

UNICORN THEATRE
147 Tooley Street, London SE1 2HZ
Website: www.unicorntheatre.com
e-mail: admin@unicorntheatre.com
Fax: 020-7645 0550   Tel: 020-7645 0500

WEST YORKSHIRE PLAYHOUSE
Playhouse Square, Quarry Hill, Leeds LS2 7UP
e-mail: gail.mcintyre@wyp.org.uk   Tel: 0113-213 7225

WIZARD THEATRE
(Director: Leon Hamilton, Company Manager: Emmy
Bradbury)
175 Royal Crescent, Ruislip, Middlesex HA4 0PN
Website: www.wizardtheatre.co.uk
e-mail: admin@wizardtheatre.co.uk   Tel: 0800 5832373

YOUNG SHAKESPEARE COMPANY
(Artistic Directors: Christopher Geelan & Sarah Gordon)
31 Bellevue Road
Friern Barnet, London N11 3ET
Fax: 020-8368 6713   Tel: 020-8368 4828

AUSTRIA
VIENNA
Vienna's English Theatre
(See website for casting requirements)
UK Representative: VM Theatre Productions Ltd
16 The Street, Ash
Canterbury, Kent CT3 2HJ
Website: www.englishtheatre.at   Tel/Fax: 01304 813330
Casting: Vanessa Mallatratt

DENMARK
COPENHAGEN
The English Theatre of Copenhagen
London Toast Theatre
Kochsvej 18, 1812 Fred C.
Copenhagen, Denmark
Website: www.londontoast.dk
e-mail: mail@londontoast.dk   Tel: + 45 33 22 8686
Artistic Director: Vivienne McKee
Administrator: Soren Hall

FRANCE
PARIS
ACT Company
25 avenue Mal Leclerc
92240 Malakoff, France
Website: www.actheatre.com
e-mail: andrew@actheatre.com   Tel: + 33 1 46 56 20 50
Artistic Director: Andrew Wilson
Administrator: Anne Wilson

FRANCE
LYON
Theatre From Oxford (Touring Europe & Beyond)
B.P. 10, F-42750 St-Denis-de-Cabanne
e-mail: theatre.oxford@virgin.net
Contact: Robert Southam (Write)

GERMANY
FRANKFURT
The English Theatre
Kaiserstrasse 34, 60329
Frankfurt, Germany
Website: www.english-theatre.org
e-mail: mail@english-theatre.org
Fax: + 49 69 242 316 14   Tel: + 49 69 242 316 15
Contact: Daniel John Nicolai

GERMANY
HAMBURG
The English Theatre of Hamburg
Lerchenfeld 14, 22081 Hamburg, Germany
Website: www.englishtheatre.de
Fax: + 49 40 227 7925   Tel: + 49 40 227 7089
Contact: Robert Rumpf, Clifford Dean

GERMANY
TOURING GERMANY
White Horse Theatre
Boerdenstrasse 17
59494 Soest-Muellingsen, Germany
e-mail: theatre@whitehorse.de
Fax: + 49 29 21 33 93 36   Tel: + 49 29 21 33 93 39
Contact: Peter Griffith, Michael Dray

HUNGARY
BUDAPEST
Merlin International Theatre
Gerloczy Utca 4, 1052 Budapest, Hungary
e-mail: angol@merlinszinhaz.hu
Fax: + 36 1 2660904   Tel: + 36 1 3179338
Contact: Laszlo Magacs

ICELAND
REYKJAVIK
Light Nights - The Summer Theatre
The Travelling Theatre
Baldursgata 37
IS-101 Reykjavik, Iceland   Tel: + 354 551 91
Artistic Director: Kristine G Magnus

ITALY
SANREMO
A.C.L.E.
Via Roma 54
18038 Sanremo (IM), Italy
Website: www.acle.org
e-mail: info@acle.org
Fax: + 39 0184 509996   Tel: + 39 0184 5060

SWITZERLAND
TANNAY
Simply Theatre
Chemin des Couleuvres 8B
1295 Tannay, Switzerland
Website: www.simplytheatre.com
e-mail: info@simplytheatre.com
Fax: + 41 22 8600519   Tel: + 41 22 86005

UNITED KINGDOM
WARWICK
Onatti Theatre Company
9 Field Close, Warwick
Warwickshire CV34 4QD
Website: www.onatti.co.uk
e-mail: info@onatti.co.uk
Fax: 0870 1643629   Tel: 01926 4952
Contact: Andrew Bardwell

DELPHI
rand, London WC2E 7NN
anager:	------------------
age Door:	020-7836 1166
ox Office:	0870 8955598

LDWYCH
dwych, London WC2B 4DF
anager:	020-7836 5537
age Door:	020-7836 5537
ox Office:	020-7379 3367
ebsite:	www.aldwychtheatre.co.uk

LMEIDA
meida Street, London N1 1TA
anager:	020-7288 4900
age Door:	------------------
ox Office:	020-7359 4404

HE AMBASSADORS
est Street, London WC2H 9ND
anager:	020-7395 5410
age Door:	020-7395 5400
ox Office:	020-7395 5405
mail:	boxofficemanager@theambassadorstheatre.co.uk

POLLO
haftesbury Avenue, London W1D 7EZ
anager:	020-7494 5834
age Door:	020-7851 2711
ox Office:	0870 8901107
mail:	enquiries@nimaxtheatres.com

POLLO VICTORIA
Wilton Road, London SW1V 1LG
anager:	020-7834 6318
age Door:	020-7834 7231
ox Office:	0870 4000650
ebsite:	www.getlive.co.uk

RTS
7 Great Newport Street, London WC2H 7JB
anager:	020-7836 2132
age Door:	020-7836 2132
ox Office:	0870 0601742
ebsite:	www.artstheatrelondon.com

ARBICAN
arbican, London EC2Y 8DS
anager:	020-7628 3351
age Door:	020-7628 3351
ox Office:	0845 1207515
ebsite:	www.barbican.org.uk

HE BLOOMSBURY
Gordon Street, London WC1H 0AH
anager:	020-7679 2777
age Door:	020-7679 2922
ox Office:	020-7388 8822
ebsite:	www.thebloomsbury.com
mail:	blooms.theatre@ucl.ac.uk

HE BUSH
hepherds Bush Green, London W12 8QD
anager:	020-7602 3703
age Door:	------------------
ox Office:	020-7610 4224
ebsite:	www.bushtheatre.co.uk
mail:	info@bushtheatre.co.uk

CAMBRIDGE
Earlham Street, Seven Dials
Covent Garden, London, WC2 9HU
Manager:	020-7850 8711
Stage Door:	020-7850 8710
Box Office:	020-7850 8715

COLISEUM (English National Opera)
St Martin's Lane, London WC2N 4ES
Manager:	020-7836 0111
Stage Door:	020-7845 9397
Box Office:	0870 1450200

COMEDY
Panton Street, London SW1Y 4DN
Manager:	020-7321 5310
Stage Door:	020-7321 5300
Box Office:	0870 0606637

CRITERION
2 Jermyn Street, Piccadilly, London SW1Y 4XA
Manager:	020-7839 8811
Stage Door:	020-7839 8811
Box Office:	0870 0602313
Website:	www.criterion-theatre.com
e-mail:	admin@criterion-theatre.co.uk

DOMINION
268-269 Tottenham Court Road, London W1T 7AQ
Manager:	------------------
Stage Door:	020-7927 0900
Box Office:	0870 1690116
Website:	www.getlive.co.uk/dominion

DONMAR WAREHOUSE
41 Earlham Street, London WC2H 9LX
Manager:	020-7240 4882
Stage Door:	020-7438 9200
Box Office:	0870 060 6624
Website:	www.donmarwarehouse.com
e-mail:	office@donmarwarehouse.com

DRURY LANE
Theatre Royal, Catherine Street, London WC2B 5JF
Manager:	------------------
Stage Door:	020-7850 8790
Box Office:	020-7494 5060

DUCHESS
Catherine Street, London WC2B 5LA
Manager:	020-7632 9601
Stage Door:	020-7632 9600
Box Office:	020-7632 9602
e-mail:	enquiries@nimaxtheatres.com

DUKE OF YORK'S
St Martin's Lane, London WC2N 4BG
Manager:	020-7836 4615
Stage Door:	020-7836 4615
Box Office:	0870 0606623

FORTUNE
Russell Street, Covent Garden, London WC2B 5HH
Manager:	020-7010 7900
Stage Door:	020-7010 7900
Box Office:	0870 0606626

GARRICK
Charing Cross Road, London WC2H 0HH
Manager:	020-7520 5692
Stage Door:	020-7520 5690
Box Office:	020-7520 5693
e-mail:	enquiries@nimaxtheatres.com

GIELGUD
Shaftesbury Avenue, London W1D 6AR
Manager: 020-7292 1321
Stage Door: 020-7292 1320
Box Office: 020-7812 7480

HACKNEY EMPIRE
291 Mare Street, London E8 1EJ
Manager: 020-8510 4500
Stage Door: 020-8510 4500
Box Office: 020-8985 2424
Website: www.hackneyempire.co.uk
e-mail: info@hackneyempire.co.uk

HAMMERSMITH APOLLO
Queen Caroline Street, London W6 9QH
Manager: -----------------
Stage Door: -----------------
Box Office: 0870 6063400
Website: www.livenation.co.uk

HAMPSTEAD
Eton Avenue, Swiss Cottage, London NW3 3EU
Manager: 020-7449 4200
Stage Door: -----------------
Box Office: 020-7722 9301
Website: www.hampsteadtheatre.com
e-mail: info@hampsteadtheatre.com

HER MAJESTY'S
Haymarket, London SW1Y 4QL
Manager: 020-7850 8750
Stage Door: 020-7850 8750
Box Office: 0870 8901106

LYCEUM
21 Wellington Street, London WC2E 7RQ
Manager: 020-7420 8100
Stage Door: 020-7420 8100
Box Office: 020-7420 8114

LYRIC
29 Shaftesbury Avenue, London W1D 7ES
Manager: -----------------
Stage Door: 020-7494 5841
Box Office: 020-7494 5842
e-mail: enquiries@nimaxtheatres.com

LYRIC HAMMERSMITH
King Street, London W6 0QL
Manager: -----------------
Stage Door: -----------------
Box Office: 0870 0500511
Website: www.lyric.co.uk
e-mail: enquiries@lyric.co.uk

NATIONAL
South Bank, Upper Ground, London SE1 9PX
Manager: 020-7452 3333
Stage Door: 020-7452 3333
Box Office: 020-7452 3000
Website: www.nationaltheatre.org.uk

NEW LONDON
Drury Lane, London WC2B 5PW
Manager: 020-7242 9802
Stage Door: 020-7242 9802
Box Office: 0870 8900141

NEW PLAYERS
The Arches, Off Villiers Street, London WC2N 6NG
Manager: 020-7930 66
Stage Door: ---------------
Box Office: ---------------
Website: www.newplayerstheatre.cc
e-mail: info@newplayerstheatre.cc

NOEL COWARD THEATRE The
85 St Martin's Lane, London WC2N 4AU
Manager: 020-7759 8C
Stage Door: 020-7759 8C
Box Office: 0870 950092

NOVELLO (Previously STRAND)
Aldwych, London WC2B 4LD
Manager: 020-7759 96
Stage Door: 020-7759 96
Box Office: 0870 95009.

OLD VIC The
The Cut, London SE1 8NB
Manager: 020-7928 26
Stage Door: 020-7928 26
Box Office: 0870 060662
Website: www.oldvictheatre.co
e-mail: info@oldvictheatre.co

OPEN AIR THEATRE
Inner Circle, Regent's Park, London NW1 4NR
Manager: 020-7935 575
Stage Door: 020-7935 575
Box Office: 08700 6018
Website: www.openairtheatre.o

PALACE
Shaftesbury Avenue, London W1D 5AY
Manager: 020-7434 008
Stage Door: 020-7434 008
Box Office: 0870 89555.
Website: www.rutheatres.co
e-mail: info@rutheatres.co

PALLADIUM
Argyll Street, London W1F 7TF
Manager: 020-7850 877
Stage Door: 020-7850 877
Box Office: 0870 89011C

PEACOCK
Portugal Street, Kingsway, London WC2A 2HT
Manager: 020-7863 82C
Stage Door: 020-7863 826
Box Office: 0844 412432
Website: www.sadlerswells.co
e-mail: info@sadlerswells.co

PHOENIX
110 Charing Cross Road, London WC2H 0JP
Manager: ---------------
Stage Door: 020-7438 96C
Box Office: 020-7438 96C

PICCADILLY
Denman Street, London W1D 7DY
Manager: 020-7478 88
Stage Door: 020-7478 88C
Box Office: 020-7478 88C

LAYHOUSE
orthumberland Avenue
ndon WC2N 5DE

anager:	020-7839 4292
age Door:	020-7839 4292
x Office:	020-7839 4401

RINCE EDWARD
Old Compton Street
ndon W1D 4HS

anager:	020-7437 2024
age Door:	020-7440 3020
x Office:	0870 8509191
ebsite:	www.delfont-mackintosh.com

RINCE OF WALES
oventry Street, London W1D 6AS

anager:	020-7766 2101
age Door:	020-7766 2100
x Office:	020-7766 2104
ebsite:	www.delfont-mackintosh.com

UEEN'S
Shaftesbury Avenue
ndon W1D 6BA

anager:	020-7292 1351
age Door:	020-7292 1350
x Office:	0870 9500930

IVERSIDE STUDIOS
risp Road, Hammersmith
ondon W6 9RL

anager:	020-8237 1000
age Door:	------------------
x Office:	------------------
ebsite:	www.riversidestudios.co.uk
mail:	info@riversidestudios.co.uk

OYAL COURT
oane Square
ndon SW1W 8AS

anager:	020-7565 5050
age Door:	020-7565 5050
x Office:	020-7565 5000
ebsite:	www.royalcourttheatre.com
mail:	info@royalcourttheatre.com

OYAL OPERA HOUSE
ovent Garden, London WC2E 9DD

anager:	020-7240 1200
age Door:	020-7240 1200
x Office:	020-7304 4000

ADLER'S WELLS
osebery Avenue
ondon EC1R 4TN

anager:	020-7863 8034
age Door:	020-7863 8198
x Office:	0870 7377737
ebsite:	www.sadlerswells.com
mail:	info@sadlerswells.com

AVOY
trand, London WC2R 0ET

anager:	020-7240 1649
age Door:	020-7836 8117
x Office:	0870 1648787

SHAFTESBURY
210 Shaftesbury Avenue, London WC2H 8DP

Manager:	020-7379 3345
Stage Door:	020-7379 3345
Box Office:	020-7379 5399
e-mail:	info@toc.dltentertainment.co.uk

SHAKESPEARE'S GLOBE
21 New Globe Walk, Bankside, London SE1 9DT

Manager:	020-7902 1400
Stage Door:	020-7902 1400
Box Office:	020-7401 9919
Website:	www.shakespeares-globe.org
e-mail:	info@shakespearesglobe.com

SOHO
21 Dean Street, London W1D 3NE

Manager:	020-7287 5060
Stage Door:	------------------
Box Office:	0870 4296883
Website:	www.sohotheatre.com

ST MARTIN'S
West Street, London WC2H 9NZ

Manager:	020-7497 0578
Stage Door:	020-7836 1086
Box Office:	0870 1628787

THEATRE ROYAL
Haymarket, London SW1Y 4HT

Manager:	020-7930 8890
Stage Door:	020-7930 8890
Box Office:	0870 4000858

TRICYCLE THEATRE
269 Kilburn High Road, London NW6 7JR

Manager:	020-7372 6611
Stage Door:	020-7372 6611
Box Office:	020-7328 1000
Website:	www.tricycle.co.uk
e-mail:	info@tricycle.co.uk

VAUDEVILLE
404 Strand, London WC2R 0NH

Manager:	020-7836 1820
Stage Door:	020-7836 3191
Box Office:	0870 8900511

VICTORIA PALACE
Victoria Street, London SW1E 5EA

Manager:	020-7828 0600
Stage Door:	020-7834 2781
Box Office:	0870 1658787

WYNDHAM'S
Charing Cross Road, London WC2H 0DA

Manager:	020-7759 8077
Stage Door:	020-7759 8010
Box Office:	0870 9500925

YOUNG VIC THEATRE
66 The Cut, London SE1 8LZ

Manager:	020-7922 2800
Stage Door:	020-7922 2800
Box Office:	020-7922 2922
Website:	www.youngvic.org
e-mail:	info@youngvic.org

ALBANY The
Douglas Way, Deptford, London SE8 4AG
Fax: 020-8469 2253
BO: 020-8692 4446   Admin: 020-8692 0231

ARCOLA THEATRE
(Artistic Director - Mehmet Ergen)
27 Arcola Street, Dalston
(Off Kingsland High Street), London E8 2DJ
e-mail: info@arcolatheatre.com
Fax/Admin: 020-7503 1645   BO: 020-7503 1646
Route: Victoria Line to Highbury & Islington, then North
London Line to Dalston Kingsland (Main Line) - 5 min walk.
Buses: 38 from West End, 149 from London Bridge or 30, 67,
76, 243

ARTSDEPOT
5 Nether St, Tally Ho Corner, N Finchley, London N12 0GA
Website: www.artsdepot.co.uk
e-mail: info@artsdepot.co.uk   BO: 020-8369 5454

BAC
Lavender Hill, London SW11 5TN
Website: www.bac.org.uk   e-mail: mailbox@bac.org.uk
Fax: 020-7978 5207
BO: 020-7223 2223   Admin: 020-7223 6557
Route: Victoria or Waterloo (Main Line) to Clapham
Junction then 5 min walk or Northern Line to Clapham
Common then 20 min walk

BARONS COURT THEATRE
'The Curtain's Up'
28A Comeragh Road, West Kensington, London W14 9HR
Fax: 020-7603 8935   Admin/BO: 020-8932 4747
Route: West Kensington or Barons Court tube

BATES Tristan THEATRE
(Theatre Manager - Suli Majithia)
The Actors Centre, 1A Tower Street, London WC2H 9NP
e-mail: act@actorscentre.co.uk
Fax: 020-7240 3896
BO: 020-7240 6283   Admin: 020-7240 3940 ext 213

BECK THEATRE
Grange Road, Hayes, Middlesex UB3 2UE
BO: 020-8561 8371   Admin: 020-8561 7506
Route: Metropolitan Line to Uxbridge then buses 427 or
607 to Theatre or Paddington (Main Line) to Hayes
Harlington then buses 90, H98 or 195 (10 min)

BEDLAM THEATRE
11B Bristo Place, Edinburgh EH1 1EZ
Website: www.bedlamtheatre.co.uk
e-mail: info@bedlamtheatre.co.uk
Admin/Fax: 0131-225 9873   BO: 0131-225 9893

BELLAIRS PLAYHOUSE
Millmead Terrace, Guildford GU2 4YT
Website: www.conservatoire.org
e-mail: enquiries@conservatoire.org
BO: 01483 444789   Admin: 01483 560701 (Mon-Fri)

BLOOMSBURY THEATRE
15 Gordon Street, Bloomsbury, London WC1H 0AH
Website: www.thebloomsbury.com
e-mail: blooms.theatre@ucl.ac.uk
BO: 020-7388 8822   Admin: 020-7679 2777
Route: Tube to Euston, Euston Square or Warren Street

BRENTWOOD THEATRE
(Theatre Administrator - Mark P Reed)
15 Shenfield Road, Brentwood, Essex CM15 8AG
Website: www.brentwood-theatre.org
SD: 01277 226658   BO: 01277 200305
Admin/Fax: 01277 230833
Liverpool Street (Main Line) to Shenfield, then 15 min walk

BRIDEWELL THEATRE The
St Bride Foundation, Bride Lane
Fleet Street, London EC4Y 8EQ
Website: www.bridewelltheatre.org
e-mail: admin@bridewelltheatre.co.uk
Fax: 020-7353 1547   Admin: 020-7353 33
Route: District & Circle Line to Blackfriars, Circle Line to
St Paul's. Thameslink. Fifteen different bus routes

BROADWAY The
Broadway, Barking IG11 7LS
Website: www.thebroadwaybarking.com
e-mail: admin@thebroadwaybarking.com
Fax: 020-8507 5611
BO: 020-8507 5607   Admin: 020-8507 561

BROADWAY THEATRE The
(Director - Martin Costello)
Catford, London SE6 4RU
Website: www.broadwaytheatre.org.uk
e-mail: martin@broadwaytheatre.org.uk
BO: 020-8690 0002   Admin: 020-8690 100
Route: Charing Cross to Catford Bridge

CAMDEN PEOPLE'S THEATRE
(Artistic Director - Matt Ball)
58-60 Hampstead Road
London NW1 2PY
Website: www.cptheatre.co.uk
e-mail: admin@cptheatre.co.uk
Fax: 020-7813 3889   Tel: 020-7419 48
Route: Victoria or Northern Line to Warren Street,
Metropolitan or Circle Line to Euston Square (2 min walk
either way)

CANAL CAFE THEATRE The
(Artistic Director - Emma Taylor)
The Bridge House, Delamere Terrace
Little Venice, London W2 6ND
Website: www.canalcafetheatre.com
e-mail: mail@canalcafetheatre.com
Fax: 020-7266 1717
BO: 020-7289 6054   Admin: 020-7289 605

CHATS PALACE ARTS CENTRE
(Nick Reed)
42-44 Brooksby's Walk, Hackney, London E9 6DF
Website: www.chatspalace.com
e-mail: info@chatspalace.com   Tel: 020-8533 022

CHELSEA THEATRE
World's End Place, King's Road, London SW10 0DR
e-mail: admin@chelseatheatre.org.uk
Fax: 020-7352 2024   Tel: 020-7349 78
Route: District or Circle Line to Sloane Square then short
bus ride 11 or 22 down King's Road

CHICKENSHED THEATRE
(Artistic Director - Mary Ward MBE)
Chase Side, Southgate, London N14 4PE
Website: www.chickenshed.org.uk
e-mail: info@chickenshed.org.uk
Fax: 020-8292 0202
Minicom: 020-8350 0676   BO: 020-8292 922
Admin: 020-8351 6161
Route: Piccadilly Line to Oakwood, turn left outside tube &
walk 8 min down Bramley Road or take 307 bus. Buses 299
299, 699 or N19. Car parking available & easy access
parking by reservation

CHRIST'S HOSPITAL THEATRE
(Director - Jeff Mayhew)
Horsham, West Sussex RH13 7LW
e-mail: jm@christs-hospital.org.uk
BO: 01403 247434   Admin: 01403 24743

Canal Café Theatre www.canalcafetheatre.com

Canal Café Theatre is one of London's leading fringe theatre venues with an award-winning reputation for comedy and increasingly for new writing. The theatre is based above the lovely Bridge House Pub, ideal for pre and post show dining. Situated in the heart of Little Venice, one of the capital's most beautiful areas, it plays host to up to fourteen shows per week. If you want to put on a show here you can download our Hiring the Theatre document and call the admin line for more information and availability: 020 7289 6056. Delamere Terrace • Little Venice • London W2 6ND

HURCHILL The
hief Executive - Derek Nicholls)
igh Street, Bromley, Kent BR1 1HA
ebsite: www.churchilltheatre.co.uk
ax: 020-8290 6968
O: 0870 0606620   Tel: 020-8464 7131

LERKENWELL THEATRE The
xmouth Market, London EC1 4QE
mail: exmouthmarketcentre@tiscali.co.uk
el/Fax: 020-7278 0829
oute: Nearest stations Angel or Farringdon. 200 yards
om Sadler's Wells

LUB FOR ACTS & ACTORS The
oncert Artistes Association) (Mark Wynter, Malcolm
night)
O Bedford Street, London WC2E 9HP
ebsite: www.thecaa.org
mail: office@thecaa.org   Admin: 020-7836 3172
oute: Piccadilly or Northern Line to Leicester Square then
w mins walk

OCHRANE THEATRE
eirdre Malynn)
outhampton Row, London WC1B 4AP
mail: info@cochranetheatre.co.uk
O: 020-7269 1606   Admin: 020-7269 1600
oute: Central or Piccadilly Line to Holborn then 3 min
alk

OCKPIT THEATRE
ateforth Street, London NW8 8EH
ebsite: www.cockpittheatre.org.uk
mail: admin@cockpittheatre.org.uk
ax: 020-7258 2921
O: 020-7258 2925   Admin: 020-7258 2920
oute: Tube to Marylebone/Edgware Road then short walk
r bus 139 to Lisson Grove & 6, 8 or 16 to Edgware Road

ORBETT THEATRE
East 15 Acting School)
he University of Essex
ectory Lane, Loughton, Essex IG10 3RY
Jebsite: www.east15.ac.uk
mail: east15@essex.ac.uk
ax: 020-8508 7521   BO & Admin: 020-8508 5983
oute: Central Line (Epping Branch) to Debden then 6 min
valk

OURTYARD THEATRE The
Artistic Director - June Abbott, General Manager - Tim Gill)
5 East Road, London N1 6AH
Jebsite: www.thecourtyard.org.uk
mail: info@thecourtyard.org.uk
O: 0870 1630717   Admin/Fax: 020-7833 0870

ROYDON CLOCKTOWER
Arts Programme Manager - Jonathan Kennedy)
Katharine Street, Croydon CR9 1ET
Jebsite: www.croydon.gov.uk/clocktower
mail: jonathan.kennedy@croydon.gov.uk
ax: 020-8253 1003
O: 020-8253 1030   Tel: 020-8253 1037

CUSTARD FACTORY
Gibb Street, Digbeth, Birmingham B9 4AA
Website: www.custardfactory.co.uk
e-mail: post@custardfactory.co.uk
Fax: 0121-604 8888   Tel: 0121-224 7777

DARTFORD ORCHARD THEATRE
(Vanessa Hart)
Home Gardens, Dartford, Kent DA1 1ED
Website: www.orchardtheatre.co.uk
Fax: 01322 227122
BO: 01322 220000   Admin: 01322 220099
Route: Charing Cross (Main Line) to Dartford

DIORAMA ARTS CENTRE
(Hire Venue)
5-7 Euston Centre, London NW1 3JG
Website: www.diorama-arts.org.uk
e-mail: admin@diorama-arts.org.uk
Fax: 020-7813 3116   Admin: 020-7916 5467
Route: Circle & District Line to Great Portland Street then 5 min walk, or Victoria/Northern line to Warren Street then 1 min walk

DRILL HALL The
16 Chenies Street, London WC1E 7EX
Website: www.drillhall.co.uk
e-mail: admin@drillhall.co.uk
Fax: 020-7307 5062
BO: 020-7307 5060   Admin: 020-7307 5061
Route: Northern Line to Goodge Street then 1 min walk

EDINBURGH FESTIVAL FRINGE
180 High Street, Edinburgh EH1 1QS
Website: www.edfringe.com
e-mail: admin@edfringe.com
Fax: 0131-226 0016   Tel: 0131-226 0026

EDINBURGH UNIVERSITY THEATRE COMPANY
(See BEDLAM THEATRE)

EMBASSY THEATRE & STUDIOS
(Central School of Speech & Drama)
64 Eton Avenue, Swiss Cottage, London NW3 3HY
Website: www.cssd.ac.uk
e-mail: enquiries@cssd.ac.uk   Tel: 020-7722 8183
Route: Jubilee Line to Swiss Cottage then 1 min walk

ETCETERA THEATRE CLUB
(Directors - Zena Barrie and Michelle Flower)
Oxford Arms, 265 Camden High Street
London NW1 7BU
Website: www.etceteratheatre.com
e-mail: etc@etceteratheatre.com
Fax: 020-7482 0378   Admin/BO: 020-7482 4857

FAIRFIELD HALLS
Ashcroft Theatre & Concert Hall
Park Lane, Croydon CR9 1DG
Website: www.fairfield.co.uk
e-mail: info@fairfield.co.uk
BO: 020-8688 9291   Admin & SD: 020-8681 0821
Route: Victoria & London Bridge (Main Line) to East Croydon then 5 min walk

FINBOROUGH THEATRE
(Artistic Director - Neil McPherson)
The Finborough, 118 Finborough Road, London SW10 9ED
Website: www.finboroughtheatre.co.uk
e-mail: admin@finboroughtheatre.co.uk
Fax: 020-7835 1853
BO: 020-7373 3842   Admin: 020-7244 7439
Route: District or Piccadilly Line to Earls Court then 5 min
walk. Buses 74, 328, C1, C3, 74 then 3 min walk

GATE THEATRE
(Artistic Directors - Carrie Cracknell & Natalie Abrahami)
Above Prince Albert Pub
11 Pembridge Road, London W11 3HQ
Website: www.gatetheatre.co.uk
e-mail: gate@gatetheatre.co.uk
Fax: 020-7221 6055
BO: 020-7229 0706   Admin: 020-7229 5387
Route: Central, Circle or District Line to Notting Hill Gate
then 1 min walk

GBS THEATRE (George Bernard Shaw)
Malet Street, London WC1E 7JN
Website: www.radaenterprises.org
e-mail: bookings@rada.ac.uk
BO: 020-7908 4800   Tel: 020-7908 4754

GIELGUD John THEATRE
Malet Street, London WC1E 7JN
Website: www.radaenterprises.org
e-mail: bookings@rada.ac.uk
BO: 020-7908 4800   Tel: 020-7908 4754

GREENWICH PLAYHOUSE
(Alice de Sousa)
Greenwich BR Station Forecourt
189 Greenwich High Road, London SE10 8JA
Website: www.galleontheatre.co.uk
e-mail: alice@galleontheatre.co.uk
Fax: 020-8310 7276   Tel: 020-8858 9256
Route: Main Line from Charing Cross, Waterloo East or
London Bridge, DLR to Greenwich

GREENWICH THEATRE
(Executive Director - James Haddrell)
Crooms Hill, Greenwich, London SE10 8ES
Website: www.greenwichtheatre.org.uk
e-mail: info@greenwichtheatre.org.uk
Fax: 020-8858 8042
BO: 020-8858 7755   Admin: 020-8858 4447
Route: Jubilee Line (change Canary Wharf) then DLR to
Greenwich Cutty Sark, 3 min walk or Charing Cross (Main
Line) to Greenwich, 5 min walk

GUILDHALL SCHOOL OF MUSIC & DRAMA
Silk Street, Barbican, London EC2Y 8DT
e-mail: info@gsmd.ac.uk
Fax: 020-7256 9438   Tel: 020-7628 2571
Route: Hammersmith & City, Circle or Metropolitan line to
Barbican or Moorgate (also served by Northern line) then 5
min walk

HACKNEY EMPIRE THEATRE
291 Mare Street, Hackney, London E8 1EJ
BO: 020-8985 2424   Press/Admin: 020-8510 4500

HEN & CHICKENS THEATRE
Unrestricted View, Above Hen & Chickens Theatre Bar
109 St Paul's Road
Islington, London N1 2NA
Website: www.henandchickens.com
e-mail: james@henandchickens.com   Tel: 020-7704 2001
Route: Victoria Line or Main Line to Highbury & Islington
directly opposite station

ICA THEATRE
(No CVs, Venue only)
The Mall, London SW1Y 5AH
Website: www.ica.org.uk
Fax: 020-7873 0051
BO: 020-7930 3647   Admin: 020-7930 049?
Route: Nearest stations Piccadilly & Charing Cross

JACKSONS LANE
269A Archway Road, London N6 5AA
Website: www.jacksonslane.org.uk
e-mail: mail@jacksonslane.org.uk   Tel: 020-8340 52▪

JERMYN STREET THEATRE
(General Manager - Penny Horner)
16B Jermyn Street, London SW1Y 6ST
Website: www.jermynstreettheatre.co.uk
Fax: 020-7287 3232
BO: 020-7287 2875   Admin: 020-7434 144▪

JERWOOD VANBRUGH THEATRE
Malet Street, London WC1E 7JN
Website: www.radaenterprises.org
e-mail: bookings@rada.ac.uk
BO: 020-7908 4800   Tel: 020-7908 475▪

KING'S HEAD THEATRE
115 Upper Street, Islington, London N1 1QN
Website: www.kingsheadtheatre.org
BO: 020-7226 1916   Admin: 020-7226 85▪
Route: Northern Line to Angel then 5 min walk. Approx
halfway between Angel and Highbury & Islington tube
stations

KING'S LYNN CORN EXCHANGE
Tuesday Market Place, King's Lynn, Norfolk PE30 1JW
Website: www.kingslynncornexchange.co.uk
e-mail: entertainment_admin@west-norfolk.gov.uk
Fax: 01553 762141
BO: 01553 764864   Admin: 01553 7655▪

KOMEDIA
(Artistic Directors: Theatre & Comedy - David Lavender.
Music, Cabaret & Children's Theatre - Marina Kobler,
Laurence Hill)
44-47 Gardner Street, Brighton BN1 1UN
Website: www.komedia.co.uk/brighton
e-mail: info@komedia.co.uk
Fax: 01273 647102
BO: 01273 647100   Tel: 01273 6471▪

LANDMARK ARTS CENTRE
Ferry Road, Teddington Lock, Middlesex TW11 9NN
Website: www.landmarkartscentre.org
e-mail: info@landmarkartscentre.org
Fax: 020-8977 4830   Tel: 020-8977 755▪

LANDOR THEATRE The
(Artistic Director - Robert McWhir)
70 Landor Road, London SW9 9PH
Website: www.landortheatre.co.uk
e-mail: info@landortheatre.co.uk   Admin/BO: 020-7737 727▪
Route: Northern Line Clapham North then 2 min walk

LEIGHTON BUZZARD THEATRE
Lake Street, Leighton Buzzard, Bedfordshire LU7 1RX
Website: www.leightonbuzzardtheatre.co.uk
BO: 01582 818807   Tel: 01582 81880▪

LILIAN BAYLIS THEATRE
(Information: Sadler's Wells Theatre)
Rosebery Avenue, London EC1R 4TN
Website: www.sadlerswells.com
e-mail: info@sadlerswells.com
BO: 0844 4124300   SD: 020-7863 819▪

VE THEATRE
' Broad Chare, Quayside, Newcastle upon Tyne NE1 3DQ
ebsite: www.live.org.uk
mail: info@live.org.uk
ax: 0191-232 2224
0: 0191-232 1232   Admin: 0191-261 2694

ACOWAN THEATRE
AMDA)
2 Logan Place, London W8 6QN
ebsite: www.lamda.org.uk
ax: 020-7370 1980   Tel: 020-7244 8744
oute: District or Piccadilly Line to Earl's Court then 6 min
alk

ADDERMARKET THEATRE
eneral Manager - Michael Lyas)
: John's Alley, Norwich NR2 1DR
ebsite: www.maddermarket.co.uk
mail: mmtheatre@btconnect.com
ax: 01603 661357
0: 01603 620917   Admin: 01603 626560

ENIER CHOCOLATE FACTORY
3 Southwark Street, London SE1 1RU
ebsite: www.menierchocolatefactory.com
mail: office@menierchocolatefactory.com
ax: 020-7378 1713   Tel: 020-7378 1712

ILLFIELD ARTS CENTRE
lver Street, London N18 1PJ
ebsite: www.millfieldtheatre.co.uk
mail: info@millfieldtheatre.co.uk
ax: 020-8807 3892
0: 020-8807 6680   Admin: 020-8803 5283
oute: Liverpool Street (Main Line) to Silver Street or tube
Turnpike Lane then bus 144, 15 min to Cambridge
oundabout

YERS STUDIO THEATRE The
layhouse Manager - Trevor Mitchell)
he Epsom Playhouse, Ashley Avenue
osom, Surrey KT18 5AL
ebsite: www.epsomplayhouse.co.uk
mail: tmitchell@epsom-ewell.gov.uk
ax: 01372 726228
0: 01372 742555   Tel: 01372 742226

ETTLEFOLD The
est Norwood Library Centre
Norwood High Street, London SE27 9JX
mail: thenettlefold@lambeth.gov.uk
ax: 020-7926 8071   Admin/BO: 020-7926 8070
oute: Victoria, West Croydon or London Bridge (Main Line)
West Norwood then 2 min walk, or tube to Brixton then
uses 2, 196, 322, 432, or buses 68, 468

EW END THEATRE
7 New End, Hampstead, London NW3 1JD
ebsite: www.newendtheatre.co.uk
ax: 020-7794 4044
0: 0870 0332733   Admin: 020-7472 5800
oute: Northern Line to Hampstead then 2 min walk off
eath Street

EW PLAYERS THEATRE The
ormerly The Players Theatre)
he Arches, Villiers Street
ondon WC2N 6NG   BO: 020-7930 6601

EW WIMBLEDON THEATRE & STUDIO
he Broadway, Wimbledon, London SW19 1QG
ebsite: www.newwimbledontheatre.co.uk
ax: 020-8543 6637
0: 0870 0606646   Admin: 020-8545 7900
oute: Main Line or District Line to Wimbledon, then 3 min
alk. Buses 57, 93, 155

NORTHBROOK THEATRE The
(Theatre Co-ordinator - Dave Manley)
Littlehampton Road
Goring-by-Sea
Worthing, West Sussex BN12 6NU
Website: www.northbrooktheatre.co.uk
e-mail: box.office@nbcol.ac.uk
Fax: 01903 606141   BO/Admin: 01903 606162

NORWICH PUPPET THEATRE
St James, Whitefriars
Norwich NR3 1TN
Website: www.puppettheatre.co.uk
e-mail: info@puppettheatre.co.uk
Fax: 01603 617578
BO: 01603 629921   Admin: 01603 615564

NOVELLO THEATRE The
(Redroofs Theatre Company)
2 High Street, Sunninghill
Nr Ascot, Berkshire
Tel: 01344 620881
Route: Waterloo (Main Line) to Ascot then 1 mile from
station

OLD RED LION THEATRE PUB
(Theatre Manager - Helen Devine)
418 St John Street
Islington, London EC1V 4NJ
BO: 020-7837 7816   Admin: 020-7833 3053
Route: Northern Line to Angel then 1 min walk

ORANGE TREE
(Artistic Director - Sam Walters)
1 Clarence Street
Richmond TW9 2SA
e-mail: admin@orange-tree.demon.co.uk
Fax: 020-8332 0369
BO: 020-8940 3633   Admin: 020-8940 0141
Route: District Line, Waterloo (Main Line) or North London
Line are virtually opposite station

OVAL HOUSE THEATRE
52-54 Kennington Oval
London SE11 5SW
Website: www.ovalhouse.com
e-mail: info@ovalhouse.com
Fax: 020-7820 0990
BO: 020-7582 7680   Admin: 020-7582 0080
Route: Northern Line to Oval then 1 min walk, Victoria Line
& Main Line to Vauxhall then 10 min walk

PAVILION THEATRE
Marine Road
Dun Laoghaire, County Dublin, Ireland
Website: www.paviliontheatre.ie
e-mail: info@paviliontheatre.ie
Fax: 353 1 663 6328   Tel: 353 1 231 2929

PENTAMETERS
Theatre Entrance in Oriel Place
28 Heath Street, London NW3 6TE
Website: www.pentameters.co.uk
BO/Admin: 020-7435 3648
Route: Northern Line to Hampstead then 1 min walk. Buses
268, 46

PLACE The
(Main London Venue for Contemporary Dance)
17 Duke's Road, London WC1H 9PY
Website: www.theplace.org.uk
e-mail: theatre@theplace.org.uk
BO: 020-7387 0031   Admin: 020-7380 1268
Route: Northern or Victoria Line to Euston or King's Cross
then 5 min walk (Opposite rear of St Pancras Church)

See London Underground Map - page 391

PLEASANCE ISLINGTON
(Anthony Alderson)
Carpenters Mews, North Road
(Off Caledonian Road), London N7 9EF
Website: www.pleasance.co.uk
e-mail: info@pleasance.co.uk
Fax: 020-7700 7366
BO: 020-7609 1800   Admin: 020-7619 6868
Route: Piccadilly Line to Caledonian Road, turn left, walk
50 yds, turn left into North Road, 2 min walk. Buses 17, 91,
259, N91, 393

POLISH THEATRE
(Polish Social & Cultural Association Ltd)
238-246 King Street
London W6 0RF
BO: 020-8741 0398   Admin: 020-8741 1940
Route: District Line to Ravenscourt Park, or District,
Piccadilly or Metropolitan Lines to Hammersmith then 7
min walk. Buses 27, 267, 190, 391, H91

POLKA THEATRE
240 The Broadway, Wimbledon SW19 1SB
Website: www.polkatheatre.com
e-mail: admin@polkatheatre.com
Fax: 020-8545 8365
BO: 020-8543 4888   Admin: 020-8545 8320
Route: Waterloo (Main Line) or District Line to Wimbledon
then 10 min walk. Northern Line to South Wimbledon then
10 min walk. Tram to Wimbledon, Buses 57, 93, 219, 493

PRINCESS THEATRE HUNSTANTON
The Green, Hunstanton, Norfolk PE36 5AH
Fax: 01485 534463
BO: 01485 532252   Admin: 01485 535937

PUTNEY ARTS THEATRE
Ravenna Road, Putney SW15 6AW
Website: www.putneyartstheatre.org.uk
e-mail: mail@putneyartstheatre.org.uk
Fax: 020-8788 6940   Tel: 020-8788 6943

QUEEN'S THEATRE
(Artistic Director - Bob Carlton)
Billet Lane, Hornchurch, Essex RM11 1QT
Website: www.queens-theatre.co.uk
e-mail: info@queens-theatre.co.uk
Fax: 01708 462363
BO: 01708 443333   SD/Admin 01708 462362
Route: District Line to Hornchurch, Main Line to
Romford/Gidea Park. 15 miles from West End take A13,
A1306 then A125 or A12 then A127

QUESTORS THEATRE EALING The
12 Mattock Lane, London W5 5BQ
Website: www.questors.org.uk
e-mail: enquiries@questors.org.uk
Fax: 020-8567 8736
BO: 020-8567 5184   Admin: 020-8567 0011
Route: Central or District Line to Ealing Broadway then 5
min walk. Buses 207, 83, 65

RICHMOND THEATRE
(Karin Gartzke)
The Green
Richmond, Surrey TW9 1QJ
Website: www.richmondtheatre.net
e-mail: richmondstagedoor@theambassadors.com
Fax: 020-8948 3601
BO: 0870 0606651   Admin & SD: 020-8940 0220
Route: 20 minutes from Waterloo (South West Trains) or
District Line or Silverlink to Richmond then 2 min walk

RIDWARE THEATRE
(Alan & Margaret Williams)
(Venue only. No resident performing company)
Wheelwright's House, Pipe Ridware
Rugeley, Staffs WS15 3QL
e-mail: alan@christmas-time.com   Tel: 01889 5043?

RIVERSIDE STUDIOS
Crisp Road
London W6 9RL
Website: www.riversidestudios.co.uk
e-mail: info@riversidestudios.co.uk
BO: 020-8237 1111   Admin: 020-8237 10(
Route: District, Piccadilly or Hammersmith & City Line to
Hammersmith Broadway then 5 min walk. Buses 9, 11, 27,
73, 91, 220, 283, 295

ROSEMARY BRANCH THEATRE
2 Shepperton Road
London N1 3DT
Website: www.rosemarybranch.co.uk
e-mail: cecilia@rosemarybranch.co.uk   Tel: 020-7704 66?
Route: Tube to Bank, Moorgate or Old Street (exit 5), then
No 21, 76 or 141 bus to Baring Street, or 271 bus from
Highbury and Islington

SCOTTISH STORYTELLING CENTRE
(Netherbow Theatre)
43-45 High Street, Edinburgh EH1 1SR
Website: www.scottishstorytellingcentre.co.uk
Tel: 0131-556 95?

SHADY DOLLS THEATRE COMPANY
9 Upper Handa Walk, London N1 2RG
Website: www.shadydolls.com
e-mail: info@shadydolls.com   Mobile: 07796 3535?

SHAW THEATRE The
100-110 Euston Road, London NW1 2AJ
Fax: 020-7388 7555
BO: 0870 0332600   Admin: 020-7388 25?

SOUTH HILL PARK ARTS CENTRE
Bracknell, Berkshire RG12 7PA
Website: www.southhillpark.org.uk
e-mail: admin@southhillpark.org.uk
BO: 01344 484123   Admin & SD: 01344 4848?
Route: Waterloo (Main Line) to Bracknell then 10 min bus
ride or taxi rank at station

SOUTH LONDON THEATRE
(Bell Theatre & Prompt Corner)
2A Norwood High Street
London SE27 9NS
Website: www.southlondontheatre.co.uk
e-mail: southlondontheatre@yahoo.co.uk
Tel: 020-8670 34?
Route: Victoria or London Bridge (Main Line) to West
Norwood then 2 min walk, or Victoria Line to Brixton then
buses 2, 68, 196, 322

SOUTHWARK PLAYHOUSE
(Chief Executive - Chris Smyrnios, Education Director - To
Wilson, Associate Education Director - Ellen Hughes)
Correspondence:
60 Great Suffolk Street, London SE1 0BL
Website: www.southwarkplayhouse.co.uk
e-mail: admin@southwarkplayhouse.co.uk
BO: 0870 0601761   Admin: 020-7620 349
Route: Trains to London Bridge, Jubilee/Northern Line to
London Bridge. Buses 47, 381, RV1, N47, N381. River service
to London Bridge City

SPACE ARTS CENTRE The
269 Westferry Road, London E14 3RS
Website: www.space.org.uk
e-mail: info@space.org.uk   Tel: 020-7515 7799

THE STAG THEATRE
(Theatre Manager - Paul Corcoran)
London Road, Sevenoaks, Kent TN13 1ZZ
Website: www.kinocinemas.co.uk
BO: 01732 450175   Admin: 01732 451548
Route: Charing Cross (Main Line) to Sevenoaks then 15 min
up the hill from station

THEATRE 503
The Latchmere Pub
503 Battersea Park Road, London SW11 3BW
Website: www.theatre503.com
e-mail: info@theatre503.com   BO: 020-7978 7040
Route: Victoria or Waterloo (Main Line) to Clapham
Junction then 10 min walk or buses 44, 219, 319, 344, 345 or
tube to South Kensington then buses 49 or 345 or tube to
Sloane Square then bus 319

THEATRE OF ALL POSSIBILITIES
(Artistic Director - Kathlin Gray)
24 Old Gloucester Street, London WC1N 3AL
Website: www.allpossibilities.org
e-mail: engage@allpossibilities.org   Tel: 020-7242 9831

THEATRE ROYAL STRATFORD EAST
(Artistic Director - Kerry Michael)
Gerry Raffles Square, London E15 1BN
Website: www.stratfordeast.com
e-mail: theatreroyal@stratfordeast.com
Fax: 020-8534 8381
BO: 020-8534 0310   Admin: 020-8534 7374
Route: Central or Jubilee Line to Stratford then 2 min walk

THEATRO TECHNIS
(Artistic Director - George Eugeniou)
26 Crowndale Road, London NW1 1TT
Website: www.theatrotechnis.com
e-mail: info@theatrotechnis.com
                    BO & Admin: 020-7387 6617
Route: Northern Line to Mornington Crescent then 3 min
walk

TRICYCLE THEATRE
(Artistic Director - Nicolas Kent,
General Manager - Mary Lauder)
269 Kilburn High Road, London NW6 7JR
Website: www.tricycle.co.uk
e-mail: admin@tricycle.co.uk
Fax: 020-7328 0795
BO: 020-7328 1000   Admin: 020-7372 6611
Route: Jubilee Line to Kilburn then 5 min walk or buses 16,
189, 32 pass the door, 98, 31, 206, 316 pass nearby

TRON THEATRE
63 Trongate, Glasgow G1 5HB
Website: www.tron.co.uk
Fax: 0141-552 6657
BO: 0141-552 4267   Admin: 0141-552 3748

UNION THEATRE The
(Artistic Director - Sasha Regan, Associate Director - Ben
De Wynter, Resident Director - Aoife Smyth, Technical
Director - Steve Miller, All Casting Enquiries - Paul Flynn)
204 Union Street, Southwark, London SE1 0LX
Website: www.uniontheatre.org
e-mail: sasha@uniontheatre.freeserve.co.uk
                    Tel/Fax: 020-7261 9876
Route: Jubilee Line to Southwark then 2 min walk

UPSTAIRS AT THE GATEHOUSE
(Ovation Theatres Ltd)
The Gatehouse Pub
Corner of Hampstead Lane/North Road, London N6 4BD
Website: www.upstairsatthegatehouse.com
e-mail: events@ovationproductions.com
BO: 020-8340 3488   Admin: 020-8340 3477
Route: Northern Line to Highgate then 10 min walk. Buses
143, 210, 214, 271

VENUE The
5 Leicester Place
Off Leicester Square
London WC2H 7BP   Tel: 0870 8993335

WAREHOUSE THEATRE
(Artistic Director - Ted Craig)
Dingwall Road
Croydon CR0 2NF
Website: www.warehousetheatre.co.uk
e-mail: info@warehousetheatre.co.uk
Fax: 020-8688 6699
BO: 020-8680 4060   Admin: 020-8681 1257
Route: Adjacent to East Croydon (Main Line). Direct from
Victoria (15 min), Clapham Junction (10 min) or by
Thameslink from West Hampstead, Kentish Town, Kings
Cross, Blackfriars & London Bridge

WATERMANS
40 High Street
Brentford TW8 0DS
Website: www.watermans.org.uk
e-mail: info@watermans.org.uk
Fax: 020-8232 1030
BO: 020-8232 1010   Admin: 020-8232 1020
Route: Buses: 237, 267, 65, N9. Tube: Gunnersbury or South
Ealing. Main Line: Kew Bridge then 5 min walk, Gunnersbury
then 10 min walk, or Brentford

WESTRIDGE (OPEN CENTRE)
(Drawing Room Recitals)
Star Lane
Highclere, Nr Newbury
Berkshire RG20 9PJ   Tel: 01635 253322

WHITE BEAR THEATRE
(Favours New Writing)
138 Kennington Park Road
London SE11 4DJ
e-mail: utopianking2002@yahoo.co.uk
                    Admin/BO: 020-7793 9193
Route: Northern Line to Kennington

WILTONS MUSIC HALL
Graces Alley
Off Ensign Street
London E1 8JB
Website: www.wiltons.org.uk
Fax: 0871 2532424   Tel: 020-7702 9555
Route: Tube: Under 10 minutes walk from Aldgate East (exit
for Leman Street)/Tower Hill. DLR: Shadwell or Tower
Gateway. Car: Follow the yellow AA signs to Wiltons Music
Hall from the Highway, Aldgate or Tower Hill

WIMBLEDON STUDIO THEATRE
(See NEW WIMBLEDON THEATRE & STUDIO)

WYCOMBE SWAN
St Mary Street
High Wycombe
Buckinghamshire HP11 2XE
Website: www.wycombeswan.co.uk
e-mail: enquiries@wycombeswan.co.uk
BO: 01494 512000   Admin: 01494 514444

ABERDEEN

His Majesty's Theatre
Rosemount Viaduct
Aberdeen AB25 1GL
Box Office: 01224 641122
Stage Door: 01224 337673
Admin: 0845 2708200
Website: www.boxofficeaberdeen.com
e-mail: info@hmtheatre.com

ABERYSTWYTH

Aberystwyth Arts Centre
University of Wales
Aberystwyth SY23 3DE
Box Office: 01970 623232
Stage Door: 01970 624239
Admin: 01970 622882
Website: www.aber.ac.uk/artscentre
e-mail: ggo@aber.ac.uk

ASHTON-UNDER-LYNE

Tameside Hippodrome
Oldham Road
Ashton-under-Lyne OL6 7SE
Box Office: 0870 6021175
Stage Door: ------------------
Admin: 0161-330 2095
Website: www.livenation.co.uk/tameside

AYR

Gaiety Theatre
Carrick Street, Ayr KA7 1NU
Box Office: 01292 611222
Stage Door: ------------------
Admin: 01292 617400
Website: www.gaietytheatre.co.uk
e-mail: gaiety.theatre@south-ayrshire.gov

BACUP

Royal Court Theatre
Rochdale Road, Bacup OL13 9NR
Box Office: 01706 874080
Stage Door: ------------------
Admin: ------------------

BASINGSTOKE

The Haymarket
Wote Street, Basingstoke RG21 7NW
Box Office: 01256 844244
Stage Door: 01256 819797
Admin: 01256 819797
Website: www.haymarket.org.uk
e-mail: info@haymarket.org.uk

BATH

Theatre Royal
Sawclose, Bath BA1 1ET
Box Office: 01225 448844
Stage Door: 01225 448815
Admin: 01225 448815
Website: www.theatreroyal.org.uk
e-mail: forename.surname@theatreroyal.org.uk

BELFAST

Grand Opera House
Great Victoria Street
Belfast BT2 7HR
Box Office: 028-9024 1919
Stage Door: 028-9024 0411
Admin: 028-9024 0411
Website: www.goh.co.uk
e-mail: info@goh.co.uk

BILLINGHAM

Forum Theatre
Town Centre
Billingham TS23 2LJ
Box Office: 01642 552663
Stage Door: ------------------
Admin: 01642 551389
Website: www.forumtheatrebillingham.co.uk
e-mail: forumtheatre@btconnect.com

BIRMINGHAM

Alexandra Theatre
Station Street, Birmingham B5 4DS
Box Office: 0870 6077533
Stage Door: 0121-230 9102
Admin: 0121-643 5536
Website: www.livenation.co.uk/birmingham

BIRMINGHAM

Hippodrome
Hurst Street, Birmingham B5 4TB
Box Office: 0870 7301234
Stage Door: ------------------
Admin: 0870 7305555

BLACKPOOL

Grand Theatre National Theatre of Variety
33 Church Street
Blackpool FY1 1HT
Box Office: 01253 290190
Stage Door: 01253 743218
Admin: 01253 290111
Website: www.blackpoolgrand.co.uk
e-mail: box@blackpoolgrand.co.uk

BLACKPOOL

Opera House
Church Street
Blackpool FY1 1HW
Box Office: 0870 3801111
Stage Door: 01253 625252 ext 148
Admin: 01253 625252
Website: www.blackpoollive.com

BOURNEMOUTH

Pavilion Theatre
Westover Road
Bournemouth BH1 2BU
Box Office: 0870 1113000
Stage Door: 01202 451863
Admin: 01202 456400

BRADFORD

Alhambra Theatre
Morley Street, Bradford BD7 1AJ
Box Office: 01274 432000
Stage Door: 01274 432375
Admin: 01274 432375
Website: www.bradford-theatres.co.uk
e-mail: administration@ces.bradford.gov.uk

BRADFORD

Theatre in the Mill
University of Bradford
Shearbridge Road, Bradford BD7 1DP
Box Office: 01274 233200
Stage Door: 01274 233187
Admin: 01274 233185
Website: www.bradford.ac.uk/theatre
e-mail: theatre@bradford.ac.uk

BRIGHTON

Theatre Royal
New Road, Brighton BN1 1SD
Box Office: 0870 0606650
Stage Door: 01273 764400
Admin: 01273 764400
Website: www.theambassadors.com/theatreroyal
e-mail: brightontheatremanager@theambassadors.com

BRIGHTON

The Dome, Corn Exchange & Pavilion Theatres
29 New Road, Brighton BN1 1UG
Box Office: 01273 709709
Stage Door: 01273 261550
Admin: 01273 700747
e-mail: info@brightondome.org

BRISTOL

Hippodrome
St Augustines Parade, Bristol BS1 4UZ
Box Office: 0870 6077500
Stage Door: 0117-302 3251
Admin: 0117-302 3310
Website: www.livenation.co.uk/bristol

BROXBOURNE (Herts)

Broxbourne Civic Hall
High Street, Hoddesdon, Herts EN11 8BE
Box Office: 01992 441946
Stage Door: ------------------
Admin: 01992 441931
Website: www.broxbourne.gov.uk/internet/whatson
e-mail: civic.leisure@broxbourne.gov.uk

BURY ST EDMUNDS

Theatre Royal
Westgate Street
Bury St Edmunds IP33 1QR
Box Office: 01284 769505
Stage Door: 01284 755127
Admin: 01284 755127
Website: www.theatreroyal.org
e-mail: admin@theatreroyal.org

BUXTON

Buxton Opera House
Water Street
Buxton SK17 6XN
Box Office: 0845 1272190
Stage Door: 01298 72524
Admin: 01298 72050
Website: www.buxtonoperahouse.org.uk
e-mail: admin@boh.org.uk

CAMBERLEY

The Camberley Theatre
Knoll Road, Camberley, Surrey GU15 3SY
Box Office: 01276 707600
Stage Door: ------------------
Admin: 01276 707512
Website: www.camberleytheatre.biz
e-mail: camberleytheatre@surreyheath.gov.uk

CAMBRIDGE

Cambridge Arts Theatre Trust Ltd
6 St Edward's Passage
Cambridge CB2 3PJ
Box Office: 01223 503333
Stage Door: 01223 578933
Admin: 01223 578903
Website: www.cambridgeartstheatre.com
e-mail: info@cambridgeartstheatre.com

CAMBRIDGE

Mumford Theatre
Anglia Ruskin University
East Road, Cambridge CB1 1PT
Box Office: 0845 1962320
Stage Door: 0845 1962848
Admin: 0845 1962848
e-mail: mumford@anglia.ac.uk

CANTERBURY

Gulbenkian Theatre
University of Kent, Canterbury CT2 7NB
Box Office: 01227 769075
Stage Door: ------------------
Admin: 01227 827861
Website: www.gulbenkiantheatre.co.uk
e-mail: gulbenkian@kent.ac.uk

CANTERBURY

The Marlowe Theatre
The Friars, Canterbury CT1 2AS
Box Office: 01227 787787
Stage Door: 01227 763262
Admin: 01227 763262
Website: www.marlowetheatre.com
e-mail: mark.everett@canterbury.gov.uk

CARDIFF

New Theatre
Park Place, Cardiff CF10 3LN
Box Office: 029-2087 8889
Stage Door: 029-2087 8900
Admin: 029-2087 8787

CARDIFF

Wales Millennium Centre
Bute Place, Cardiff CF10 5AL
Box Office: 0870 0402000
Stage Door: 029-2063 4700
Admin: 029-2063 6400
Website: www.wmc.org.uk

CHELTENHAM

Everyman Theatre
Regent Street, Cheltenham GL50 1HQ
Box Office: 01242 572573
Stage Door: 01242 512515
Admin: 01242 512515
Website: www.everymantheatre.org.uk
e-mail: admin@everymantheatre.org.uk

CHICHESTER

Festival Theatre
Oaklands Park, Chichester PO19 6AP
Box Office: 01243 781312
Stage Door: 01243 784437
Admin: 01243 784437
Website: www.cft.org.uk
e-mail: admin@cft.org.uk

CRAWLEY

The Hawth
Hawth Avenue, Crawley, West Sussex RH10 6YZ
Box Office: 01293 553636
Stage Door: ------------------
Admin: 01293 552941
Website: www.hawth.co.uk
e-mail: info@hawth.co.uk

CREWE

Lyceum Theatre
Heath Street, Crewe CW1 2DA
Box Office: 01270 537333
Stage Door: 01270 537336
Admin: 01270 537243

DARLINGTON

Civic Theatre
Parkgate, Darlington DL1 1RR
Box Office: 01325 486555
Stage Door: ------------------
Admin: 01325 387775
Website: www.darlingtonarts.co.uk

DUBLIN

Gaiety Theatre
South King Street, Dublin 2
Box Office: 00 353 1 6771717
Stage Door: 00 353 1 6795622
Admin: 00 353 1 6795622
Website: www.gaietytheatre.ie

DUBLIN

Gate Theatre
1 Cavendish Row, Dublin 1
Box Office: 00 353 1 8744045
Stage Door: ------------------
Admin: 00 353 1 8744368
Website: www.gate-theatre.ie
e-mail: info@gate-theatre.ie

DUBLIN

Olympia Theatre
72 Dame Street, Dublin 2
Box Office: 00 353 1 6793323
Stage Door: 00 353 1 6771400
Admin: 00 353 1 6725883
Website: www.olympia.ie
e-mail: info@olympia.ie

EASTBOURNE

Congress Theatre
Admin: Winter Garden
Compton Street, Eastbourne BN21 4BP
Box Office: 01323 412000
Stage Door: 01323 410048
Admin: 01323 415500
Website: www.eastbournetheatres.co.uk
e-mail: theatres@eastbourne.gov.uk

EASTBOURNE

Devonshire Park Theatre
Admin: Winter Garden
Compton Street, Eastbourne BN21 4BP
Box Office: 01323 412000
Stage Door: 01323 410074
Admin: 01323 415500
Website: www.eastbournetheatres.co.uk
e-mail: theatres@eastbourne.gov.uk

EDINBURGH

King's Theatre
2 Leven Street
Edinburgh EH3 9LQ
Box Office: 0131-529 6000
Stage Door: 0131-229 3416
Admin: 0131-662 1112
Website: www.eft.co.uk
e-mail: empire@eft.co.uk

EDINBURGH

Playhouse Theatre
18-22 Greenside Place
Edinburgh EH1 3AA
Box Office: 0870 6063424
Stage Door: 0131-524 3324
Admin: 0131-524 3333
Website: www.livenation.co.uk/edinburgh

GLASGOW

King's Theatre
297 Bath Street
Glasgow G2 4JN
Box Office: 0141-240 1111
Stage Door: 0141-240 1300
Admin: 0141-240 1300
Website: www.kings-glasgow.co.uk

GLASGOW

Theatre Royal
282 Hope Street
Glasgow G2 3QA
Box Office: 0870 0606647
Stage Door: 0141-332 3321
Admin: 0141-332 3321
Website: www.theambassadors.com

RAYS THURROCK

hameside Theatre
rsett Road, Grays Thurrock RM17 5DX
ox Office:	01375 383961
tage Door:	-----------------
dmin:	01375 382555
ebsite:	www.thurrock.gov.uk/theatre
mail:	mallinson@thurrock.gov.uk

ARLOW

he Playhouse
layhouse Square, Harlow CM20 1LS
ox Office:	01279 431945
tage Door:	-----------------
dmin:	01279 446760
ebsite:	www.playhouseharlow.com
mail:	playhouse@harlow.gov.uk

ARROGATE

arrogate International Centre
ngs Road, Harrogate HG1 5LA
ox Office:	01423 537230
tage Door:	-----------------
dmin:	01423 500500
ebsite:	www.harrogateinternationalcentre.co.uk
mail:	sales@harrogateinternationalcentre.co.uk

ASTINGS

hite Rock Theatre
hite Rock, Hastings TN34 1JX
ox Office:	0870 1451133
tage Door:	-----------------
dmin:	01424 462280

AYES (Middlesex)

eck Theatre
range Road, Hayes, Middlesex UB3 2UE
ox Office:	020-8561 8371
tage Door:	-----------------
dmin:	020-8561 7506
ebsite:	www.getlive.co.uk/hayes

IGH WYCOMBE

ycombe Swan
Mary Street, High Wycombe HP11 2XE
ox Office:	01494 512000
tage Door:	01494 514444
dmin:	01494 514444
ebsite:	www.wycombeswan.co.uk
mail:	enquiries@wycombeswan.co.uk

UDDERSFIELD

ragrats Ltd
he Mill, Dunford Road, Holmfirth, Huddersfield HD9 2AR
tage Door:	-----------------
D:	-----------------
dmin:	01484 686451
ebsite:	www.cragrats.com
mail:	info@cragrats.com

UDDERSFIELD

awrence Batley Theatre
ueen Street, Huddersfield HD1 2SP
ox Office:	01484 430528
tage Door:	01484 484501
dmin:	01484 484412
mail:	theatre@lbt-uk.org

HULL

Hull New Theatre
Kingston Square, Hull HU1 3HF
Box Office:	01482 226655
Stage Door:	01482 318300
Admin:	01482 613818
e-mail:	theatre.management@hullcc.gov.uk

HULL

Hull Truck Theatre
Spring Street, Hull HU2 8RW
Box Office:	01482 323638
Stage Door:	-----------------
Admin:	01482 224800
Website:	www.hulltruck.co.uk
e-mail:	admin@hulltruck.co.uk

ILFORD

Kenneth More Theatre
Oakfield Road, Ilford IG1 1BT
Box Office:	020-8553 4466
Stage Door:	020-8553 4465
Admin:	020-8553 4464
Website:	www.kenneth-more-theatre.co.uk
e-mail:	kmtheatre@aol.com

IPSWICH

Sir John Mills Theatre (Hire Only)
Gatacre Road, Ipswich IP1 2LQ
Box Office:	01473 211498
Stage Door:	-----------------
Admin:	01473 218202
Website:	www.easternangles.co.uk
e-mail:	admin@easternangles.co.uk

JERSEY

Opera House
Gloucester Street, St Helier, Jersey JE2 3QR
Box Office:	01534 511115
Stage Door:	-----------------
Admin:	01534 511100
Website:	www.jerseyoperahouse.co.uk
e-mail:	ian@jerseyoperahouse.co.uk

KIRKCALDY

Adam Smith Theatre
Bennochy Road, Kirkcaldy KY1 1ET
Box Office:	01592 583302
Stage Door:	-----------------
Admin:	01592 583301

LEATHERHEAD

The Leatherhead Theatre
7 Church Street, Leatherhead, Surrey KT22 8DN
Box Office:	01372 365141
Stage Door:	-----------------
Admin:	01372 365130
Website:	www.the-theatre.org
e-mail:	info@the-theatre.org

LEEDS

City Varieties Music Hall
Swan Street, Leeds LS1 6LW
Box Office:	0845 6441881
Stage Door:	-----------------
Admin:	0845 1260696
Website:	www.cityvarieties.co.uk
e-mail:	info@cityvarieties.co.uk

LEEDS

Grand Theatre & Opera House
46 New Briggate
Leeds LS1 6NZ
Box Office: 0844 8482700
Stage Door: 0113-245 6014
Admin: 0113-245 6014
Website: www.leedsgrandtheatre.com
e-mail: boxoffice@leedsgrandtheatre.com

LICHFIELD

The Lichfield Garrick
Castle Dyke
Lichfield WS13 6HR
Box Office: 01543 412121
Stage Door: ------------------
Admin: 01543 412110
Website: www.lichfieldgarrick.com

LINCOLN

Theatre Royal
Clasketgate
Lincoln LN2 1JJ
Box Office: 01522 525555
Stage Door: 01522 545490
Admin: 01522 523303
Website: www.theatreroyallincoln.com
e-mail: trl@dial.pipex.com

LIVERPOOL

Empire Theatre
Lime Street
Liverpool L1 1JE
Box Office: 0870 6063536
Stage Door: 0151-708 3200
Admin: 0151-708 3200
Website: www.livenation.co.uk/liverpool

MALVERN

Malvern Theatres (Festival & Forum Theatres)
Grange Road
Malvern WR14 3HB
Box Office: 01684 892277
Stage Door: ------------------
Admin: 01684 569256
Website: www.malvern-theatres.co.uk
e-mail: post@malvern-theatres.co.uk

MANCHESTER

Manchester Apollo
Stockport Road
Ardwick Green, Manchester M12 6AP
Box Office: 0870 4018000
Stage Door: 0161-273 2416
Admin: 0161-273 6921
Website: www.livenation.co.uk

MANCHESTER

Opera House
Quay Street
Manchester M3 3HP
Box Office: 0870 4019000
Stage Door: 0161-828 1700
Admin: 0161-828 1700
Website: www.manchesteroperahouse.org.uk

MANCHESTER

Palace Theatre
Oxford Street
Manchester M1 6FT
Box Office: 0870 4013000
Stage Door: 0161-245 6600
Admin: 0161-245 6600
Website: www.manchesterpalace.org.uk

MARGATE

Theatre Royal
Addington Street
Margate, Kent CT9 1PW
Box Office: 0845 1301786
Stage Door: 01843 293397
Admin: 01843 293397
Website: www.theatreroyalmargate.co.uk

MILTON KEYNES

Milton Keynes Theatre
500 Marlborough Gate
Central Milton Keynes MK9 3NZ
Box Office: 0870 0606652
Stage Door: 01908 547500
Admin: 01908 547500

NEWARK

Palace Theatre
Appletongate
Newark NG24 1JY
Box Office: 01636 655755
Stage Door: ------------------
Admin: 01636 655750
Website: www.palacenewark.com
e-mail: david.piper@nsdc.info

NEWCASTLE UPON TYNE

Northern Stage
Barras Bridge
Haymarket
Newcastle upon Tyne NE1 7RH
Box Office: 0191-230 5151
Stage Door: ------------------
Admin: 0191-232 3366
Website: www.northernstage.co.uk
e-mail: info@northernstage.co.uk

NEWCASTLE UPON TYNE

Theatre Royal
Grey Street
Newcastle upon Tyne NE1 6BR
Box Office: 0870 9055060
Stage Door: 0191-244 2500
Admin: 0191-232 0997

NORTHAMPTON

Royal & Derngate Theatres
19-21 Guildhall Road
Northampton NN1 1DP
Box Office: 01604 624811
Stage Door: ------------------
Admin: 01604 626222
Website: www.royalandderngate.co.uk
e-mail: postbox@royalandderngate.co.uk

RWICH

eatre Royal
eatre Street
rwich NR2 1RL
x Office: 01603 630000
age Door: 01603 598500
Imin: 01603 598500
ebsite: www.theatreroyalnorwich.co.uk

OTTINGHAM

eatre Royal & Royal Concert Hall
eatre Square, Nottingham NG1 5ND
x Office: 0115-989 5555
age Door: 0115-989 5500
Imin: 0115-989 5500
ebsite: www.royalcentre-nottingham.co.uk
mail: enquiry@royalcentre-nottingham.co.uk

KFORD

w Theatre
orge Street, Oxford OX1 2AG
x Office: 0870 6077484
age Door: 01865 320760
Imin: 01865 320763

'FORD

ford Playhouse
aumont Street, Oxford OX1 2LW
x Office: 01865 305305
age Door: 01865 305301
'min: 01865 305300
ebsite: www.oxfordplayhouse.com
mail: admin@oxfordplayhouse.com

OLE

ghthouse, Poole's Centre for The Arts
ngland Road, Poole BH15 1UG
x Office: 0870 0668701
age Door: ------------------
Imin: ------------------
ebsite: www.lighthousepoole.co.uk

ADING

e Hexagon
een's Walk, Reading RG1 7UA
x Office: 0118-960 6060
age Door: 0118-939 0018
Imin: 0118-939 0123

CHMOND (N Yorks)

orgian Theatre Royal
ctoria Road, Richmond
rth Yorkshire DL10 4DW
x Office: 01748 825252
age Door: ------------------
Imin: 01748 823710
ebsite: www.georgiantheatreroyal.co.uk

CHMOND (Surrey)

chmond Theatre
e Green, Richmond, Surrey TW9 1QJ
x Office: 0870 0606651
age Door: 020-8940 0220
Imin: 020-8940 0220
ebsite: www.richmondtheatre.net

SHEFFIELD

Sheffield Theatres - Crucible, Lyceum & Crucible Studio
55 Norfolk Street, Sheffield S1 1DA
Box Office: 0114-249 6000
Stage Door: 0114-249 5999
Admin: 0114-249 5999
Website: www.sheffieldtheatres.co.uk
e-mail: info@sheffieldtheatres.co.uk

SHERINGHAM

The Little Theatre
2 Station Road
Sheringham, Norfolk NR26 8RE
BO: 01263 822347
Stage Door: 01263 826173
Admin: 01263 822117
Website: www.sheringhamlittletheatre.com
e-mail: enquiries@sheringhamlittletheatre.com

SOUTHAMPTON

The Mayflower
Commercial Road
Southampton SO15 1GE
Box Office: 023-8071 1811
Stage Door: ------------------
Admin: 023-8071 1800
Website: www.the-mayflower.com
e-mail: info@mayflower.org.uk

SOUTHEND

Southend Theatres
(Cliffs Pavilion, Palace & Dixon Theatres)
Cliffs Pavilion
Station Road, Westcliff-on-Sea, Essex, SS0 7RA
Box Office: 01702 351135
Stage Door: 01702 347394
Admin: 01702 390657
Website: www.thecliffspavilion.co.uk
e-mail: info@cliffspavilion.demon.co.uk

ST ALBANS

Abbey Theatre
Holywell Hill, St Albans AL1 2DL
Box Office: 01727 857861
Stage Door: ------------------
Admin: 01727 847472
Website: www.abbeytheatre.org.uk
e-mail: manager@abbeytheatre.org.uk

ST ALBANS

Alban Arena
Civic Centre, St Albans AL1 3LD
Box Office: 01727 844488
Stage Door: ------------------
Admin: 01727 861078
Website: www.alban-arena.co.uk
e-mail: alban.arena@leisureconnection.co.uk

ST HELENS

Theatre Royal
Corporation Street, St Helens WA10 1LQ
Box Office: 01744 756000
Stage Door: ------------------
Admin: 01744 756333
Website: www.sthelenstheatreroyal.co.uk

STAFFORD

Stafford Gatehouse Theatre
Eastgate Street, Stafford ST16 2LT
Box Office: 01785 254653
Stage Door: ------------------
Admin: 01785 253595
Website: www.staffordgatehousetheatre.co.uk
e-mail: gatehouse@staffordbc.gov.uk

STEVENAGE

Gordon Craig Theatre
Arts & Leisure Centre
Lytton Way, Stevenage SG1 1LZ
Box Office: 08700 131030
Stage Door: 01438 242629
Admin: 01438 242679
Website: www.gordon-craig.co.uk
e-mail: gordoncraig@stevenage-leisure.co.uk

SUNDERLAND

Sunderland Empire
High Street West
Sunderland SR1 3EX
Box Office: 0870 6021130
Stage Door: 0191-566 1050
Admin: 0191-566 1040

SWANAGE

Mowlem Theatre
Shore Road, Swanage BH19 1DD
Box Office: 01929 422239
Stage Door: ------------------
Admin: 01929 422229

TAMWORTH

Assembly Rooms
Corporation Street, Tamworth B79 7BX
Box Office: 01827 709618
Stage Door: ------------------
Admin: 01827 709620

TEWKESBURY

The Roses
Sun Street, Tewkesbury GL20 5NX
Box Office: 01684 295074
Stage Door: ------------------
Admin: 01684 290734
e-mail: admin@rosestheatre.org

TORQUAY

Babbacombe Theatre
Babbacombe Downs, Torquay TQ1 3LU
Box Office: 01803 328385
Stage Door: 01803 328385
Admin: 01803 322233
Website: www.babbacombe-theatre.com
e-mail: mail@matpro-show.biz

TORQUAY

Princess Theatre
Torbay Road, Torquay TQ2 5EZ
Box Office: 0870 2414120
Stage Door: 01803 290068
Admin: 01803 290288
Website: www.livenation.co.uk/torquay

TRURO

Hall For Cornwall
Back Quay
Truro, Cornwall TR1 2LL
Box Office: 01872 262466
Stage Door: 01872 262465
Admin: 01872 262465
Website: www.hallforcornwall.co.uk
e-mail: admin@hallforcornwall.org.uk

WINCHESTER

Theatre Royal
21-23 Jewry Street
Winchester SO23 8SB
Box Office: 01962 840440
Stage Door: ------------------
Admin: 01962 844600
e-mail: marketing@theatre-royal-winchester.co.u

WOLVERHAMPTON

Grand Theatre
Lichfield Street
Wolverhampton WV1 1DE
Box Office: 01902 429212
Stage Door: 01902 573320
Admin: 01902 573300
Website: www.grandtheatre.co.uk
e-mail: marketing@grandtheatre.co.uk

WORCESTER

Swan Theatre
The Moors
Worcester WR1 3EF
Box Office: 01905 611427
Stage Door: ------------------
Admin: 01905 726969
Website: www.worcesterlive.co.uk
e-mail: chris@worcesterlive.co.uk

WORTHING

Connaught Theatre
Union Place
Worthing BN11 1LG
Box Office: 01903 206206
Stage Door: ------------------
Admin: 01903 231799
Website: www.worthingtheatres.co.uk

YEOVIL

Octagon Theatre
Hendford, Yeovil BA20 1UX
Box Office: 01935 422884
Stage Door: ------------------
Admin: 01935 845900
Website: www.octagon-theatre.co.uk
e-mail: octagontheatre@southsomerset.gov.

YORK

Grand Opera House
Cumberland Street, York YO1 9SW
Box Office: 0870 6063595
Stage Door: ------------------
Admin: 01904 678700
Website: www.livenation.co.uk/york

UTHENTIC PUNCH & JUDY
uppets, Booths & Presentations) (John Styles)
2 Christchurch Road
dcup
ent DA15 7HQ
ebsite: www.johnstylesentertainer.co.uk
Tel/Fax: 020-8300 3579

UCKLEY Simon
reelance Puppeteer/Presenter)
College Green
5-57 Barrington Road
ondon SW9 7JG
ebsite: www.simonbuckley.co.uk
mail: puppet.buckley@virgin.net   Mobile: 07976 290351

OMPLETE WORKS CREATIVE COMPANY Ltd The
rtistic Director: Phil Evans)
he Old Truman Brewery
Brick Lane
ondon E1 6QL
ebsite: www.tcw.org.uk
mail: info@tcw.org.uk
ax: 0870 1431979   Tel: 0870 1431969

ORNELIUS & JONES
9 Carters Close
herington
ewport Pagnell
uckinghamshire MK16 9NW
ebsite: www.corneliusjones.com
mail: admin@corneliusjones.com   Tel/Fax: 01908 612593

YNAMIC NEW ANIMATION
nit 13
he Watermark
bbleton Lane
reston PR1 5EZ
ebsite: www.dynamicnewanimation.co.uk
mail: info@dynamicnewanimation.co.uk
obile: 07976 946003   Tel: 01772 253100

RIFFITHS Marc
entriloquist & Motivational Speaker)
he Mega Centre
ernard Road
heffield S2 5BQ
ebsite: www.mega-u.com
Tel: 0114-284 6007

NDIGO MOON THEATRE
5 Waltham Court
everley
st Yorkshire HU17 9JF
ebsite: www.indigomoontheatre.com
mail: info@indigomoontheatre.com   Mobile: 07855 328552

ACOLLY PUPPET THEATRE
rkella Road
elverton
est Devon PL20 6BB
ebsite: www.jacolly-puppets.co.uk
mail: theatre@jacolly-puppets.co.uk   Tel: 01822 852346

TTLE ANGEL THEATRE
Dagmar Passage
oss Street
ondon N1 2DN
ebsite: www.littleangeltheatre.com
mail: info@littleangeltheatre.com   Tel: 020-7226 1787

MAJOR MUSTARD'S TRAVELLING SHOW
1 Carless Avenue
Harborne, Birmingham B17 9EG
e-mail: mm@majormustard.com
Fax: 0121-427 2358   Tel: 0121-426 4329

NORWICH PUPPET THEATRE
St James
Whitefriars
Norwich NR3 1TN
Website: www.puppettheatre.co.uk
e-mail: info@puppettheatre.co.uk
Fax: 01603 617578   Tel: 01603 615564

PEKKO'S PUPPETS
(Director: Stephen Novy)
92 Stanley Avenue, Greenford
Middlesex UB6 8NP   Tel: 020-8575 2311

PICCOLO PUPPET COMPANY
Maythorne Higher Park Road
Braunton
North Devon EX33 2LF
e-mail: flychek@yahoo.co.uk   Tel: 01271 815984

PLAYBOARD PUPPETS
2 Ockenden Mews
London N1 3JL
Website: www.buttonmoon.tv
e-mail: thebuttonmoon@aol.com   Tel/Fax: 020-7226 5911

POM POM PUPPETS
9 Fulham Park Gardens
London SW6 4JX
Mobile: 07974 175247   Tel: 020-7736 6532

PROFESSOR PATTEN'S PUNCH & JUDY
(Puppetry & Magic)
14 The Crest
Goffs Oak
Herts EN7 5NP
Website: www.dennispatten.co.uk   Tel: 01707 873262

PUPPET THEATRE WALES
22 Starling Road, St Athan
Vale of Glamorgan CF62 4NJ
Website: www.puppettheatrewales.com
e-mail: puppetwales@aol.com   Tel: 01446 790634

TALK TO THE HAND PRODUCTIONS
24 Burstead Close
Brighton BN1 7HT
Website: www.talktothehandproductions.com
e-mail: talktothehandproductions@hotmail.com
Mobile: 07813 682293   Mobile: 07855 421454

TICKLISH ALLSORTS SHOW
57 Victoria Road
Wilton, Salisbury
Wiltshire SP2 0DZ
Website: www.ticklishallsorts.co.uk
e-mail: garynunn@ntlworld.com   Tel/Fax: 01722 744949

TOPPER Chris PUPPETS
(Puppets Created & Performed)
75 Barrows Green Lane
Widnes
Cheshire WA8 3JH
Website: www.christopperpuppets.co.uk
e-mail: christopper@ntlworld.com   Tel: 0151-424 8692

ALDEBURGH
Summer Theatre (July & August)
The Jubilee Hall
Crabbe Street, Aldeburgh IP15 5BW
BO: 01728 453007/454022　Admin: (Oct-May) 020-7724 5432
　　　　　　　　　　　Admin: (June-Sept) 01502 723077
Website: www.southwoldtheatre.org

BELFAST
Lyric Theatre
55 Ridgeway Street, Belfast BT9 5FB
Fax: 028-9038 1395
BO: 028-9038 1081　　　　　Admin: 028-9038 5685
Website: www.lyrictheatre.co.uk
e-mail: info@lyrictheatre.co.uk
Production Manager: Marianne Crosslé
Administration Manager: Clare Gault
Executive Director: Michael Diskin
Finance Manager: David McIlwrath

BIRMINGHAM
Birmingham Stage Company
London Office:
Suite 228 The Linen Hall
162 Regent Street, London W1B 5TB
Fax: 020-7437 3395　　　　　Admin: 020-7437 3391
Website: www.birminghamstage.net
e-mail: info@birminghamstage.net
Actor/Manager: Neal Foster
Executive Producer: Philip Compton

BIRMINGHAM
Birmingham Stage Company
The Old Rep Theatre
Station Street, Birmingham B5 4DY
BO: 0121-303 2323　　　　　Admin: 0121-643 9050
Website: www.birminghamstage.net
e-mail: info@birminghamstage.net
Actor/Manager: Neal Foster

BIRMINGHAM
Repertory Theatre
Centenary Square
Broad Street, Birmingham B1 2EP
Press Office: 0121-245 2075
BO: 0121-236 4455　　　　　Tel: 0121-245 2000
e-mail: info@birmingham-rep.co.uk
Artistic Director: Rachel Kavanaugh
Executive Director: Stuart Rogers
Casting Director: Hannah Miller

BOLTON
Octagon Theatre
Howell Croft South, Bolton BL1 1SB
Fax: 01204 556502
BO: 01204 520661　　　　　Admin: 01204 529407
Artistic Director: Mark Babych
Executive Director: John Blackmore
Head of Administration: Lesley Etherington
Head of Production: Paul Sheard

BRISTOL
Theatre Royal and Studio
(Closed for refurbishment until December 2008)
Bristol Old Vic, King Street
Bristol BS1 4ED
Fax: 0117-949 3996
BO: 0117-987 7877　　　　　Tel: 0117-949 3993
Website: www.bristol-old-vic.co.uk
e-mail: admin@bristol-old-vic.co.uk

CARDIFF
Sherman Theatre
Senghennydd Road CF24 4YE
Fax: 029-2064 6902
BO: 029-2064 6900　　　　　Tel: 029-2064 6901
Director: Chris Ricketts
General Manager: Margaret Jones

CHICHESTER
Chichester Festival Theatre
Oaklands Park
Chichester, West Sussex PO19 6AP
Fax: 01243 787288
BO: 01243 781312　　　　　SD & Admin: 01243 784437
Website: www.cft.org.uk
e-mail: admin@cft.org.uk
Artistic Director: Jonathan Church
Executive Director: Alan Finch
Theatre Manager: Janet Bakose

CHICHESTER
Minerva Theatre at Chichester Festival Theatre
Oaklands Park
Chichester
West Sussex PO19 6AP
Fax: 01243 787288
BO: 01243 781312　　　　　SD & Admin: 01243 784437
Website: www.cft.org.uk
e-mail: admin@cft.org.uk
Artistic Director: Jonathan Church
Executive Director: Alan Finch
Theatre Manager: Janet Bakose

COLCHESTER
Mercury Theatre
Balkerne Gate
Colchester
Essex CO1 1PT
Fax: 01206 769607
BO: 01206 573948　　　　　Admin: 01206 577006
Website: www.mercurytheatre.co.uk
e-mail: info@mercurytheatre.co.uk
Chief Executive: Dee Evans
General Manager: Adrian Grady

COVENTRY
Belgrade Theatre & Belgrade Studio
Belgrade Square
Coventry
West Midlands CV1 1GS
BO: 024-7655 3055　　　　　Admin: 024-7625 643
Website: www.belgrade.co.uk
e-mail: admin@belgrade.co.uk
Theatre Director & Chief Executive: Hamish Glen
Executive Director: Joanna Reid
Director of Marketing: Antony Flint

DERBY
Derby Playhouse
(4 Weekly)
Theatre Walk
Eagle Centre
Derby DE1 2NF
Fax: 01332 547200
BO: 01332 363275　　　　　SD/Admin: 01332 3632
Website: www.derbyplayhouse.co.uk
e-mail: admin@derbyplayhouse.co.uk
Creative Producer: Stephen Edwards
Chief Executive: Karen Hebden

Dominic Marsh   Chook Sibtain   Canterville Ghost   Patrick Stewart

Pascal Mollière // Photography ●

Theatre // Film Stills // Dance // Circus // Stage // Actors Headshots
m: 07713 242948   e: info@pascalphoto.co.uk   www.pascalphoto.co.uk

DUBLIN
Abbey Theatre & Peacock Theatre
The National Theatre Society Limited
26 Lower Abbey Street
Dublin 1, Ireland
Fax: 00 353 1 872 9177
BO: 00 353 1 878 7222   Admin: 00 353 1 887 2200
Website: www.abbeytheatre.ie
e-mail: mail@abbeytheatre.ie
Artistic Director: Fiach MacConghail

DUNDEE
Dundee Repertory Theatre
Tay Square, Dundee DD1 1PB
Fax: 01382 228609
BO: 01382 223530   Admin: 01382 227684
Website: www.dundeereptheatre.co.uk
Artistic Directors: James Brining, Dominic Hill
Executive Director: Graeme Wallace

EDINBURGH
Royal Lyceum Theatre Company
30B Grindlay Street, Edinburgh EH3 9AX
Fax: 0131-228 3955
BO: 0131-248 4848   SD & Admin: 0131-248 4800
Website: www.lyceum.org.uk
e-mail: info@lyceum.org.uk
Artistic Director: Mark Thomson

EDINBURGH
Traverse Theatre
(New Writing, Own Productions, Touring & Visiting
Companies)
10 Cambridge Street
Edinburgh EH1 2ED
Fax: 0131-229 8443
BO: 0131-228 1404   Admin: 0131-228 3223
Website: www.traverse.co.uk
e-mail: admin@traverse.co.uk
Artistic Director: Philip Howard
Administrative Director: Mike Griffiths

EXETER
Exeter Northcott Theatre
Stocker Road
Exeter
Devon EX4 4QB
Fax: 01392 223996
BO: 01392 493493   Admin: 01392 223999
Website: www.northcott-theatre.co.uk
Artistic Director: Ben Crocker

FRINTON
Frinton Summer Theatre
(July-Sept)
The McGrigor Hall
Fourth Avenue, Frinton-on-Sea
Essex CO13 9EB   BO: 01255 674443 (July-Sept Only)
e-mail: ed.max@frintonsummertheatre.co.uk
Producer/Artistic Director: Edward Max

GLASGOW
Citizens Theatre
Gorbals
Glasgow G5 9DS
Fax: 0141-429 7374
BO: 0141-429 0022   Admin: 0141-429 5561
Website: www.citz.co.uk
e-mail: info@citz.co.uk
Artistic Directors: Jeremy Raison, Guy Hollands
General Manager/Administrative Director: Anna Stapleton

GUILDFORD
Yvonne Arnaud Theatre
Millbrook
Guildford
Surrey GU1 3UX
Fax: 01483 564071
BO: 01483 440000   Admin: 01483 440077
Website: www.yvonne-arnaud.co.uk
e-mail: yat@yvonne-arnaud.co.uk
Director: James Barber

HARROGATE
Harrogate Theatre
(3-4 weekly) 2.30pm Sat
Oxford Street
Harrogate HG1 1QF
Fax: 01423 563205
BO: 01423 502116   Admin: 01423 502710
e-mail: info@harrogatetheatre.co.uk
Chief Executive: David Bown

HULL
Hull Truck Theatre
Spring Street, Hull HU2 8RW
Fax: 01482 581182
Tel: 01482 224800
Website: www.hulltruck.co.uk
e-mail: admin@hulltruck.co.uk
Artistic Directors: John Godber & Gareth Tudor Price
Executive Director: Joanne Gower
Associate Director: Nick Lane

IPSWICH
The New Wolsey Theatre
Civic Drive
Ipswich
Suffolk IP1 2AS
Admin Fax: 01473 295910   Admin: 01473 295911
BO: 01473 295900
Website: www.wolseytheatre.co.uk
e-mail: info@wolseytheatre.co.uk
Artistic Director: Peter Rowe
Chief Executive: Sarah Holmes

KESWICK
Theatre by the Lake
Lakeside
Keswick
Cumbria CA12 5DJ
Fax: 017687 74698
BO: 017687 74411   Admin: 017687 72282
Website: www.theatrebythelake.com
e-mail: enquiries@theatrebythelake.com
Artistic Director: Ian Forrest

LANCASTER
The Dukes, Moor Lane, Lancaster
Lancashire LA1 1QE
Fax: 01524 598519
BO: 01524 598500   Admin: 01524 598505
Website: www.dukes-lancaster.org
e-mail: info@dukes-lancaster.org
Artistic Director: Ian Hastings
Chief Executive: Amanda Belcham

LEEDS
The West Yorkshire Playhouse
Playhouse Square
Quarry Hill, Leeds LS2 7UP
Fax: 0113-213 7250
BO: 0113-213 7700   Admin: 0113-213 7800
Website: www.wyp.org.uk
Artistic Director (Chief Executive): Ian Brown
Executive Director: Lesley Jackson
Producer: Henrietta Duckworth

LEICESTER
Leicester Theatre Trust
Suite 1A
Rutland Centre
56 Halford Street, Leicester LE1 1TQ
Fax: 0870 7065241   Admin: 0116-253 0021
Website: www.leicestertheatretrust.co.uk
e-mail: enquiries@leicestertheatretrust.co.uk
Artistic Director: Paul Kerryson
Chief Executive: Ruth Eastwood

LIVERPOOL
Everyman & Playhouse Theatres
Everyman: 13 Hope Street
Liverpool L1 9BH

Playhouse: Williamson Square
Liverpool L1 1EL
Fax: 0151-709 0398
BO: 0151-709 4776   Admin: 0151-708 0338
Website: www.everymanplayhouse.com
e-mail: reception@everymanplayhouse.com
Artistic Director: Gemma Bodinetz
Executive Director: Deborah Aydon

MANCHESTER
Contact Theatre Company
Oxford Road, Manchester M15 6JA
Fax: 0161-274 0640
BO: 0161-274 0600   Admin: 0161-274 0623
Website: www.contact-theatre.org
e-mail: info@contact-theatre.org
Chief Executive/Artistic Director: John Edward McGrath

MANCHESTER
Library Theatre Company
St Peter's Square, Manchester M2 5PD
Fax: 0161-228 6481
BO: 0161-236 7110   Admin: 0161-234 1913
Website: www.librarytheatre.com
e-mail: ltcadmin@manchester.gov.uk
Artistic Director: Chris Honer
General Manager: Adrian J. P. Morgan

MANCHESTER
Royal Exchange Theatre
St Ann's Square, Manchester M2 7DH
Fax: 0161-832 0881
BO: 0161-833 9833   Admin: 0161-833 9333
Website: www.royalexchange.co.uk
Artistic Directors: Braham Murray, Gregory Hersov
Executive Director: Paul Clay
Associate Artistic Directors: Sarah Frankcom,
Jacob Murray
Producer (Studio): Richard Morgan
Casting Director: Jerry Knight-Smith

MILFORD HAVEN
Torch Theatre, St Peter's Road
Milford Haven, Pembrokeshire SA73 2BU
Fax: 01646 698919
BO: 01646 695267   Admin: 01646 694192
Website: www.torchtheatre.org.uk
e-mail: info@torchtheatre.co.uk
Artistic Director: Peter Doran

MOLD
Clwyd Theatr Cymru
(Repertoire, 4 Weekly, also touring)
Mold, Flintshire, North Wales CH7 1YA
Fax: 01352 701558
BO: 0845 3303565   Admin: 01352 75633
Website: www.clwyd-theatr-cymru.co.uk
e-mail: drama@celtic.co.uk

MUSSELBURGH
The Brunton Theatre
(Annual programme of Theatre, Dance, Music, Comedy &
Children's Work)
Ladywell Way, Musselburgh EH21 6AA
Fax: 0131-653 5265
BO: 0131-665 2240   Admin: 0131-665 990
General Manager: Lesley Smith

NEWBURY
Watermill Theatre
(4-7 Weekly) (Feb-Jan)
Bagnor, Nr Newbury, Berkshire RG20 8AE
Fax: 01635 523726
BO: 01635 46044   Admin: 01635 4583
Website: www.watermill.org.uk
e-mail: admin@watermill.org.uk
Executive Director: James Sargant
General Manager: Clare Lindsay

NEWCASTLE UPON TYNE
Northern Stage (Theatrical Productions) Ltd
Barras Bridge, Newcastle upon Tyne NE1 7RH
Fax: 0191-261 8093
BO: 0191-230 5151   Admin: 0191-232 3366
Website: www.northernstage.co.uk
e-mail: info@northernstage.co.uk
Chief Executive: Erica Whyman

NEWCASTLE-UNDER-LYME
New Vic Theatre
(3-4 Weekly)
Theatre in the Round
Etruria Road, Newcastle-under-Lyme
Staffordshire ST5 0JG
Fax: 01782 712885
BO: 01782 717962   Tel: 01782 717954
Website: www.newvictheatre.org.uk
e-mail: casting@newvictheatre.org.uk
Artistic Director: Theresa Heskins
Managing Director: Nick Jones

NORTHAMPTON
Royal & Derngate Theatres
Guildhall Road, Northampton
Northamptonshire NN1 1DP
BE: 01604 655740
BO: 01604 624811   Admin: 01604 626222
Chief Executive: Donna Mundy
Artistic Director: Laurie Sansom
Associate Director: Dani Parr

NOTTINGHAM
Nottingham Playhouse
(3/4 Weekly)
(Nottingham Playhouse Trust Ltd)
Wellington Circus
Nottingham NG1 5AL
Fax: 0115-947 5759
BO: 0115-941 9419   Admin: 0115-947 4361
Website: www.nottinghamplayhouse.co.uk
Chief Executive: Stephanie Sirr
Artistic Director: Giles Croft
Roundabout TIE Director: Andrew Breakwell

OLDHAM
Coliseum Theatre
(3-4 Weekly)
Fairbottom Street
Oldham, Lancashire OL1 3SW
Fax: 0161-624 5318
BO: 0161-624 2829   Admin: 0161-624 1731
Website: www.coliseum.org.uk
e-mail: mail@coliseum.org.uk
Chief Executive: Kevin Shaw

PERTH
Perth Repertory Theatre
(2-3 Weekly)
185 High Street
Perth PH1 5UW
Fax: 01738 624576
BO: 0845 6126328   Admin: 01738 472700
Website: www.horsecross.co.uk
e-mail: info@horsecross.co.uk
Artistic Director: Ian Grieve
Head of Planning & Resources: Paul Hackett
Chief Executive: Jane Spiers

PETERBOROUGH
Key Theatre
(Touring & Occasional Seasonal)
Embankment Road
Peterborough, Cambridgeshire PE1 1EF
Fax: 01733 567025
BO: 01733 552439   Admin: 01733 552437
e-mail: michael.cross@peterborough.gov.uk

PITLOCHRY
Pitlochry Festival Theatre
Pitlochry, Perthshire PH16 5DR
Fax: 01796 484616
BO: 01796 484626   Admin: 01796 484600
Website: www.pitlochry.org.uk
e-mail: admin@pitlochry.org.uk
Chief Executive/Acting Artistic Director: John Durnin

PLYMOUTH
Theatre Royal & Drum Theatre
Royal Parade
Plymouth, Devon PL1 2TR
Fax: 01752 230506   Admin: 01752 668282
Website: www.theatreroyal.com
e-mail: info@theatreroyal.com
Artistic Director: Simon Stokes
Chief Executive: Adrian Vinken

SALISBURY
Playhouse & Salberg Studio
(3-4 Weekly)
Malthouse Lane
Salisbury, Wiltshire SP2 7RA
Fax: 01722 421991
BO: 01722 320333   Admin: 01722 320117
Website: www.salisburyplayhouse.com
e-mail: info@salisburyplayhouse.com
Artistic Director: Philip Wilson
Executive Director: Michelle Carwardine-Palmer

SCARBOROUGH
Stephen Joseph Theatre
(Repertoire/Repertory)
Westborough, Scarborough
North Yorkshire YO11 1JW
Fax: 01723 360506
BO: 01723 370541   Admin: 01723 370540
e-mail: enquiries@sjt.uk.com
Artistic Director: Alan Ayckbourn
Executive Director: Stephen Wood

SHEFFIELD
Crucible, Studio & Lyceum Theatres
55 Norfolk Street, Sheffield S1 1DA
Fax: 0114-249 6003
BO: 0114-249 6000   Admin: 0114-249 5999
Website: www.sheffieldtheatres.co.uk
e-mail: info@sheffieldtheatres.co.uk
Chief Executive: Angela Galvin

SHERINGHAM
Summer Repertory
The Little Theatre
2 Station Road
Sheringham, Norfolk NR26 8RE   BO: 01263 822347
Website: www.sheringhamlittletheatre.com
e-mail: enquiries@sheringhamlittletheatre.com
Producer: Sheringham Little Theatre
Artistic Director: Debbie Thompson

SIDMOUTH
Manor Pavilion Theatre
(Weekly) (July-Sept)
Manor Road, Sidmouth, Devon EX10 8RP
BO: 01395 579977 (Season Only)
                              Tel: 020-7636 4343 Charles Vance

SONNING THEATRE
The Mill at Sonning Theatre
(5-6 Weekly)
Sonning Eye, Reading RG4 6TY
BO: 0118-969 8000   Admin: 0118-969 6039
Artistic Director: Sally Hughes
Assistant Administrator: Ann Seymour

SOUTHAMPTON
Nuffield Theatre
(Sept-July, Sunday Night Concerts, Occasional Tours)
University Road
Southampton SO17 1TR
Fax: 023-8031 5511
BO: 023-8067 1771   Admin: 023-8031 5500
Website: www.nuffieldtheatre.co.uk
Artistic Director: Patrick Sandford
Administrative Director: Kate Anderson

SOUTHWOLD
Summer Theatre
(July-Sept)
St Edmund's Hall, Cumberland Road
Southwold IP18 6JP   Admin: (Oct-May) 020-7724 5432
Admin: (June-Sept) 01502 723077
Website: www.southwoldtheatre.org
e-mail: jill@southwoldtheatre.org
Producer: Jill Freud & Company

ST ANDREWS
Byre Theatre
(Not producing, Co-productions only)
Abbey Street
St Andrews KY16 9LA
Fax: 01334 475370
BO: 01334 475000   Admin: 01334 475000
Website: www.byretheatre.com
e-mail: enquiries@byretheatre.com
Chief Executive: Jacqeuline McKay

STRATFORD-UPON-AVON
Swan Theatre & Courtyard Theatre
Waterside, Stratford-upon-Avon CV37 6BB
Fax: 01789 294810
BO: 0870 6091110   Admin: 01789 29665
Website: www.rsc.org.uk
e-mail: info@rsc.org.uk

WATFORD
Watford Palace Theatre
(3-4 Weekly) Weds 2.30pm, Sat 3pm
Clarendon Road, Watford, Herts WD17 1JZ
Fax: 01923 819664
BO: 01923 225671   Admin: 01923 23545
Website: www.watfordpalacetheatre.co.uk
e-mail: enquiries@watfordpalacetheatre.co.uk
Artistic Director & Chief Executive: Brigid Larmour
Executive Director: Anne Gallacher

WINDSOR
Theatre Royal, Thames Street
Windsor, Berkshire SL4 1PS
Fax: 01753 831673
BO: 01753 853888   Admin: 01753 86344
Website: www.theatreroyalwindsor.co.uk
e-mail: info@theatreroyalwindsor.co.uk
Director: Angela Edwards

WOKING
New Victoria Theatre
The Ambassadors, Peacocks Centre, Woking GU21 6GQ
SD: 01483 545855
BO: 0870 0606645   Admin: 01483 5458C
Website: www.theambassadors.com/woking
e-mail: boxoffice@theambassadors.com

YORK
Theatre Royal
St Leonard's Place
York YO1 7HD
Fax: 01904 550164
BO: 01904 623568   Admin: 01904 65816
Website: www.yorktheatreroyal.co.uk
e-mail: admin@yorktheatreroyal.co.uk
Artistic Director: Damian Cruden
Chief Executive: Daniel Bates

CTION CARS Ltd
(even Royffe)
om 586
st Side Complex
newood Studios, Pinewood Road
er Heath, Bucks SL0 0NH
ebsite: www.actioncars.co.uk
mail: info@actioncars.co.uk
x: 01753 652027   Tel: 01753 785690

MERICAN DREAMS
Wilsons Lane
ark's Tey, Essex CO6 1HP
ebsite: www.americandreams.co.uk
mail: tphj47@aol.com   Tel: 0800 8488032

NGLO PACIFIC INTERNATIONAL Plc
reight Forwarders to the Performing Arts)
9 Willenfield Road
rk Row
ndon NW10 7BQ
ebsite: www.anglopacific.co.uk
mail: info@anglopacific.co.uk
x: 020-8965 4945   Tel: 020-8965 1234

JTOMOTIVE ACTION
uppliers of H1 Hummers)
Sheffield House
rk Road, Hampton Hill
ddlesex TW12 1HA
ebsite: www.carstunts.co.uk
mail: carstunts@hotmail.co.uk
bile: 07974 919589   Tel: 020-8977 6186

ANCHI AVIATION FILM SERVICES
storic & Other Aircraft)
vcombe Air Park
oker, Nr Marlow
ckinghamshire SL7 3DP
ebsite: www.bianchiaviation.com
mail: info@bianchiaviation.com
x: 01494 461236   Tel: 01494 449810

UEBELL RAILWAY Plc
eam Locomotives, Pullman Coaches, Period Stations.
ch Film Experience)
effield Park Station
st Sussex TN22 3QL
ebsite: www.bluebell-railway.co.uk
x: 01825 720804   Tel: 01825 720800

RUNEL'S THEATRICAL SERVICES
it 8
cklechurch
stol BS16 9QH
ebsite: www.brunelsremovalservices.co.uk
mail: enquiries@brunelsremovalservices.co.uk
x: 0117-907 7856   Tel: 0117-907 7855

ARLINE & CREW TRANSPORTATION
elebrity Services)
A Bridge Industrial Estate
lcombe Road
est Sussex RH6 9HU
ebsite: www.carlineprivatehire.co.uk
mail: carlinehire@btconnect.com
x: 01293 400508   Tel: 01293 400505

Vehicles & Transport

[CONTACTS2008]

CLASSIC CAR AGENCY The
(Film, Promotional, Advertising, Publicity)
PO Box 427
Dorking
Surrey RH5 6WP
Website: www.theclassiccaragency.com
e-mail: theclassiccaragency@btopenworld.com
Mobile: 07788 977655   Tel: 01306 731052

CLASSIC CAR HIRE
(Classic & Vintage Cars including 1927 Rolls Royce Phantom 1)
Unit 2 Hampton Court Estate
Summer Road
Thames Ditton KT7 0RG
Website: www.classic-hire.com
e-mail: info@classic-hire.co.uk
Fax: 020-8398 9234   Tel: 020-8398 8304

CLASSIC OMNIBUS
(Vintage Open-Top Buses & Coaches)
44 Welson Road
Folkestone
Kent CT20 2NP
Website: www.opentopbus.co.uk
Fax: 01303 241245   Tel: 01303 248999

DEVEREUX DEVELOPMENTS Ltd
(Removals, Haulage, Trucking)
Daimler Drive
Cowpen Industrial Estate
Billingham
Cleveland TS23 4JD
e-mail: mike.bell@kdevereux.co.uk
Fax: 01642 566664   Tel: 01642 560854

DREAM DESTINATIONS
(Corporate & Stretch Limousines)
PO Box 6990
Mansfield
Nottinghamshire NG19 9EW
Website: www.dreamdestinationsonline.co.uk
e-mail: info@dreamdestinationsonline.co.uk
    Tel: 0800 0191345

EST Ltd
(Trucking - Every Size & Country)
Bell Lane
Off North Woolwich Road
London E16 2AB
Website: www.yourockweroll.com
e-mail: delr@est-uk.com
Fax: 020-8522 1002   Tel: 020-8522 1000

FELLOWES Mark TRANSPORT SERVICES
(Transport/Storage)
59 Sherbrooke Road
London SW6 7QL
Website: www.fellowesproductions.com
Mobile: 07850 332818   Tel: 020-7386 7005

FRANKIE'S YANKEES
(Classic 1950s American Cars, Memorabilia & New
Superstretch Limos)
283 Old Birmingham Road
Bromsgrove B60 1HQ
Mobile: 07970 062142   Tel: 0121-445 5522

HOME JAMES CHAUFFEUR SERVICE
Moor Lane, Witton
Birmingham B6 7HH
Website: www.homejamescars.com
e-mail: julie.homejames@virgin.net   Tel: 0121-323 4717

IMPACT
(Private & Contract Hire of Coaches)
1 Leighton Road
Ealing, London W13 9EL
Website: www.impactgroup.co.uk
e-mail: sales@impactgroup.co.uk
Fax: 020-8840 4880   Tel: 020-8579 9922

JASON'S
(Up-market Cruising Canal Wideboat, Daily Scheduled Trips
to Camden Lock) (3 Boats Available)
Opposite 60 Blomfield Road
Little Venice
London W9 2PD
Website: www.jasons.co.uk
e-mail: enquiries@jasons.co.uk
Fax: 020-7266 4332   Tel: 020-7286 3428

KEIGHLEY & WORTH VALLEY LIGHT RAILWAY Ltd
(Engines, Stations, Carriages, Props & Crew)
The Railway Station
Haworth
Keighley, West Yorkshire BD22 8NJ
Website: www.kwvr.co.uk
e-mail: admin@kwvr.co.uk
Fax: 01535 647317   Tel: 01535 645214

LUCKINGS
(Transporters/Storage/Stage Hands)
63 Kew Green
Richmond, Surrey TW9 3AH
Website: www.luckings.co.uk
e-mail: enquiries@luckings.co.uk
Fax: 020-8332 3000   Tel: 020-8332 2000

LUCKINGS SCREEN SERVICES
(Artists' Trailers/Splits/2-3 Ways)
63 Kew Green
Richmond, Surrey TW9 3AH
Website: www.luckings.co.uk
e-mail: enquiries@luckings.co.uk
Fax: 020-8332 3000   Tel: 020-8332 2000

MAINSTREAM LEISURE GROUP
(Riverboat/Canal Boat Hire)
5 The Mews
6 Putney Common
London SW15 1HL
Website: www.mainstreamleisure.co.uk
Fax: 020-8788 0073   Tel: 020-8788 266

McNEILL Brian
(Vintage Truck & Coaches)
Hawk Mount
Kebcote
Todmorden
Lancashire OL14 8SB
Website: www.rollingpast.com
e-mail: autotrans@uk2.net
Fax: 01706 812292   Tel: 01706 8122

ODDED MOTORS AGENCY
3 Williamson Way
ckmansworth
ertfordshire WD3 8GL
ebsite: www.moddedmotorsagency.com
mail: danielle@moddedmotorsagency.com
obile: 07989 128131   Tel: 01923 681454

OTORHOUSE HIRE Ltd
eriod Vehicles 1900-80) (Michael Geary)
eston Underwood
ney
uckinghamshire MK46 5LD
mail: michael@motorhouseltd.co.uk
ax: 01234 240393   Tel: 020-7495 1618

V DIXIE QUEEN
hames Luxury Charters
The Mews
Putney Common
ndon SW15 1HL
ebsite: www.thamesluxurycharters.co.uk
mail: sales@thamesluxurycharters.co.uk
ax: 020-8788 0072   Tel: 020-8780 1562

ATIONAL MOTOR MUSEUM
ohn Montagu Building
eaulieu
ockenhurst
ampshire SO42 7ZN
ebsite: www.beaulieu.co.uk
mail: info@beaulieu.co.uk
ax: 01590 612624   Tel: 01590 612345

NE-NINE CARS Ltd
de Meadow Farm
de Lane
emel Hempstead HP3 8SA
mail: david@nineninecars.com   Tel: 01923 266373

CKFORDS REMOVALS Ltd
eritage House
15 Southbury Road
field
ddlesex EN1 1UP
ebsite: www.pickfords.com
mail: enquiries@pickfords.com
ax: 020-8219 8001   Tel: 020-8219 8000

LUS FILM Ltd
ll Periods Vehicle Hire)
ill House Cottages
inchester Road
shop's Waltham SO32 1AH
mail: stephen@plusfilms7.freeserve.co.uk
                                  Tel/Fax: 01489 895559

TOKE BRUERNE BOAT COMPANY Ltd
assenger & Commercial Boats)
9 Main Road
hutlanger
orthamptonshire NN12 7RU
ebsite: www.stokebruerneboats.co.uk
ax: 01604 864098   Tel: 01604 862107

THAMES LUXURY CHARTERS Ltd
5 The Mews
6 Putney Common, London SW15 1HL
Website: www.thamesluxurycharters.co.uk
e-mail: sales@thamesluxurycharters.co.uk
Fax: 020-8788 0072   Tel: 020-8780 1562

THE WAY TO GO LIMOUSINES
Queenshead Cottage,
43 The Street
Wittersham, Kent TN30 7EA
Website: www.thewaytogolimousines.co.uk
e-mail: twtg@aol.com
Fax: 01797 270190   Tel: 01797 270672

TOTAL LOGISTICS MANAGEMENT
(Close Proximity to Heathrow)
Unit 1
Lakeside Industrial Estate
Colnbrook, Berkshire SL3 0ED
Website: www.tlmltd.co.uk
e-mail: sales@tlmltd.co.uk
Fax: 01753 689004   Tel: 01753 689003

TRACK THAT
(Tracking Vehicle/Camera Car Supplier)
Wandsworth
London SW18 1JH
Website: www.trackthat.co.uk
e-mail: info@trackthat.co.uk
Mobile: 07941 234254   Tel: 020-8870 0673

UK SAME DAY DELIVERY SERVICE
(Philip Collings)
18 Billingshurst Road
Broadbridge Heath
West Sussex RH12 3LW
Fax: 01403 266059   Mobile: 07785 717179

VINTAGE CARRIAGES TRUST
(Owners of the Museum of Rail Travel at Ingrow Railway
Centre)
Keighley
West Yorkshire BD22 8NJ
Website: www.vintagecarriagestrust.org
e-mail: admin@vintagecarriagestrust.org
Fax: 01535 610796   Tel: 01535 680425

Index To Advertisers

ANIMALS

CASTING SERVICES

CONSULTANTS

COSTUMIERS/WARDROBE SERVICES

DENTISTS & DENTAL SERVICES

ENTERTAINERS/ACTORS/ CHOREOGRAPHERS

FESTIVALS

HAIR & MAKE UP

HEALTH & WELLBEING

ORGANISATIONS

PHOTOGRAPHERS

A

B

C

THE SPOTLIGHT

PARTNERS
Nigel Seale, Ben Seale, Emma Smith, Philppa Burton

EDITOR
Kate Poynton

DESIGN & LAYOUT
Kathy Norrish

ACCOUNTS
Maggie Hillier - Head of Accounts
Amelia Barnham
Sally Barnham

CLIENT RELATIONS
Pippa Harrison - Head of Client Relations
Joe Bates
Will Davies
Eleanor Garrett
Thom Hammond
Micki Ling
Lisa McGeoch
Joan Queva

DATA PROCESSING
Joanna MacLeod - Head of Data Processing
Caroline Taylor
Angie Drake
Amanda Lawrence
Emma McCumiskey
Sharon Mulcahy
Helene Van De Langenberg

EDITORIAL
Cindy Lemmer
Christine Barry
Elaine Compton
Angela Cottrell
Nick Goldfinch
Martin Pavey
Elinor Samuels
Cherene Suljkanovic

IT
Dylan Beattie - Head of IT
Scott Lilly
Owen Roberts
Dan Woodhead

MARKETING
Laura Albery - Head of Marketing
Thomas Bracewell
Kelly Taylor

PRODUCTION
Hannah Witzenfeld
Louise Fairweather
Neill Kennedy
David McCarthy
Jaime Robb

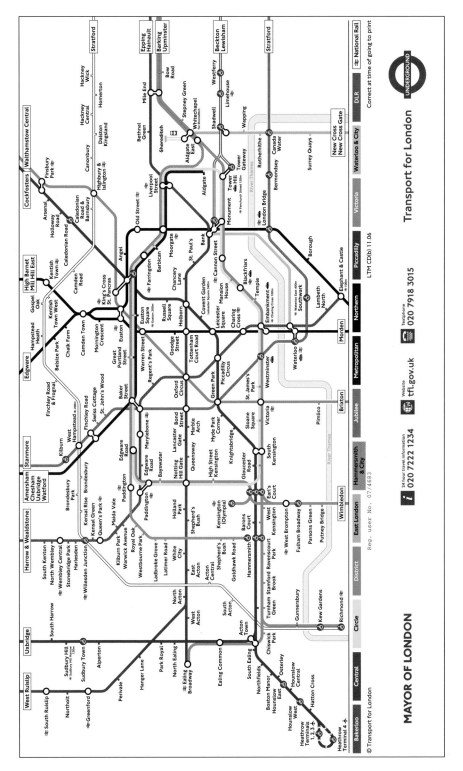

MAYOR OF LONDON

Transport for London

© Transport for London

Reg. user No. 07/4683

i 24 hour travel information
020 7222 1234

Website
tfl.gov.uk

Textphone
020 7918 3015

LTM CD(b) 11.06

Correct at time of going to print

UNDERGROUND

Bakerloo Central District East London Hammersmith & City Jubilee Metropolitan Northern Piccadilly Victoria & City Waterloo & City DLR National Rail

Circle